Experimental Stress Analysis and Motion Measurement

EXPERIMENTAL STRESS ANALYSIS AND MOTION MEASUREMENT

(Theory, instruments and circuits, techniques)

Richard C. Dove

Paul H. Adams

Charles E. Merrill Books, Inc., Columbus, Ohio

Library of Congress Catalog Card Number: 64-12874

PRINTED IN THE UNITED STATES OF AMERICA

Preface

The vast amount of experimental work being done in Mechanics and the number of new experimental tools and techniques perfected during the past few years seem to dictate a broader treatment of what has been called "Experimental Stress Analysis." Just as the field expanded from photoelasticity to experimental stress analysis, so now must it include the concerns of the many experimentalists whose work in the field of mechanics goes beyond stress analysis.

The material covered in Part I, "Experimental Stress Analysis," is the material commonly covered in courses and books of the same title. In this section, the authors have attempted to relate the extent of coverage of a given topic to the extent of application that a practicing experimentalist will likely find for this topic. Hence, mechanical and optical gages are given limited mention, whereas electrical resistance gages are discussed in detail. New experimental methods such as the moiré fringe method and semiconductor gages are given more than cursory attention; these new methods show great promise, but have not been dealt with in other books of this kind. Since the photoelastic method of stress analysis is well treated in several books, the principal aim of this section has been to up-date the material, thereby acquainting the reader with the extension of the photoelastic method into dynamic stress analysis, thermostress analysis, and surface-coating techniques.

To accommodate the notable expansion of the field of experimental mechanics, the second part of this book covers the techniques and tools used for measuring and analyzing displacements, velocities, and accelerations. The basic theory of seismic instruments is presented and extended to cover the transient motion case. Piezoelectric accelerometers and associated circuitry are discussed in detail.

Since most course work in experimental stress analysis is taught using problems and laboratory work, this book has taken this into account. The suggested experiments have been designed so that a wide variety of equipment can be used in conducting them. All of the experiments listed have been performed in the authors' laboratory and, in most cases, the data obtained have been presented in the form of problems which are designed to amplify the material contained in each chapter.

It has been assumed that the reader has a normal background of applied mechanics and basic electrical circuits. Work in elasticity and vibrations is not requisite to an understanding and use of this book. It is hoped that the coverage of the most modern instruments, equipment and circuits, and techniques will be of value to both students and engineers engaged in experimental stress analysis and/or shock and vibrations test work.

R. C. Dove
P. H. Adams

Table of Contents

PART I

EXPERIMENTAL STRESS ANALYSIS

Part I

Experimental Stress Analysis

CHAPTER 1

Stress Analysis by Strain Measurement

1-1 Introduction

Stress analysis is the solution for the state of stress at a point, or points, under a given set of conditions. That is, to make a stress analysis of a machine part (such as a connecting rod) or of a structural member (such as a roof truss) means to establish the kinds, magnitudes, and directions of the stresses at all points of interest under all conditions of loading of interest. Information concerning the kinds, magnitudes, and directions of the stresses at a point defines the state of stress at that point. This information, made available by stress analysis, is combined with the known material properties in order to predict or explain the behavior of a stressed machine part or structural member. That is, stress magnitudes are compared with the elastic limit to predict the limit of elastic action, with the ultimate strength to predict or explain rupture, with the creep limit to predict or explain excessive growth at elevated temperatures, or with the endurance limit to predict or explain fatigue failure.

If the state of stress at a point can be established from theoretical considerations, theoretical stress analysis is possible. The theory of elasticity can be, and is, used to solve for the state of stress in elastic materials subjected to many conditions of loading. Plastic and viscoelastic theories are also available for solving for the state of stress in materials which behave plastically or viscoelastically. However, stress analysis by theoretical means alone is limited for several reasons. First, the classical theories of elasticity, plasticity, and viscoelasticity all involve numerous restrictive assumptions. Second, the theories are very difficult, or impossible, to apply in any but a relatively simply shaped part.

If the state of stress at a point is established by the use of experimentally determined quantities, then the procedure is referred to as experimental stress analysis. Experimental stress analysis almost never involves the measurement of stress, as such. Rather, experimental stress analysis involves the measurement of some quantity which can in turn be related to stress. *This is a most important point.* In relating the measured quantities to stresses, computations based on theory are required, and hence experimental stress analysis is not 100 per cent experimental and does not overcome all the objections just raised to theoretical stress analysis.

The quantity most often measured in experimental stress analysis is axial strain. In this case, stress analysis involves experimentally determining the state of strain at a point and deducing the state of stress at this same point. It is perhaps unfortunate that most engineers' backgrounds are such that they have a "feel" for stress values rather than strain values, since many of the common material properties could be defined in terms of strain as well as in terms of stress.

Axial strain is the change in length of a given original length and, as such, the most direct experimental method involves two measurements of length: the first, to establish the reference or gage length before straining, and the second, to establish the change in this gage length during straining. Measurement of a change in finite length obviously does not give the strain at a point, but rather the average strain over the length. How closely this average strain represents the true strain at any point within the gage length depends upon the strain gradient along the gage length and the length involved.

The experiments of Robert Hooke in 1660 which led to the formulation of Hooke's law are excellent examples of the experimental determination of strain by direct measurement without magnification. Hooke suspended 20 to 40 ft lengths of wire and loaded them in tension; the change in length produced by loading was measured by measuring the change in distance between the bottom of the wires and the floor by means of a drawing compass. In spite of the success enjoyed by Hooke, experimentalists since his time have realized that, when strain is to be determined experimentally, the nature of the strain gradient will not in general be known. Therefore, the trend has been to measurements over the shortest possible gage lengths, and this has made magnification of the change in length imperative.

Strain gages of all types are devices which provide for the magnification of a change in length, and strain gages are most often classified according to the type of magnification system which they employ. The three most important methods of magnification and, hence, the three principal types of commercially available strain gages are mechanical, optical, and electrical. Strain gages of these three types are discussed briefly in the next three sections.

Since strain gages function at a point, it is obvious that in many studies large numbers of strain gages must be used. That is, strain measurement using strain gages is a point-by-point method of analysis. Methods for determining some strain information at every point on a surface of considerable area have also been developed. These methods, referred to as whole field methods, are discussed briefly in the last three sections of this chapter.

1-2 Mechanical strain gages

Strain gages employing mechanical means for magnification appear to have had their origin in England. In 1802, Dr. Thomas Young of London, England proposed the ratio of stress to strain below the proportional limit as a property of the material. Thomas Tredgold, an English experimentalist and a contemporary of Young, attempted to evaluate Young's modulus for several materials using stress-strain data computed from load deflection tests. Certain assumptions (locations of neutral axis) on which his computations were based were attacked, and the experimental work, which these attacks caused Tredgold to undertake, led to the beginning of strain gage development.

In about 1850, Peter Barlow, an English experimentalist, designed, constructed, and used a single mechanical lever type of extensometer. This extensometer produced a magnification of 10 to 1, contained a vernier on a scale divided into tenths of inches, and was used over a 100 in. gage length.

The development of mechanical gages during the period 1870 to 1950, which is discussed in detail by M. Hetényi [1],* can be briefly summarized

* Bracketed numerals identify references at the end of each chapter.

as follows: a single lever gage patented in 1883 and used by Paine in tests on the New York East River Bridge gave a magnification of 100 to 1. The next major improvement in lever gages occurred in about 1890 with the introduction of single lever gages in which one end of the lever actually rested on the test piece. This principle, together with the use of compound levers (which was introduced by Berry in about 1910) and/or dial indicators, has given us our present-day mechanical lever gages which have magnifications up to 2000 to 1 and gage lengths as small as one-half inch.

The modern mechanical strain gages can be studied by a more detailed inspection of one widely used type. Figure 1-1 shows a Huggenberger

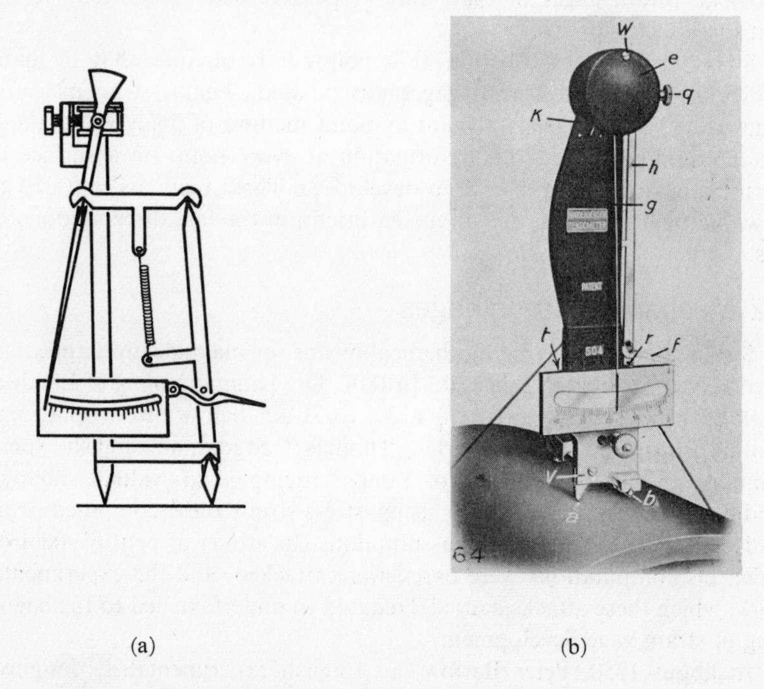

Fig. 1-1. **Compound lever, mechanical strain gage.** (*Courtesy of A. V. Huggenberger.*)

gage. As shown in Fig. 1-1, the height of the gage is considerable; this is because long levers are used to obtain a high magnification factor. The schematic (Fig. 1-1a) shows that this gage uses a compound lever system, in which one lever actually rests on the test piece. Figure 1-1b shows a

Huggenberger in use. In this case it is held in place by means of an electromagnet; other mounting fixtures may employ suction cups, screw clamps, or spring-loaded clips. Huggenberger and other gages employing compound levers are available, having magnifications as high as 2000 to 1 and gage lengths as small as 0.5 in. Gages of this type weigh as little as 0.4 oz.

The mechanical gages just described, and mechanical gages in general, have an advantage over all other types of strain gages in that their magnification system is self-contained. With mechanical gages no auxiliary equipment is necessary, whereas with all other gage types and particularly with electrical strain gages, the auxiliary equipment which must be used in conjunction with the strain gage dwarfs the gage in physical proportion, in cost, and in complexity. This feature of self-containment is sufficient reason for the stress analyst carefully to consider, at least, the use of mechanical gages whenever the test conditions will permit their use. The conditions under which mechanical gages may be profitably used can be briefly summarized as follows:

1. The stress gradient is expected to be sufficiently small so that the average strain over the gage length (which will be one-half inch or larger for commercially available gages) can be used as the strain at the desired point.
2. There is sufficient surface area on the test specimen and clearance above it for the mechanical gage together with its mounting fixture.
3. The additional mass introduced by the gage and its mounting fixture is so small compared to the mass of the test item as to have a negligible effect on the test conditions.
4. The rate of straining is so low that the relatively large mechanical inertia of the gage does not effect its response, and the rate of change of strain is such that visual observation and manual recording is feasible.

This statement of the conditions under which mechanical gages can be used immediately calls attention to the most important shortcoming of mechanical gages—namely, the poor adaptability of mechanical gages for measuring dynamic or varying strains. Here the difficulties involved in securely mounting the gages are considerable, the inertia introduced by the gage mass and the slow response of the gage due to its own inertia become important, and the lack of a good method of automatically recording the gage output is a severe handicap. To summarize, mechanical gages are best suited for use in static tests on those test specimens where the surface area and clearance are available for mounting and observing gages at points of interest which are removed from notches, grooves, corners, and similar stress raisers which produce areas of high stress gradient.

However, having dwelt upon the poor adaptability of mechanical gages in general to varying strains, we must mention the "deForest scratch recording strain gage." This single lever gage lacks the sensitivity of the modern mechanical gages previously described, but it can be used to record varying strains. Figure 1-2 shows a deForest scratch gage.

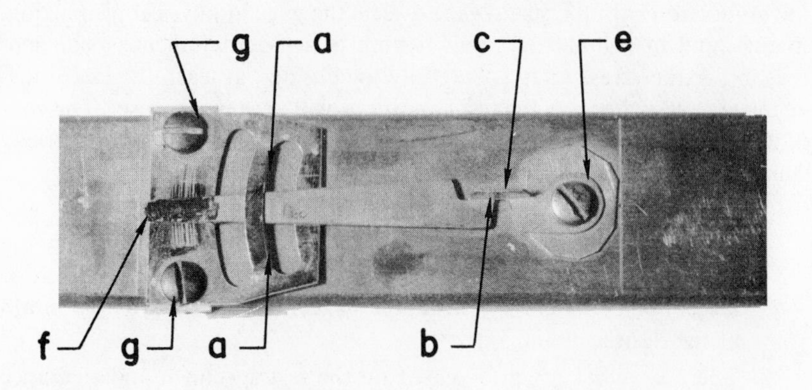

Fig. 1-2. Target and scratch arm of deForest scratch recording strain gage.

According to the manufacturer (Baldwin Southwark Corporation):

> This simple instrument records deformations below the elastic limit of from 0.0001 in. to 0.050 in., over a 2 in. gage length. The record is in the form of a scratch, the exact size of the deformation, which is measured or photographed at suitable magnification under a metallographic microscope. The recorder weighs two grams, and is therefore light enough to attach to rapidly moving parts. The scratch gage consists of two parts: one, the target; the other, the scratch arm carrying a special abrasive held under spring contact with the polished chrome plated recording surface. The particular feature of this gage is the method of causing the scratch arm to progress over the target at right angles to the direction of the strain record. The drive is obtained by using the difference between the coefficients of static and

moving friction. Between the clip bar on the target, *a* in Fig. 1-2, and the spring arm *b* is a generous amount of friction. The device is fastened in place on the surface to be strained with the arm in the center of its travel. The arm is then moved over to one side or the other of the target, bending the spring fulcrum *c*. The friction is sufficient to prevent the return of the arm to the center under static conditions, but when the distance between the gage points *g* and *e* is changed, the transverse force due to spring *c* causes arm *b* to move slightly toward the center with each longitudinal slip of the arm under the clip bar *a*.

The record consists of a scratch pattern on the target plate, and this record is read by means of a microscope. Figure 1-3 is a photomicrograph

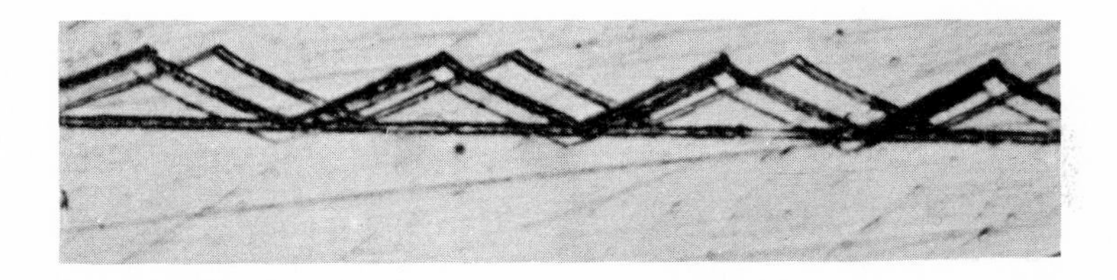

Fig. 1-3. Scratch record of repeated loading of a steel bar held in vise as a cantilever (magnified 175 times).

of a scratch pattern. This gage retains the advantage of self-containment while overcoming some of the difficulties discussed in connection with other mechanical gages.

1-3 Optical strain gages

Magnifying lens to permit more accurate reading of mechanical gages have been used almost since the start of mechanical gage development. Those mechanical gages which incorporated magnification in their viewing system might be classed as mechanical-optical gages, but the use of magnifying lens is not the most important application of optics to strain measurements.

Optical levers have been used for many years in physics laboratories to measure small displacements; however, it was the development of a new optical lever system by L. B. Tuckerman of the National Bureau of Standards which made possible the development of a strain gage which combines mechanical and optical levers. The Tuckerman optical strain gage is shown in Fig. 1-4a. According to the manufacturer (American Instrument Company, Incorporated),

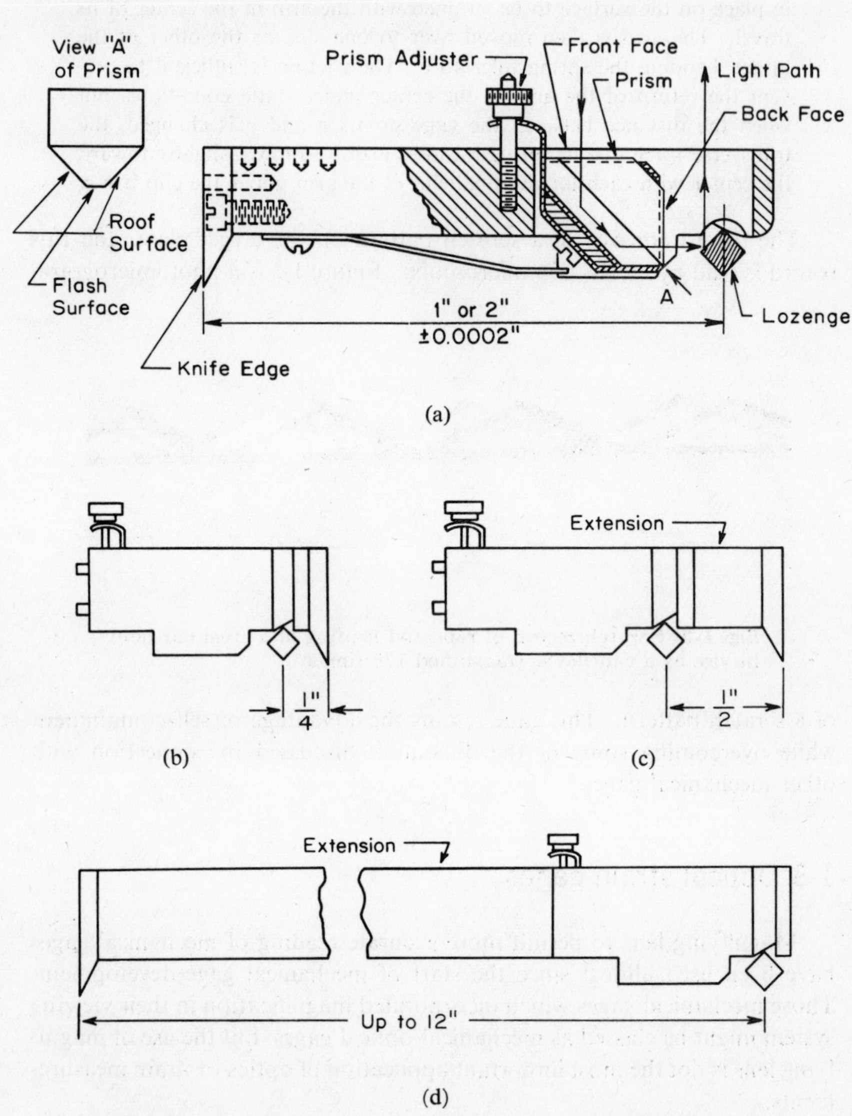

Fig. 1-4. Tuckerman optical strain gage. (*Courtesy of American Instrument Co., Inc.*)

This gage is made of either steel or aluminum alloy, in two standard lengths—1 and 2 inches. In every case the distance from the knife edge to the point of contact of the lozenge is the nominal length of the gage, plus or minus 0.0002 in.

By placing the knife edge on the lozenge end of the extensometer body, the 1-in. extensometer becomes a $\frac{1}{4}$-in. extensometer (see Fig. 1-4b) and by adding a $\frac{1}{4}$-in. spacer the 1-in. extensometer becomes a $\frac{1}{2}$-in. extensometer (see Fig. 1-4c).

By adding extensions to a standard extensometer it may be made to any gage length up to 12 in., in increments of 1 in. (see Fig. 1-4d). Either the 1-in. or the 2-in. extensometer may be used as the basis for the longer extensometer. These extensions are made of steel, aluminum alloy, or invar. The smallest strain (movement) measurable with this device is 1/500,000 in. Each gage is calibrated by means of a precision interferometer. A calibration factor is supplied with each extensometer or lozenge, in which case the calibration may be relied upon to at least plus or minus 0.1 per cent of the full scale deflection. The scale has 125 graduations (every fifth graduation being numbered) giving 25 numbered divisions.

Table 1-1 gives typical ranges for various gage lengths and lozenges. Note that the total range of strain varies inversely with the gage length.

Table 1-1*

Gage Length in.	Lozenges in.	Total Range of Strain in.
0.25	0.2	0.0816
2.00	0.2	0.0102
10.00	0.2	0.00204
2.00	0.4	0.0204
2.00	0.5	0.02550

* Courtesy of American Instrument Co., Inc.

The gage is read by using the auto-collimator as shown in Fig. 1-5.

The true optical gage (as distinguished from the mechanical-optical gage just described) is an interferometer type. These gages, which depend on the interference fringes produced when two optical flats undergo relative motion equal to one-half the wavelength of light, are suited only for the most sensitive laboratory work. The first use of the interferometer as a strain gage was made in 1935 by R. V. Vose, who used it to measure the change in thickness of photoelastic models under test. Since 1935 interferometer strain gages have been used in various laboratories to determine Young's modulus and Poisson's ratio, but they are not commercially available.

The mechanical-optical gages are subjected to the same limitations in use as are the mechanical gages; in addition, some additional auxiliary devices are required for the observations of the results. However, the

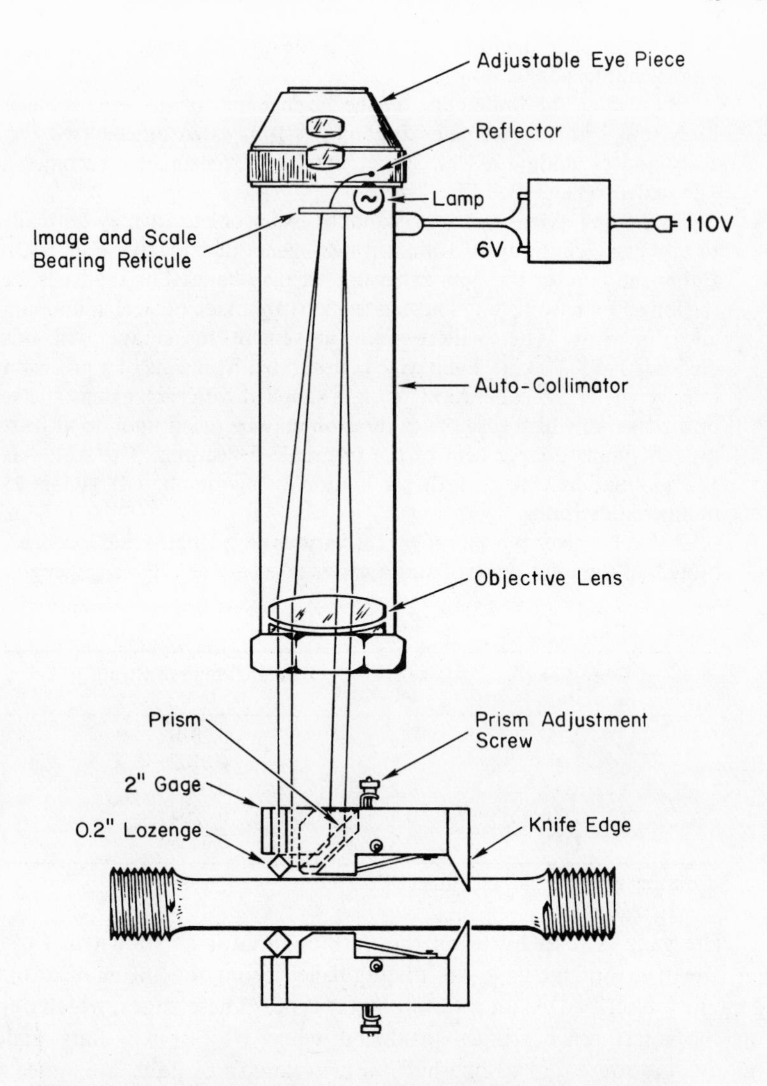

Fig. 1-5. Relationship of auto-collimator and extensometers, and relative positions of auto-collimator optical components. Three images are visible on the reticule. The reading or "steady" image lies on the scale and its position relative to the scale is governed only by the rocking of the lozenge and the prism, and is not affected by relative motion between the specimen and the auto-collimator. The other images are used mainly in eliminating errors due to rotation of the extensometers or for qualitative purpose in problems involving vibrations. The two extensometers, mounted as shown, are read alternately and averaged, thus automatically compensating for any bending of the specimen. (*Courtesy of American Instrument Co., Inc.*)

Tuckerman optical gage has good sensitivity, and a gage of the interferometer type has the greatest inherent sensitivity of any type of strain gage yet devised.

1-4 Electrical strain gages

An electrical strain gage is a device in which a change in length (strain) produces a change in some electrical characteristic. Magnification of the signal is then accomplished by electronic means. The important advantage common to all electric gages is the relative ease with which the output can be amplified, displayed, and recorded. Grouping electrical strain gages according to the particular electrical property affected by straining, we have: (1) capacitance gages, (2) inductance (or magnetic) gages, (3) piezoelectric gages, and (4) resistance gages. All of the electrical gages are of comparatively recent origin.

Of the four types, the first (capacitance gages) have found very little use as strain gages and are not commercially available. However, variable capacitance transducers are used to measure pressure, force, and displacement; see Refs. [2] and [3].

The inductance type of gage was developed as a strain gage about 1930 and has been used for various applications since then. The inductance gage can take several forms, but in all cases the gage functions as an inductive element in the electrical circuit. Straining produces a change in the magnitude of the inductance associated with the gage, and it is this inductance change which permits magnification and recording. Figure 1-6a shows a commercially available inductance strain gage of the variable air gap type, and Fig. 1-6b shows the basic electrical circuit into which this type of strain gage is connected. In this particular design the laminated iron cores (E_1 and E_2 in Fig. 1-6b) are carried on the frame piece which is mounted to the test specimen at one end. The laminated iron armature (A in Fig. 1-6b) is carried on the frame piece which is mounted to the test specimen at the opposite end. When a change in length between the two ends occurs, the air gap between the armature and one core increases while the gap between the armature and the other core decreases. This change in air gap changes the inductance of the two coils on E_1 and E_2 with a resultant change in the current flow in the external loop (I_5 in Fig. 1-6b). It is this change in current that is measured and related to the relative motion between the gage attachment points (i.e., strain).

For a discussion of other forms of inductance strain gages and a detailed discussion of the circuitry used with inductance gages, see Ref.

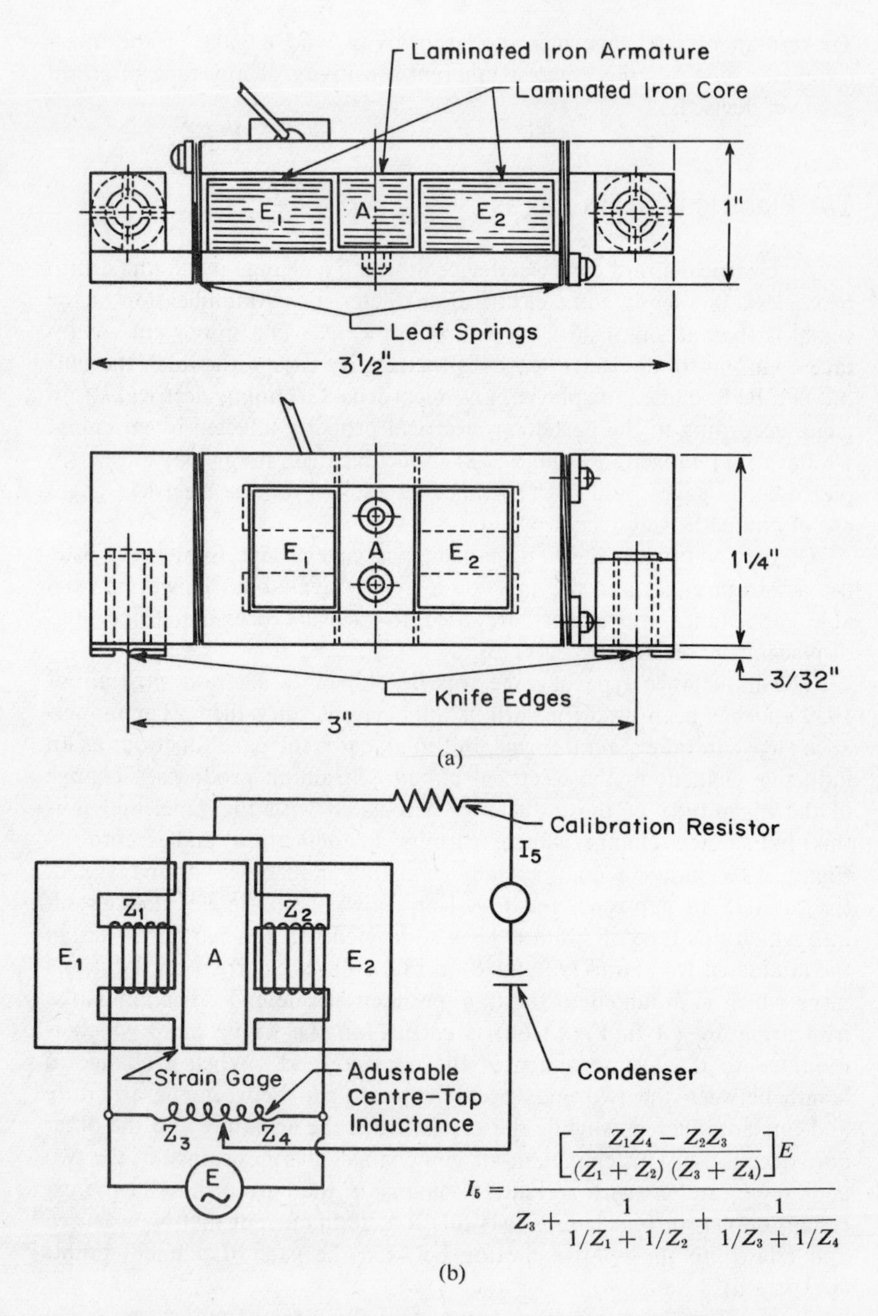

$$I_5 = \frac{\left[\dfrac{Z_1 Z_4 - Z_2 Z_3}{(Z_1 + Z_2)\,(Z_3 + Z_4)}\right] E}{Z_3 + \dfrac{1}{1/Z_1 + 1/Z_2} + \dfrac{1}{1/Z_3 + 1/Z_4}}$$

(b)

Fig. 1-6. Inductance-type strain gage. (*Courtesy of Society for Experimental Stress Analysis.*)

[4]. In common with all electrical strain gages, the inductance gage has the advantage of easy readout and recording and, compared to the resistance gage (to be discussed later in this section), the inductance gage has a very high output, which simplifies the associated readout circuit. However, as was the case with mechanical and optical gages, the inductance type of strain gage has appreciable size, mass, and gage length. For this reason, variable inductance transducers are more used in motion measuring devices than as strain gages. Hence, this principle will be discussed further in Chap. 8.

The ability of certain materials to generate an electrical charge when strained was observed before 1900 by the Curies. This effect is known as the piezoelectric effect, and materials exhibiting this effect are referred to as piezoelectric materials. Certain crystalline materials are naturally piezoelectric, and certain polycrystalline ceramics can be given piezoelectric properties artificially during manufacture (see Sect. 9-2). Since the 1940's, the piezoelectric principle has been widely used in various kinds of transducers, particularly for measurement of pressure and acceleration. The use of a piezoelectric material as the transducer element in an accelerometer is discussed in detail in Chap. 9, and information on piezoelectric properties and electrical circuitry for use with piezoelectric devices appears there.

The piezoelectric principle is mentioned here because recently piezoelectric materials have been used as strain gages. A small wafer of piezoelectric material is bonded with electrically insulating cement to the surface of a part at a point where the strain is to be measured. With suitable circuitry and recording equipment,* the electrical charge produced by strain can be measured and related to the magnitude of strain at the gaged point. E. A. Ripperger [5] used thin (0.01 in.) wafers of barium titanate bonded with Duco (cellulose nitrate) to measure very small strains (10^{-6} in./in.) produced by impact. J. W. Mark and W. Goldsmith [6] made a more detailed study of the use of barium titanate as a strain gage with particular emphasis on calibration of such gages.

Piezoelectric strain gages are of interest because of the very high signal produced per unit of strain and because they are self-generating; i.e., no power supply is needed. They are not in wide use for several reasons. (1) They are not suitable for measuring static strains and, because of this, they are difficult to calibrate.† (2) They have not been precalibrated because mounting affects the sensitivity. (3) They produce considerable reinforcement at the point to which they are attached, and this changes

* See Sect. 9-3.

† For a discussion of the low frequency response of piezoelectrics, see Sect. 9-3b.

the strain field that is to be studied. For these reasons, piezoelectric gages are most frequently used to provide a control signal when strain is sensed and to provide qualitative measurements of strain. Uncalibrated piezoelectric strain gages are commercially available (Gulton Mfg., Metuchen, New Jersey).

The resistance type of strain gage functions as a resistive element in an electrical circuit. Strain produces a change in the magnitude of the resistance associated with the gage. In the past, both metals and nonmetals have been used as the resistive element. A nonmetallic, unbonded resistance gage (an extensometer) was used in 1924 by McCollum and Peters. This gage consisted of a stack of precompressed carbon blocks through which an electric current passed; when the stack was relieved or further compressed by straining, the resistance change was recorded and related to strain.

A nonmetallic, bonded resistance gage was developed in 1935 by A. Block and was used shortly thereafter by Hamilton Standard for determining strains in rotating aircraft propellers. In this type, a plastic, impregnated with carbon particles, is deposited directly on the test specimen (i.e., bonded); the resistance of this "patch" to electrical current is found to be a function of strain. These nonmetallic resistance-type gages are not commercially available, due to their poor stability. However, these gages have a greater sensitivity (high signal output per unit strain) than any other resistance gage, and they have been used in experimental work for providing control signals and a qualitative indication of strain. Nonmetallic resistance gages may be made by mixing powdered graphite in rubber cement and brushing the mixture on the point of interest. Leads are attached by using conducting silver paint. If the object on which the gage is placed is an electrical conductor (metal), it is necessary only to place an insulating film between the gage and the conductive surface—Duco cement may be used for this purpose.

The principle leading to the development of metallic resistance strain gages was first noted by Lord Kelvin in 1856, when he observed that the electrical resistance of various metal wires was influenced by their state of strain (piezoresistive effect). The first use of this principle for strain measurement was not made until in 1930 by R. W. Carlson and E. C. Eaton. This first metallic resistance gage consisted of a fine wire looped between two pins which were in turn fixed to the test piece. This unbonded type (wire not fixed directly to the test specimen) is still in use and is commercially available. Figure 1-7 shows a commercially available strain gage of the unbonded wire type. Unbonded, variable resistance strain gages have appreciable size, mass, and gage length and, as a result, the unbonded variable resistance transducer is more used in motion measuring gages than

Illustrated approximately actual size.

(a)

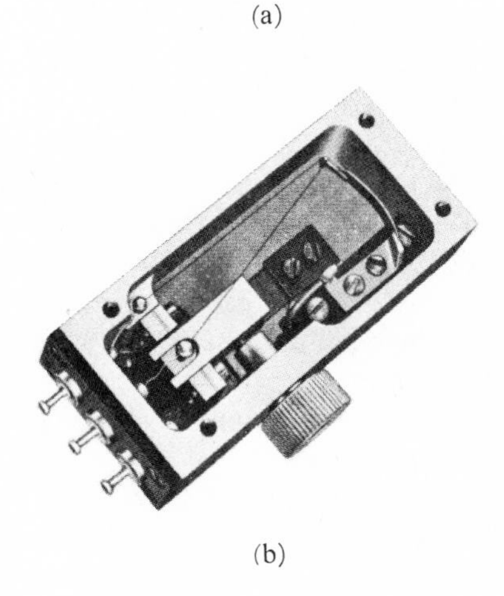

(b)

Fig. 1-7. Resistance strain gage, unbonded wire type. (*Courtesy of Statham Laboratories, Inc.*)

in strain gages.* The electrical circuitry and recording equipment used with unbonded resistance gages is the same as that used with the bonded resistance gages.†

A bonded, metallic resistance gage in which the wire was bonded directly to the test piece was invented by Simmons in 1940. At about the same time, Ruge conceived the idea of bonding the wire to a thin paper

* See Sect. 8-2.

† See Sect. 2-2.

base and then bonding the paper to the test piece. Because of the advances made in the art of printed electrical circuits during the 1940's and 1950's, metallic resistance strain gages are now available with foil elements as well as wire elements.

In 1954 C. S. Smith [7] reported on the piezoresistive properties of two semiconductors, silicon and germanium. In 1957, W. P. Mason and R. N. Thurston [8] reported on the use of semiconductors in variable resistance transducers.

Various metals (in the form of both wire and foil) and semiconductors are now widely used in bonded, variable resistance strain gages. Typical examples of three types are shown in Fig. 2-2 on page 55. This type of strain gage is certainly the most widely used at the present time, and the next four chapters are devoted exclusively to bonded resistance gages, their associated circuitry, recording equipment, problems, and data reduction methods.

The bonded, resistive type of strain gage serves to surmount most of the shortcomings enumerated for the mechanical and optical gages. Gages of this type approach negligible mass, and gage lengths as low as $\frac{1}{32}$ in. are available. These gages respond faithfully to rapidly fluctuating strains, and the output signal is easily recorded. However, when any electrical strain gage is used, the gage will almost always be dwarfed by the associated equipment necessary to operate and record from the gage. This will be true with respect to size, cost, and complexity.

1-5 Grid techniques

As we mentioned in the introduction, strain gages of all types function to measure strain at a point (actually, average strain over a given gage length); therefore, many gages must be used to investigate a strain field of finite area. When strain data are required over a field of finite area, an experimental method that will yield data at many points simultaneously is desired. Such techniques are referred to as "whole field methods."

The most obvious whole field method consists of placing reference marks on the specimen over the area of interest, measuring the distance between the marks before straining and again after straining, and computing the strain as the change in length divided by the original length (the distance between the marks is the gage length over which the strain is averaged). If the reference marks are in the form of a continuous grid pattern, rectangular, polar, or other, sufficient information becomes available to determine the principal strain magnitudes and directions at every point. For example, with a rectangular grid, the normal strain in three directions can be determined by the measurement of the change in length of the sides and a diagonal. With the normal strain in three directions known, the principal strains can be determined by using the usual rosette equation.*

To use the grid technique two problems must be solved: first, forming the grid on the surface of interest and second, measuring the deformation of the grid that is produced by the environment of interest. Before we discuss the solutions to either of these problems, it is important to emphasize the magnitude of dimensional changes that are likely to be involved. As a reference, consider a mild steel having a yield point stress S_y of 30,000 psi and a modulus of elasticity E of 30×10^6 psi. The yield point strain ϵ_y is 1000×10^{-6} in./in., which is more commonly written as 1000 μin./in. or 1000 microstrain. If a one in. square grid were laid out on this material, the length change of a one in. side at the yield point would be 0.001 in. Clearly, a one in. gage length is unsuitable for use in regions of high strain gradient, such as near points of stress concentration, since the maximum strain will differ from the average over the one in. length by large and unknown amounts. However, if a 0.01 in. square grid is used, the change in length at the yield point will be only 0.00001 in. The limit of resolution on these measurements has functioned to restrict the application of the grid method to problems involving very large strains—hence, plastic strains in metals or elastic strains in materials capable of very large elastic deformation, i.e., rubberlike. If large strains in a certain rubberlike material are of interest, the grid method may be an obvious choice; if, however, the rubberlike material is selected only as a model for a material that will undergo much smaller strains, the problem is complicated by the additional problem of relating strains in the model to the strains in the prototype. The similarity requirements between model and prototype and the difference between large and small strains must be considered.

Grids may be formed on the surface of interest by drawing or scribing [9] by photographic printing ([10], [11], [12], [13]), or by cementing a grid network to the surface [14].

Hand drawing or scribing is suitable only when relatively coarse grids are used. In general, when grids are hand drawn or scribed, each element in the grid will have to be measured both before and after straining. With flat and cylindrical surfaces, grids can be machine scribed by using ruling engines. With machine scribed grids, the individual elements in the grid may be identical within close tolerances and, hence, measurements need be made only after straining. Scribed grids are often used

* See Chap. 5 for the development and application of the rosette equations.

when the test is carried to the point of rupture, since most other grids are damaged near the rupture line.

Grids are applied photographically by painting a light-sensitive emulsion on the surface, covering the surface with a master grid negative, exposing to strong light, and developing the resultant print in the usual manner. The term "photogrid" is used for a grid so applied. The master grid negative may be prepared by drawing the grid to a very large scale and then photographically reducing to obtain the desired grid spacing and accuracy. More commonly, master grid negatives are made by contact printing from master grids on glass plates which are machine ruled. J. A. Miller [13] describes the way in which a glass master is produced. Several emulsions and step-by-step procedures for applying the grid to the specimen are given in Refs. [10], [11], [12], and [13]. Photogrids have remarkable tenacity and have been applied to metal which was then deep drawn. The strain pattern produced by the deep draw can be determined in this way; see Fig. 1-8.

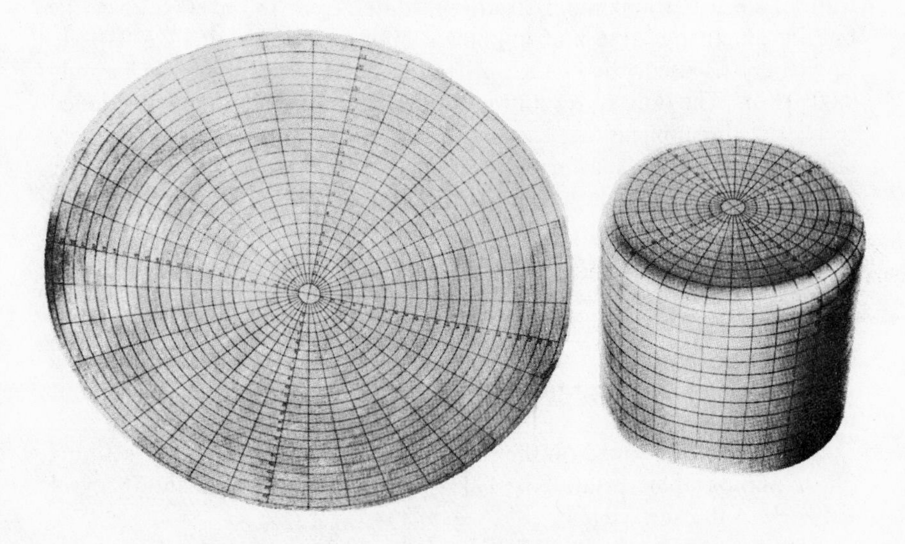

Fig. 1-8. Photogrid on blank and deep drawn cup. (*Courtesy of Metal Progress, Ref.* [*15*].)

A. J. Durelli and W. F. Riley [14] cast a grid of extruded rubber threads in a plastic material so that the grid method could be used in conjunction with the photoelastic method of stress analysis.*

* See Chap. 6 for a discussion of the photoelastic method.

After straining, the necessary grid dimensions can be measured in any of several ways. In some cases the measurements can be made on the model by using a micrometer-microscope or a microscope with a graduated reticle. Care must be taken to insure that magnification is the same when the before and after readings are taken. More often, photographs are made as the test progresses and then measurements are made on the photograph. A micrometer-microscope or an optical comparator can be used in this case. Extreme care must be taken to make sure that photographic magnification and effect of film shrinkage are allowed for in comparing the before and after measurements.

For making measurements in areas where the grid lines are contoured on a curved surface, as around a corner produced during a forming operation, Miller [13] suggests and describes a replica method. A plastic solution which will harden is pressed and held on the grid surface with a flexible tape. When the solution has hardened, this grid replica is peeled off, straightened, and pressed between glass plates, and measurements are made.

1-6 Moiré fringe method

The method of "whole field" strain measurement to be discussed in this section has been discussed in the literature under various titles. Among the titles applied are "mechanical interferometry" [16], "photoscreen method" [17], and "moiré method." All titles refer to the identical method, and the title "moiré method" is currently in most common use. In some respects the moiré fringe method of strain measurement is similar to the grid method just discussed. A grid, or grids, must be applied to the area of interest (photographic printing is most often used); a pattern produced by straining must be measured (a micrometer-microscope is most often used); this method is best suited to measuring relatively large strains. The moiré fringe method has two distinct advantages as compared to the grid method, however. First, the point in the test area of greatest interest (point of largest strain) and the general nature of the strain gradient can be determined without any measurements. Second, the measurements required are much less tedious to make than in the grid method. A relative disadvantage of the moiré method is the fact that two sets of grids must be applied and measured to define the strain field completely.

The moiré fringe effect is the formation of alternately light and dark patterns that are observed when two similar line patterns are laid one on top of the other and one is rotated relative to the other, as with two pieces of screen wire. This effect, produced by mechanical interference, has been known for a very long time, but Weller and Shepard [16] appear to have been the first to use it as a tool for experimental stress analysis. References [17], [18], [19], and [20] contain complete analyses for relating interference patterns to displacement and/or strain.

The moiré fringe phenomena can be explained in terms of the array of lines shown in Fig. 1-9. The linear sets shown in Fig. 1-9a are assumed to be identical; one set S is on the surface to be studied; the other set M, applied to a transparent sheet (usually a hard film negative), will be called the master grid. The opaque line width and the transparent space width are equal (this equality is not necessary, but it gives the best resolution; see Ref. [17]). Now assume that the master grid M is slid to the left so as to overlap the surface grid S with all lines parallel, as in Fig. 1-9b. Next assume that the surface grid S is subjected to a uniform strain in the y direction (ϵ_y). Figure 1-9c shows the resulting pattern for $\epsilon_y = 0.1$ tension. In general, the distance d between the centers of adjacent lines of maximum density (fringe lines) will be given by

$$d = \frac{p}{\epsilon}(1 + \epsilon),$$

in which d is the fringe spacing;

p is the unstrained grid pitch;

and ϵ is the strain perpendicular to the grid lines, + for tension and — for compression.

For the complete development of this equation see Ref. [19]. For Fig. 1-9c, since $\epsilon_y = +0.1$, and taking p as 2 units ($t = 1$ unit), we have

$$d = \frac{2}{0.1}(1 + 0.1) = 22 \text{ units}.$$

In general, normal strain in a direction perpendicular to the grid lines can be determined if p is known and d is measured; thus

$$\epsilon_T = \frac{p}{d - p}$$

for tensile strains, and

$$\epsilon_c = \frac{p}{d + p}$$

for compressive strains.

To explain the moiré fringe pattern that results from relative rotation of two grids, we shall start again with the two unstrained grids, Fig. 1-9a. Now assume that the master grid M is slid to the left to cover the surface

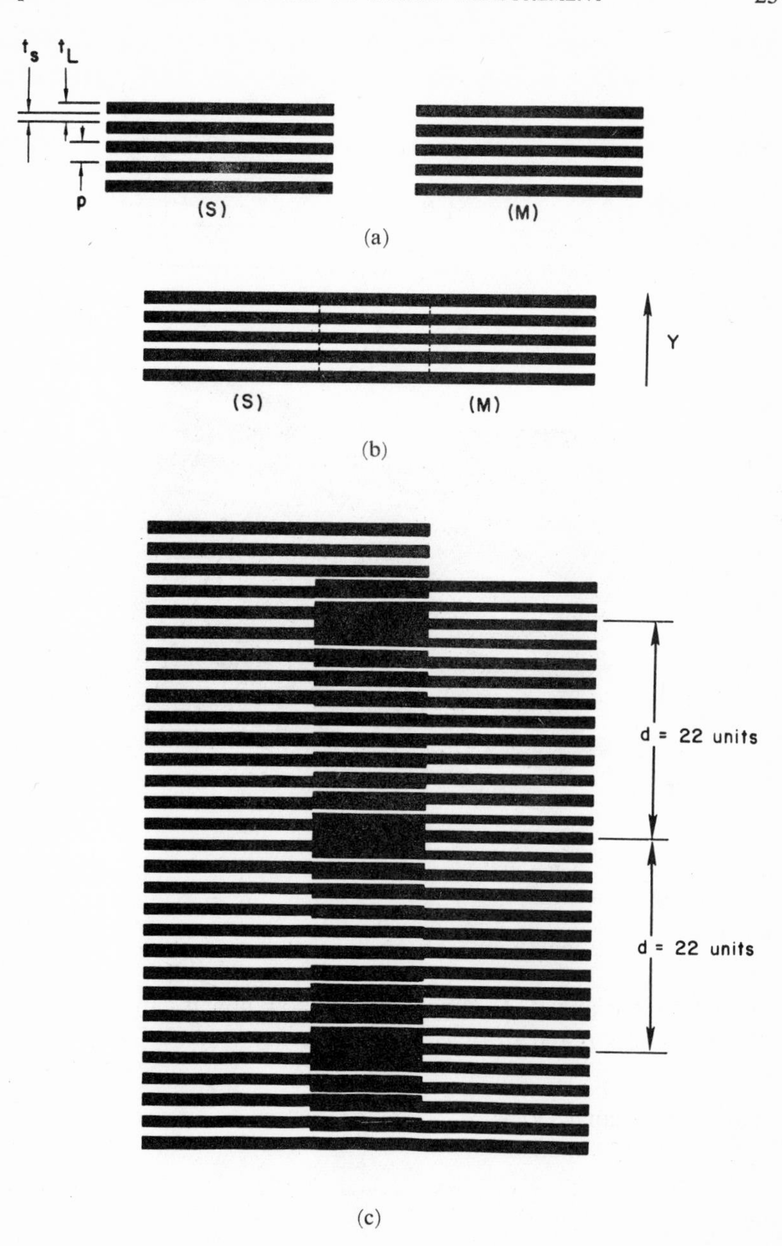

Fig. 1-9. Moiré fringe effect, normal strain.

grid S, and the surface grid is then rotated through an angle θ. The resultant fringe pattern and its geometry are shown in Fig. 1-10. Consideration

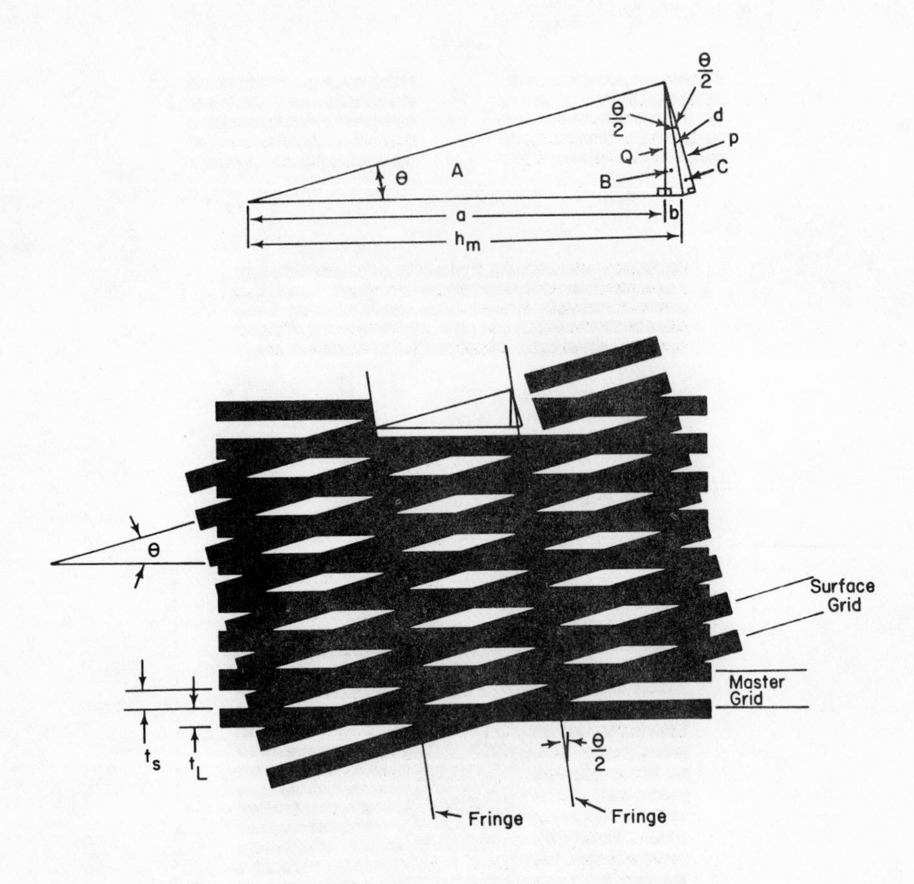

Fig. 1-10. Moiré fringe effect, rotation.

of the three triangles A, B, and C will show how θ can be determined. Since triangles B and C are equal triangles,

$$q = p.$$

Then from triangle A:

$$a = \frac{q}{\tan\,\theta},$$

or

$$a = \frac{p}{\tan\,\theta}.$$

If the distance between the fringes, measured parallel to the master grid lines, is denoted as h_m, then

$$h_m = a + b,$$

and

$$h_m = \frac{p}{\tan\theta} + p \tan\frac{\theta}{2},$$

or

$$h_m = \frac{p\cos\theta}{\sin\theta} + p\,\frac{1 - \cos\theta}{\sin\theta},$$

or

$$h_m = \frac{p}{\sin\theta}.$$

In general, rotation of the surface relative to the master grid M can be determined if p is known and h_m, the distance between fringes, measured parallel to the master grid lines, is measured.
Thus,

$$\theta = \sin^{-1}\frac{p}{h_m}.$$

Notice that fringes produced by rotation make an angle of $\theta/2$ with a line which is perpendicular to the master grid. The fringes are rotated from this perpendicular in the same sense as the surface was rotated to produce the fringes. Since shear strain γ results in rotation, moiré fringes can now be related to shear strain. A surface element distorted by shear is shown in Fig. 1-11a. By definition, $\gamma_{xy} = \tan^{-1}\alpha$. If grid lines were originally horizontal on both surface and master, the fringe pattern would be as shown in Fig. 1-11b and the angle, $\theta_x = (\alpha/2)_x$, can be evaluated as

$$\theta_x = \left(\frac{\alpha}{2}\right)_x = + \left|\sin^{-1}\frac{p}{h_x}\right|.$$

We shall call this "plus," since the fringes are rotated counterclockwise from a co-ordinate perpendicular to the master grid. If the grid lines were originally vertical on both surface and master, the fringe pattern would be as shown in Fig. 1-11c and the angle, $\theta_y = (\alpha/2)_y$, can be evaluated as

$$\theta_y = \left(\frac{\alpha}{2}\right)_y = - \left|\sin^{-1}\frac{p}{h_y}\right|.$$

We shall call this "minus," since the fringes are rotated clockwise from a co-ordinate perpendicular to the master grid. In this case

$$\gamma_{xy} = \tan^{-1}\alpha = \tan^{-1}\left[\left|\left(\frac{\alpha}{2}\right)_x\right| + \left|\left(\frac{\alpha}{2}\right)_y\right|\right].$$

In general, the shear strain γ_{xy} is

$$\gamma_{xy} = \tan^{-1}\alpha = \tan^{-1}(\theta_x - \theta_y),$$

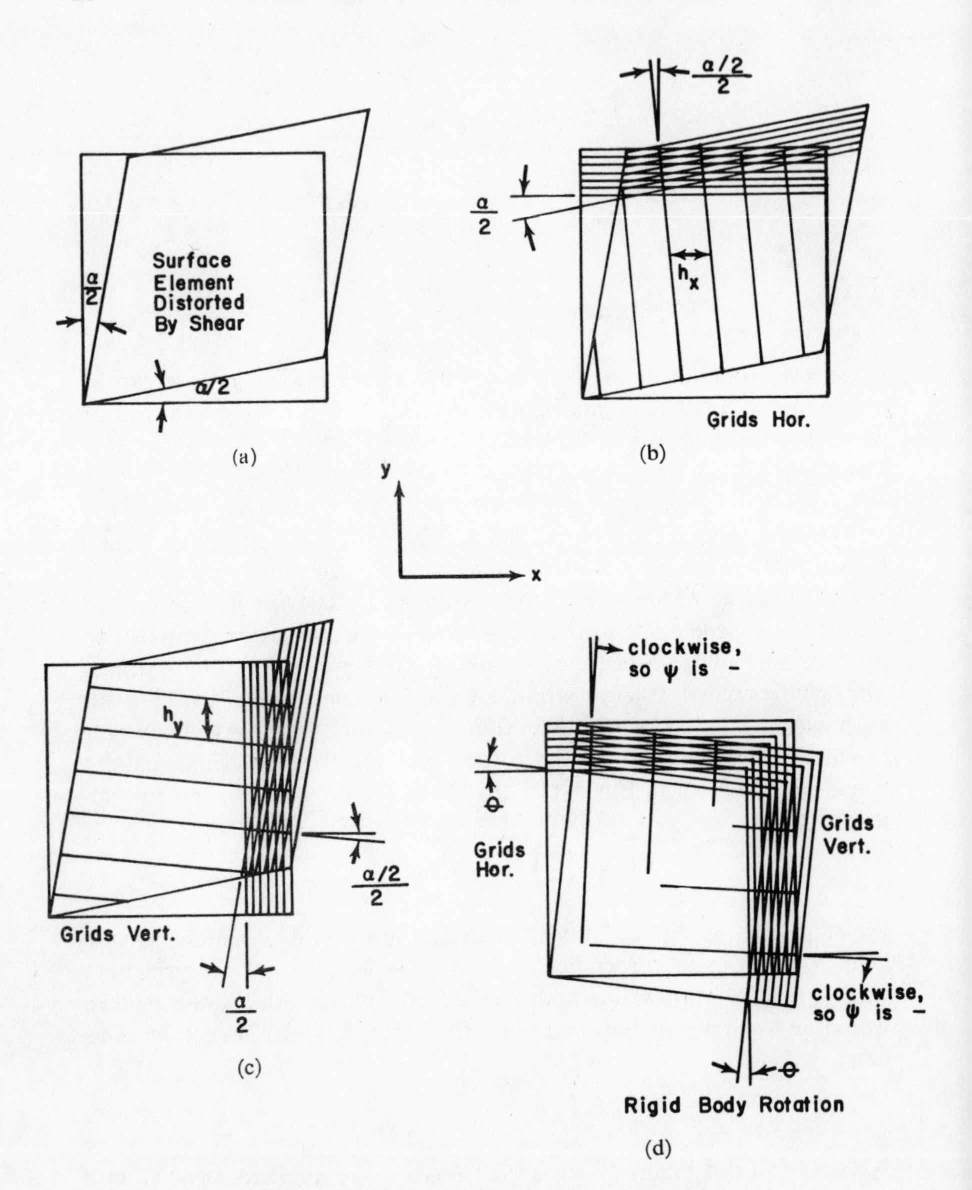

Fig. 1-11. Moiré fringe effect, shear strain.

in which θ_x and θ_y can be either plus or minus. Notice that if rigid body rotation accompanies the rotation produced by shear, the expression just developed will still be correct, because rigid body rotation produces the same fringe effect with either horizontal or vertical grids, and hence the effect of rigid body rotation is cancelled in the above equation; see Fig. 1-11d. Indeed, any rigid body rotation ϕ, could be determined as

$$\phi = \tfrac{1}{2}(\theta_x + \theta_y),$$

in which we evaluate θ_x, using horizontal (x) grids, as

$$\theta_x = \sin^{-1}\frac{p}{h_x};$$

and we evaluate θ_y, using vertical (y) grids, as

$$\theta_y = \sin^{-1}\frac{p}{h_y}.$$

In the usual case, both normal and shear strains will occur simultaneously, and the strain will not be uniform over the surface. A rigorous analysis for this most general case, which applies regardless of the magnitude of the normal and shear strains and rigid body rotations, is given in Ref. [19]. For those cases where the rigid body rotation and the strains are small, the fringe pattern can be interpreted by superimposing the results previously obtained and considering normal strain and rotation to be applied separately. If the strain is not uniform over the area of interest, the results represent average values of the strain components over the length between any two adjacent fringes. Figure 1-12 shows a deformed surface. In Fig. 1-12a the surface grid was originally oriented in the x direction, and the fringe pattern is viewed through an x-oriented master grid. In Fig. 1-12b the surface grid was originally oriented in the y direction, and the fringe pattern is viewed through a y-oriented master grid. Using the equations previously developed, we have, from Fig. 1-12a,

$$\epsilon_y = \frac{p}{d_y \mp p},$$

in which the "minus" applies for tensile strain and the "plus" for compressive strain.

$$\theta_x = +\left|\sin^{-1}\frac{p}{h_x}\right|.$$

From Fig. 1-12b:

$$\epsilon_x = \frac{p}{d_x \mp p},$$

$$\theta_y = +\left|\sin^{-1}\frac{p}{h_y}\right|.$$

Then

$$\gamma_{xy} = \tan^{-1}\left[\left(\sin^{-1}\frac{p}{h_x}\right) - \left(\sin^{-1}\frac{p}{h_y}\right)\right].$$

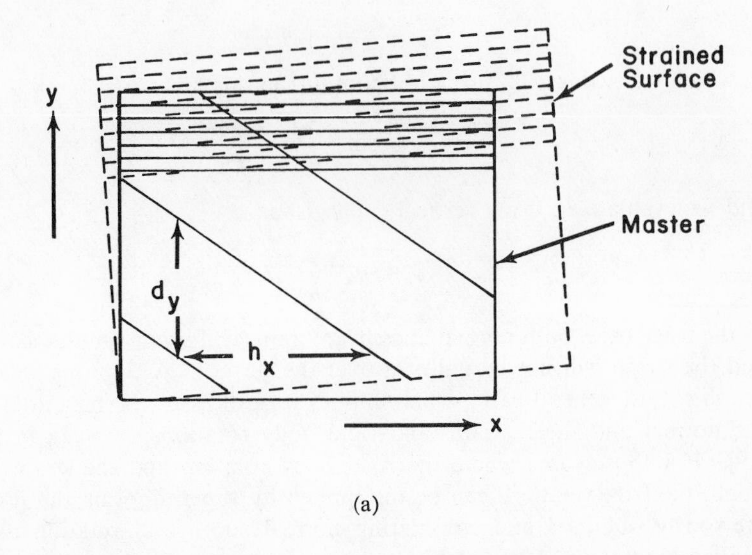

(a)

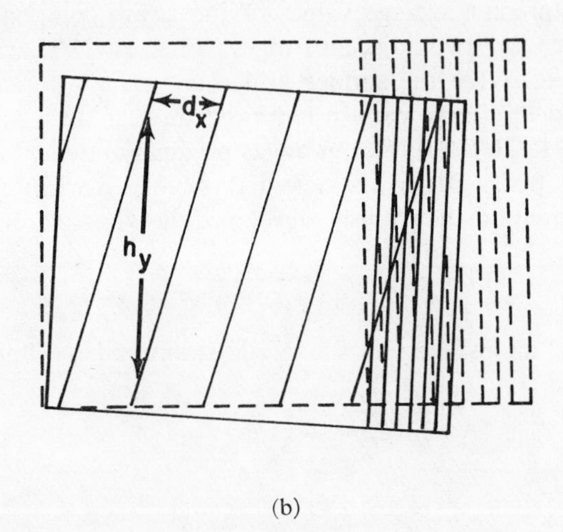

(b)

Fig. 1-12. Moiré fringe effect, combined normal and shear strain.

In cases where $d >> p$ (small ϵ), the normal strain becomes

$$\epsilon_x = \frac{p}{d_x}$$

and

$$\epsilon_y = \frac{p}{d_y},$$

for either tension or compression.

In cases where $h_x >> p$ and $h_y >> p$ (small angle of rotation),

$$\theta_x = \frac{p}{h_x},$$

$$\theta_y = \frac{p}{h_y},$$

and

$$\gamma_{xy} = (\theta_x - \theta_y),$$

since the sine and tangent functions of small angles are nearly equal to the value of the angle itself. With ϵ_x, ϵ_y, and γ_{xy} known, the principal strains can be computed in the usual manner.*

Complete analysis requires patterns formed by each of two orthogonal grid sets. Two identical tests can be made: the first with a y set of grids, the second with an x set of grids; or with a symmetrical strain field, one side of the test item can be studied with an x set of grids, while the other side can be studied with a y set of grids. Figure 1-13 is an

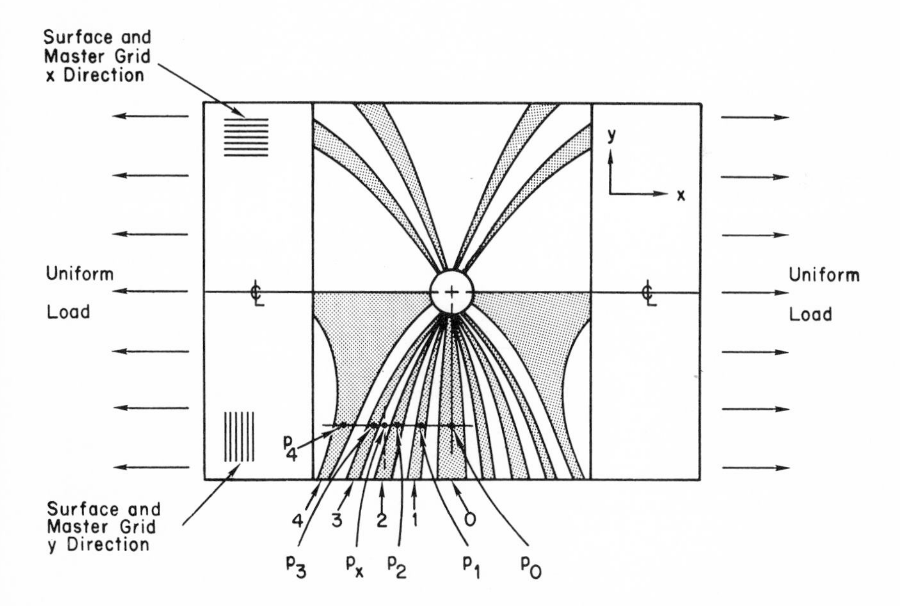

Fig. 1-13. Moiré fringe pattern on a plate containing a small hole.

* See Chap. 5.

example of this last case. The resolution of the moiré method depends upon the grid pitch p used. One hundred to 2000 lines per inch are used, i.e., p from 0.01 to 0.0005, but resolution is always limited by the accuracy with which the fringe spacing (d and h) can be measured. It must also be remembered that the strain values determined represent averaged values over the distance between fringes. The normal strain value at a point can best be found by plotting position versus fringe number and taking d (in./fringe) as the slope of this plot at the position of interest. If we use Fig. 1-13 as an example, the fringes are numbered arbitrarily as shown and the positions of points along a line of interest are determined from the arbitrary starting point, 0. See Fig. 1-14.

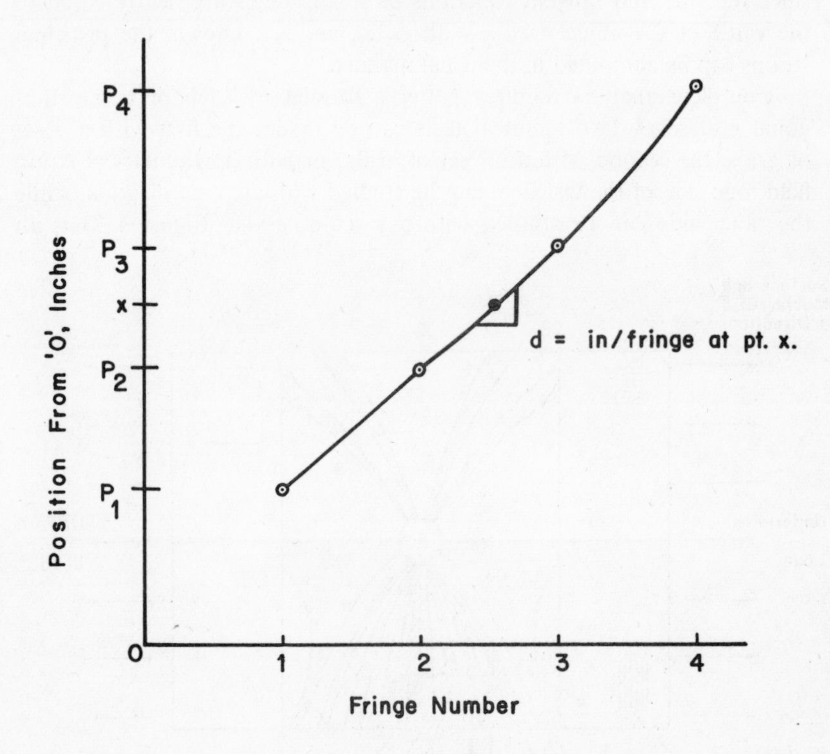

Fig. 1-14. Reduction of moiré fringe data.

This simplified method of analysis presented here gives best results for *normal* strains when the *fringe lines* are nearly *parallel* to the grid lines (i.e., with a given grid, at a given point $h > d$). In this case, however, there may be considerable error in evaluating rigid body rotation or shear strain. Conversely, rigid body rotation and/or *shear* strains are most accurately determined when the *fringe lines* are nearly *perpendicular* to the grid lines. In this case there may be considerable error in evaluating normal strains.

The moiré fringe method has been used to study strain distribution during high rate of loading tests by photographing the changing fringe pattern with a high-speed camera. Figure 1-15 shows a frame of film

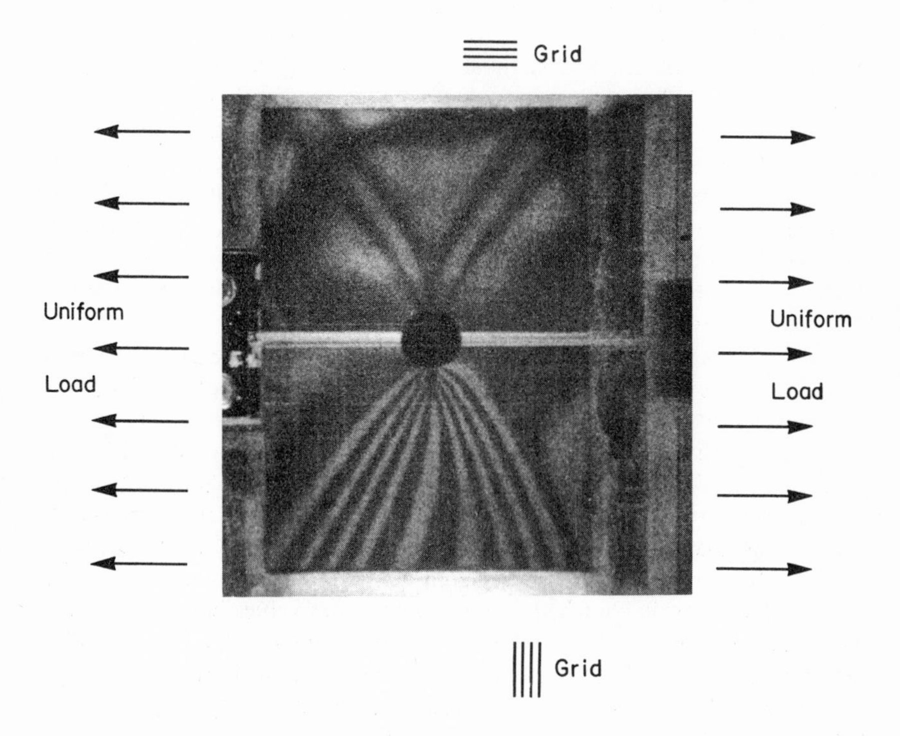

Fig. 1-15. Photograph of moiré fringe pattern taken at 1200 frames/second.

taken at a rate of 1200 frames per second. The lower half of the specimen carries a grid perpendicular to the direction of the applied load; the upper half carries a grid parallel to the direction of the applied load.

1-7 Brittle coatings for strain indication

The term "brittle coating" is used to describe a coating which will fail or crack when a certain value of tensile stress is exceeded without an appreciable yielding or inelastic action preceding the actual cracking. If an actual structure coated with such a brittle material were subjected to loads, the initiation of cracks in the coating could be related to tensile stress in the structure. The proper use of brittle coatings will then graphically show the distribution, magnitude, direction, and gradient of stresses on an actual structure. This graphical illustration of the state of stress over the whole surface of an actual structure is useful for several purposes. (A photoelastic coating may also be used for this purpose, but reduction of the observed data to actual strain values is somewhat more complicated.) First, the crack patterns can be used to determine the location and direction of electric resistance strain gages for the more accurate determination of stresses at desired locations. Second, the approximate values of stress indicated by the initiation of cracks at particular values of load may be used to redesign the structure to reduce the magnitude of the stresses around stress concentrations. Finally, the use of closely controlled conditions may allow the determination of stress values at stress concentration points where electric resistance strain gages would be too large to provide accurate data.

The flaking of the brittle oxide scale on hot rolled steel has long been recognized as an indication of local yielding. Other materials such as whitewash or cement paste may be used, but their usefulness is limited by the fact that the yield point of the material must be exceeded before cracking of the brittle coating occurs. Work on more sensitive brittle coatings began to appear in the 1930's and culminated in the development of Stresscoat (trademark of Magnaflux Corporation; to the authors' knowledge Stresscoat is the only room temperature curing brittle coating commercially available which will crack at strain values below the elastic limit of most engineering materials) by Greer Ellis in 1937.

Stresscoat is a mixture of a natural resin obtained from a reaction of rosin with zinc oxide, carbon disulfide, and dibutyl phthalate. This mixture can be sprayed on the structure to be analyzed and after drying will crack at strain levels as low as 0.0004 inch per inch. By using special techniques (see p. 39), the sensitivity can be lowered to 0.0001 in./in.

Although Stresscoat possesses the more important characteristics of an ideal brittle coating, it also has several limitations which must be allowed for during usage. The strain value at which cracking of the coating starts is dependent upon temperature, humidity, thickness of coating, time to maximum load, curing conditions, and the inherent sensitivity of the coating. Although these characteristics may at first glance appear to complicate the application of Stresscoat beyond usefulness, a simple calibrate procedure, reasonable care and advance planning make Stresscoat a highly useful experimental tool. The calibrator itself

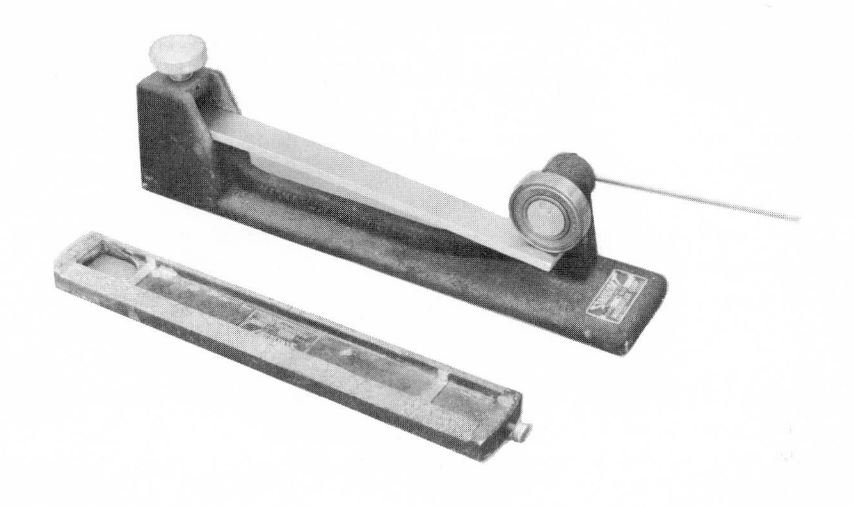

Fig. 1-16. Stresscoat calibrator with calibration bar in the deflected position.

is shown in Fig. 1-16. It consists of an aluminum beam $\frac{1}{4}$ by 1 by 12 in. and a loading device which is used to deflect the end of the beam a fixed maximum amount. The other piece of calibration equipment is simply a scale graduated in strain. Thus, the initiation of cracks in the Stresscoated calibration beam can be compared with the strain scale, and the value of threshold sensitivity, or the minimum value of strain which will cause cracking of the Stresscoat, can be readily determined. Of course, the calibration bars must be treated exactly the same as the test structure throughout the whole testing procedure.

A typical Stresscoat test is conducted as follows. The test structure and calibration bars are cleaned of all grease, dirt, and loose paint. They are painted with an undercoat lacquer to provide the optimum viewing conditions for the visual observation of the crack patterns. The Stresscoat is sprayed on and allowed to cure, preferably at a slightly higher temperature than the anticipated test conditions. Room temperature curing requires a minimum of eighteen hours. Accelerated curing in as short as three hours may be accomplished by using temperatures up to 140°F. After curing and stabilizing at the test temperature, a calibration bar is loaded to verify that the Stresscoat sensitivity is the desired value. The test structure is then loaded in increasing increments with observation and marking of the crack initiation being made between load increments.

Actual strain values assigned to Stresscoat crack ends on the test structure should be corrected to take into account the loss in strain sensitivity due to creep of the coating. This correction may be accomplished by use of the creep correction chart or by loading a calibration strip in the same length of time as load increments were applied on the test structure. Apparent stresses on the test structure are then obtained by multiplying the creep-corrected strain sensitivity by tension modulus of elasticity of the material used in the structure.

Stresscoat can be used on any structural material which can be satisfactorily coated with lacquer. As with any painting operation, the surfaces

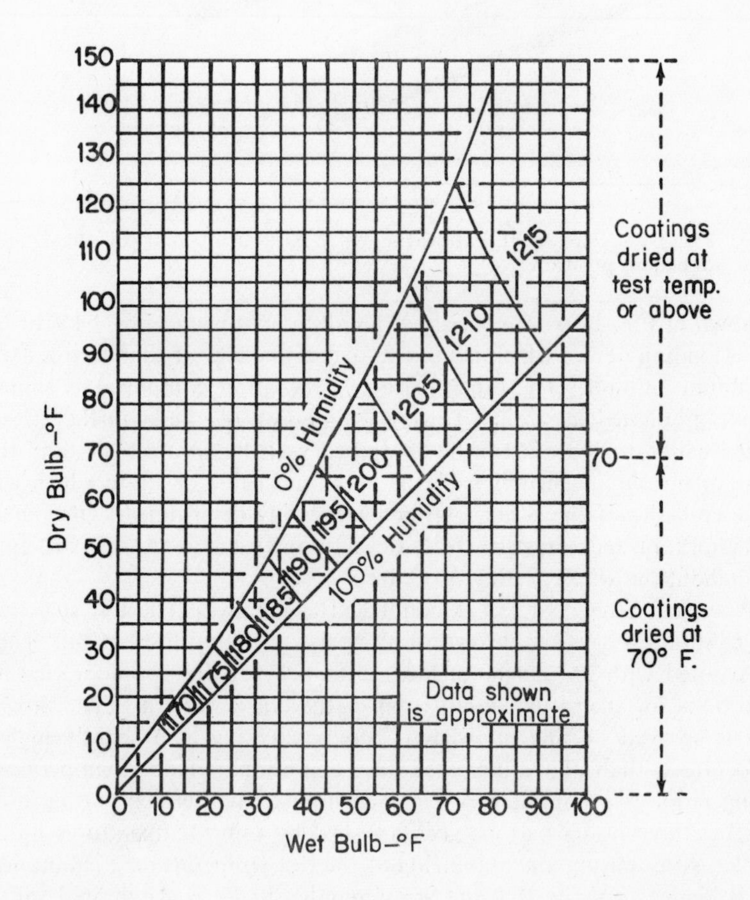

Fig. 1-17. Full range coating selection chart. (*Courtesy of Magnaflux Corporation.*)

should be clean and free from any loose scale or dirt. Most well-cured painted surfaces can be sprayed over with the Stresscoat materials without affecting test results. Smoothing of very rough surfaces is necessary to insure the attaining of a uniform thickness of the Stresscoat.

Differences in test conditions are accommodated through the use of a number of different coatings. Figure 1-17 shows the selection chart for the available coatings covering the full range of temperature and humidity conditions at the time of test.

Figure 1-18 shows the selection chart for coatings used in the normal working range.

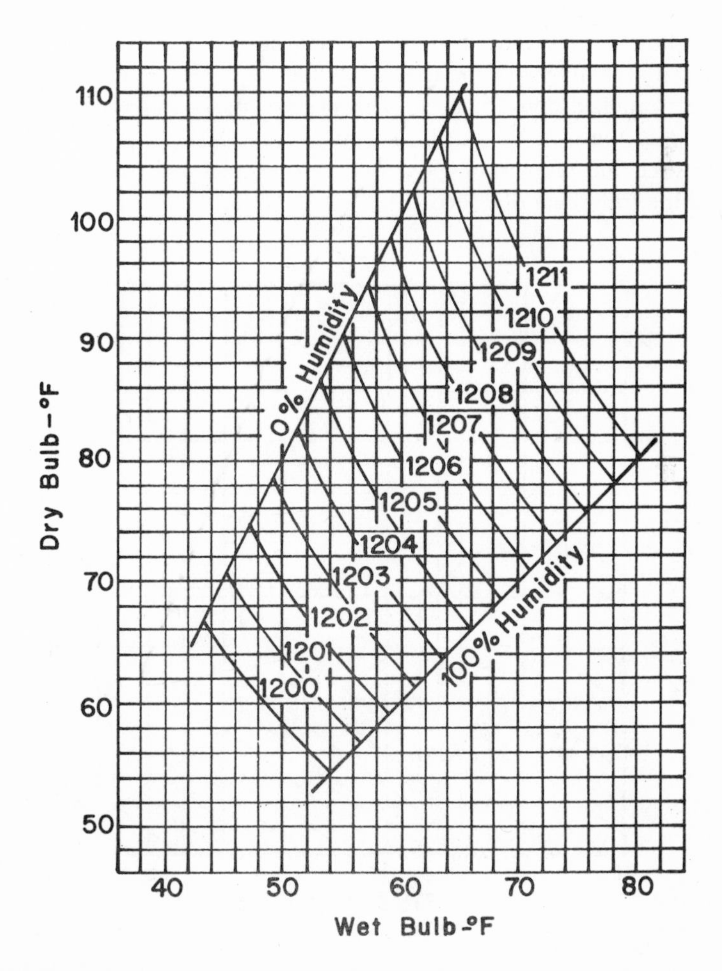

Fig. 1-18. Normal range coating selection chart. (*Courtesy of Magnaflux Corporation.*)

Particular care must be exercised to assure easy and positive recognition of the Stresscoat cracks, since Stresscoat is almost transparent and the cracks are minute. There are two crack-detection methods in common use. The first and oldest method utilizes a red dye etchant which is applied over the whole stresscoated surface and then wiped off, the red dye being left in the cracks. The red dye etchant (ST-1300A) is most useful if the test specimen is first coated with the aluminum-pigmented lacquer ST-840. The dull aluminum lacquer produces a uniformly colored surface and provides contrast with the red dye etchant. The principal disadvantage of the dye etchant is that it attacks and sensitizes the Stresscoat and makes it unusable for further use at higher test loads. Thus, it is customary to make Stresscoat cracks visible for photography by dye etching with the red dye etchant after all the load increments have been applied and crack ends have been marked at each successive load application. The shaded portion of Fig. 1-19 shows the area of elapsed time and temperature rise that can be tolerated with satisfactory dye etching still being obtained.

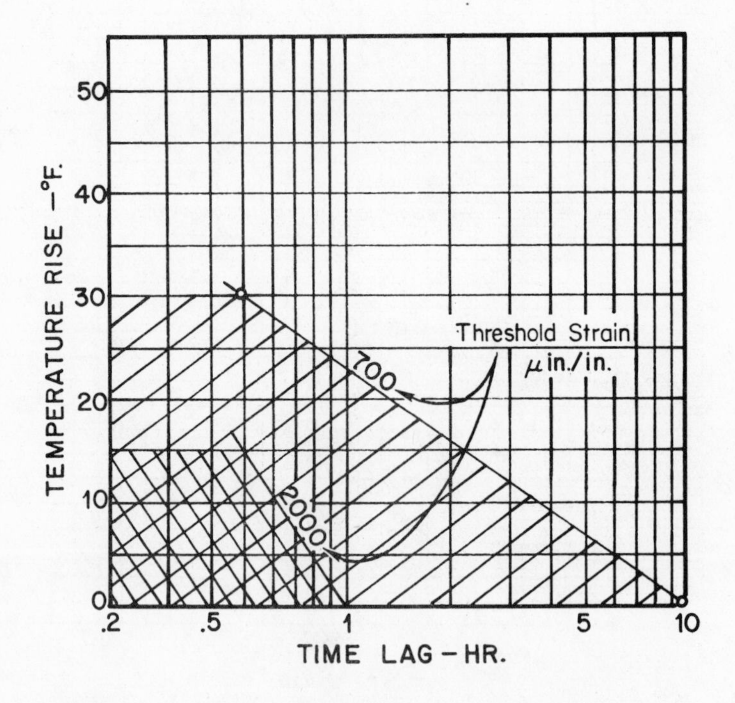

Fig. 1-19. Allowable time lag and temperature rise between loading and dye etching. (*Courtesy of Magnaflux Corporation.*)

The second method of crack detection is known as the electrified particle inspection method. The electrified particle inspection method known as Statiflux* overcomes the disadvantages of the dye etchant. Statiflux may be used repeatedly to detect cracks in Stresscoat without harming the coating. Since the special water-based penetrant, which is a mild electrolyte, does not actually attack the Stresscoat, it is desirable in some cases to apply the penetrant before loading the specimen so that the penetrant will enter the cracks as they open under load. After the test load is released, the penetrant is wiped dry. Statiflux powder SXP-1 is blown from a special gun onto the test surface. The electrified particles are attracted to the negative ions in the penetrant which has been collected in the Stresscoat cracks. Thus, each crack becomes covered with the white Statiflux powder. A flat black undercoat lacquer is used to provide a contrasting background for the white Statiflux powder.

As we have previously pointed out, the test structure and calibration bars should undergo the same treatment throughout the whole test procedure. If it is not convenient to load the test structure in a few seconds, the creep correction chart shown in Fig. 1-20 may be used to obtain a

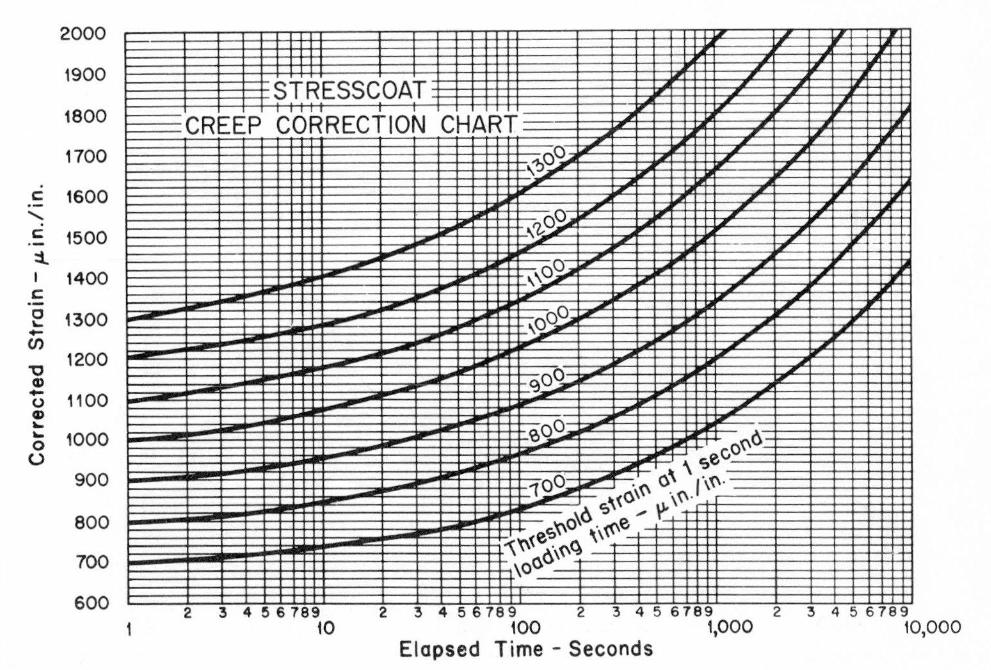

Fig. 1-20. Creep correction chart. (*Courtesy of Magnaflux Corporation.*)

* Trademark of Magnaflux Corporation.

corrected value of threshold strain on the test structure based on a one-second loading time of the calibration bar.

For the detection of compression strains the Stresscoated structure is loaded very slowly to maximum load and held at maximum load a period of time, and then the load is released quickly in increments. Cracks are marked at each increment as in the static tension loading test. Calibration bars should be loaded in a similar manner, with the Stresscoated surface being the lower surface of the cantilever beam. Figure 1-21a shows the variation of threshold sensitivity with various tension threshold sensitivities and varying compression hold time. Figure 1-21b shows the variation in threshold sensitivity with varying release time.

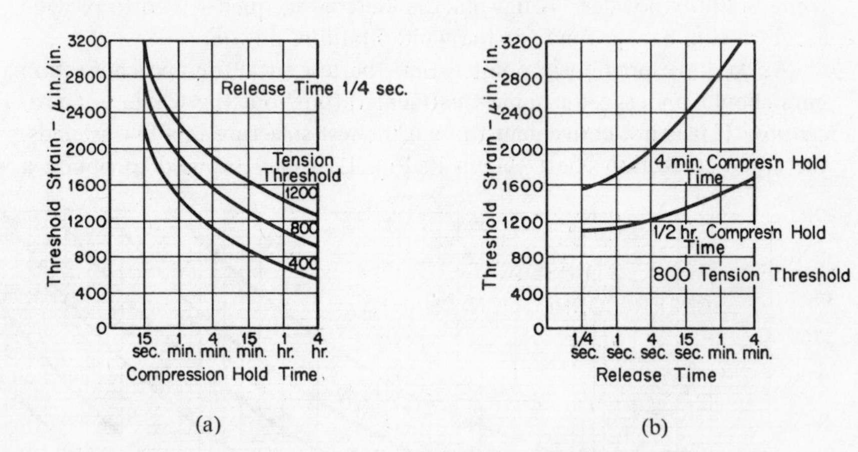

Compression threshold versus hold time — Compression threshold versus release time

Fig. 1-21. Compression threshold charts. (*Courtesy of Magnaflux Corporation.*)

The load and crack initiation data from a test are customarily converted to stress values in the test specimen by multiplication of the threshold sensitivity of the coating, as determined from the calibration bars, by the modulus of elasticity of the specimen material.* If the calibration bars and test specimen are of the same material, i.e., Poisson's ratio of equal value, the stress values will be accurate provided that the specimen stress field is essentially uniaxial. The error of the calculated stress value in a biaxial stress field increases to 15 per cent as the absolute magnitude of the smaller principal stress approaches the absolute magnitude of the

* See Ref. [21] for a complete discussion of the law of failure of Stresscoat.

larger principal stress. If the calibration bars and specimen are of different materials, the stress values should be calculated by using the following equation:

$$S = \frac{1 - \mu_c \mu_o}{1 - \mu_c \mu_s} E_s \epsilon_o,$$

where S is the stress in the test specimen.

μ_c is the Poisson's ratio of the Stresscoat (from Ref. [21], $\mu_c = 0.42$).

μ_o is the Poisson's ratio of the calibration bar material.

μ_s is the Poisson's ratio of the test specimen material.

ϵ_o is the threshold strain measured on the calibration bar.

E_s is the modulus of the test specimen material.

For commonly used metallic test specimen materials and aluminum calibration bars, the maximum error encountered by not correcting for the differences in Poisson's ratio is about four per cent.

Dynamic tests with Stresscoat may be conducted in basically the same manner as static loading tests. Frequently, however, variation of the load is not an available method for the determination of relative strain levels on a structure. Different coating sensitivities applied on symmetrical parts of the assembly or tested sequentially can be used to determine relative values of strain during dynamic loading, when the variation of load is not possible. For impact loading it is desirable to apply Statiflux penetrant prior to the load application so that cracks which may close upon cessation of the impact load may still be detected, since the penetrant will have entered the cracks while the test specimen was under load. As we have pointed out previously, Stresscoat sensitivity is affected by the rate of loading; thus, we can expect that dynamic loading conditions will produce lower strain sensitivities than the standard calibration system.* If Stresscoat is to be used to determine quantitative values of strain under dynamic loading conditions, calibration of the coating should be made under identical conditions, so far as time of load application, temperature, and humidity are concerned.

The normal sensitivity range of Stresscoat is between 400 μin./in. and 2000 μin./in. Sensitization of a coating by use of ice water, cold air, snow from a carbon dioxide fire extinguisher, or dye etchant may be used to get rough quantitative data. Careful water cooling of the coating on the test specimen and the calibrate strip can yield good quantitative

* See Refs. [22], [23], and [24] for detailed studies of the dynamic sensitivity of Stresscoat.

results down to strains of 100 μin./in. Thus, a single increment of load may be used to produce a series of crack patterns by successively bathing the test item and calibrate strip with water at a series of temperatures below room temperature. Reference [25] illustrates this method by using water at temperatures 3°, 6°, 9°, and 12°F below room temperature. Better accuracy in reading the calibrate bars was obtained by using half the normal deflection on the Stresscoat calibrate loading device.

Very insensitive (2000 to 10,000 μin./in.) coatings may be attained by simply using coating numbers 25 to 40 lower than those indicated by the coating selection chart. Calibration of the coating is achieved by utilizing 21 by 0.050 by 1 in. calibration strips which are bent around an involute which produces strains from 2000 to 10,000 μin./in. (see Ref. [25]). Since the calibrate strips are strained beyond their elastic limit, they are not reusable.

Since the Statiflux method of crack detection is based on the difference in charge between the top coating surface and the bottom, if the coating is applied to a nonconducting surface, special techniques must be used to achieve charge distribution throughout the bottom of the

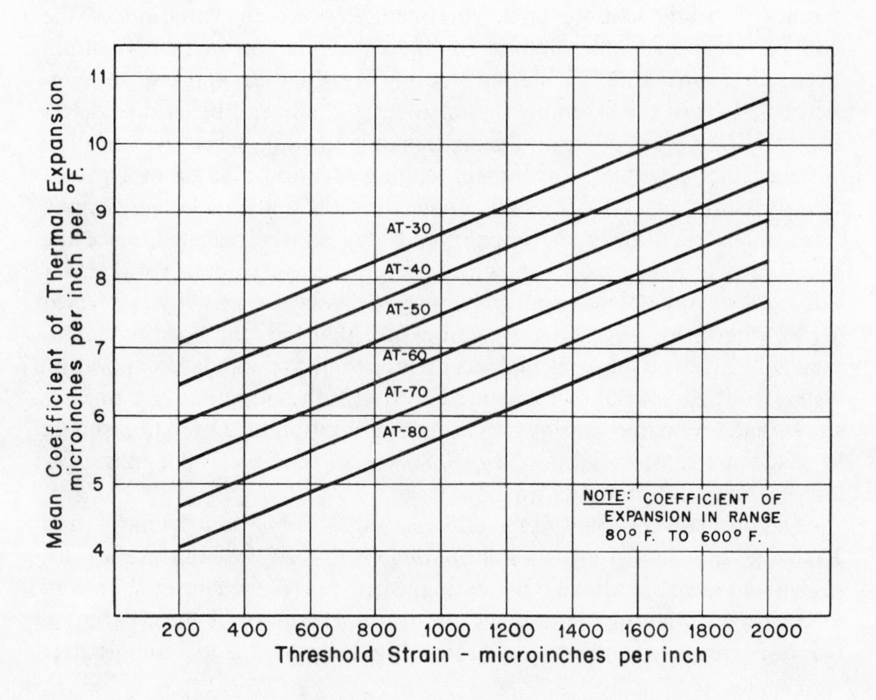

Fig. 1-22. Stresscoat All-Temp coating selection chart. (*Courtesy of Magnaflux Corporation.*)

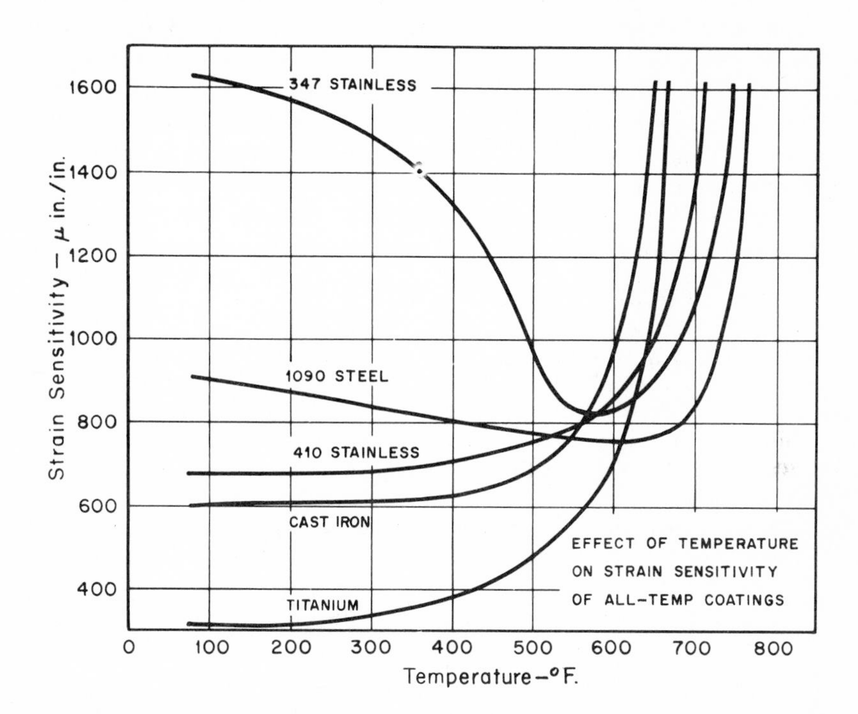

Fig. 1-23. Effect of temperature on strain sensitivity of All-Temp coatings. (*Courtesy of Magnaflux Corporation.*)

coating surface. It has been found that by using wet cloth strips at about six-inch intervals and in contact with the black lacquer undercoat as ground strips, Statiflux can be used for detecting cracks on nonconducting base material such as polyester resin (see Ref. [26]).

In 1952 ceramic-base materials that were usable from $-50°$ to 600°F with sensitivity from 200 to 1800 μin./in. were developed (see Ref. [27]). Coating selection is based on the coefficient of thermal expansion of the material of the structure, as shown in Fig. 1-22, since cracking of the coating is dependent upon the difference in coefficient of expansion of the coating and the base metal.

Conduct of a Stresscoat All-Temp* test is similar to the conventional Stresscoat test described on page 33. The surface to be coated must first be cleaned and roughened by a mild sandblast. The selected ceramic

* Trademark by Magnaflux Corporation.

coating is then sprayed on. After air drying for fifteen minutes, the parts are placed in an oxidizing furnace at 950° to 1100°F for fifteen minutes. After cooling they are ready for test. For tests at various temperatures or determination of thermally induced strains, the variation in strain sensitivity with temperature, shown in Fig. 1-23, must be taken into account. Crack detection is accomplished with Statiflux, as in the case of conventional Stresscoat tests.

1-8 References listed in Chapter 1

1. Hetényi, M. (ed.), *Handbook of Experimental Stress Analysis*, Chap. 3, "Mechanical Gages," by Donnell and Savage. New York: John Wiley and Sons, Inc., 1950.
2. Hetényi, M. (ed.), *Handbook of Experimental Stress Analysis*, Chap. 7, "Capacitance Gages," by Carter, Forshaw, and Shannon. New York: John Wiley and Sons, Inc., 1950.
3. Harris, C. M. and C. E. Crede (eds.), *Shock and Vibration Handbook*. Vol. 1, Chap. 14, by C. S. Duckwald and B. S. Angell. New York: McGraw-Hill Book Co., Inc., 1961, pp. 14-1–14-10.
4. Hetényi, M. (ed.), *Handbook of Experimental Stress Analysis*, Chap. 6, "Inductance Gages," by B. F. Langer. New York: John Wiley and Sons, Inc., 1950.
5. Ripperger, E. A., "A Piezoelectric Strain Gage," *Proceedings of the Society for Experimental Stress Analysis*, Vol. 12, No. 1, pp. 117–24.
6. Mark, J. W. and W. Goldsmith, "Barium Titanate Strain Gages," *Proceedings of the Society for Experimental Stress Analysis*, Vol. 13, No. 1, pp. 139–150.
7. Smith, C. S., "Piezoresistive Effect in Germanium and Silicon," *Phys. Rev.* **94**, 42 (Apr. 1, 1954).
8. Mason, W. P. and R. N. Thurston, "Use of Piezoresistive Materials in the Measurement of Displacement, Force and Torque." *Journal of Acoustical Society of America*, Vol. 29 (1957).
9. Box, W. A., "The Effect of Plastic Strains on Stress Concentrators," *Proceedings of the Society for Experimental Stress Analysis*, Vol. 8, No. 2, pp. 99–110.
10. Brewer, G. A., "Measurement of Strain in the Plastic Range," *Proceedings of the Society for Experimental Stress Analysis*, Vol. 1, No. 2, pp. 105–115.
11. O'Haven, C. P. and J. F. Harding, "Studies of Plastic Flow Problems by Photo Grid Methods," *Proceedings of the Society for Experimental Stress Analysis*, Vol. 2, No. 2, pp. 59–70.
12. MacLaren, D. D., "The Photo-Grid Process for Measuring Strain Caused by Underwater Explosions," *Proceedings of the Society for Experimental Stress Analysis*, Vol. 5, No. 2, pp 115–24.
13. Miller, J. A., "Improved Photogrid Techniques for Determination of Strain Over Short Gage Lengths," *Proceedings of the Society for Experimental Stress Analysis*, Vol. 10, No. 1, pp. 29–34.

14. Durelli, A. J. and W. F. Riley, "Developments in the Grid Method of Experimental Stress Analysis," *Proceedings of the Society for Experimental Stress Analysis*, Vol. **14**, No. 2, pp. 91–100.

15. Brewer, G. O. and M. M. Rockwell, "Measurement of the Drawing Properties of Aluminum Sheet," *Metal Progress*, Vol. **41**, No. 5 (May 1942), pp. 663–8.

16. Weller, R. and B. M. Shepard, "Displacement Measurement by Mechanical Interferometry," *Proceedings of the Society for Experimental Stress Analysis*, Vol. 6, No. 1, pp. 35–38.

17. Crisp, J. D. C., "The Measurement of Plane-Strains by a Photo-Screen Method," *Proceedings of the Society for Experimental Stress Analysis*, Vol. **15**, No. 1, pp. 65–76.

18. Vinckier, A. and R. Dechaene, "Use of the Moiré Effect to Measure Plastic Strains," *Journal of Basic Engineering, Trans. ASME*, Series D (June 1960), pp. 426–34.

19. Morse, S., A. J. Durelli, and C. A. Sciammarella, "Geometry of Moiré Fringes in Strain Analysis," *Journal Engr. Mech. Div., Proc. ASCE*, Vol. **86**, No. EM4 (Aug. 1960), Part 1, pp. 105–126.

20. Sciammarella, C. A. and A. J. Durelli, "Moiré Fringes as a Means of Analyzing Strains," *Journal Engr. Mech. Div. Proc. ASCE*, Vol. **87**, No. EM1 (Feb. 1961), pp. 54–74.

21. Durelli, A. J., E. A. Phillips, and C. H. Tsao, *Analysis of Stress and Strain*. New York: McGraw-Hill Book Co., Inc., 1958, pp. 329–467.

22. Durelli, A. J. and J. W. Dally, "Some Properties of Stresscoat Under Dynamic Loading," *Proceedings of the Society for Experimental Stress Analysis*, Vol. **15**, No. 1, pp. 43–56.

23. Dally, J. W., A. J. Durelli, and V. S. Parks, "Further Studies of Properties of Stresscoat Under Dynamic Loading," *Proceedings of the Society for Experimental Stress Analysis*, Vol. **15**, No. 2, pp. 57–66.

24. Brown, G. W. and D. M. Cunningham, "Calibration of Stresscoat by Impact," *Experimental Mechanics*, Vol. **2**, No. 5 (May 1962), pp. 137–41.

25. Parks, V. J., K. E. Hofer, and A. J. Durelli, "Extending the Stress Analysis Range of Brittle Coatings," *Experimental Mechanics*, Vol. **2**, No. 5 (May 1962), pp. 137–41.

26. Clark, E. C., "Advances in the Art of Stresscoat Analysis," *Proceedings of the Society for Experimental Stress Analysis*, Vol. **13**, No. 1, pp. 59–66.

27. Singdale, F. M., "Improved Brittle Coatings for Use Under Widely Varying Temperature Condition," *Proceedings of the Society for Experimental Stress Analysis*, Vol. **11**, No. 2, pp. 173–8.

1-9 Problems

1-1 The sketch of equipment setup, the data sheet, and the tracing of moiré fringe pattern taken during the performance of Experiment 1-1 are given. Write the report asked for.

Equipment Setup:

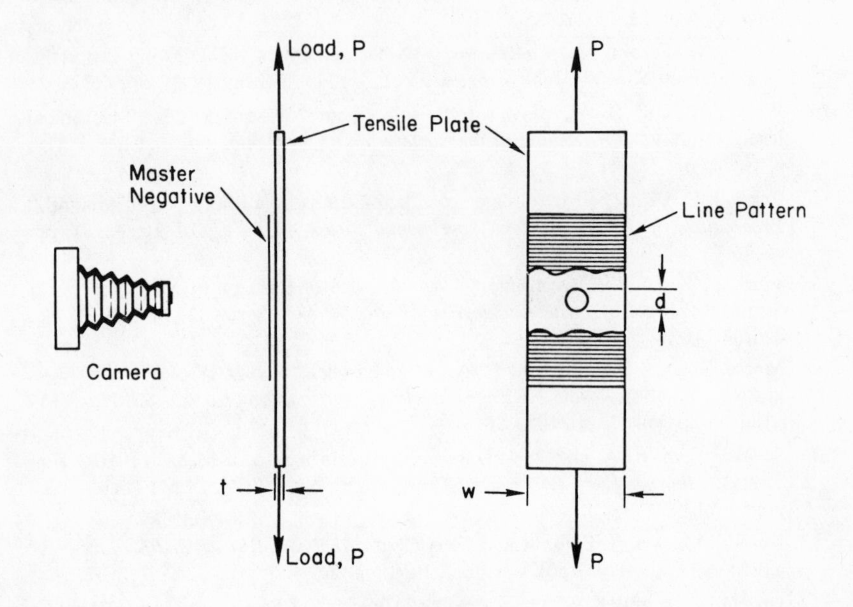

Fig. 1-24.

Data:

$t = 0.032$ in.
$w = 1.5$ in.
$d = \frac{3}{16}$ in.
Grid pitch = 200 lines per in.
Load, $P = 1725$ lb.
For material used (Al), $E = 10 \times 10^6$ psi.
$\mu = \frac{1}{3}$.

Fringe Pattern:

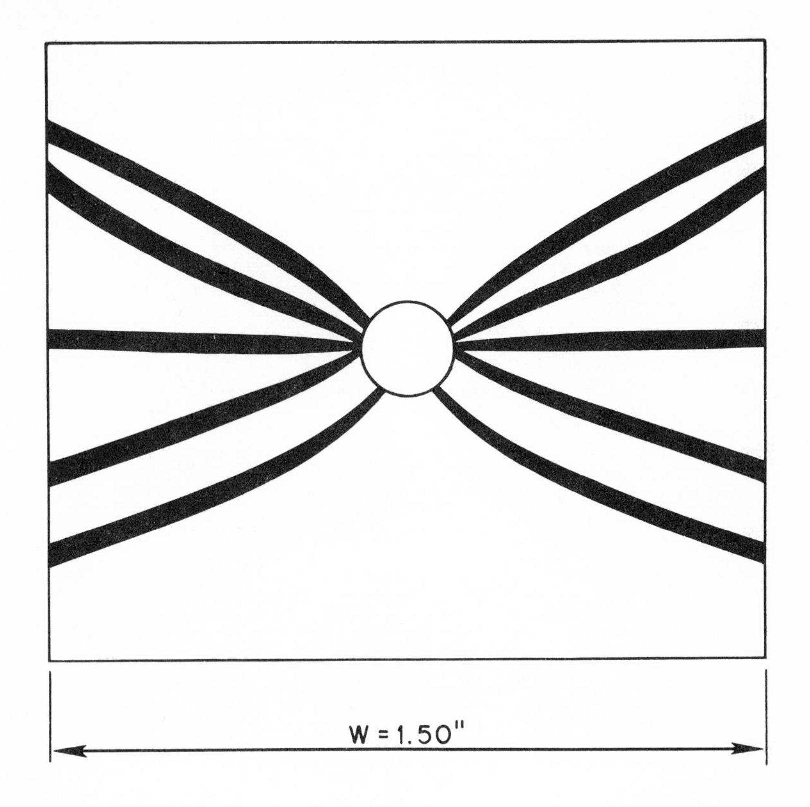

Fig. 1-25.

1-2 The sketch of equipment setup, the data sheet, and the tracing of moiré fringe pattern taken during the performance of Experiment 1-2 are given. Write the report asked for.

Equipment Setup:

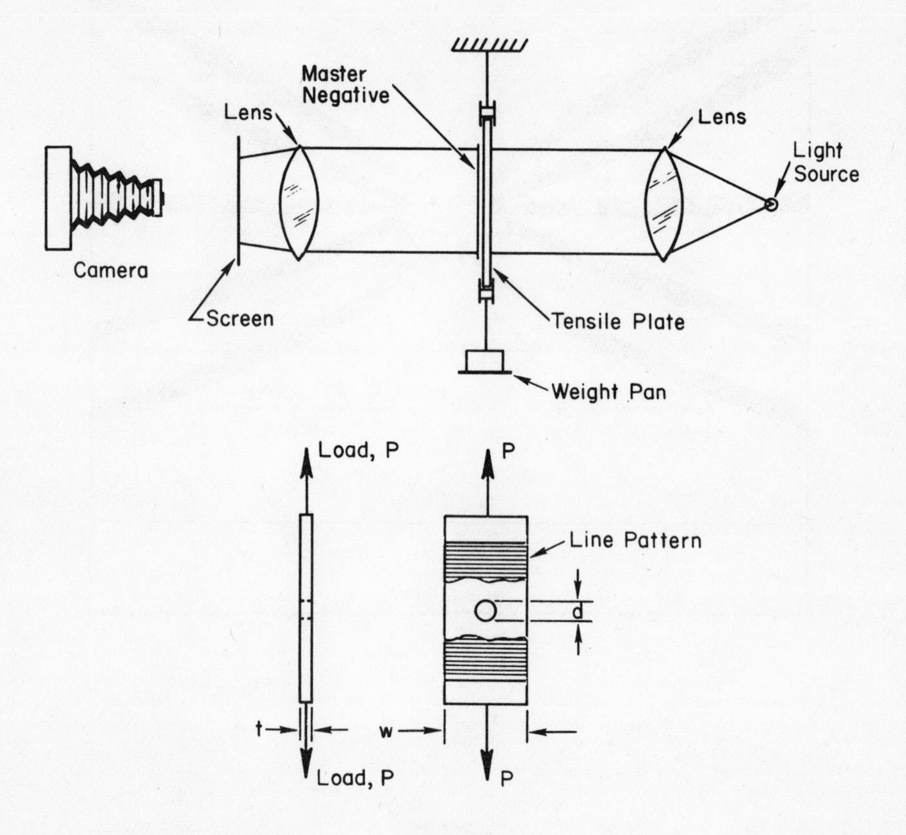

Fig. 1-26.

Data:

$t = 0.5$ in.
$w = 5$ in.
$d = 0.97$ in.
Grid pitch = 200 lines per in.
Load, $P = 20$ lb.
For material used (urethane rubber), $E = 618$.
$\mu = 0.474$.

Fringe Pattern:

Fig. 1-27.

1-10 Suggested laboratory experiments

Experiment 1-1 Study of plastic strain distribution using the moiré fringe method

EQUIPMENT NECESSARY

1. A flat plate tensile specimen containing a centrally located circular hole on which a suitable line pattern has been printed.*
2. A tensile test machine.
3. A master negative through which the moiré fringe pattern can be viewed and photographed.
4. Camera for photographing the moiré fringe pattern.†

---

* Lines perpendicular to the longitudinal or load axis; 200 or more lines per inch is suitable.

† A Polaroid camera with short focal length is excellent, since the fringe pattern can be enlarged and traced by using a standard opaque projector.

PROCEDURE

1. Pull the specimen so that the strain in the area near the hole is in the plastic region.
2. Photograph the fringe pattern.
3. Enlarge and trace the fringe pattern in preparation for measurement of the fringe spacing.

REPORT

Plot the ratio of strain at a point to nominal strain (strain at points removed from discontinuity), $\epsilon/\epsilon_{NOMINAL}$, versus position along a transverse axis through the hole. Use experimentally determined values and values computed using elastic theory (Kirsch theory) so that plastic strain distribution can be compared to elastic strain distribution.

Experiment 1-2* Study of elastic strain distribution using the moiré fringe method

EQUIPMENT NECESSARY

1. A flat plate tensile specimen (the plate is a low modulus material so that large elastic strains can be produced),† containing a centrally located circular hole, and on which a suitable line pattern has been printed (lines perpendicular to load axis).
2. A tensile test machine or dead weight tensile loading fixture.
3. A master negative through which the moiré fringe pattern can be viewed and photographed.
4. Camera for photographing the moiré fringe pattern.

PROCEDURE

1. Pull the specimen so that the maximum strain is elastic.
2. Photograph the fringe pattern.
3. Enlarge and trace the fringe pattern in preparation for measurement of the fringe spacing.

---

* The problem of elastic strain distribution around a circular hole in a plate in tension is solved in this and four other experiments (1-3, 5-1, 6-3, and 7-1). Solving this same problem by using several experimental methods gives the student some feel for the relative advantages and disadvantages of the several methods.

† A $\frac{1}{4}$ to $\frac{1}{2}$ in. thick sheet of rubberlike plastic may be used. A urethane rubber will serve both the present purpose and as a photoelastic model for Experiment 6-3.

REPORT

Plot the ratio of strain at a point to nominal strain (strain at points removed from discontinuity), $\epsilon/\epsilon_{\text{NOMINAL}}$, versus position along a transverse axis through the hole. Use both experimentally determined values and values computed by using elastic theory (Kirsch theory).

Experiment 1-3 Study of strain distribution using the brittle lacquer method

EQUIPMENT NECESSARY

1. A flat plate tensile specimen containing a centrally located hole. The specimen has been coated with a brittle lacquer.
2. A tensile test machine.
3. Camera for photographing the crack pattern.

PROCEDURE

Pull the specimen, stopping at preselected load increments to mark and photograph the crack pattern.

REPORT

1. Plot the ratio of strain at a point to nominal strain (strain at points removed from the discontinuity) versus position along several selected radial lines.
2. Determine principal stress directions at points along several selected radial lines.
3. Compare results obtained in items 1 and 2 to elastic theory.

CHAPTER 2

Variable-Resistance Strain Gages

2-1 Gage characteristics and types

A variable-resistance strain gage is a device whose electrical resistance changes in proportion to the strain to which it is subjected. In the case of the bonded resistance-type strain gage, the resistive element consists of a length of fine metal wire, a metal foil, or a whisker of semiconductive material. To reduce the length of the gage while its sensitivity is retained (by maintaining a relatively large resistance), the wire, or foil, is usually formed in a grid pattern. The resistive element is fixed to a suitable base, usually paper, plastic, or ceramic. The complete gage consists of the resistive element fixed to a base. For use, the gage base is bonded to the point at which strain is to be measured, or the base may be stripped away and the resistive element placed directly in a bonding agent at the point where strain is to be measured.

2-1a Gage factor

The essential property of the resistive element is that the resistance varies with strain. This property is defined in terms of the gage factor F. By definition:

$$F = \frac{\Delta R/R}{\Delta L/L} = \frac{\Delta R/R}{\epsilon}, \tag{2-1}$$

in which F = gage factor.
R = electrical resistance.
L = length of strain-sensitive element.
ϵ = normal or axial strain.

That is, the gage factor is a measure of the change in resistance per unit of original resistance that will occur per unit of strain applied. With semiconductor gages, "gage sensitivity," defined as $S = \Delta R/\epsilon$, is often used; the reason for this difference in approach is discussed in Section 2-2.

We may develop the following expression for the change in resistance that will accompany strain.

The resistance of any conductive path is a function of the path length L, the path area A, and the specific resistance of the material ρ.

$$R = \rho\frac{L}{A}. \tag{2-2}$$

To obtain the total change in resistance, we may differentiate Eq. (2-2), treating all terms as variables. Thus,

$$dR = \frac{\rho A\,dL + LA\,d\rho - L\rho\,dA}{A^2}. \tag{2-3}$$

Since this expression for change in resistance involves original length, original area, and changes in length and area, we shall next consider other expressions for dL and dA. The change in volume (dV) of the conductive path may be expressed in terms of L, A, dL, and dA.

$$V = AL,$$

and (2-4)

$$dV = A\,dL + L\,dA.$$

In addition,

$$dV = V_{\text{final}} - V = L_{\text{final}}A_{\text{final}} - LA,$$

or (2-5)

$$dV = L(1 + \epsilon)\,A(1 - \mu\epsilon)^2 - LA,$$

since as the length increases by the factor $(1 + \epsilon)$ under the action of normal strain, the transverse dimension is reduced by the factor $(1 - \mu\epsilon)$ due to the Poisson effect, and the area is proportional to the transverse dimension squared. If the first term on the right side of Eq. (2-5) is expanded and terms containing ϵ^2 are neglected, we have

$$dV = LA\epsilon(1 - 2\mu),$$

or

$$dV = A\,dL(1 - 2\mu), \tag{2-6}$$

since

$$\epsilon = \frac{dL}{L}.$$

Equating Eqs. (2-4) and (2-6), we have

$$L\,dA = -2\mu A\,dL,$$

which can be substituted into Eq. (2-3), yielding

$$dR = \frac{\rho A\,dL + LA\,d\rho + 2\mu A\rho\,dL}{A^2}.$$

Dividing this last expression by Eq. (2-2), we have

$$\frac{dR}{R} = \frac{dL}{L} + \frac{d\rho}{\rho} + 2\mu\frac{dL}{L},$$

or

$$\frac{\frac{dR}{R}}{\frac{dL}{L}} = 1 + 2\mu + \frac{\frac{d\rho}{\rho}}{\frac{dL}{L}};$$

that is,

$$F = 1 + 2\mu + \frac{\frac{d\rho}{\rho}}{\epsilon}. \tag{2-7}$$

The expression just developed indicates that the change in resistance which accompanies strain is due both to geometrical changes of the resistive element and to changes in its specific resistivity.

One approach to determining the gage factor for a given material would be first to evaluate the material's specific resistivity as a function of strain. The alternative, and the method actually used, is to shape the resistance element into the gage form desired, to subject this gage to a known strain, to measure the change in resistance as a function of strain, and to compute the gage factor F, using Eq. (2-1).

The gage factor of various materials has been obtained experimentally, and values for F from -140 to $+175$ have been obtained. A negative value for F indicates that resistance decreases as the strain increases in a positive sense. As in most work, tensile strain is taken as positive.

It is interesting to note that any positive value of F less than approximately 1.6 and any negative value indicate a decrease in specific resistivity with increase in strain for that particular material (i.e., $\mu \simeq 0.3$; hence $1 + 2\mu = 1.6$). Any value of F greater than 1.6 indicates an increase in specific resistivity with an increase in strain.

Since strain gages will be used to measure both tensile and compressive strains, how the gage factor in tension F_t compares with the gage factor in compression F_c is an important question. This question must be answered anew for each new gage material and form. Metal element gages now available are considered to have identical values of F_c and F_t unless otherwise stated. Semiconductor element gages show a lower gage factor at large compressive strains than at large tensile strains.

Strain gages may be used to measure large strains, so how gage factor F is affected by amount of strain is also an important question. Kuczyski [1] has investigated this question in connection with metal gage materials, and his findings may be summarized as follows: in the region of plastic deformation where $\mu = 0.5$ (i.e., volume remains constant), continuous relaxation of the material insures that the specific resistivity remains constant (i.e., $\frac{d\rho/\rho}{\epsilon} = 0$). Therefore, the gage factor will be equal to 2 for all metals in their plastic range.

$$F = 1 + 2\mu + \frac{d\rho/\rho}{\epsilon};$$

$$F = 1 + (2)(0.5) + 0 = 2.$$

Again, this question must be answered anew for each new gage material and form; but in general it may be said that, as a metal strain-sensitive element is strained beyond its proportional limit, the gage factor will vary—usually F approaches 2 as the strain increases. It follows that, for all metal gages having a gage factor of 2 in the elastic region, little change in gage factor will occur over a wide range of strain. All others will show a change in gage factor when plastic deformation of the gage element begins. Semiconductor gages tend to show a continuous change in gage factor with strain, even though they are nearly perfectly elastic over a very wide strain range.

If the gage factor is determined by using any gage shape other than a single length of element, an additional factor must be considered. Consider the flat grid shown in Fig. 2-1 mounted on a surface subjected to a uniaxial stress field in the direction shown.

This grid now finds itself in a biaxial strain field, the strain perpendicular to the grid axis being equal to μ (Poisson's ratio) times the strain in the direction of the applied stress and opposite in sense. The change

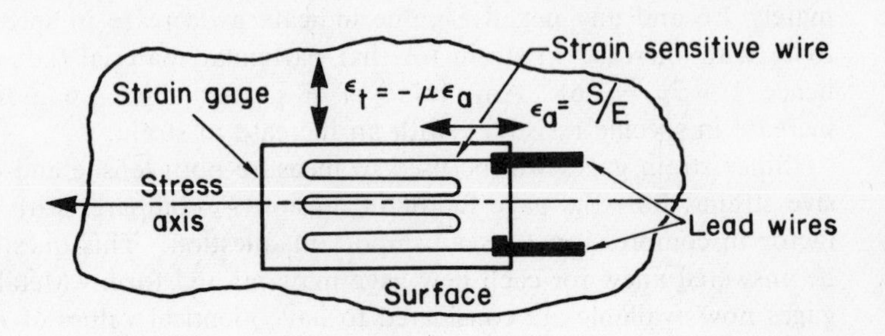

Fig. 2-1. Flat grid mounted on a surface subjected to a uniaxial stress field. (The grid of a gage placed in a uniaxial stress field is actually subjected to strains in two perpendicular directions because of the Poisson effect.)

in resistance which this grid will undergo will depend on both the amount of strain in the longitudinal direction and on the amount of strain in the transverse direction. This influence of transverse strain on the gage output (resistance change) is referred to as transverse sensitivity K. The effect of transverse sensitivity on the evaluation of the strains and stresses from gage readings is discussed in detail in Sect. 5-2.

It must not be assumed that neglect of transverse sensitivity will result only in "small" errors. Visualize a gage mounted in a direction along which the true strain is $+500$ μin./in. (500×10^{-6} in./in.). If the true strain perpendicular to the gage axis is $-2{,}500$ μin./in. and the gage's transverse sensitivity K is three per cent, the gage will give a reading which is 15 per cent less than the true strain. This is a fairly common strain condition in thin-skinned members. In any case, the magnitude of stress cannot be computed from a single strain-gage reading, and this is the quantity most often desired.

2-1b Gage materials

Having discussed the basic principle (gage factor) of resistance-type gages, we shall now consider other important factors that enter into the selection of material to be used as the gage element, into the methods of gage construction, and into the requirements of the gage bond. Figure 2-2 shows three typical strain gages, one of the wire-grid type, one of the foil type, and one of the semiconductor type.

Any of these gages can be discussed in terms of the following items: (1) the material used to form the strain-sensitive grid, (2) the base material

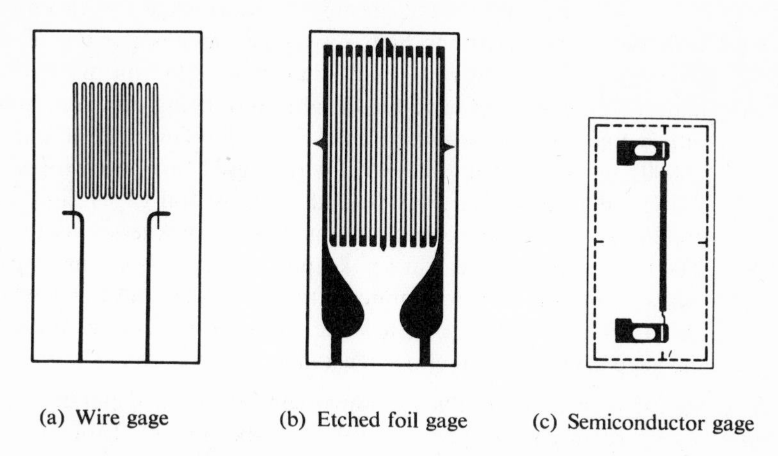

(a) Wire gage (b) Etched foil gage (c) Semiconductor gage

Fig. 2-2. Three types of electric resistance strain gages.

on which the grid is carried, and (3) the bonding adhesive used to mount the gage on the surface where strain is to be measured.

First let us consider the selection of the strain-sensitive material. A list of requirements would include the following items:

1. High gage factor.
2. High resistance per unit length. Notice that when the gage factor definition is rearranged, we have $\Delta R = FR\epsilon$. Hence, for a given gage factor F and strain ϵ, the change in resistance ΔR which must be measured will be directly proportional to the original resistance R.
3. Gage factor stability over a wide temperature range.
4. Resistance a function of strain only. If this is not the case, it will be difficult to separate strain from other phenomena which may be contributing to the observed ΔR. Change in gage resistance due to change in specific resistance of the wire with temperature is an example of a resistance change that is not a function of strain.
5. No electrical effects other than change in resistance ΔR produced by strain or other phenomena. Since strain gages are generally connected in circuits in which the ΔR produced by strain is sensed as a potential difference ΔE between two points, it would be disconcerting to have potentials simultaneously generated by piezoelectric, thermoelectric, or other means.
6. Large strain range. Since it is desirable to have a gage factor which remains constant over the entire strain range, this requirement may give preference to those materials having a gage factor of 2.

7. Ease of manufacture. The desire for short gage length coupled with the requirement for high resistance dictates the use of very thin foil or wire of very small diameter. This means that the material chosen must have the capability of being drawn or etched into a fine wire or produced as a thin foil. One-half or one mil (0.0005 in. or 0.001 in. diameter) wire is used for most wire gages; foil less than 0.001 in. thick is used for most foil gages; and semiconductor wafers are commonly etched to thicknesses as thin as 0.0005 in. Another reason for keeping the cross-sectional area of the wire or foil to a minimum is to insure that the bond will be able to force the grid to follow the strain on the surface on which the gage is mounted in either tension or compression.

Table 2-1 is included to allow comparison of several materials on the basis of the requirements just discussed. Inspection of Table 2-1 will show that all of the metallic materials which are used in wire and foil gages have somewhat similar characteristics. Indeed, with metallic gages, methods of gage construction, styles available, and electrical circuitry (including calibration and temperature compensating techniques)* can all be discussed without regard to the specific metal used for the gage element. However, as shown in Table 2-1, silicon, which is used for most semiconductor strain gages, has properties which are considerably different from those of the metals—so different, in fact, that gage construction, styles available, and electrical circuitry used with semiconductor gages must be considered as separate items.

The principal advantage of the semiconductor strain gage is its high sensitivity as compared to the metal gages, an order of 60 times as great—$F_{\text{semiconductor}} = 120$, as compared to $F_{\text{metal}} = 2$. Semiconductors show promise of producing gages with very low hysteresis (because they function in elastic strain region almost to failure), and their properties can be easily altered through wide ranges (by proper doping of the crystal during manufacture—gage factor from -140 to $+175$ is just one example—resistance can be varied by more than 1000 to 1 with the same physical geometry). Semiconductor gages have three serious drawbacks, however. They are fragile compared to metal gages, and are not capable of functioning to as large strains as are the metal gages.† The semiconductor gages show more variation of gage factor with strain and temperature than do the metal gages, and they are inherently more temperature-sensitive.‡ Considerable progress has been made on all three of these

* See Sect. 2-2a.

† See Sect. 4-2.

‡ See Sect. 2-2e.

problems. In addition to these three drawbacks, semiconductor gages suffer from the handicap of having been introduced after considerable amounts of specialized circuitry, equipment, and techniques had been developed for use with metal strain gages, and semiconductor gages have so much greater sensitivity than the metal gages that some of these circuits and techniques are either not suitable or at least not the most advantageous.* This latter handicap will undoubtedly be eliminated as the use of semiconductor strain gages becomes more widespread.

2-1c Method of gage construction and gage style—metal gages

Next, let us discuss the method by which the gage is constructed. Two techniques have been used for making wire-wound gages. In the first, the grid is formed by winding the wire around pins on a jig. The grid is then lowered on a base and cemented to it, and the pins are withdrawn; the grid may then be covered with a suitable protective cover. In the second technique, the wire is wound in the form of a helix around a thin-walled cylinder of insulating material; this cylinder is then flattened and bonded between sheets of suitable insulating material. Figure 2-3 shows the result of these two methods of construction.

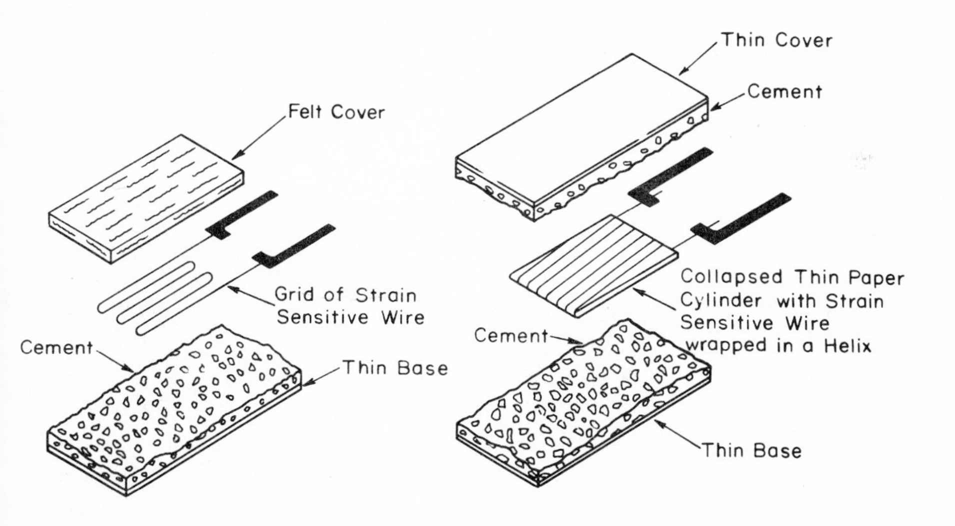

Fig. 2-3. Two methods used for constructing wire strain gages.

* Section 2-2 discusses circuitry and techniques for use with both types of gages.

The flat-grid construction is much preferred, since it places the strain-sensitive grid nearer the surface on which the strain is to be measured, and all elements are in the same plane. This is especially important when the gage is used on thin sections subjected to bending and when transient or rapidly varying strain and/or temperatures are involved. In addition, the flat-grid type shows less creep, less hysteresis, better high-temperature performance, better hydrostatic stability, and greater current-carrying capacity. The helical construction was originally devised to permit the use of a relatively long length of wire (and hence high resistance) in gages having short gage lengths (less than $\frac{3}{8}$ in.). Fortunately, even gages of the shortest gage length are now available in the flat-grid type, and hence this preferred form can be used exclusively.

The foil gages are made by etching or punching the desired grid form out of a foil of strain-sensitive material. For most situations foil or flat-grid wire gages are equally suitable. The foil gages are easier to mount, come in more compact patterns, and show greater stability during long time and elevated temperature tests.

Gages are available with gage lengths from $\frac{1}{32}$ to 9 in. The larger gages are the easier to bond and have greater capacity for dissipating the heat produced by the gage current. Hence, as large a gage as is suitable for the problem at hand should be used. Remember, however, that the gage averages the strain over the gage length. If the peak strain at a point in an area of high strain gradient is required, then the shortest gage length possible should be used.

Gage resistances from 60 to 5000 ohms are available. One hundred twenty ohms is considered a standard, and most commercially available strain-gage reading equipment has been designed with the 120-ohm gage in mind. When most commercially available strain-indicating equipment is used, there is very little to be gained by the use of strain gages of resistance other than 120 ohms. It is possible to use other resistance values, however. The high-resistance gages are primarily intended for use in special circuits designed to maximize the electrical output per unit of strain. The gages of less than 120 ohms are the inherent result of very short gage length or the use of only a single length of wire instead of a grid.

Various gage lead styles are available, and all are intended to serve a specific purpose. The gage lead arrangements shown in Fig. 2-2 may be considered standard. Figure 2-4 shows some additional gage lead styles with sufficient comment to indicate their special purpose.

Gages are made with *dual leads*, as shown in Fig. 2-5, to improve their fatigue resistance. Experience has demonstrated that in vibration environments the weak point of the gage is the point at which the small (0.001 or 0.0005 in. diameter) filament is connected to the gage lead.

TABLE 2-1

Properties of Materials Used for Variable-Resistance Strain Gages

Basic Alloy Type	Trade Name and/or Supplier	Designation Used by Strain Gage Manufacturer	Principal Strain Gage Use	Approx. Gage Factor (F)	Resistance (R—ohm/in. of 0.001 in. diameter)	Temperature Coefficient of Resistance [β—(ohms/ohm/°F) 10^6]	REMARKS
Copper-nickel	"Advance" Driver-Harris (57% Cu, 43% Ni) Constantan	BLH*-A Type Budd†-100 Series	Used for most gages intended for service below 500°F.	2.0	$\simeq 25$	$\simeq 6$	No other electrical effects; F is constant over wide range of strain; easy to manufacture.
Nickel-chrome Iron	"Isoelastic" John Chatillon & Sons (36% Ni, 8% Cr, ½% Mo, rest Fe)	BLH-C Type	Used because of large gage factor. Intended for service below 400°F, but see REMARKS	3.5	$\simeq 60$	$\simeq 175$	F changes in plastic region. More difficult to form; a magnetic material which may give false signals when used in magnetic fields.
Nickel-chrome	"Nichrome-V" Driver-Harris (80% Ni, 20% Cr)	BLH-N Type Budd-400 Series Budd-600 Series	Used for high-temperature gages — above 500°F. Is stable to higher temperature than is any other commercially available alloy.	2.0	$\simeq 60$	$\simeq 250$	Greater stability at elevated temperatures than Cu-Ni and hence, used in most strain gages for service above 500°F.
Nickel-chrome Aluminum-iron	"Karma" Driver-Harris Small additions of Al and Fe to Nichrome V	Budd-500 Series	Used for high-temperature gages instead of nickel-chrome where the lower temperature coefficient is desired.	2.0	>60	< 250	Lower β than Ni-chrome-V.
Alloys of platinum		BLH-HT 1200 Series	For very high temperature strain gages, above 1000°F.	4.0	$\simeq 10$	$\simeq 1500$	This and other new alloys under development treated as trade secrets.
Silicon	Kulite-Bytrex Corp. Micro-Systems, Inc. Century Electronics	(Kulite) (MS) (Strainistor)	Semiconductor gages	−140 to +170. Varies with temperature.	Very brittle; hence, not available as wire. Gages made of wafers less the 0.010" have resistance of 120 ohms.	$\simeq 60{,}000$	Very low coefficient of thermal expansion. A fairly new product (as of June 1961); will change rapidly, and up-to-date literature should be consulted.

* BLH: Baldwin-Lima-Hamilton Corporation.

† Budd: Instruments Division, The Budd Company.

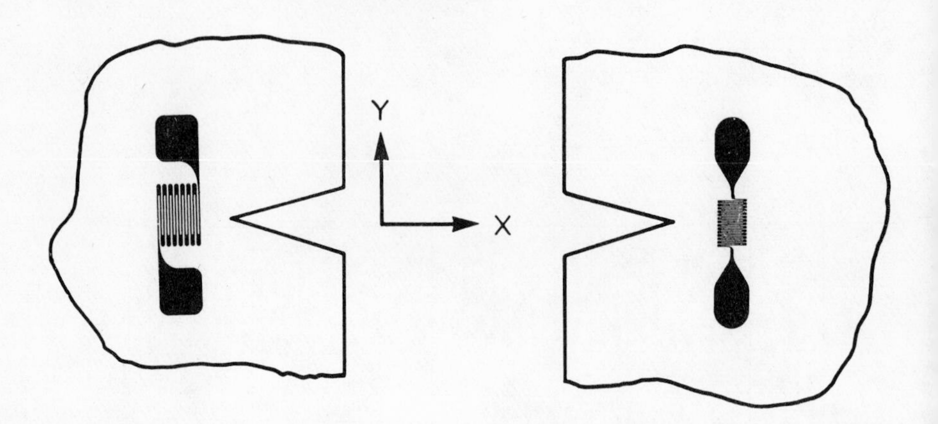

Gage leads positioned to allow measurement of strain in the Y direction at the discontinuity.

Gage leads positioned to allow measurement of strain in the X direction at the discontinuity.

Fig. 2-4. Two gage lead styles.

Inclusion of the intermediate-size wire between the filament and lead, as in Fig. 2-5, increases the life of the gage in vibration environments.

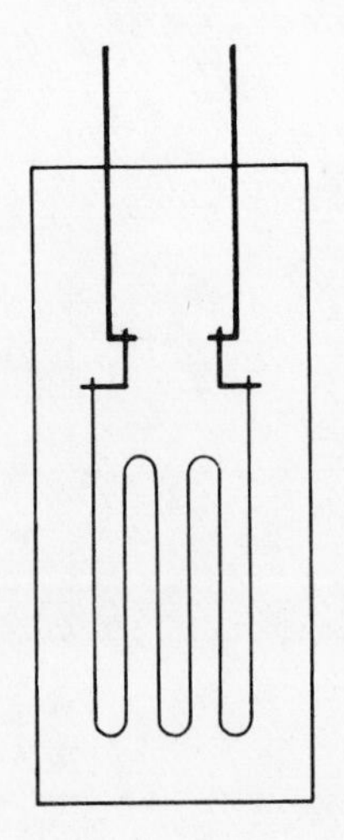

Fig. 2-5. Dual lead gage.

For measuring very large strains, a special post yield gage has been designed. Figure 2-6 shows such a gage. Whereas conventional gages fail when the applied strain exceeds from 1.5 to 3 per cent, these gages (called post yield gages) can measure strains as large as 10 per cent (100,000 μ in./in.). These gages must be bonded with a special flexible cement, which is not suitable for use at elevated temperatures.

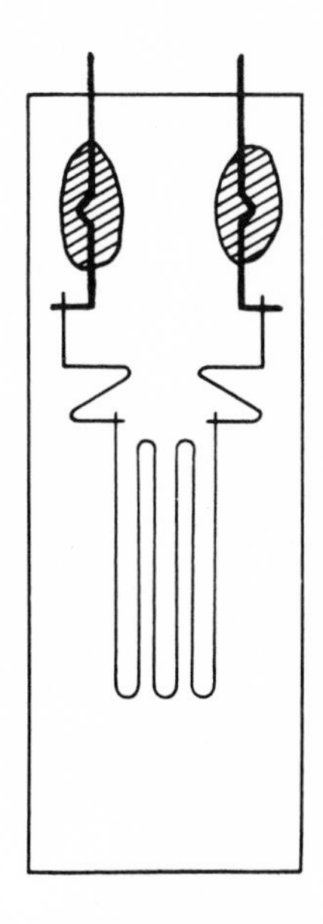

Fig. 2-6. Post yield gage. (High elongation gages also available in foil.)

Gage styles containing more than one element (rosette gages) are discussed in more detail in Sect. 5-3, since their use is related to the method chosen to reduce strain gage readings to stress values. For the present, the following remarks will be adequate.

Single-element gages (Fig. 2-2) are for use individually in *uniaxial stress fields*, or for making up rosettes.

Two-element rosette gages (Fig. 2-7) are for use in *biaxial stress fields* in which the directions of principal stress are known. The style shown in Fig. 2-7a, in which the grids are stacked one on top of the other (insulated between the grids), is intended for use at a location where there is a high strain gradient along the surface and hence where it is important to approach a "point" as nearly as possible. The style in which the grids are all in one plane, Fig. 2-7b, is intended for use at a location where there is a high strain gradient perpendicular to the surface and hence where it is important to keep all elements as near the surface as possible.

Fig. 2-7. Two styles of two-element rosettes.

Three-element rosette gages (Fig. 2-8) are for use in a general biaxial stress field.* As was the case with the two-element rosettes, the choice of overlapping or single-plane style is determined by the nature of the strain gradient at the point where the gage is to be mounted.

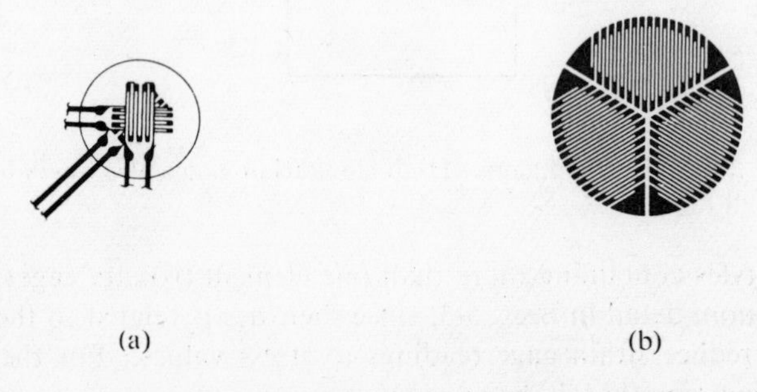

Fig. 2-8. Two styles of three-element rosettes.

Figure 2-9 shows a grid design which gives a signal proportional to the magnitude of stress along the gage axis, regardless of the direction of principal stress. This gage, called a stress gage, is discussed in detail in Sect. 5-3.

* The term "general biaxial stress field" is used here to indicate the situation at a point where neither magnitude nor directions of principal stresses are known.

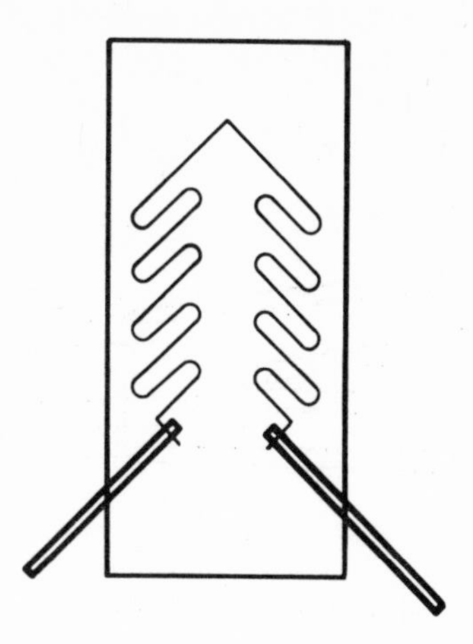

Fig. 2-9. Stress gage.

Figure 2-10 shows a special spiral gage for measuring tangential strains in diaphragms.

Fig. 2-10. Spiral gage.

Figure 2-11 shows a strain gage-thermocouple combination for reading both strain and temperature at the same location.

Variable-resistance strain gages are also produced in a form which is said to be self-temperature-compensating. These gages are not essentially different in form from the single-element gages already discussed; therefore, a discussion of their special purpose will be deferred. The subject of temperature compensation is discussed in Sect. 2-2e.

2-1d Method of gage construction and gage style—semiconductor gages

As pointed out in Sect. 1-4, semiconductors started being used for strain gages in 1957, and semiconductor strain gages have been

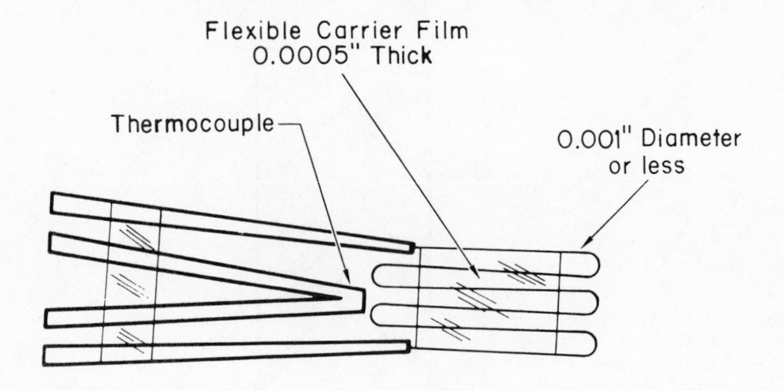

Fig. 2-11. High-temperature thermocouple-strain gage.

commercially available since 1960. It is to be expected, therefore, that construction techniques and styles available will change very rapidly.

The first semiconductor strain gage elements were grown as individual whiskers by the vapor transport process, and these whiskers were fitted with leads for evaluation and use [2]. See Figs. 2-12a and b.

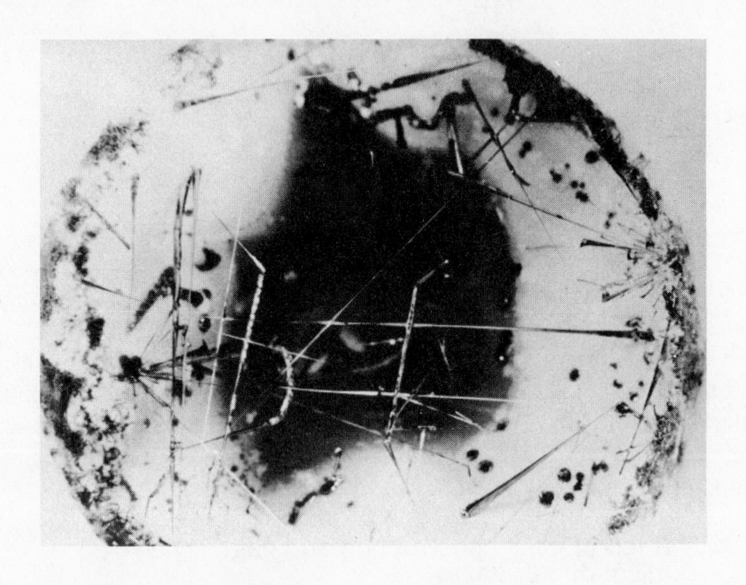

(a) Vapor growth silicon whiskers in crucible. (*Courtesy of Micro Systems, Incorporated.*)

(**b**) Semiconductor strain gage. (*Courtesy of Micro Systems, Incorporated.*)

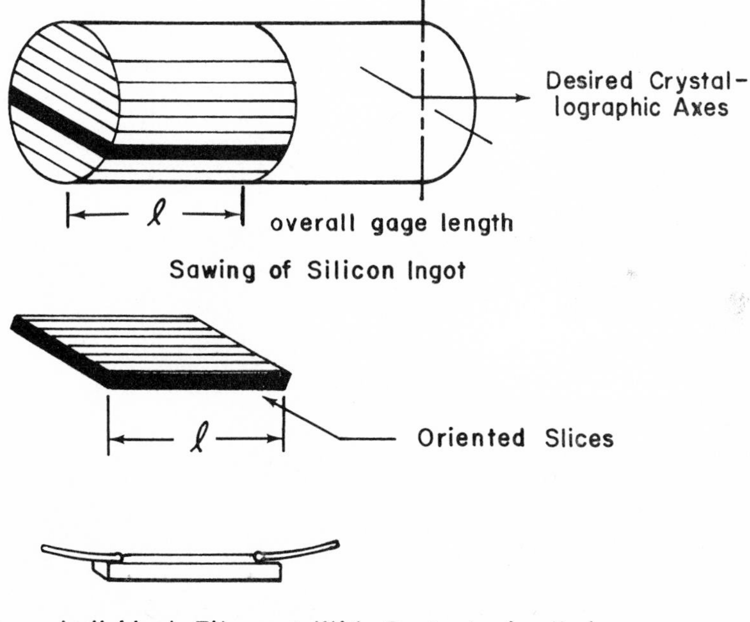

(**c**) Silicon ingot semiconductor strain gage construction.*

Fig. 2-12. Semiconductor strain gage construction.

---

* From Sanchez, J. C., "Semiconductor Strain Gages: A State of the Art Summary," *Strain Gage Readings*. Vol. **IV**, No. 4 (Oct.–Nov. 1961), p. 5.

Semiconductor elements are now cut from more massive silicon ingots which have been grown with controlled crystal orientation and doped with impurities to give the desired properties. The element is sized by etching, leads are attached, and the element is furnished either unbacked or mounted on a suitable carrier. This method of construction is sketched in Fig. 2-12c. Figure 2-13 shows several types.

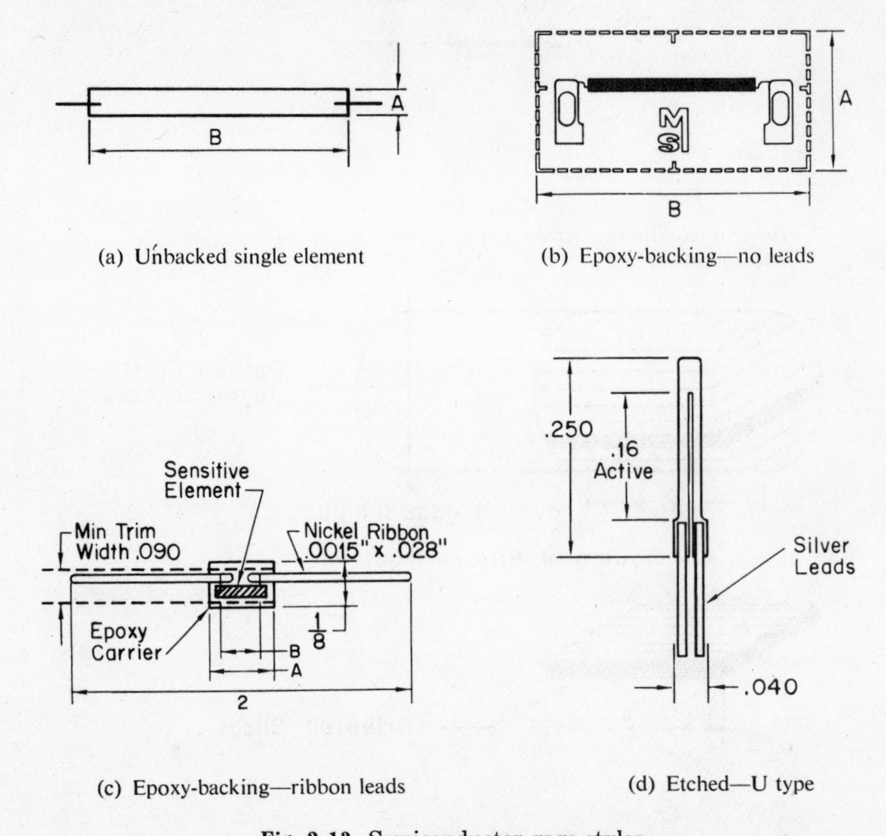

(a) Unbacked single element

(b) Epoxy-backing—no leads

(c) Epoxy-backing—ribbon leads

(d) Etched—U type

Fig. 2-13. Semiconductor gage styles.

Semiconductor gages can also be produced by the diffusion of certain impurity elements into the surface of a parent silicon piece. For a discussion of this technique, see Refs. [3] and [4].

Semiconductor gages are available with gage lengths from 0.02 to 0.5 in. As yet, semiconductor gages are not available in rosette pattern. Semiconductor gages containing either two or four gage elements on the same backing are available for obtaining increased output and temperature compensation. These types are discussed in Sect. 2-2b.

2-1e Grid-backing materials

Both wire-wound and metal foil gages are constructed on a *paper base*. The grid is usually cemented to the paper with cellulose nitrate cement (Duco), and the gage in turn is ordinarily bonded to the test surface with a cellulose nitrate cement. However, almost any of the common bonding cements can be used. Paper-based gages are suitable for use at temperatures between −320° and +180°F. The usable upper temperature limit is very much affected by the magnitude and time duration of the applied strain and by the quality of the bond obtained in mounting the gage.

The lead wires are ordinarily soft-soldered to the strain-sensitive filament of paper-backed gages, since the softening point of solder is compatible with the upper temperature limit of the paper backing and cellulose nitrate cement. Paper-backed gages are reasonably flexible and hence can be applied to curved surfaces.

Metal foil and semiconductor gages are most commonly constructed on an *epoxy base*. Several cements can be used to bond these epoxy-backed gages to the test surface, but cellulose nitrate *must not* be used with this type. Cellulose nitrate cement cures by evaporation of solvent, and an epoxy-backed gage is essentially impervious to this solvent; hence, the cement will not set and cure below the gage.

Epoxy-backed gages are suitable for use at temperatures between −320° and +200°F. Here again, the usable upper temperature limit is a function of the magnitude and duration of the applied strain and the quality of the bond between the gage and the test surface. Epoxy-backed gages are very flexible and are superior to all other types for mounting on surfaces of considerable curvature. Lead wires are ordinarily attached to the strain-sensitive filament with soft solder, since this is compatible with the upper temperature limit of the epoxy back.

Gages are available in a *phenol-resin impregnated fiber carrier* (commonly called Bakelite gages). The strain-sensitive element is encased between two sheets of the phenol-impregnated fiber. Several cements can be used to bond Bakelite gages to the test surface, but those containing an evaporative solvent (cellulose nitrate) *must not* be used.

Gages of this type are usable at temperatures from −400°F to +450°F, again depending on magnitude and time duration of strain, upon the bond to test surfaces, and upon the method of lead attachment. Bakelite gages are not as flexible as the epoxy-backed gages. As regularly supplied by Baldwin-Lima-Hamilton Corporation,* these gages have soft-soldered

* Baldwin-Lima-Hamilton Corporation, Electronics and Instrument Division, Waltham 54, Mass.

lead wires, and the softening temperature of the joint may limit the operating temperature of the gage. On special order, Baldwin-Lima-Hamilton Corporation will supply Bakelite gages with joints made of high-temperature solder.

Gages are furnished without a backing or on a backing that can be stripped away when the gage is mounted. These are called *free-filament* and *strippable-backed* gages. They are intended for use in high-temperature environments, usually above 400°F, and they have been successfully used to measure strains above 1000°F. The strain-sensitive element is chosen for its high-temperature stability (see Table 2-1). The lead wires are attached by spot welding or mechanical crimping, or the strain-sensitive filament and the leads are integral. These gages are bonded to the test surface by means of a ceramic cement. They are the most difficult to handle and bond, and are especially difficult to bond under field conditions. As a result, strippable-backed gages are available already bonded to a thin (0.005 in. thick) metal tab. This bond is made by the manufacturer under laboratory conditions; the user then welds the metal tab with prebonded gage to the test surface.

Another form of metal-backed gage is called the *weldable* gage, consisting of a single-filament strain-sensitive wire encased in an insulation-filled metal tube. The metal tube is welded to the test surface (see Fig. 2-14). These gages are not flexible, but because they are narrow they can be mounted on surfaces having considerable curvature in a plane perpendicular to the gage axis. These gages are available in a limited range of sizes, the shortest having a gage length of $\frac{9}{16}$ in.

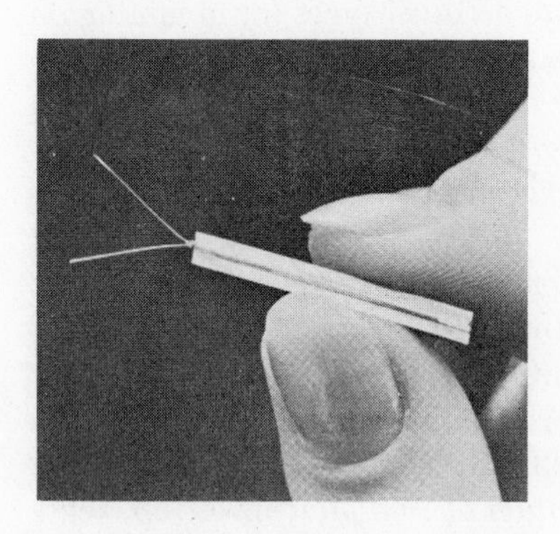

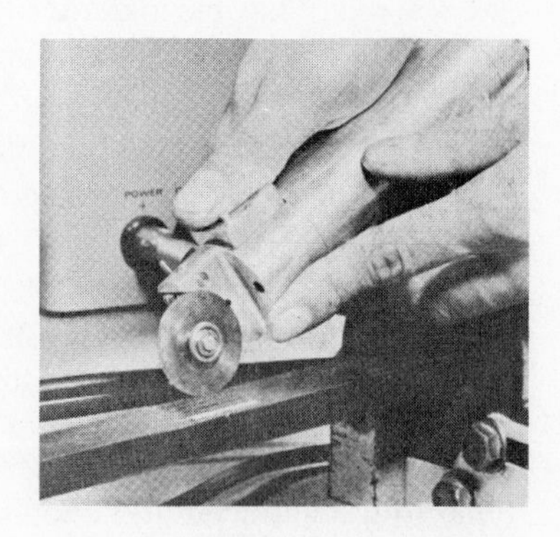

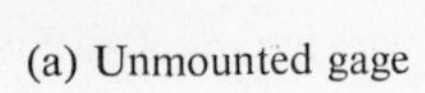

(a) Unmounted gage

(b) Welding gage to test bar

Fig. 2-14. Weldable strain gage. (*Courtesy of Microdot, Incorporated.*)

Weldable gages can be temperature-cycled or subjected to other environments before mounting for use. This "preconditioning" may increase the gage's stability when it is first used in the environment of interest. These gages may also be heat-treated after fabrication to reduce temperature-induced resistance change, and, since they can be calibrated without mounting, it is possible to measure the effect of temperature on resistance for an individual gage and to supply this information to the user.

2-1f Gage-bonding materials

Cellulose nitrate cement (*Duco or SR-4*), which sets by means of solvent evaporation, is most often used to bond paper-base gages. This type of bond is usable at temperatures between −320°F and +180°F. A combination of paper-backed gages and cellulose nitrate cement is well suited for field application and short-term tests at ambient temperatures. Under favorable conditions of low humidity and sunshine, this combination will "air-dry" sufficiently in 24 hours to give results compatible with the resolution available in most strain recording systems.

Whenever possible, paper-base gages bonded with cellulose nitrate cement and air-dried should be strain-cycled a few times before the actual test. This is necessary to obtain the highest possible accuracy and to minimize zero shift, since when paper-based gages bonded with air-dried cellulose nitrate cement are strained for the first few times, there is a change in the bond, which causes a change in the gage's zero reading. However, gages bonded with cellulose nitrate cement show very little first-loading zero-shift and very little long-term creep, even at high-strain levels, if the bond is properly cured at 140°F for 12 to 24 hours. See Sect. 2-1g for a step-by-step procedure for mounting gages with cellulose nitrate cement.

Phenol-resin (*Bakelite*) sets under the combined action of pressure and heat. Formerly, this was used exclusively as the bonding agent for the Bakelite-backed gages, but it has been largely replaced in this use by high-temperature epoxy cements. Bakelite cement is difficult to use because it requires that high bond pressure (150 psi) be maintained during a long and carefully controlled high-temperature (up to 400°F) cure. This is generally not possible under field conditions, and the user must realize that an improper Bakelite bond may be inferior to a proper cellulose nitrate bond. Bakelite bonds are not discussed further, because it is felt that the epoxy bonds are superior.

Several *epoxy resins* are available for use as strain-gage adhesives. In general, these materials set by chemical action, which is initiated by the addition of a catalyst. No solvent evaporation is involved. The cure is generally accelerated at elevated temperatures, but the time-temperature cycle for proper cure is rather flexible. Very little pressure is needed during the cure. Epoxy resins can be used to bond paper-backed gages, epoxy-backed gages, and Bakelite gages. If the proper epoxy resin is chosen, a bond can be made which has temperature capabilities at least as great as the temperature capability of any of these three gage types. Epoxies and phenol-epoxy mixtures (Shell 422) are available for producing bonds good to 700–800°F, but these must be used with the free-filament or strippable-backed gages to effect any increase in the upper temperature limit of the completed gage installation. Gages can be bonded with epoxy resins and properly cured under field conditions if the proper resin is chosen for the job at hand. See Sect. 2-1g for step-by-step mounting instructions.

Cyanoacrylate (*Eastman 910*) can be used to bond paper-based and Bakelite gages, but it is not recommended for these types. It is best suited for use with the epoxy-backed gages. This cement bonds under the action of modest contact pressure and gives a gage installation that is ready for immediate use. Several gage manufacturers caution against using cyanoacrylate bonds when either thermal or mechanical shock is involved, when large strains are to be measured, or in long-time installations. Baldwin-Lima-Hamilton Corporation recommends an upper temperature limit of 150°F; others use 200°F as an upper limit for static work and 250°F for dynamic work. Bakelite-backed gages bonded with Eastman 910 have been evaluated in the authors' laboratory at strains as high as 1800 μin./in., and held for one hour at 210°F. Creep was negligible, and the gage performance was satisfactory. The authors have used cyanoacrylate-bonded gages to measure static strains as large as 3000 μin./in., and dynamic strains (rise time, approximately 1 millisecond) as high as 2000 μin./in. They have used these gages in outdoor locations (but waterproofed) for two years. We conclude that although cyanoacrylate bonds may be somewhat inferior to epoxy bonds with regard to shock, maximum strain, and long-time stability, they are adequate for a very large percentage of the problems encountered. Cyanoacrylate bonds are the most convenient to make under either laboratory or field conditions. Although cyanoacrylate will bond to most materials, it should be recognized that it is a poor gap filler, and hence the test surface should be reasonably smooth. Also, preparing the surface chemically is extremely important.

Ceramic adhesives are used to bond the free-filament or strippable-backed gages for use in high-temperature (usually above 400°F) or nuclear radiation environments (organic materials, hence the cements previously discussed, are very sensitive to nuclear radiation). These cements consist of ceramic fillers (such as aluminum or magnesium oxide) carried in various binders. The gage is mounted in the cement and the installation baked at high temperature (up to 1200°F) to produce a bond. The resultant bond will permit strain measurement up to 1500°F, but since the ceramic is brittle, these installations are not suitable for use when measuring large strains or when thermal or mechanical shock may be encountered. (For measuring high-temperature strains under shock conditions, the weldable gage is the proper choice.) Ceramic adhesives are definitely not suited for field installation of strain gages. Indeed, use of ceramic cement bonds requires considerable skill even under laboratory conditions.

The following are some specific suggestions as to gage and bond for several typical applications:

1. For service between subzero and 120°F, paper, epoxy, or Bakelite gages may be used. The paper-based gages should be bonded with Duco or SR-4 cement. If large strains are to be measured, air-drying is *not* sufficient (see Sect. 2-1g). The epoxy-based gages should be bonded with Eastman 910 or one of the epoxy cements. The Bakelite gages should be bonded with an epoxy cement. The Bakelite or epoxy-based gages bonded with epoxy cement are recommended for the most severe environments (large strains, short rise-time shock, many cycles), but under most conditions epoxy-based gages bonded with Eastman 910 will be adequate.
2. All outdoor installations and all installations to be used over a long period of time should be waterproofed (see Sect. 2-1g).
3. Gage installations to be used in vibration and shock environments should be made with special attention to lead wire installation. The use of a flexible link between gage tab and main lead wire is essential (see Sect. 2-1g).
4. For service between 120°F and 350°F, Bakelite gages bonded with an elevated-temperature-curing epoxy are recommended.
5. For service above 350°F, free-filament or strippable gages mounted in ceramic cement can be used for static measurements. For shock or impact at elevated temperatures the weldable gages are recommended.

2-1g Mounting, wiring, moistureproofing, and checking techniques

A. PAPER-BASED GAGES

Use cellulose nitrate cement (Duco or BLH SR-4 cement). The steps are as follows:

1. Prepare area larger than gage with emery cloth.
2. Clean with acetone and cotton swabs.

3. Apply excess of cement.
4. Place gage and press excess cement from center of gage outward; use thumb.
5. Hold in place until bond is set. Apply *light* pressure and allow to dry at room temperature.

CAUTION: DO NOT COVER GAGE SO AS TO INTERFERE WITH EVAPORATION OF SOLVENT AND DO NOT APPLY LARGE CLAMPING PRESSURE.

For short-time static tests air-drying may be adequate; however, the drying time depends on humidity conditions and gage type (thin or thick paper back). The best procedure is to dry until the gage-to-specimen resistance reaches 5000 megohms (a low-voltage megohmmeter must be used in order not to damage gage). Air-dried gages *should not be waterproofed*, since they still contain solvent which would be trapped under the waterproofing.

For long-time tests and greatest accuracy the following cure is recommended (from Ref. [5]):

1. The surface of the test specimen is rubbed with 00 or 000 garnet paper.
2. The surface is then cleaned with acetone and absorbent cotton.
3. The gages are trimmed and applied to the test bar with SR-4 cement. (Preliminary tests at lower strains indicated better gage performance with SR-4 cement than with Duco cement. Because the cements have the same constituents, this is attributed to the fact that the SR-4 was thinner and allowed the gage to be mounted with less distance between the paper base of the gage and the test specimen.)
4. The gages are air-dried for two hours and then placed in an oven and gradually brought to 140°F. The oven temperature is left at 140°F until the resistance between the gage grid and the test specimen is in excess of 10,000 megohms. The time required depends on moisture conditions, but in general a minimum of 12 hours for thin paper-base gages (A3 or A5-1) or 24 hours for thick paper-base gages (A7 or A8) should be used.
5. When the gages are properly dried, the temperature of the oven is raised to 160°F and held there for about one hour. The SR-4 cement around the gage is cleaned off with garnet paper, and the gages and the surrounding metal surface are coated with petrosene wax. On specimens which cannot be conveniently placed in an oven, the drying can be accomplished with thermostatically-controlled heat lamps or with hair driers.

In addition to the check made of the gage-to-specimen resistance, several other checks are in order. The gage resistance should check that given by the manufacturer. This check is most easily made by connecting two identical gages (from the same package) to a static strain indicator; if the indicator cannot be balanced near the midrange, one of the gages is outside resistance tolerance. This indicates mechanical damage of the grid element and is a sufficient reason for discarding the gage. *Do not use* gages which require use of shunt resistors to balance the bridge.

Another useful check consists of gently tapping and pressing the gage and lead wire terminal with a rubber pencil eraser. If erratic resistance (indicated by indicator pointer fluctuation) is produced by this probing, spotty bond and/or shorting of leads is indicated. If the situation cannot be corrected, the gage must be rejected or replaced.

B. EPOXY AND BAKELITE GAGES

With epoxy cements, regardless of the type, the steps are as follows:

1. Mechanically clean surface in gage area (remove scale, rust, paint, etc.).
2. Chemically clean (remove grease, oxides, etc.).
3. Roughen surface with medium grade emery paper and clean with acetone.
4. Clean gage back with acetone.
5. Spread cement, place gage, squeeze out excess cement, cover with thin teflon tape and apply light (5 to 10 psi) pressure.
6. Cure bond according to instructions given for the particular epoxy.

The same checks discussed for use on paper-based gage installations should be used here.

With cyanoacrylate cement (*Eastman 910*), the chemical condition of specimen surface and gage backing is of the greatest importance, and hence the use of one of the Eastman 910-based kits is recommended. These kits contain appropriate metal conditioners and cleaners. Specific instructions for use of such a kit are given by the manufacturers (see Sect. 2-1g, D).

Gage installation. The terminal strip, if used, should be applied at the same time as the gage. The back of the terminal should be sanded lightly and cleaned with acetone and then placed $\frac{1}{16}$ in. from the tab end of the gage. Cut a piece of transparent tape 1 to 2 in. longer than the gage. The tape should be wider than the gage. Place the tape over the top of the gage and terminal strip, and pick up the pair. Remove the heavy plastic gage carrier, and again clean the gage back and terminal strip back before the accelerator is applied to both. The accelerator should be allowed to dry for a minute or two.

The tape should now be oriented on the test specimen, and the tape near the rear end of the gage pressed down; the tape should be stuck to within about one-eighth inch of the end of the gage. One drop of Eastman 910 should be placed on the specimen at the point where the tape is stuck. With moderate pressure of the thumb and in one wiping motion starting at a point beyond where the tape has been placed, wipe the tape down, moving the thumb over the gage and the terminal strip (be sure that the surface is not wrinkled as the thumb slides along). The tape may be peeled off, starting at one corner, after one minute.

After the tape has been removed, the area around the gage and between the terminal strip should be sanded to remove the cement. This insures a good bond for the waterproofing material.

The hookup of the gage and terminal strip is done by first tinning the gage tabs and terminal strip tabs. A fine-gage resin core solder such as Divco No. 233 and a 30- to 40-watt soldering iron with a smooth-tinned tip should be used. The end of the solder is placed on the tab. The iron is then placed on the solder, gently touching the tab. The wire between the gage and the terminal strip should be a small tinned wire, such as one conductor of a No. 30 stranded wire. Before soldering, wipe the fine wire with a solvent (preparation for waterproofing). Now gently touch the wire and soldering iron to the gage tab. Leave some slack between the gage tabs and the terminal strip, and solder to the terminal strip. The wire should be slightly above the surface to prevent electrical shorting to the specimen and to allow the waterproofing to flow around the wires.

The gages should now be checked for correct bonding, gage resistance, and gage-to-specimen resistance. One of the best indications of a good bond is if the tape peels off cleanly. A close visual inspection for any areas not bonded is useful. A knife point at the corner of the gage should break off small parts of the gage backing material, but no large flakes of the gage should come off. The resistance of the gage can be measured with a bridge to see if the resistance of the gage is as specified on the package. The gage-to-gage specimen resistance should be measured with a low-voltage type of megohm meter. This reading should be greater than 10,000 megohms. If this reading is lower than 10,000 megohms, one possibility is that too much heat was applied to the tabs of the gage.

Waterproofing material such as an epoxy, a silicon, or di-jell may be used.

The waterproofing material should be applied so that it will cover from the center of the terminal tabs back, covering the entire gage area and enclosing the area that has been previously sanded. The gage is now ready for the main lead wires to be soldered on (see Fig. 2-15).

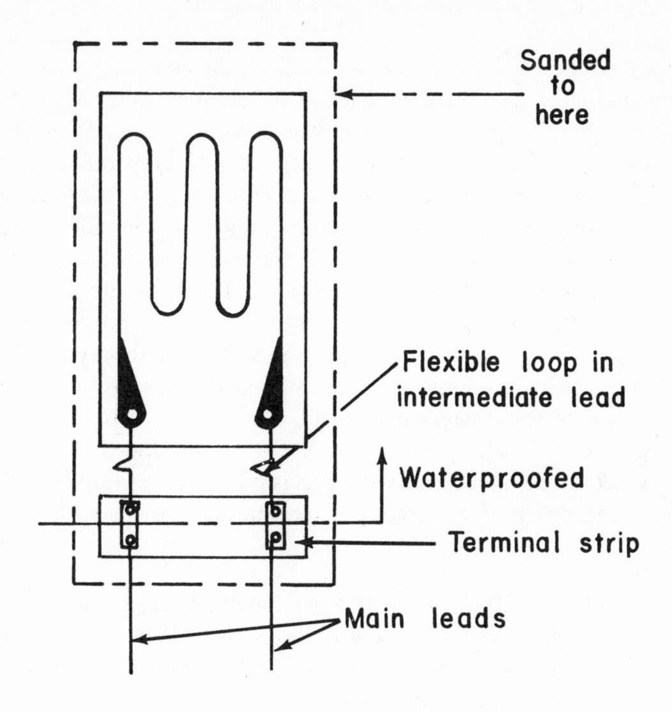

Fig. 2-15. Proper lead wire layout.

C. FREE-FILAMENT AND STRIPPABLE-BACKED GAGES—CERAMIC CEMENT

Bonding gages with ceramic cement requires considerable skill, which can only be developed with practice. For the user who does not have the time to develop the technique, the use of weldable gages is recommended. Free-filament gages are somewhat easier to use than the strippable gages, because the steps involved in stripping the back are eliminated. Specific instructions are given by gage manufacturers; see Sect. 2-1g, D.

D. MATERIALS AVAILABLE FROM GAGE MANUFACTURERS

Gage manufacturers have done an excellent job of making available to gage users detailed instructions on how best to mount their products. These instructions are available upon request from the manufacturers. For example, from Baldwin-Lima-Hamilton Corporation, the "BLH Handbook—Strain Gages," and from the Instruments Division of the Budd Company, the "BG-3100 Instruction Manual."

2-2 Circuitry for resistance strain gages

As we have pointed out in the last section, the characteristics of metal and semiconductor gages are sufficiently different to make it convenient to consider circuitry for the two types as separate items. The difficulty stems from the fact that metal gages, which were developed first, normally undergo very small changes in resistance during use (i.e., low gage factor). As a result, most of the circuit theory originally applied for strain gage use was simplified for the case of small changes in resistance, and most of the equipment and techniques developed were adequate only for this case. The semiconductor gages undergo large changes in resistance (i.e., high gage factor) and, as a result, the simplified theory, equipment, and techniques which assume small resistance changes are not adequate.

To use any of these gages effectively, it is necessary to connect them in an electric circuit which will allow the strain-produced change in the resistance ΔR to be measured with precision. Two examples will serve to indicate the order of magnitude of resistance changes with which we must deal.

Example 2-1. A 120-ohm metal gage having a gage factor of 2.0 is mounted on a low carbon steel. What change in gage resistance will be produced by straining the material to its yield point?

Solution: Assume that the yield-point stress is 30,000 psi and the modulus of elasticity E is 30×10^6 psi. Then

$$\epsilon_{\text{yield point}} = \frac{\text{stress}}{E} = \frac{30 \times 10^3}{30 \times 10^6} = 1 \times 10^{-3} \text{ in./in.}$$

$$= 1000 \ \mu\text{in./in.}$$

Rearranging the equation for gage factor, we have

$$\Delta R = FR\epsilon$$

or

$$\Delta R = (2)(120)(1 \times 10^{-3}) = 0.24 \text{ ohm.}$$

This represents a total change of 0.2 per cent over the strain region of interest; hence, circuits must be capable of measuring small changes of resistance to a high degree of accuracy.

Example 2-2. A 120-ohm semiconductor gage having a gage factor of 100 is used in the same way as the gage in Example 2-1. What change in gage resistance is produced?

Solution:

$$\begin{aligned}\Delta R &= FR\epsilon \\ &= (100)(120)(1 \times 10^{-3}) \\ &= 12 \text{ ohms.}\end{aligned}$$

This represents a change of 10 per cent in gage resistance.

2-2a Circuit analysis—metal strain gages

The circuit most commonly used with metal variable-resistance strain gages is a four-arm bridge with a *constant voltage* power supply.

The basic bridge-type circuit is shown in Fig. 2-16.

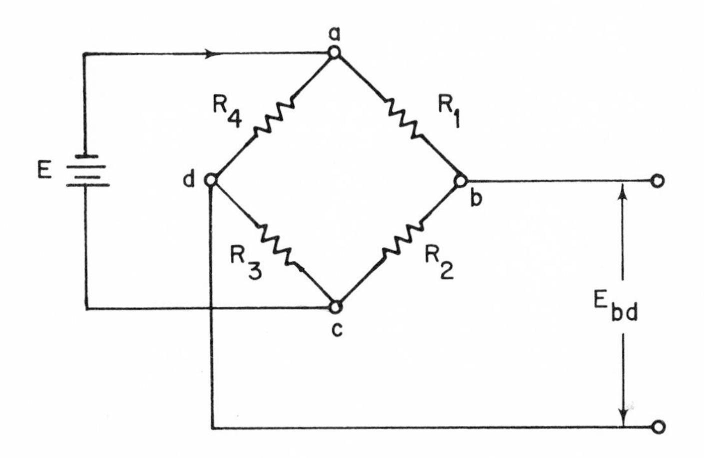

Fig. 2-16. Wheatstone-bridge circuit.

The power supply can be either AC or DC, but we assume it to be DC so that equations may be written in terms of resistance R rather than in terms of impedance Z.* Let us begin by establishing the condition which makes the potential across the diagonal b-d equal to zero ($E_{bd} = 0$).

To do this, we first write the equations for the potential drops across the individual elements:

$$\begin{aligned} E_{ad} &= I_4R_4, \quad \text{or} \quad I_4 = \frac{E_{ad}}{R_4}; \\ E_{dc} &= I_3R_3, \quad \text{or} \quad I_3 = \frac{E_{dc}}{R_3}; \\ E_{ab} &= I_1R_1, \quad \text{or} \quad I_1 = \frac{E_{ab}}{R_1}; \end{aligned} \tag{2-8}$$

* For a discussion of AC-powered bridges, see p. 124.

$$E_{bc} = I_2R_2, \quad \text{or} \quad I_2 = \frac{E_{bc}}{R_2}.$$

But for an open circuit between points b and d,

$$I_4 = I_3,$$

and (2-9)

$$I_1 = I_2.$$

So

$$\frac{E_{ad}}{R_4} = \frac{E_{dc}}{R_3},$$

and (2-10)

$$\frac{E_{ab}}{R_1} = \frac{E_{bc}}{R_2}.$$

If E_{bd} is to equal zero, the potential at d must equal that at b; hence, the drop from a to d must equal that from a to b, and the drop from d to c must equal that from b to c; i.e.,

$$E_{ad} = E_{ab},$$

and (2-11)

$$E_{dc} = E_{bc}.$$

Substituting Eq. (2-11) into Eq. (2-10), we obtain

$$\frac{R_1}{R_2} = \frac{R_4}{R_3}, \tag{2-12}$$

which is the condition for a balanced bridge.

Next, we establish the expression for the change in the potential across the diagonal b-d (dE_{bd}) due to *small* changes in R_1; i.e., dR_1. Since R_4 and R_3 remain constant, the potential at point d is unchanged. The current flow through R_1 is

$$I_1 = \frac{E}{(R_1 + R_2)}, \tag{2-13}$$

and the potential drop across R_1 is

$$E_{ab} = I_1R_1 = \frac{ER_1}{(R_1 + R_2)}. \tag{2-14}$$

The change in E_{ab} due to *small* changes in R_1 may be determined by differentiation:

$$dE_{ab} = \frac{R_2\, dR_1}{(R_2 + R_1)^2}\, E. \tag{2-15}$$

Since $E_b = E_d$ at balance and E_d remains constant, the difference between b and d due to dR_1 is equal to the change in potential of b, and the change in potential at b is equal to the change across ab, since the potential at a remains constant; i.e.,

$$E_{bd} = E_d - (E_b + dE_b),$$

$$E_{bd} = -dE_b = -dE_{ab}.$$

So

$$E_{bd} = -\frac{R_2\,dR_1}{(R_2 + R_1)^2}E.$$

Using the same approach, we can write this equation successively for changes in R_2, R_3, and R_4.
Thus,

$$E_{bd} = +\frac{R_1\,dR_2}{(R_2 + R_1)^2}E,$$

$$E_{bd} = -\frac{R_4\,dR_3}{(R_4 + R_3)^2}E,$$

and

$$E_{bd} = +\frac{R_3\,dR_4}{(R_4 + R_3)^2}E.$$

If R_1, R_2, R_3, and R_4 undergo small changes simultaneously, the total effect on E_{bd} is the sum of these individual effects. Thus,

$$E_{bd} = \left[\frac{-R_2\,dR_1}{(R_1 + R_2)^2} + \frac{R_1\,dR_2}{(R_1 + R_2)^2} - \frac{R_4\,dR_3}{(R_3 + R_4)^2} + \frac{R_3\,dR_4}{(R_3 + R_4)^2}\right]E. \quad (2\text{-}16)$$

By substituting the definition of gage factor

$$F = \frac{dR/R}{\epsilon}$$

into Eq. (2-16), we obtain

$$E_{bd} = \left[\frac{-R_2R_1F_1\epsilon_1}{(R_1 + R_2)^2} + \frac{R_1R_2F_2\epsilon_2}{(R_1 + R_2)^2} - \frac{R_4R_3F_3\epsilon_3}{(R_3 + R_4)^2} + \frac{R_3R_4F_4\epsilon_4}{(R_3 + R_4)^2}\right]E. \quad (2\text{-}17)$$

In many cases, this bridge circuit is made up using equal resistances ($R_g = R_1 = R_2 = R_3 = R_4$). For this special case, the sensitivity, Eq (2-17) can be reduced to the following:

$$E_{bd} = \frac{FE}{4}(-\epsilon_1 + \epsilon_2 - \epsilon_3 + \epsilon_4), \quad (2\text{-}17a)$$

or, in terms of current to the bridge I,*

* The permissible gage current depends upon the power that the gage can dissipate as heat without becoming overheated. The permissible power ($P = I^2R$) depends on a number of factors which include the size of the gage, the method of bonding, the thermal conductivity of the surface to which it is bonded, and whether or not the gage is cooled or insulated on its unbonded side. Hence, no fixed value of maximum power may be set, but 50 mw may be taken as a reasonable value for both metal and semiconductor gages.

$$E_{bd} = \frac{FIR_g}{4}(-\epsilon_1 + \epsilon_2 - \epsilon_3 + \epsilon_4), \tag{2-17b}$$

since

$$E = IR_{\text{bridge}}$$

and

$$R_{\text{bridge}} = \left(\frac{1}{R_1 + R_2} + \frac{1}{R_3 + R_4}\right)^{-1} = R_g.$$

We conclude that the unbalance of the bridge (E_{bd}) is proportional to the sum of strain (or resistance) changes in opposite arms and to the difference of strain (or resistance) changes in adjacent arms.

The sensitivity of the bridge circuit when the bridge is balanced or is very near the balance point is expressed in Eq. (2-17). This is true, since in the derivation we assumed $E_b = E_d$; hence, the value obtained from Eq. (2-17) is referred to as the null or balance point sensitivity. It must also be remembered that Eq. (2-17) was derived by using differentiation and assuming that no current flows through the instrument used to measure E_{bd}. Hence, the value of E_{bd} obtained from Eq. (2-17) is the no-load (or open circuit) potential for small changes in R.

The solution for E_{bd} associated with change in ΔR of any size with the bridge voltage E held constant can be investigated in the following manner. Refer to Fig. 2-16. The initial (before straining) voltage drop across ab is

$$E_{ab_i} = \frac{R_1}{R_1 + R_2} E,$$

and the final (after straining) voltage drop across ab is

$$E_{ab_f} = \frac{(R_1 + \Delta R_1)E}{[(R_1 + \Delta R_1) + R_2]},$$

in which it has been assumed that the active strain gage was R_1 and a change in resistance of ΔR_1 was produced. Since the potential at point d remains constant, the change in potential at point b is the same as the change between b and d, and hence

$$E_{bd} = \frac{(R_1 + \Delta R_1)E}{[(R_1 + \Delta R_1) + R_2]} - \frac{R_1}{R_1 + R_2} E. \tag{2-18}$$

This reduces to

$$\frac{E_{bd}}{E} = \frac{\Delta R_1}{4R + 2\Delta R_1}, \qquad \text{for } R_1 = R_2,$$

whereas Eq. (2-16) reduces to

$$\frac{E_{bd}}{E} = \frac{dR_1}{4R}, \qquad \text{for } R_1 = R_2.$$

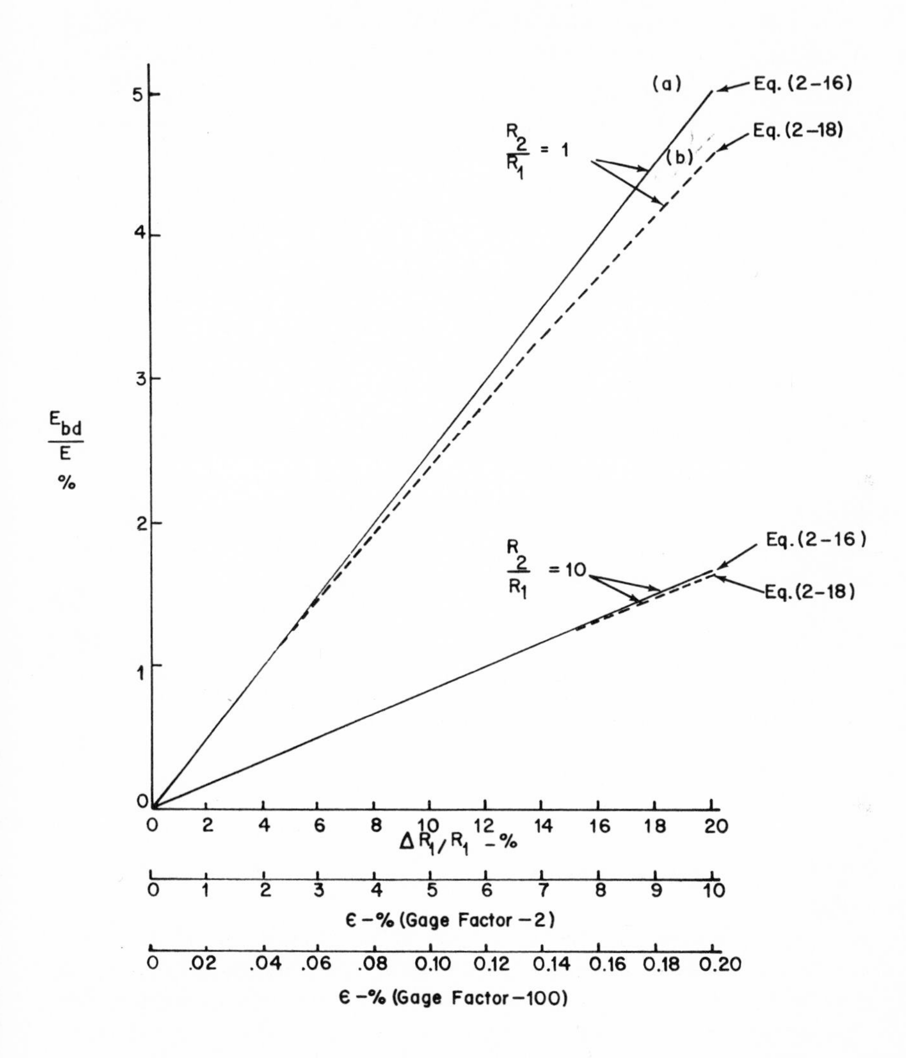

Fig. 2-17. Bridge output as a function of strain for several gage factors—comparison of differential and finite difference equations.

Equations (2-16) and (2-18) have been plotted in Fig. 2-17 for several values of R_2/R_1. From this plot we make the following observations:

1. With a four-arm bridge the voltage output is a nonlinear function of resistance change in one arm. Equation (2-16), which predicts linear output, is a good approximation only for small $\Delta R/R$.

2. The nonlinearity is largest for $R_1 = R_2$ (the case most frequently encountered in strain gage work) and is reduced as R_2/R_1 is increased. If the supply voltage E remains fixed, the output E_{bd} is reduced, however.

As shown in Table 2-2, the percentage of deviation from linearity is less than five per cent even for strain in a single gage as large as five

Table 2-2. Percentage of deviation from linearity of E_{bd} for $R_2/R_1 = 1$

$\Delta R/R$	ϵ–μin./in. Gage Factor = 2	ϵ–μin./in. Gage Factor = 100	% Deviation*,†
0.02	10,000	200	1.00
0.04	20,000	400	2.00
0.06	30,000	600	2.94
0.08	40,000	800	3.90
0.10	50,000	1000	4.80
0.12	60,000	1200	5.66
0.14	70,000	1400	6.57
0.16	80,000	1600	7.50
0.18	90,000	1800	8.22
0.20	100,000	2000	9.00

* Percentage of deviation computed as value from curve (*a*), Fig. 2-17, minus value from curve (*b*), divided by value from (*a*), times 100.

† Percentage of deviation is approximately one-half of $\Delta R/R$, expressed in per cent.

per cent (50,000 μin./in.) if $F = 2$; but if $F = 100$, a strain of only 0.2 per cent (2000 μin./in.) produces a deviation from linearity of nine per cent.

Since the use of a single, active gage is the worst* case, we conclude that, except in cases where strains are very large and where the highest degree of precision is required *and warranted*, Eq. (2-16) is adequate for analysis of and use with variable-resistance strain gages having gage factors in the neighborhood of 2.0. If greater precision is required and warranted, then the variable-resistance strain gages having low gage factors should be analyzed and treated in the same way as are semiconductor gages. See Sect. 2-2b. Even when accuracy of greater than one per cent is desired, correction of Eq. (2-16) only may still be of little real value, unless errors in calibration, reading, reduction of data, and conversion of strains to stress are all reduced accordingly.

* Use of two or four active gages connected in the bridge so that their outputs are additive will reduce or even eliminate the nonlinearity effect. See p. 95.

To determine the effect of a finite load resistance, we may analyze a loaded circuit using Thevenin's theorem. Thevenin's theorem states that the actual current flow through the load (the indicating instrument in this case) can be obtained by first finding the no-load potential (switch S in Fig. 2-18 open) and then applying this potential across the entire circuit, with the supply potential (F) shorted. See Ref. [6], pp. 3-11. See Fig. 2-18.

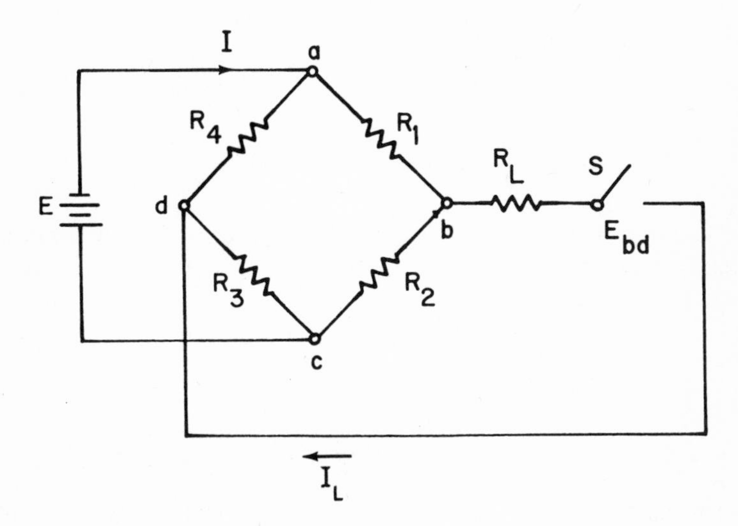

Fig. 2-18. Bridge circuit with load resistance.

We apply the no-load potential (E_{bd}) at point S and compute the current flow through the instrument.

$$I_L = \frac{E_{bd}}{R_L + R_{\text{bridge}}}, \tag{2-19}$$

in which

$$R_{\text{bridge}} = \frac{R_1 R_2}{R_1 + R_2} + \frac{R_3 R_4}{R_3 + R_4}.$$

Now, applying Ohm's law, we have

$$E_L = I_L R_L,$$

or

$$E_L = \frac{R_L}{R_L + R_{\text{bridge}}} E_{bd}, \tag{2-20}$$

in which E_L is the potential across the indicating instrument. The factor

$$\frac{R_L}{R_L + R_{\text{bridge}}}$$

is the factor by which the open circuit (or no-load potential) is reduced, due to the load resistance. For the special case $R_g = R_1 = R_2 = R_3 = R_4$, thus,

$$E_L = \frac{FE}{4}(-\epsilon_1 + \epsilon_2 - \epsilon_3 + \epsilon_4) \times \frac{R_L}{R_L + R_g}, \tag{2-21}$$

or

$$E_L = \frac{FIR_g}{4}(-\epsilon_1 + \epsilon_2 - \epsilon_3 + \epsilon_4) \times \frac{R_L}{R_L + R_g}. \tag{2-21a}$$

The term $-\epsilon_1 + \epsilon_2 - \epsilon_3 + \epsilon_4$ may be defined as the net strain (ϵ_{net}) affecting the bridge.

Then

$$E_L = \frac{FE}{4} \times \frac{R_L}{R_L + R_g} \times \epsilon_{\text{net}}, \tag{2-22}$$

or

$$E_L = \frac{FIR_g}{4} \times \frac{R_L}{R_L + R_g} \times \epsilon_{\text{net}}. \tag{2-22a}$$

The net strain (ϵ_{net}) will depend upon the number of gages being strained and the strain in each. Figure 2-19 indicates ways in which more than one gage may be made active for various types of loading.

In (a) of Fig. 2-19,

$$\epsilon_1 = \epsilon_3, \quad \text{and} \quad \epsilon_{\text{net}} = 2\epsilon_1.$$

In (b) of Fig. 2-19,

$$\epsilon_1 = -\epsilon_2, \quad \text{and} \quad \epsilon_{\text{net}} = 2\epsilon_1,$$

or

$$\epsilon_1 = \epsilon_3 = -\epsilon_2 = -\epsilon_4, \quad \text{and} \quad \epsilon_{\text{net}} = 4\epsilon_1.$$

In (c) of Fig. 2-19,

$$\epsilon_2 = -\mu\epsilon_1, \quad \text{and} \quad \epsilon_{\text{net}} = (1 + \mu)\epsilon_1,$$

or

$$\epsilon_2 = \epsilon_4 = -\mu\epsilon_1 = -\mu\epsilon_2 \quad \text{and} \quad \epsilon_{\text{net}} = 2(1 + \mu)\epsilon_1,$$

in which μ is Poisson's ratio.

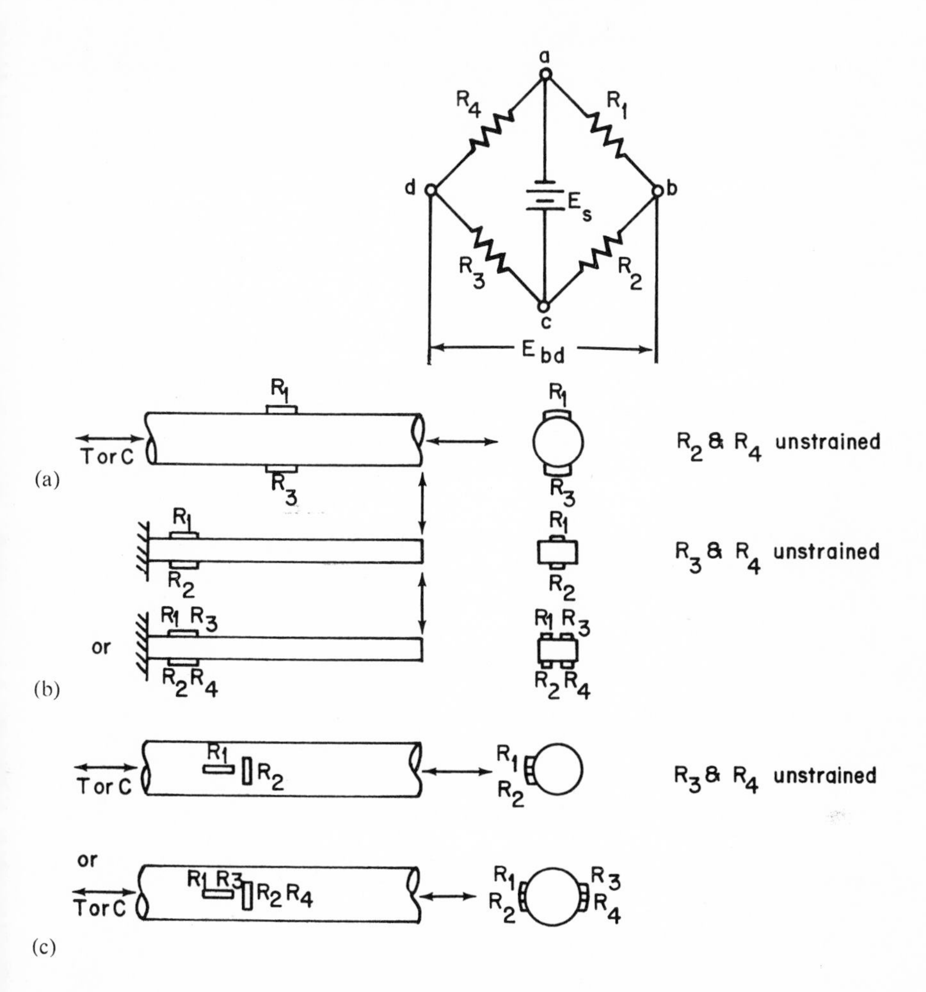

(a) Positioning of gages to measure axial strain.
(b) Positioning of gages to measure bending strain.
(c) Positioning of gages to measure axial strain and to provide temperature compensation.

Fig. 2-19. Strain-gage locations for various measured quantities.

The output of a bridge-type circuit is often measured by using a current-sensitive instrument (a galvanometer); for this reason it is advantageous to have the sensitivities in terms of current to the galvanometer. Again, for the case of $R_g = R_1 = R_2 = R_3 = R_4$: since $I_L = E_L/R_L$,

$$I_L = \frac{FE}{4} \times \frac{1}{R_L + R_g} \times \epsilon_{\text{net}}, \tag{2-23}$$

or

$$I_L = \frac{FIR_g}{4} \times \frac{1}{R_L + R_g} \times \epsilon_{\text{net}}. \tag{2-23a}$$

The following example will illustrate the application of the equations just derived.

Example 2-3. (Refer to Fig. 2-18.)
Assume that we make a bridge using four 120-ohm gages, that $F = 2.0$, and that the current through a gage is to be held to 20 ma. Find the sensitivity of this circuit: first, when a cathode-ray oscilloscope is used as an indicator, and second, when a low-impedance microammeter is used.

Solution: The current to the bridge will be twice the current through the gages.

$$I = 2I_{\text{gage}} = 40 \text{ ma.}$$

The required supply potential is

$$E = IR_{\text{bridge}} = IR_g$$
$$= (40 \times 10^{-3})(120) = 4.8 \text{ v.}$$

The sensitivity is

$$E_L = \frac{FE}{4}(\epsilon_{\text{net}})\frac{R_L}{R_L + R_g},$$

or

$$I_L = \frac{FE}{4}(\epsilon_{\text{net}})\frac{1}{R_L + R_g},$$

in which ϵ_{net} is used to replace $(-\epsilon_1 + \epsilon_2 - \epsilon_3 + \epsilon_4)$.

The load resistance (R_L) of a cathode-ray oscilloscope (CRO) is very large; hence,

$$\frac{R_L}{R_L + R_g} \to 1.$$

So, for the CRO system,

$$\frac{E_L}{\epsilon_{\text{net}}} = \frac{FE}{4} = \frac{(2)(4.8)}{4} = 2.4 \text{ v/in./in.}$$

or

$$0.0024 \text{ mv}/\mu\text{in./in.}$$

The load resistance (R_L) of microammeters varies over a wide range and hence must be determined for the specific instrument being used; however, it is often low and must be considered. Assume $R_L = 120$ ohms when a microammeter is used as the indicating instrument. So, for the microammeter system,

$$\frac{I_L}{\epsilon_{\text{net}}} = \frac{FE}{4} \times \frac{1}{R_L + R_g}$$

$$= \frac{(2)(4.8)}{4} \times \frac{1}{120 + 120} = 0.01 \text{ amp/in./in.}$$

$$= 0.01 \ \mu\text{amp}/\mu\text{in./in.}$$

The example just given was for the case of an equal bridge ($R_g = R_1 = R_2 = R_3 = R_4$). To analyze an unequal bridge, Eq. (2-17) must be used. How an unequal bridge may be used to increase the circuit output under certain conditions is considered in the following analysis. If only one active gage is used (say, R_1 in Fig. 2-18), Eq. (2-17) reduces to

$$\frac{E_{bd}}{\epsilon_1} = \frac{-R_2 R_1 F_1}{(R_1 + R_2)^2} E, \tag{2-24}$$

which shows that the open circuit output is not dependent upon R_3 and R_4, except that for balance,

$$\frac{R_4}{R_3} = \frac{R_1}{R_2}.$$

The question now arises as to the effect on open-circuit output of varying the ratio R_1/R_2.

First, consider the case in which E is held constant. We may write

$$\frac{E_{bd}}{\epsilon_1} = \frac{R_2 R_1}{(R_1 + R_2)^2} K,$$

in which $K = -F_1 E$. By dividing both numerator and denominator by R_2^2, this reduces to

$$\frac{E_{bd}}{\epsilon_1} = \frac{\dfrac{R_1}{R_2}}{\left(\dfrac{R_1}{R_2} + 1\right)^2} K. \tag{2-25}$$

Figure 2-20, which is a plot of

$$\frac{\dfrac{R_1}{R_2}}{\left(\dfrac{R_1}{R_2} + 1\right)^2} \quad \text{versus} \quad \frac{R_1}{R_2},$$

shows that for this case (when E = constant),

$$\frac{R_1}{\left(\frac{R_1}{R_2} + 1\right)^2}$$

is a maximum for $R_1/R_2 = 1$; hence, the open-circuit signal output per unit of strain (E_{bd}/ϵ) is greatest for $R_1 = R_2$.

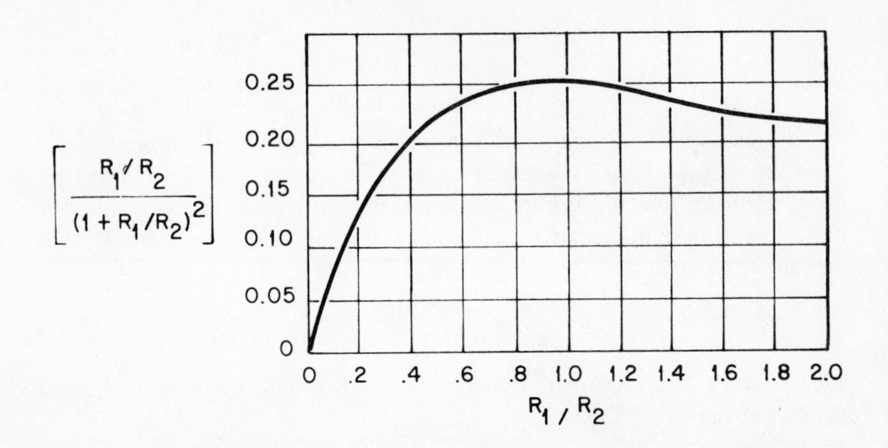

Fig. 2-20. Effect of the R_1/R_2 ratio on the sensitivity of a bridge with a constant supply voltage. (R_1 = active gage resistance.)

Next, consider the case in which the current through the gage is held constant.* The current through the gage (R_1) is related to the applied potential by Ohm's law:

$$E = I_1(R_1 + R_2). \tag{2-26}$$

Substituting this into Eq. (2-24) yields

$$\frac{E_{bd}}{\epsilon_1} = -\frac{R_2 R_1 F_1 I_1}{(R_1 + R_2)},$$

which may be written as

$$\frac{E_{bd}}{\epsilon_1} = \frac{R_2}{(R_1 + R_2)} K_1'$$

in which $K_1' = -F_1 I_1 R_1$.

* In this case "constant current" is used to mean that the supply potential is set so that for any value of $(R_1 + R_2)$, I is the same before strain is applied. It does not mean that I remains constant as strain, and hence ΔR, is applied.

Dividing both numerator and denominator by R_2, we obtain

$$\frac{E_{bd}}{\epsilon_1} = \frac{1}{\left(\frac{R_1}{R_2} + 1\right)} K_1'. \qquad (2\text{-}27)$$

Figure 2-21, which is a plot of

$$\frac{1}{\left(\frac{R_1}{R_2} + 1\right)} \quad \text{versus} \quad \frac{R_1}{R_2},$$

shows how

$$\frac{1}{\left(\frac{R_1}{R_2} + 1\right)}$$

varies with R_1/R_2.

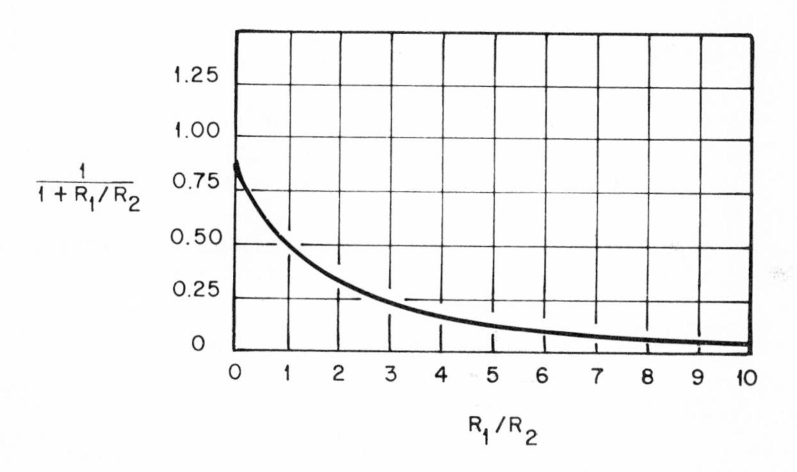

Fig. 2-21. Effect of the R_1/R_2 ratio on the sensitivity of a bridge with a constant gage current. (R_1 = active gage resistance.)

For this case (I_1 = constant), the open-circuit signal output per unit strain E_{bd}/ϵ_1 is proportional to

$$\frac{1}{\left(\frac{R_1}{R_2} + 1\right)}.$$

As R_1/R_2 approaches zero, E_{bd}/ϵ_1 approaches its maximum value of $F_1 I_1 R_1$. For $R_1 = R_2$ (an equal bridge),

$$\frac{E_{bd}}{\epsilon_1} = \frac{F_1 I_1 R_1}{2}$$

or half the maximum possible. It must be remembered, however, that as R_1/R_2 varies, the potential (E) required to hold I_1 constant also varies. This variation is readily investigated by rewriting Eq. (2-26). Thus,

$$E = I_1 R_1 \left(1 + \frac{1}{R_1/R_2}\right). \tag{2-26a}$$

As $R_1/R_2 \to 0$, the required potential approaches infinity.

If an unequal bridge is to be used in conjunction with a low-impedance (R_L small) indicating instrument, we need to investigate the effect on the closed (loaded) circuit output. For a single active gage (say R_1),

$$\frac{E_L}{\epsilon_1} = -\frac{-R_2 R_1 F_1}{(R_1 + R_2)^2} E \times \frac{R_L}{R_L + R_{\text{bridge}}}, \tag{2-28}$$

which shows that the loaded-circuit output is not independent of the value of R_3 and R_4, since R_{bridge} is dependent on R_3 and R_4. Specifically, the larger the value chosen for R_3 and R_4, the larger the value of R_{bridge} and the more the closed-circuit output is reduced.

The bridge circuit just discussed is used as the basis for two types of strain-measuring systems. In the first of these (the deflection system), the potential produced by strain causes a deflection of the indicating device. As has already been indicated by the examples given, the available signal will, in general, be in the range of microvolts or microamperes. In addition to the rather high sensitivity required of the indicating instrument, the instrument deflection should be proportional to the input signal over a wide range. It should also be pointed out that the resolution obtainable is directly related to the maximum possible deflection of the indicator. Equation (2-17) indicates that in the deflection system the output is directly proportional to E as well as to strain ϵ.

In the second system of strain measurement utilizing the bridge circuit, the indicating instrument is used only to determine whether the bridge is in balance or out of balance. This system is referred to as a null or null balance system. With the system initially balanced (before straining occurs), the indicating instrument shows zero deflection. Straining unbalances the bridge, and the indicator is deflected. Equation (2-17) indicates that unbalance produced by strain in any arm of the bridge can be compensated for by introduction of a suitable ΔR in some other arm of the bridge—this is the basis of the null system. To illustrate the possibilities of this system, we shall assume that the initially balanced bridge is unbalanced by a tensile strain in the arm $ab(+\Delta R_1)$. See Fig. 2-22.

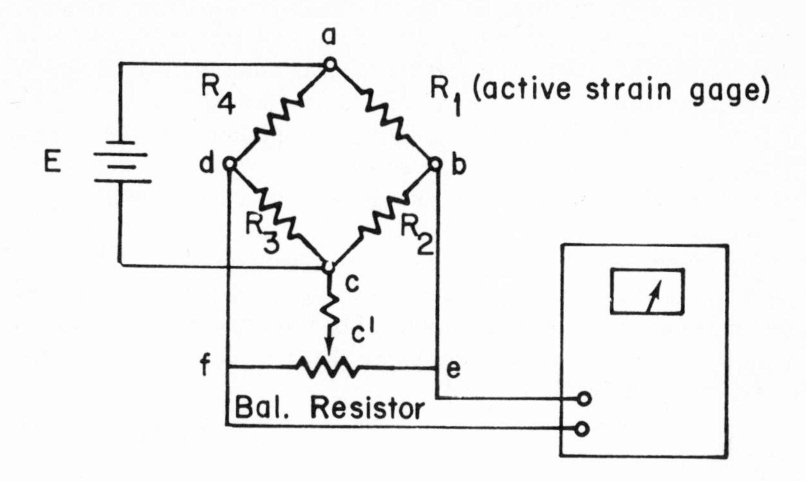

Fig. 2-22. Bridge circuit with balancing resistor in parallel with two arms of the bridge.

The system can be rebalanced in either of two ways: (1) by the introduction of a suitable* value of $+\Delta R$ in either R_2 or R_4, or (2) by the introduction of a suitable value of $-\Delta R$ in R_3. In this system, the strain is determined by measuring the value of ΔR required to rebalance the bridge. This measured value of ΔR is related to the applied strain by Eq. (2-16) and the definition of gage factor.

Theoretically, the ΔR required to rebalance the bridge may be introduced in any of several ways, but we must remember that we are concerned with very small values which must be continuously variable with great precision. Several balance systems are discussed in Sect. 2-2d, but for the present we shall look briefly at one possible method. See Fig. 2-22. A large resistor (balancing resistor) is connected so that the portion in parallel with R_3 and R_2 may be continuously varied. Again, assume unbalance due to $+\Delta R_1$. As c' (Fig. 2-22) is moved from its initial position toward position f, a $+\Delta R_{bc}$ and a $-\Delta R_{dc}$ will result. Since bridge output is proportional to the difference of resistance change in adjacent arms [see Eq. (2-16)], balance is restored more rapidly than if either R_2 or R_3 were varied individually. Also note that unbalance due to a $-\Delta R_1$ could be offset by moving c' from its initial position toward

* In the case of an equal bridge, the required value would be equal to $|\Delta R_1|$; in an unequal bridge the required value could be determined by using Eq. (2-16).

point *e*. In this system the indicating instrument need have only sufficient sensitivity to allow the balance point to be established with accuracy, and the instrument need not be linear. Also, note that the variation in bridge potential (E) will not affect the system calibration or accuracy. However, the network used for rebalancing the bridge should be such that ΔR (and hence strain) will be linearly proportional to the motion of point c'.* Also, this system can be used only when the strain to be measured remains constant long enough for the balance point to be re-established.

A potentiometer (or half bridge circuit) which consists of two resistances in series with a potential source (see Fig. 2-23) is most often used in the measurement of dynamic strains. For this application, the output is capacitance-coupled to the indicator so that only changes in potential across the gage (ΔE_g) are recorded.

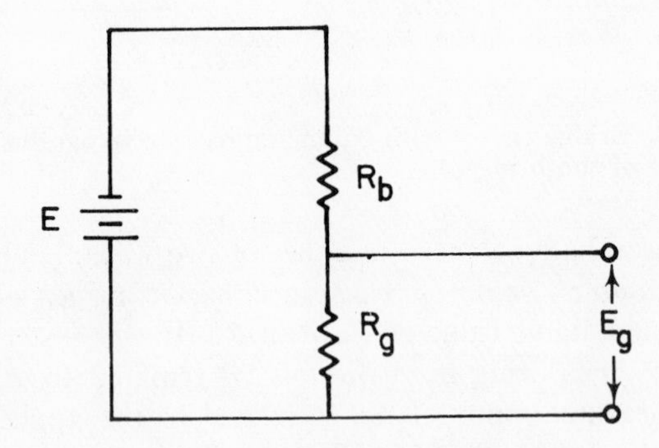

Fig. 2-23. Potentiometer-type circuit with one active gage.

In practice the potential source may be either alternating or direct current, but we shall assume it to be direct current so that equations may be written in terms of resistance (R) instead of total impedance (Z). The symbol R_g represents the strain gage and R_b represents a resistive element of fixed value which is referred to as a ballast resistance. E_g is the potential difference across the strain gage. This circuit can be analyzed in the same manner as the bridge circuit. The resulting sensitivity equation is

$$\frac{dE_g}{\epsilon} = \frac{R_b R_g F E}{(R_b + R_g)^2}, \tag{2-29}$$

* With the balancing network shown in Fig. 2-22, strain may *not* be linearly related to motion of c′ over a wide range. See Laboratory Experiment 2-3.

or, in terms of gage current,

$$\frac{dE_g}{\epsilon} = \frac{R_b R_g F I_g}{(R_b + R_g)}. \tag{2-29a}$$

Notice that for the case of $R_b/R_g \to \infty$, Eq. (2-29a) becomes

$$\frac{dE_g}{\epsilon} = R_g F I_g, \tag{2-29b}$$

which is twice the sensitivity of an equal bridge circuit for the same gage current (I_g).

Equations (2-29) and (2-29a) give the sensitivity of this circuit for small changes in R_g and for the condition of no load connected across the gage element. This circuit can be used in the measurement of static strains if a zeroing circuit is added to reduce the initial value E_g to zero. A suitable zeroing circuit is shown in Fig. 2-24. The potential E_z is selected to be somewhat larger than the IR_g drop across points bc. The potentiometer R_2 is then adjusted to produce zero potential between points $b'c'$.

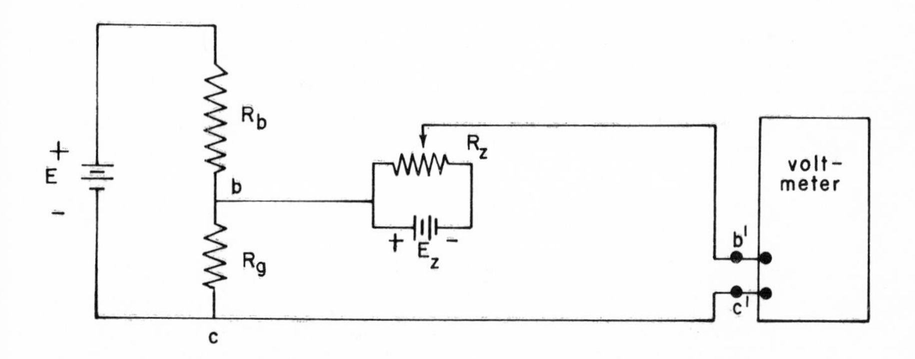

Fig. 2-24. Potentiometer circuit showing position of zeroing circuit.

The zero circuit tends to be unstable due to variation of R_z (thermal effects) and E_z (battery or power supply drift); hence, this circuit is not used to measure strain variations over long periods of time. Indeed, for static use this circuit would have no advantage over an unequal bridge.

The effect of large changes in ΔR and of load (R_L) on the circuit can be investigated in the same way that these effects were evaluated with the full bridge circuit. The effect of loading is to reduce the open-circuit potential output Eq. (2-29) by the factor

$$\left[\frac{R_L}{R_L + \dfrac{R_b R_g}{R_b + R_g}}\right]$$

The nonlinearity of potential output with ΔR will again be found to be small for values of ΔR likely to be encountered with metallic variable-resistance strain gages, particularly for the case of $R_b >> R_g$. However, with semiconductor gages and other variable-resistance transducers, the nonlinearity of this circuit should certainly be investigated; the same method as that on p. 80 should be used.

2-2b Circuit analysis—semiconductor strain gages

As pointed out in the previous section, with a constant-voltage four-arm bridge the voltage output is nonlinear with changes in R in one bridge arm. Since semiconductor gages undergo larger changes in R for the same applied strain, this nonlinearity is more troublesome with the semiconductor gages. As shown in Examples 2-1 and 2-2, a metal gage ($R = 120\Omega$, $F = 2.0$) and a semiconductor gage ($R = 120$, $F = 100$), both subjected to a strain of 1000 μin./in., give

$$\Delta R_{F=2} = FR\epsilon = 0.24 \text{ ohms},$$

or 0.2 per cent change in R.

$$\Delta R_{F=100} = 12 \text{ ohms},$$

or 10 per cent change in R.

Using Table 2-2 or Fig. 2-17, we find that, with $F = 2$ and $R_1/R_2 = 1$, the deviation from linearity of circuit potential output is less than one per cent, whereas with $F = 100$ the comparable figure is 4.8 per cent.

In spite of this difficulty, constant-voltage bridge circuits are used with semiconductor gages under certain circumstances. First, if the strain to be measured is sufficiently small, this circuit may still be adequate. Since the amount of nonlinearity is dependent upon the value ΔR, and since $\Delta R = F\epsilon R$, the maximum strain that can be tolerated before the permissible deviation from linearity is exceeded is inversely proportional to gage factor. This use of semiconductor gages to measure small strain should not be considered to be a trivial application. Indeed, measurement of small strains (<500 μin./in., where the percentage of deviation from linearity is less than two per cent) is one of the two applications where semiconductor gages, as they now function, have any advantage over the metal gages. The other application is the case where a new system is to be designed and built, and a large output signal will eliminate the need for amplifiers.

Second, semiconductor gages can be used in constant-voltage, four-arm bridge circuits to measure larger strains if the ratio of R_2/R_1 is increased; this, of course, also increases both bridge output and supply voltage required (see Figs. 2-20 and 2-21).

Third, semiconductor gages may be used in constant-voltage four-arm bridge circuits when two or four gages are used in adjacent arms and strained so that their outputs are additive. Just as the potential signal (E_{bd}) produced by a given ΔR in one bridge arm is opposite in sign to the potential sign produced by the same ΔR in an adjacent arm, so also is the sign of nonlinearity of E_{bd} dependent on the arm in which the ΔR occurs. Therefore, if gages in adjacent arms are subjected to equal but opposite values of ΔR, the output signal is doubled, and the nonlinearity of E_{bd} with ΔR is eliminated.

The requirement is that each current-carrying half bridge as seen from the input "diagonal" *ac* must undergo no resistance change so that gage current remains constant (see Fig. 2-16). In this case $\Delta E = I$ (a constant) $\times \Delta R$.

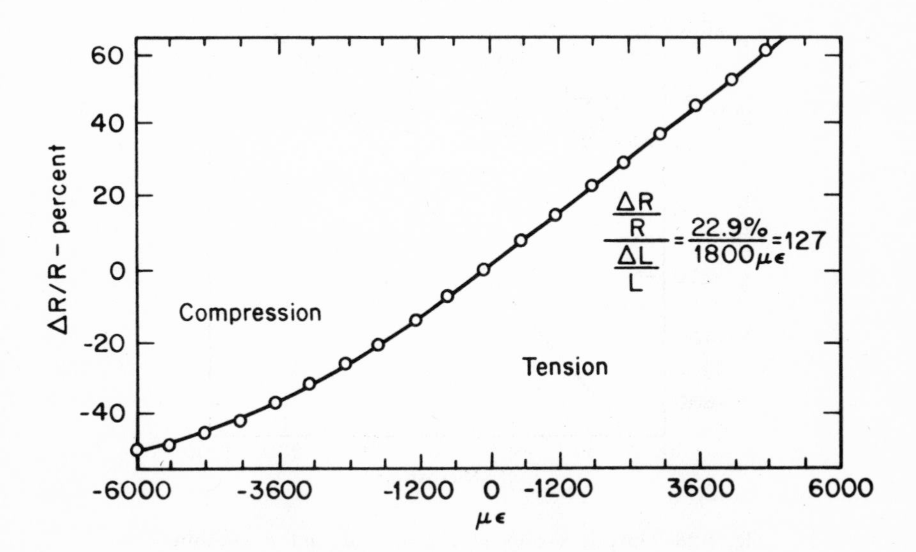

Fig. 2-25. Strain sensitivity of a semiconductor gage ($\Delta R/R$ versus strain ϵ) bonded to aluminum with Eastman 910 cement tested in constant moment fixture from -6000 to $+6000$ microstrain. (*Courtesy of ISA, Ref.* [3].)

With semiconductor gages, arrangement for additive output can be made in either of two ways. Two or four identical gages can be mounted at locations where the applied strain is equal in magnitude but opposite in sign (see p. 85). This scheme completely eliminates the nonlinearity of potential output (E_{bd}) with ΔR. However, it may not make E_{bd} a linear function of strain, since the gage factor (F) of most semiconductor gages is a function of strain, and the variation with compressive strains is greater than with tensile strains, and the effect is considerable with large strains. See Fig. 2-25.

Since semiconductor gages can be produced with either positive or negative gage factors, it is possible to obtain additive output while constant gage current is maintained by mounting two or four gages at a point where, subjected to the same strain, they produce ΔR's of opposite sign. Gages of this type (two elements having gage factors of opposite sign) are commercially available (type DC, Micro-Sensor, Micro Systems, Incorporated). However, to accomplish temperature compensation (see Sect. 2-2e) it is necessary that gage factors of the two elements be different, and hence the ΔR's produced by equal strains are not equal and again the cancelling of nonlinearity is not complete. See Fig. 2-26.

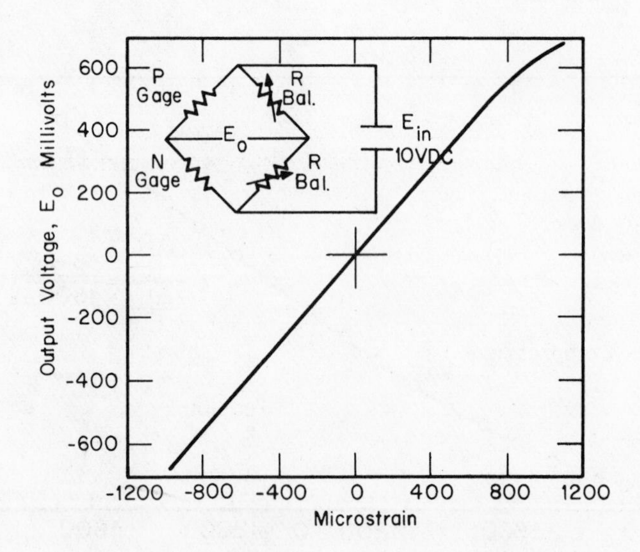

Fig. 2-26. Output versus strain of a *p* and *n* combination. (*Courtesy of ISA, Ref.* [4].)

The fourth circumstance under which semiconductor gages may be used in constant-voltage four-arm bridge circuits is the case when nonlinearity of bridge output can be utilized just to counterbalance nonlinearity produced by the nonlinearity of gage factor with strain. Comparison of Figs. 2-17 and 2-25 will show that the nonlinear bridge effect is opposite to the nonlinear gage-factor effect, and since the nonlinear bridge effect can be controlled by varying the ratio R_2/R_1, it should be possible to reduce the nonlinearity of voltage output with strain to a small value over a limited strain range.

In the final analysis, however, if voltage output is to be linear over the entire range of resistance change produced by semiconductor strain gages, a constant-voltage four-arm bridge circuit is not adequate. The simplest solution to this problem of nonlinearity is to design a circuit in which the *current through the gage is constant.* In this case the change in voltage across the gage will be an absolutely linear function of change in gage resistance; i.e., $E = I\Delta R$. Then with semiconductor gage "sensitivity" given as

$$S = \frac{\Delta R}{\epsilon},$$

output signal is related to strain by the simple expression

$$\frac{\Delta E}{\epsilon} = IS. \tag{2-30}$$

Figure 2-27 shows such a circuit in its simplest form. The disadvantages of this circuit are as follows: the constant-current power supply must have very low ripple, since supply ripple is superimposed directly on the output signal, i.e., ΔE due to ripple $= \Delta I_{\text{ripple}} R$; the constant-current power supply must have very good regulation, since if I varies with load it defeats the purpose of the circuit; the signal output is not zero at zero strain, i.e., $E_{\text{out}} = IR_g$ at zero strain. Fortunately, constant-current supplies that will meet the stringent requirements mentioned above have recently become available. Ripple is held as low as 10 microvolts (rms), and regulation is such as to hold I constant within 0.1 per cent with

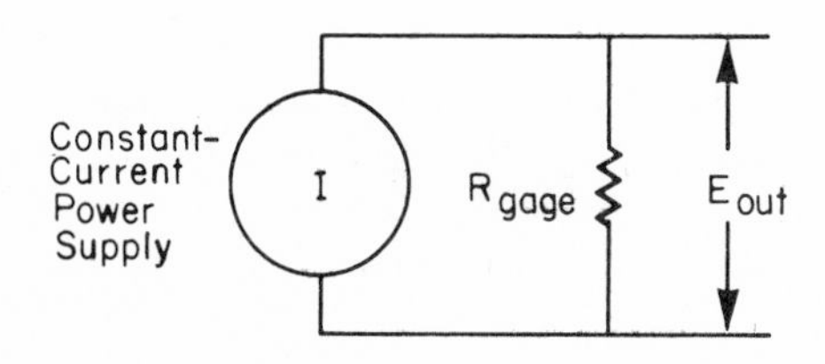

Fig. 2-27. Basic constant-current circuit.

resistance changes of 50 per cent occurring at frequencies as high as 20,000 cps (see Ref. [7]). The output signal at zero strain can be reduced to zero by using two constant-current power supplies and the circuit shown in Fig. 2-28. In this circuit, power supply I_2 is variable so that the voltage drop across R_2 can be made equal to the drop across R_{gage} and hence E_{out} can be adjusted to zero. This last system also allows for temperature compensation (see Sect. 2-2e) and permits the output of two active gages to be added, since the potential developed across the output is equal to the difference in the changes of potential that occur across arms 1 and 2. Thus, if R_1 is subjected to $+\Delta R_1$ and R_2 to $-\Delta R_2$, $E_{ou} \simeq 2\Delta R$.

If it is desired to sum the output of several gages subjected to the same sense of strain, all gages which will be subjected to ΔR's of like sign are series-connected in position R_1, and all gages subjected to ΔR's of the opposite sign are series-connected in position R_2.

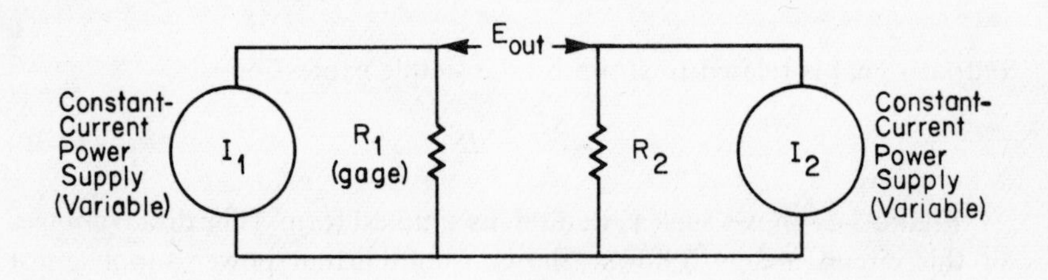

Fig. 2-28. Null balanced, constant-current circuit.

The circuit shown in Fig. 2-28 is the basis for strain indicators of both the deflection and null type which have been specifically designed for use with semiconductor strain gages. These instruments are discussed in detail in Sect. 3-2d.

Two important points should be repeated. A circuit that provides constant *gage current* will provide a voltage output which is linear with ΔR, but this does not guarantee linearity with strain. This is the case since with most semiconductor gages ΔR is nonlinear with strain. Using a constant-current power supply with a four-arm bridge does not produce a voltage output from the bridge diagonal, which is linear with ΔR. This is the case, because *gage* current will still vary with ΔR.

2-2c Calibrating strain-gage circuits

Equations (2-17) and (2-20) can be used to compute the output of constant-voltage bridge circuits. Equation (2-29) can be used to compute the output of potentiometer circuits, and Eq. (2-30) can be used to compute the output of constant-gage current circuits, provided that all of the necessary parameters are known. Then, with the sensitivity (units of deflection/mv or /μamp) of the indicator known, the indicator deflection can be related to strain. This is the method used for designing strain-gage circuits and selecting recording or indicating equipment. However, it is not suitable for final calibration of a system, since with this method the final accuracy of the system would depend upon the accuracy with which all of the parameters involved could be measured and held constant during the period of test. Hence, a handy, reliable, and direct calibration is extremely important.

The calibration method most often used involves producing a known change in resistance by means of a parallel resistor and then relating the known ΔR to equivalent strain, using the definition of gage factor. When this system is used to calibrate a bridge-type circuit, the calibrate resistor or resistors are usually connected in parallel with one of the active gages, as shown in Fig. 2-29.

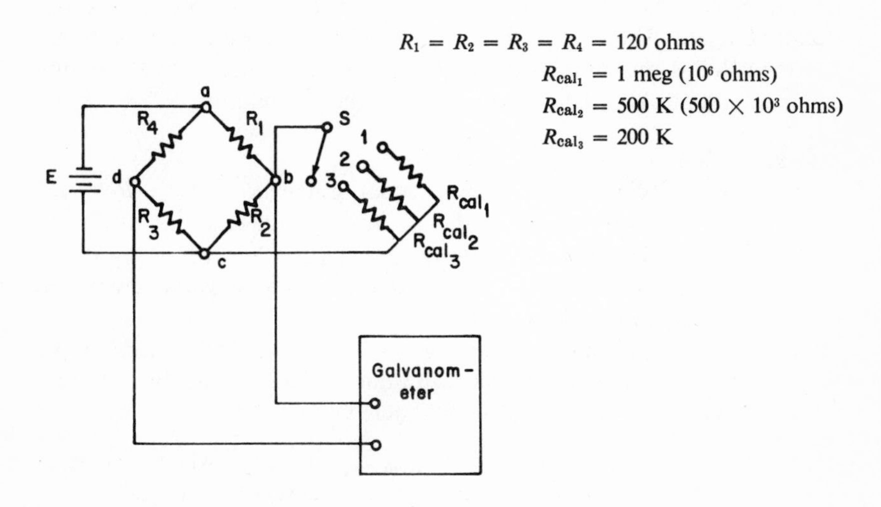

Fig. 2-29. Bridge circuit with several resistors which can be paralleled with one arm.

The change in resistance produced by connecting a calibrate resistor as shown is easily computed by using the parallel resistance law:

$$\frac{1}{R_{(g+\text{cal})}} = \frac{1}{R_g} + \frac{1}{R_{\text{cal}}},$$

or

$$R_{(g+\text{cal})} = \frac{R_g R_{\text{cal}}}{R_g + R_{\text{cal}}};$$

then,

$$\Delta R_{bc} = R_{(g+\text{cal})} - R_g,$$

or

$$\Delta R_{bc} = \frac{R_g^2}{R_g + R_{\text{cal}}}.$$

Substituting the result into the definition of gage factor

$$\left(F = \frac{\Delta R_g/R_g}{\epsilon}\right),$$

we have

$$\epsilon_{\text{equivalent}} = -\frac{R_g}{F(R_g + R_{\text{cal}})}, \tag{2-31}$$

in which $\epsilon_{\text{equivalent}}$ is the strain required in the single gage to produce the same signal as is produced by connection of R_{cal}. The minus sign indicates that the unbalance produced by connection of the calibrate resistor has the same sense of direction as that produced by compressive strain. It can be readily shown that the percentage of tolerance on the calibrate-resistor value is the same as the percentage of tolerance on the resulting calibrate strain. An example will illustrate the procedures.

Example 2-4. (Refer to Fig. 2-29.)

We shall assume an equal bridge ($R_1 \simeq R_2 \simeq R_3 \simeq R_4$) in which R_2 is the active gage (gage to be strained). The three calibrate resistors ($R_{c_1} = 1 \times 10^6$, $R_{c_2} = 0.5 \times 10^6$, and $R_{c_3} = 0.2 \times 10^6$ ohms) can be selectively placed in parallel with R_2.

Calibrate this system; i.e., units of deflection per unit strain for use with one active gage (R_2) of 120 ohms resistance and with a gage factor of 2.0.

Solution: First, solve for the $\epsilon_{\text{equivalent}}$ simulated when each R_c is paralleled with R_2, using Eq. (2-31).

$$\epsilon_{\text{equivalent}} \text{ of } R_{c_1} = -\frac{120}{(2)(120 + 1 \times 10^6)}$$

$$\simeq -\frac{60}{1 \times 10^6} = -60\ \mu\text{in./in.}$$

compression in arm R_2.

$$\epsilon_{\text{equivalent}} \text{ of } R_{c_2} = \frac{120}{2(120 + 0.5 \times 10^6)} \simeq -120\ \mu\text{in./in.}$$

$$\epsilon_{\text{equivalent}} \text{ of } R_{c_3} = \frac{120}{2(120 + 0.2 \times 10^6)} \simeq -300 \ \mu\text{in./in.}$$

Assume that when R_{c_1} was paralleled with R_2 the deflection of the galvanometer was 2 units, 4 units when R_{c_2} was paralleled with R_2, and 10 units when R_{c_3} was paralleled with R_2. Then the sensitivity of this system is

$$S = \frac{\text{deflection}}{\text{strain}} = \frac{2}{60} = \frac{1 \text{ unit}}{30 \ \mu\text{in./in.}},$$

or

$$S = \frac{4}{120} = \frac{1 \text{ unit}}{30 \ \mu\text{in./in.}},$$

and

$$S = \frac{10}{300} = \frac{1 \text{ unit}}{30 \ \mu\text{in./in.}},$$

which indicates that the indicating galvanometer is linear over the range calibrated. Since the equivalent strain introduced in R_2 is compression, the sense of deflection is the same as would be associated with a tensile strain in the arm R_1.

It must be remembered that the sensitivity established by calibration of a bridge-type circuit is for *one* active gage. When the output of two gages which are equally strained is made additive, the deflection per unit of strain is, of course, twice that when only one gage is active, etc. This must be taken into account when the calibration data are used. Specifically, if N gages (usually $N = 2$ or 4) are equally strained and connected so that their outputs are additive, the strain that must be applied to each of the N gages to produce a signal equal to the calibration signal is

$$\epsilon = \frac{R_g}{F(R_g + R_{\text{cal}})} \times \frac{1}{N}.$$

Parallel resistors can be used to calibrate unequal-bridge systems ($R_1 \neq R_2 \neq R_3 \neq R_4$), but in this case R_{cal} *must* be paralleled with the active gage (say R_1) unless the effect (E_{bd}) of paralleling R_{cal} with another resistor not equal to the gage resistance is computed by means of Eq. (2-17). Additional computation defeats the purpose of calibration.

When bridge-type circuits are calibrated by using paralleled resistors, and long lead wires are being used, some correction of Eq. (2-31) may be necessary. The effect of lead wires on circuit calibration is discussed in detail in Sect. 2-2f.

When parallel resistors are used to calibrate potentiometer circuits, they are connected as shown in Fig. 2-30.

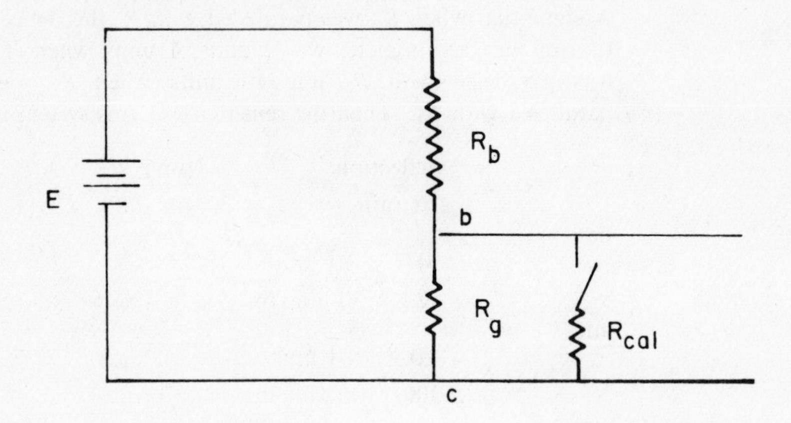

Fig. 2-30. Use of a parallel resistor to calibrate a potentiometer circuit.

The computations involved are identical to those used when a bridge-type circuit is calibrated. However, it must be remembered that when several gages are connected in potentiometer, they are series-connected between points b and c and act as *one* gage having a resistance equal to the total resistance of the gages in series. Hence, the equivalent strain simulated by calibration is

$$\epsilon_{\text{equivalent}} = -\frac{R_{\text{Total}}}{F(R_{\text{Total}} + R_{\text{cal}})},$$

in which R_{Total} is the sum of the resistances of the gages connected in series between points b and c.

When parallel resistors are used to calibrate constant gage current circuits, they are connected as shown in Fig. 2-31. As before, the change in resistance, ΔR, produced by connecting R_{cal} is

$$\Delta R = \frac{R_g^2}{R_g + R_{\text{cal}}}$$

Then, in terms of gage sensitivity ($S = \Delta R/\epsilon$), the equivalent strain is

$$\epsilon_{\text{equivalent}} = \frac{\Delta R}{S} = \frac{R_g^2}{S(R_g + R_{\text{cal}})}. \tag{2-32}$$

With semiconductor gages, the gage resistance of the unmounted gage (given by the manufacturer) may be considerably different from the resistance of the mounted gage due to strains induced during the bonding operation. Since the calibration resistors are parallel with the mounted gage, it is most important that the resistance of the gage as mounted be measured and this value used for R_g in Eq. (2-32).

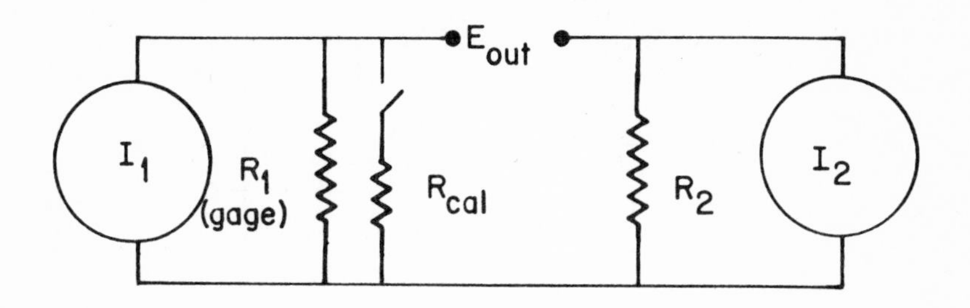

Fig. 2-31. Use of a parallel resistor to calibrate a constant-current circuit.

2-2d Balancing strain-gage circuits

Up to this point in our discussion of the bridge-type circuit, we have assumed that R_1, R_2, R_3, and R_4 are chosen so that the equation

$$\frac{R_1}{R_2} = \frac{R_4}{R_3}$$

is satisfied, and, therefore, the bridge is perfectly balanced before straining occurs. It is impractical to satisfy this equation perfectly by the proper selection of four gages or resistors. Hence, the problem we have circumvented is how the bridge can be initially balanced. There are two methods in use for accomplishing initial balance:

1. Series balancing, which is illustrated in Fig. 2-32.

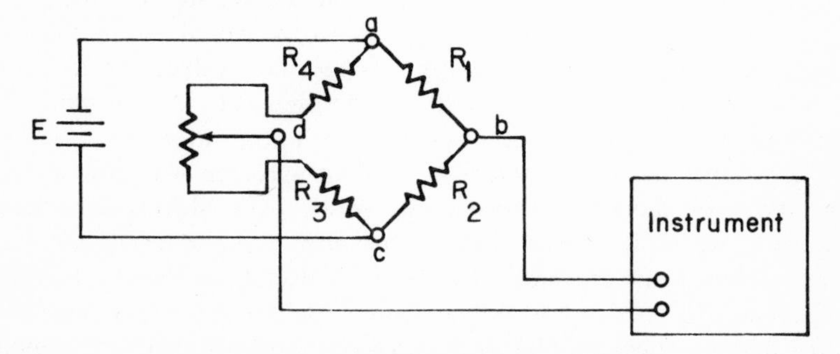

Fig. 2-32. Series bridge-balancing method.

2. Parallel balancing, which is illustrated in Fig. 2-33.

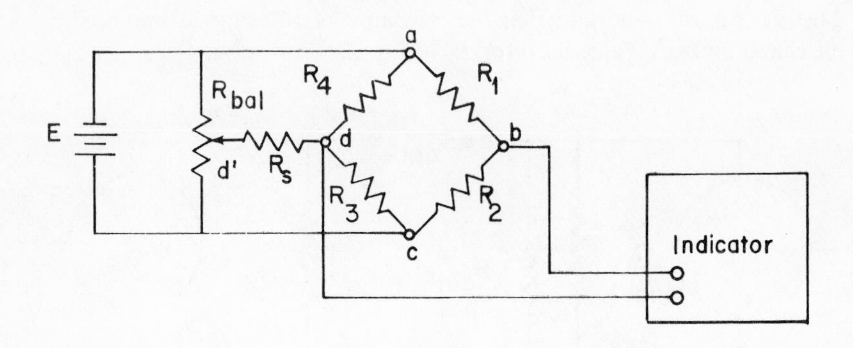

Fig. 2-33. Parallel bridge-balancing method.

A series-balancing network is a common element in commercially available strain-indicating equipment, where it is usually a part of the readout system in a null balance indicator. It is less frequently used to obtain initial balance because of the difficulty in obtaining the small and precise variations in resistance required. The parallel method is often used to obtain initial bridge balance because, by using a large value for R_{bal}, very small changes in resistance between points *ad* and *dc* can be produced by moving the center tap (d').

When a parallel balancing network is being used, several facts should be kept in mind. Placing R_{bal} across the bridge as shown will change the values of R_{ad} and R_{dc}. Indeed, this is the purpose: to balance the bridge. But we no longer have an equal bridge, and any equations previously developed for $R_1 = R_2 = R_3 = R_4$ do not *strictly* apply. We can see from Eq. (2-17) that if only R_1 and R_2 are active gages, the open-circuit output will be independent of the remaining resistance values.

How the balancing-resistor network affects the closed (loaded) circuit output can be seen from Eq. (2-20). Using small values for R_{bal} and R_S will reduce R_{bridge} and increase the load voltage (E_L). This gain will be at the expense of increased power-supply load, however.

If a parallel balancing system is used on a bridge with four active arms, its effect should be thoroughly investigated. Murray and Stein have made a complete analysis of this problem and the results are presented in convenient graphical form by Stein, Ref. [8]. The effect of the parallel balancing network is to desensitize gages 3 and 4 relative to gages 1 and 2, and this effect must be taken into account or reduced to a negligible amount. In general, both R_{bal} and R_S (R_S is a limiting resistor which prevents shorting points a and d or d and c at the extreme position of d') should be as large as possible and still permit initial balance. By calibrating the system, first across one of the unshunted gages (R_1 or R_2), then across R_3, and finally across R_4, and comparing results, the amount of desensitization can be established. The values R_{bal} and R_S should be chosen to give differences among these three calibrates which are less than the resolution of the indicating system.

It should also be noted that the use of a parallel balance network to establish true balance of a bridge is a different matter from the use of parallel balance networks to bring several bridges to a common point on a single indicator. Two bridges which can be switched to a common indicator are shown in Fig. 2-34.

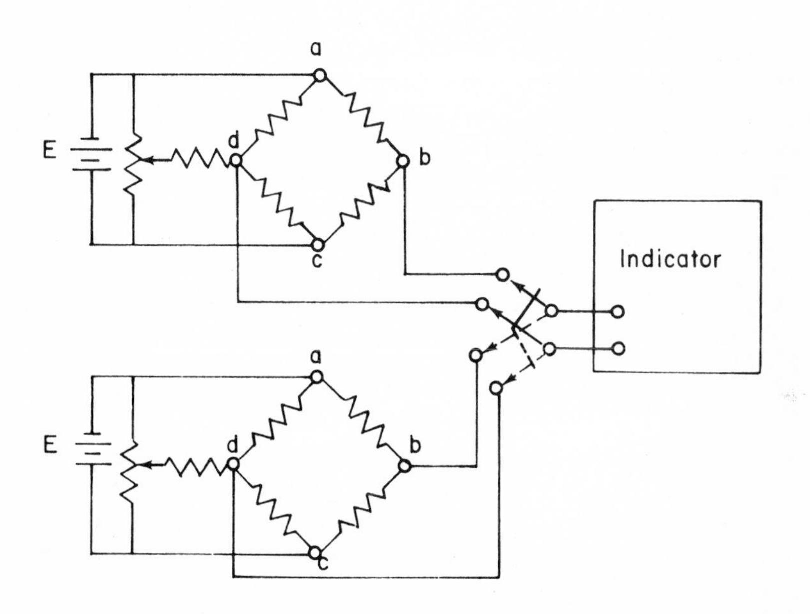

Fig. 2-34. Several bridges to be read on a common indicator.

If an arbitrary starting point is selected on the indicator and several bridges are brought to this point by adjustment of their parallel balancing circuits, all of the bridges will be in a state of unbalance ($E_{bd} \neq 0$) at this starting point. When we remember that one of the restrictions placed on the linear-output equations developed is that they apply at or near the null or true balance point, we realize that this system may not give a signal which is linearly related to strain. In *most* cases this departure from linearity will be insignificant, but it is good practice to investigate by using several calibrate resistors (see Example 2-4 on p. 100). Potentiometer circuits that are connected to the recording equipment through a DC blocking capacitance are not initially balanced. If a zeroing circuit is used (Fig. 2-23), initial balance is established by using the zeroing circuit. With the constant-gage current circuit shown in Fig. 2-28, initial balance is obtained by adjustment of I_2.

2-2e Temperature compensation of strain-gage circuits

In the preceding discussion of strain-gage circuits, it was assumed that the only source of a change in resistance was a stress-produced strain. This would be the case with an ideal strain gage, but most available gages undergo change in resistance due to changes in temperature. This false strain signal arises from three sources: (1) the specific resistance of the gage element changes with temperature; (2) a difference in coefficient of linear expansion of the gage and the surface to which the gage is bonded causes a change in grid length, which produces the same ΔR as would be produced by a stress-induced change of gage length; (3) gage factor or sensitivity changes with temperature. With the metallic strain gages, the third effect is ordinarily very small except at temperature extremes and, hence, will not be considered here. With metal gages the effect of change in gage factor (the third effect) is considered in Sect. 4-2.

With the semiconductor strain gages the change in gage factor

$$F = \frac{\Delta R/R}{\epsilon}$$

or sensitivity

$$S = \Delta R/\epsilon$$

with temperature may be considerable and can not be ignored, even when only modest changes in temperature are involved. See Fig. 2-35.

When a circuit is designed so that no output results from any variation of temperature of the strain gage and/or the object on which the gage is mounted, the circuit is said to be temperature-compensated. The oldest and probably most common temperature compensation in use is the dummy, or compensating, gage method. The bridge-type circuit can be temperature-compensated because of the principle expressed in Eq. (2-16); namely, the unbalance of the bridge (E_{bd}) is proportional to the sum of resistance changes in opposite arms and *to the difference of resistance changes in adjacent arms.* If two identical gages are mounted in an identical manner on identical materials, and if both gage locations (gage and material on which it is mounted) are subjected to identical temperatures, the change in resistance of the two gages, due to temperature effects, will be identical. If these two gages are connected as adjacent arms in a bridge circuit, the output (E_{bd}) due to temperature effects (false

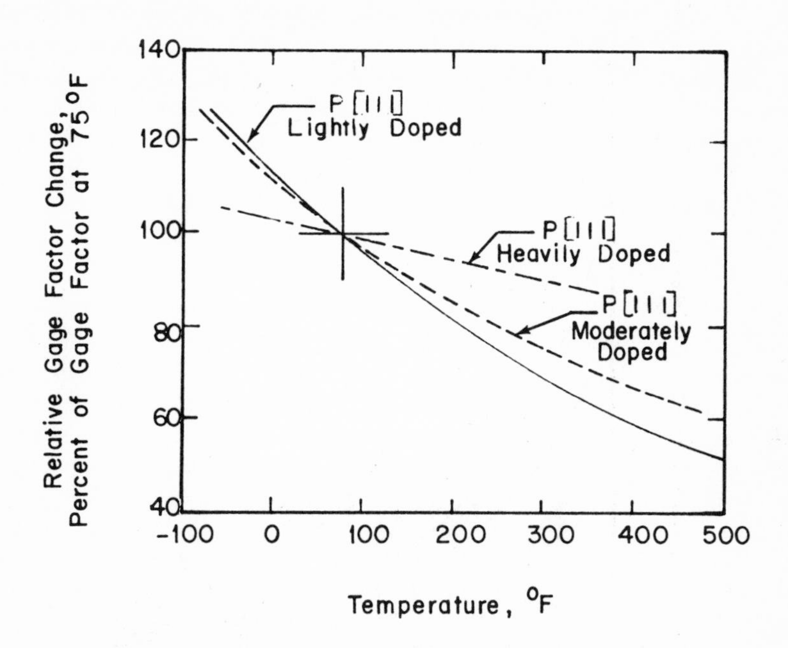

Fig. 2-35. Gage factor versus temperature of semiconductors using various dopant concentrations, bonded to 17-4 PH steel. (*Courtesy of ISA, Ref.* [*4*].)

strain) will be zero. It must be emphasized, however, that to accomplish temperature compensation, the gages must be identical (i.e., same type, same gage factor, preferably two from the same package); they must be bonded in the same manner (i.e., same adhesive type and thickness and same cure cycle) to the same kind of material (so that the differential coefficient of linear expansion will be the same); they must be mounted on surfaces with the same radius of curvature* (see Fig. 2-36); the structure on which the dummy or compensating gage is mounted must expand freely when temperature changes occur; and they must both be at the same temperature.

The constant-gage current circuit (Fig. 2-28) can be temperature-compensated by using a compensating gage in position R_2, since the potential output is again proportional to the difference of ΔR_1 and ΔR_2. The necessary conditions for compensation discussed in connection

* See Ref. [9].

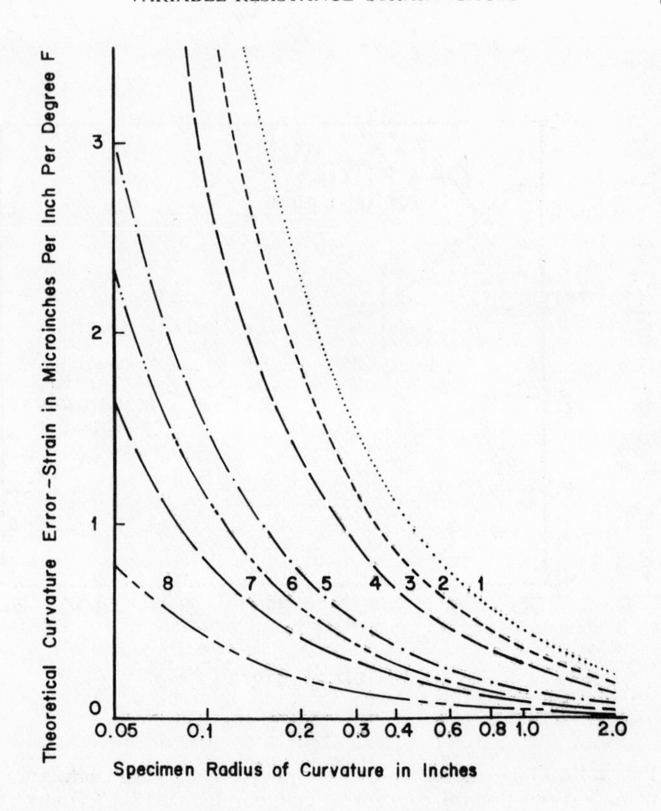

1. Wire, wrap-around, cellulose nitrate and paper matrix, cellulose nitrate bonded (A-7, etc.)
2. Wire, flat-grid, cellulose nitrate and paper matrix, cellulose nitrate bonded (A-1, etc.)
3. Wire, flat-grid, cellulose nitrate and thin paper matrix, cellulose nitrate bonded (A-3, etc.)
4. Foil, cellulose nitrate and thin paper matrix, cellulose nitrate bonded (FAP series)
5. Wire, wrap-around, paper-phenolic matrix, phenolic or EPY-400 bonded (AB-7, etc.)
6. Foil, epoxy matrix, EPY-150 bonded (FA-)
7. Wire, flat-grid, paper-phenolic matrix, phenolic or EPY-400 bonded (AB-, EBF-)
8. Foil, glass-phenolic matrix, phenolic or EPY-400 bonded (FAB series)

Error is positive for outside radius.
Error is negative for inside radius.
All curves are for gages on mild steel.

Fig. 2-36. Theoretical effect of specimen curvature on the temperature coefficient of bonded strain gages. (*Courtesy of Baldwin-Lima-Hamilton Corporation, Ref.* [9].)

with the bridge circuit (identical gages mounted on same material, same temperatures, etc.) still apply.

The potentiometer circuit can be temperature-compensated by using a gage identical to the active gage for the ballast resistor (R_b); see Fig. 2-23. However, with $R_b = R_g$ the sensitivity of the potentiometer circuit is reduced to one-half its maximum value. See Eq. (2-29). However, since the potentiometer circuit is primarily useful for measurement of strain over short periods of time, during which the temperature may not vary, they are often used without any provision for temperature compensation.

Temperature compensation by means of the compensating-gage method is more difficult when semiconductor gages are used than when metal gages are used. This is true because semiconductor gages have greater temperature sensitivity, and as a result any departure from the conditions required for complete compensation becomes more important.

The requirement that the active and the compensating gages be at the same temperature cannot be filled in some cases, and then a temperature-compensated circuit is impossible. In any case, this requirement of identical temperature is difficult to fulfill, since the temperature of the gage results from two heat sources: (1) the temperature environment in which the stress measurements are desired, and (2) current flow in the gage itself. Consider the circuit shown in Fig. 2-37.

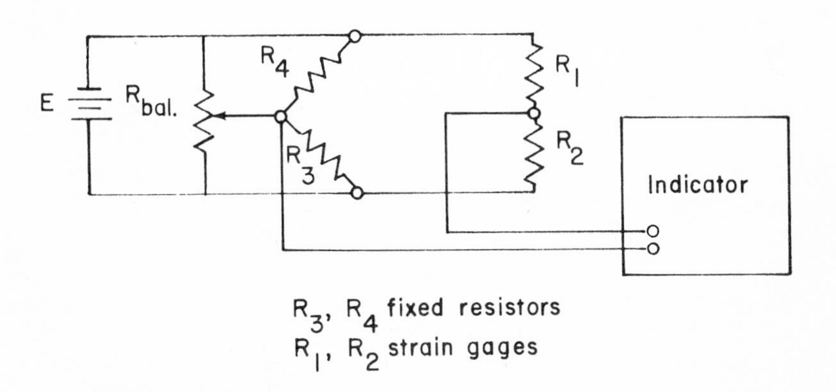

Fig. 2-37. Temperature-compensated circuit.

The circuit is properly designed for temperature compensation, but care must be taken to insure that R_1 and R_2 remain at the same temperature throughout the test. If one is insulated, as when it is covered by tape, the other must be so treated; otherwise, self-heating will cause a difference in temperature. If one is exposed to sunshine or other external heating, the other must be so treated. If one is cooled by forced or natural convection, the other must also be cooled, etc. Furthermore, the structures to which the gages are mounted must have no major difference in thermal capacities. For example, if very thin or very small specimens are gaged, the dummy gage should also be on thin or very small samples of the same material.

The inherent advantages of this method of temperature compensation, which cannot be obtained with a single gage having a selected best-fit temperature coefficient (discussed in the following paragraphs), are

1. Nonlinearity in temperature response is eliminated. All strain-sensing materials used in electrical-resistance strain gages possess nonlinear thermal coefficients of resistance.
2. Effective compensation is obtained over a broad temperature range.
3. Effective compensation is obtained on all test specimen materials.

It must be remembered that temperature compensation of a circuit does not eliminate the problem of change in gage factor or sensitivity with temperature.

In those cases where it is impossible to locate two gages in such a way as to accomplish temperature compensation, it is necessary to use either a self-temperature-compensating gage or to correct the measured output. Three basic types of self-temperature-compensating metallic gages are available: (1) the two-element type; (2) the single-element, selected-melt type; and (3) the universally compensated type.

In the first (two-element) type the grid is made of two wire elements in series. One of the elements has a negative temperature coefficient of resistance ($+\Delta T$ results in $-\Delta R$), and the other element has a positive temperature coefficient of resistance. The lengths of the two elements are adjusted so that the net temperature coefficient of resistance will just compensate for the change in resistance due to differential coefficient of expansion when the gage is mounted on a particular metal. Gages of this type are intended for use *only on the metal for which they have been designed.* They are adjusted to give the least false strain over a prescribed temperature range. Figure 2-38 shows a typical gage grid of this type and a typical plot of false (or apparent) strain versus temperature.

Gages of this type are available from Baldwin-Lima-Hamilton (BLH) for use on mild steel (EBF- _____ *S*), titanium (EBF- _____ *T*), and duraluminum (EBF- _____ *D*) and quartz (EBF- _____ *Q*). Since quartz has essentially a zero coefficient of linear expansion, gages that are compensated for quartz can be mounted on any material to measure the free expansion of that material with temperature.

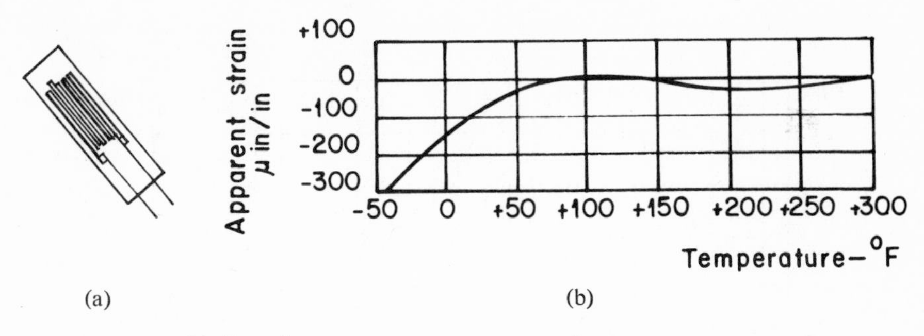

(a) (b)

(a) Two-element temperature-compensating gage
(b) False strain versus temperature performance curve

Fig. 2-38. Two-element temperature-compensating gage and performance curve. (*Courtesy of Baldwin-Lima-Hamilton Corporation.*)

The single-element, selected-melt type of self-temperature-compensating metallic gage is made by producing a grid for which the change in resistance due to change in specific resistance* will be just equal in magnitude but opposite in sense to the change due to difference in coefficient of linear expansion of the gage and the metal on which it is mounted. Obviously, these gages are also designed for use on a specific material and for least false strain over a prescribed temperature range. It is important to observe the temperature limits specified by the manufacturer, since the compensation may be altered by exceeding the last heat treatment conditions to which the manufacturer subjected the particular type of gage. Figure 2-39 shows a typical plot of false (apparent) strain versus temperature for gages on this type. An S-6 is compensated for use on mild steel, an S-9 for use on stainless steel, and an S-13 for use on aluminum alloys.

Gages of this type are available from Baldwin-Lima-Hamilton Corporation, Instruments Division, from Budd Co., and from Microdot, Incorporated. From BLH, they are available in either wire or foil, on paper, epoxy or Bakelite; for use on materials having coefficients of linear expansion of 6μin./in./°F (plain steel), 9 μin./in./°F (stainless steel), 13 μin./in./°F (aluminum alloys), 15 to 55 μin./in./°F (plastics). In addition, BLH offers weldable gages (FABW-) for use on plain steel and stainless steel in the temperature range from +50° to +250°F. From Budd, they are available as foil gages on epoxy backs or with a strippable back for use on materials having coefficients of linear expansion of 6

* The temperature coefficient of resistance of certain gage element metals can be varied by alloying, heat treatment, and cold working.

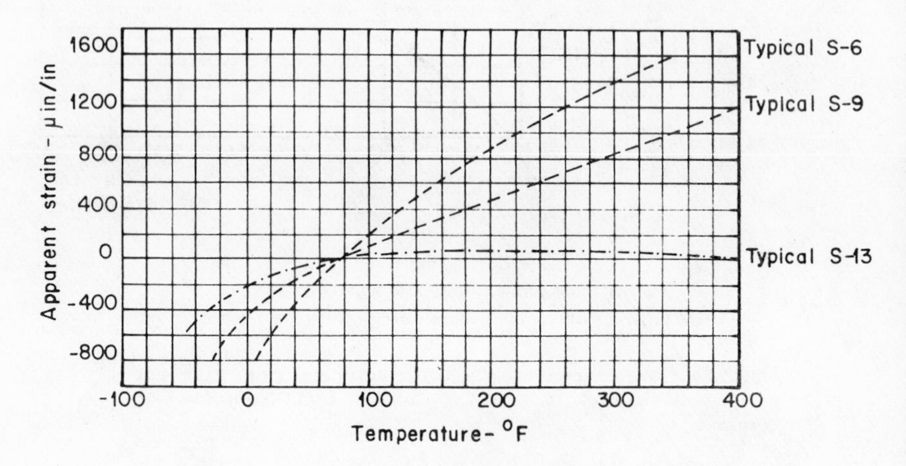

Fig. 2-39. False strain versus temperature for three selected-melt gages mounted on 2024-T4 aluminum. (*Courtesy of Baldwin-Lima-Hamilton Corporation.*)

μin./in./°F (plain steel), 9 μin./in./°F (stainless steel), 12 μin./in./°F (aluminum alloys), 15 μin./in./°F (magnesium alloys), and 18 and 40 μin./in./°F (plastics). From Microdot they are available as weldable gages which can be temperature-compensated for almost any specified material upon request.

The third type of self-temperature-compensating (universally compensated) gage is again a two-element gage, but in this case the relative effect of the two elements can be adjusted by making changes in the external circuitry. Figure 2-40 shows a gage of this type and the circuit into which it is connected.

The value of change in resistance per unit resistance per unit temperature change is known for both the gage element and the temperature-compensating element (ΔG and ΔT) when the unit is mounted on a particular material. Equation (2-16) can be used to explain how such a gage-circuit combination can be made self-compensating. Since only two arms are subjected to change in resistance, only the first two terms of Eq. (2-16) apply. Rewriting Eq. (2-16) in terms of the nomenclature used in Fig. 2-40, we have

$$\frac{E_{bd}}{E} = -\frac{(R_T + R_{LT} + R_B)\,dR_G}{[R_G + R_{LG} + (R_T + R_{LT} + R_B)]^2} + \frac{(R_G + R_{LG})\,dR_T}{[R_G + R_{LG} + (R_T + R_{LT} + R_B)]^2}.$$

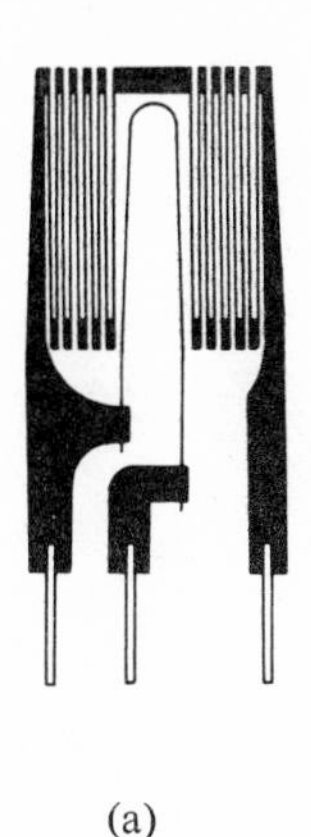

(a)

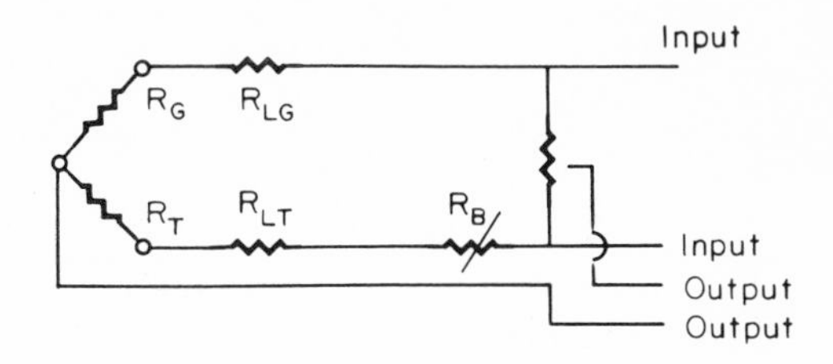

R_T = Resistance of compensating element
R_G = Resistance of active element
R_{LT} = Resistance of compensating arm lead wire
R_{LG} = Resistance of active arm lead wire
R_B = Ballast resistor

(b)

(a) Two-element temperature-compensating gage
(b) Typical circuit for installation

Fig. 2-40. Universally temperature-compensating gage and circuit. (*Courtesy of Baldwin-Lima-Hamilton Corporation.*)

For zero output due to temperature change

$$(R_T + R_{LT} + R_B)\,dR_G = (R_G + R_{LG})\,dR_T.$$

Both dR_G and dR_T due to temperature change may be written as

$$dR_G = \Delta G R_G\,\Delta\theta_G,$$
$$dR_T = \Delta T R_T\,\Delta\theta_T,$$

in which $\Delta\theta$ is the temperature change. Hence, we may write

$$(R_T + R_{LT} + R_B)\,\Delta G R_G = (R_G + R_{LG})\,\Delta T R_T,$$

since

$$\Delta\theta_G = \Delta\theta_T.$$

Rearranging, we find the required value of R_B for temperature compensation:

$$R_B = \frac{\Delta T R_T}{\Delta G R_G}(R_G + R_{LG}) - (R_T + R_{LT}).$$

If the temperature coefficient of specific resistance and the differential coefficient of linear expansion were constant over a temperature range, then, once the value of R_B had been set, this gage-circuit system would be perfectly compensating for a given metal. Since both of these factors vary, we can only set R_B to give the least false (or apparent) strain over the range of interest. Figure 2-41 shows a typical plot of apparent strain versus temperature for a gage circuit of this type.

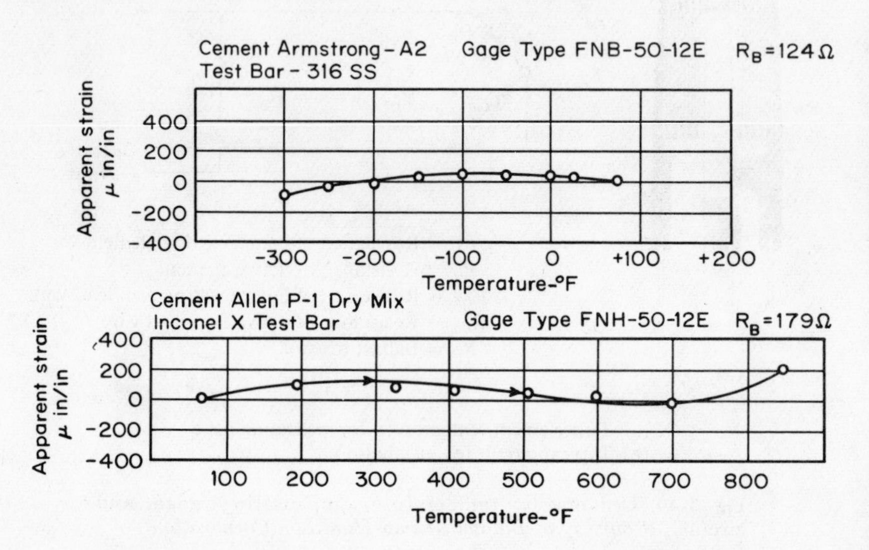

Fig. 2-41. **Apparent strain versus temperature for a universally temperature-compensating gage.** (*Courtesy of Baldwin-Lima-Hamilton Corporation.*)

Several possible methods for making self-temperature-compensating semiconductor gages have been proposed, and semiconductor gages which accomplish temperature compensation to some degree are available.

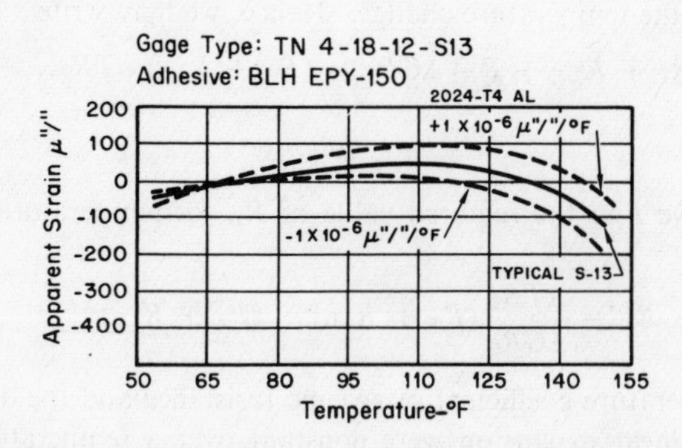

Fig. 2-42. **False strain versus temperature for self-temperature-compensating semiconductor gage.** (*Courtesy of Baldwin-Lima-Hamilton Corporation.*)

W. P. Mason [10] suggests that by cutting the crystals along selected crystal orientations the transverse effect can be made to just cancel thermal effects. Temperature sensitivity can be reduced by doping (adding impurities), but unfortunately temperature sensitivity is reduced at the expense of reduced gage factor. See Refs. [2] and [11]. Self-temperature-compensated gages of this type show least temperature sensitivity when they are mounted on the specific material for which they were designed. Figure 2-42 shows typical apparent strain versus temperature curves for gages of this type.

A semiconductor gage has been specifically designed for use in a temperature-compensating bridge circuit.* This gage, which is shown in Fig. 2-43, is made of two semiconductor filaments: one, a P-type

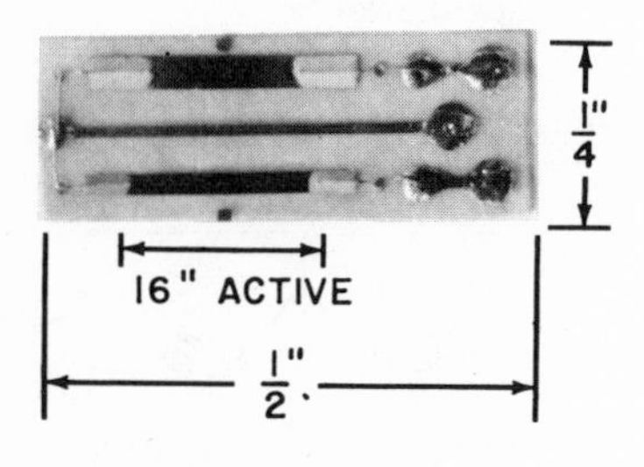

- Equivalent gage factor of 250.
- Apparent strain $\leqq 1\mu\epsilon/°F$ on aluminum.
- Integral terminal construction for 3 wire leads.
- Temperature-compensated from $-65°F$ to $+160°F$.
- Negligible transverse sensitivity.

Fig. 2-43. P- and N-type self-temperature-compensating half bridge. (*Courtesy of Micro Systems, Incorporated.*)

silicon with a positive gage factor $[(+\Delta R/R)/\epsilon]$ and a positive temperature coefficient $[(+\Delta R/R)/°T]$ and the other a N-type silicon with negative gage factor and a positive temperature coefficient. When these two filaments are connected as shown in Fig. 2-44, the output due to temperature effects will be zero if $\Delta R/°T$ is the same for both elements, whereas the output due to strain will be proportional to the sum of the $|\Delta R_1|$ and $|\Delta R_2|$ produced by strain. This particular gage (half bridge, with one +F and one −F) also functions to reduce the nonlinearity of output associated with strain, since the two elements are nonlinear with strain in different directions, and the two effects tend to cancel. See Fig. 2-45.

* Type DC, Micro Sensor, Micro Systems, Incorporated.

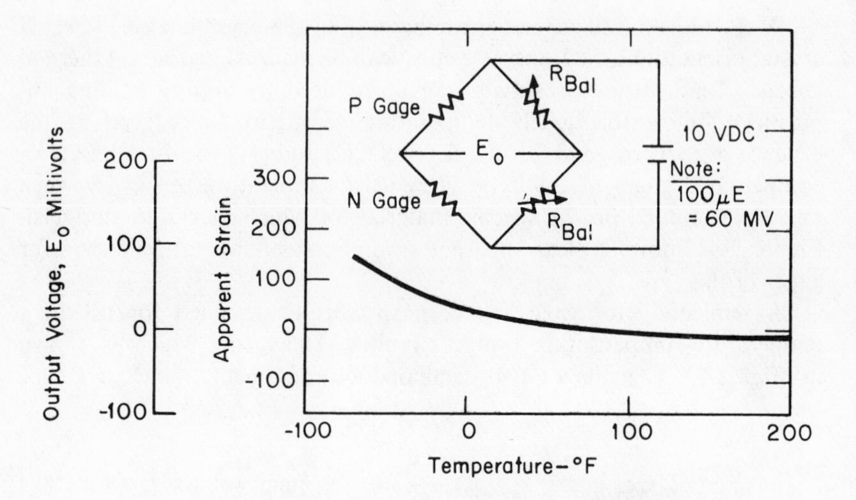

Fig. 2-44. False strain versus temperature for a P- and N-type half bridge. (*Courtesy of ISA, Ref.* [4].)

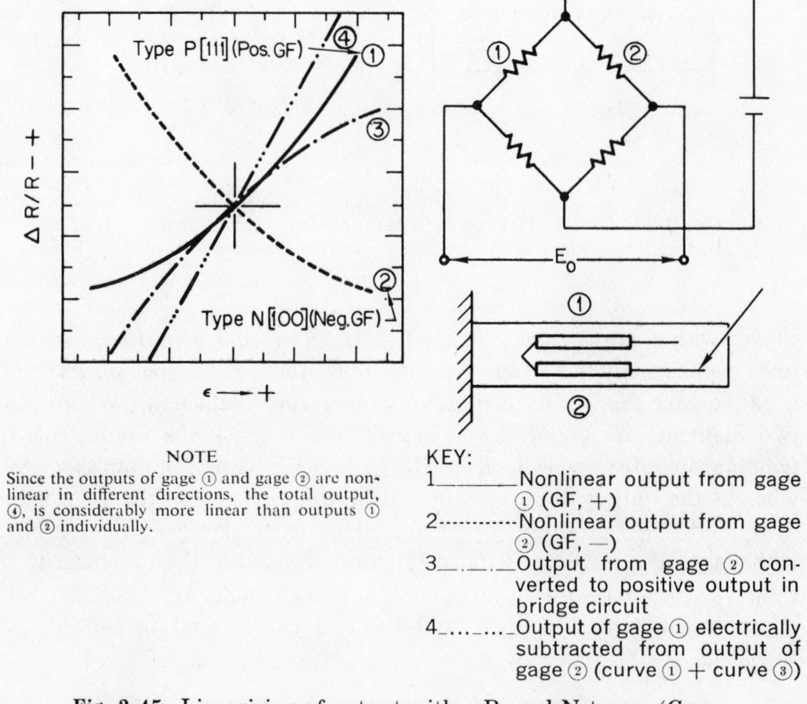

Fig. 2-45. Linearizing of output with a P- and N-type. (*Courtesy of ISA, Ref.* [3].)

A self-temperature-compensating circuit can also be made by using a strain gage and thermocouple combination.* See Fig. 2-46. The strain-

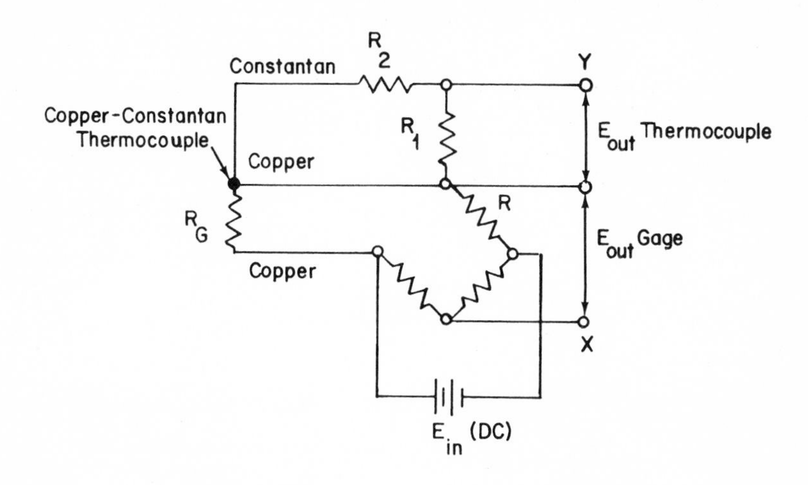

Fig. 2-46. Self-temperature-compensating circuit.

gage bridge output (E_{out} gage) due to temperature effects (false strain) can be expressed in the same way as the thermocouple output (E_{out} thermocouple); i.e., mv/°F.

If the strain-gage bridge is DC-powered, these two signals will be similar functions, and with proper adjustment of the resistors R_1 and R_2 (which divides the thermocouple output), the value E_{out} thermocouple can be made equal and opposite to E_{out} gage. The total output across points x and y will then be independent of temperature.

The presence of lead wires may also influence temperature compensation. This problem is discussed in detail in Sect. 2-2f.

2-2f Effect of leads, switches, and slip rings in strain-gage circuits

In all of our work up to this point we have assumed that the only resistive elements in the strain-gage circuit were the gages themselves, which, practically speaking, is an impossibility; therefore, we shall now consider the effect of the resistance of necessary lead wires. The presence of leads affects the strain-measuring system in three distinct ways:

* Material taken from a paper by R. F. Hines and L. J. Weymouth, Ref. [12].

1. The presence of leads affects the sensitivity of the circuit.
2. The presence of leads affects the calibration procedure.
3. The presence of leads may introduce another temperature-compensating problem.

These are important problems, because strain signals are often recorded at a location removed from the point at which the strain is measured. In the case of DC-powered circuits, we need be concerned only with the resistance of the lead wire. When the circuit is AC-powered, the total impedance of the leads become important.

One possibility for remote recording is illustrated in Fig. 2-47 (4 arms,

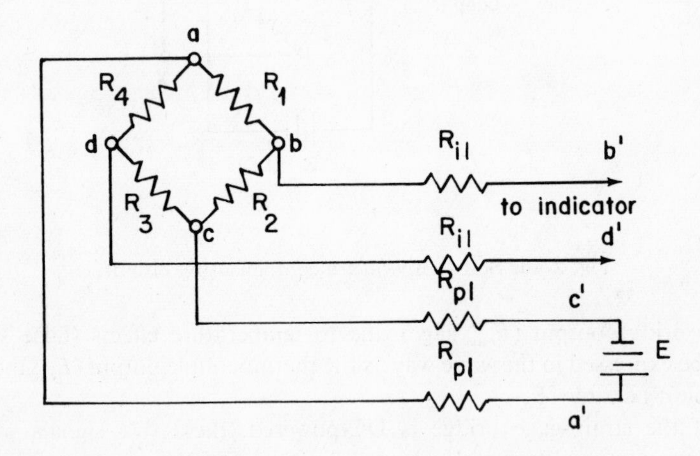

Fig. 2-47. Bridge circuit with lead resistances external to the bridge.

remote). Here the bridge is completed at the test location. This will always be the case when four gages are used actively, but it has several advantages even when less than four gages are active. In this case the lead-wire resistance will all be in series with the recording equipment and the power supply. Therefore, the only effects of the lead-wire resistance will be (1) to change the load resistance associated with the indicator from R_L to $(R_L + 2R_{il})$, and (2) to change the resistance in series with the power supply (E) from R_{bridge} to $(R_b + 2R_{pl})$. These changes can easily be investigated by using Eqs. (2-17) and (2-20). From Eq. (2-17) it is apparent that the open-circuit output (E_{bd}) must be computed, by using the potential actually applied at the bridge (E); therefore, the potential drop in the power leads (across $2R_{pl}$) must be accounted for.

The simplest method of handling the correction is to rewrite Eq. (2-17), replacing E by $(I_{\text{bridge}} \times R_{\text{bridge}})$ and then actually measuring the current (I_{bridge}) to the bridge. From Eq. (2-20) it is apparent that the indicator signal depends upon the actual load resistance; therefore, the presence of leads in series with the instrument load requires that a total load resistance of $(R_L + 2R_{il})$ be used in computing the indicator signal. Clearly, this is an unnecessary correction if the indicator is of the high impedance ($\simeq$ zero load) type, since $2R_{il}$ will be negligible compared to R_L.

In the system shown in Fig. 2-47 (four arms, remote), calibration can be accomplished by paralleling a calibration resistor (R_c) with one of the arms *at the bridge;* say, across *ab*. In this case, the computations for change in resistance (ΔR_{ab}) and equivalent strain $(\epsilon_{\text{equivalent}})$ are all identical to those previously discussed. However, in practice it is sometimes convenient to calibrate the system by placing the calibrate across $a'b'$ at the instrument location. In this case the calibrate resistance is in parallel with $R_1 + (R_{il} + R_{pl})$; hence,

$$\epsilon_{\text{equivalent}} = -\frac{(R_1 + R_{il} + R_{pl})^2}{FR_1(R_1 + R_{il} + R_{pl} + R_c)}.$$

This correction implies a knowledge of the lead resistance (impedance in the case of an AC bridge), a quantity which must usually be obtained by measurement on the completed system. A more convenient procedure is as follows: a calibrate resistance (R_c) is paralleled across one of the resistances at the bridge (*ab*) and the indicating device is deflected L units. The same calibrate resistance (R_c) is then paralleled across $a'b'$, and the indicating device is deflected H units (for any real lead resistance $H > L$, as can be seen from the equation for $\epsilon_{\text{equivalent}}$ given above). In all future work this circuit may be calibrated by paralleling calibration resistors across $a'b'$ only, and computing the equivalent strain as

$$\epsilon_{\text{equivalent}} = -\frac{R_1}{F(R_1 + R_c)} \times \frac{H}{L},$$

thus eliminating the necessity of knowing the lead resistance. (It is imperative that the lead resistance does not vary, however.)

In the system shown in Fig. 2-47 (four arms, remote), if the value of lead-wire resistance changes due to temperature changes that the lead wire may undergo, the potential to the bridge (E_{bridge}) will change, and the load resistance $(R_L + 2R_{il})$ will change. Both of these changes affect the bridge output, as shown by Eqs. (2-17) and (2-20). Since the lead resistance is usually small compared to either the bridge or the load resistance, and since the change due to normal temperature variation is small, this temperature effect is in turn *usually* small. However, each case should be considered separately; the worst cases involve long small leads (high R_l) combined with low bridge and load resistance (low R_B and low R_L), where the leads may undergo considerable temperature change during the test duration.

Another possibility for remote recording is illustrated in Fig. 2-48.

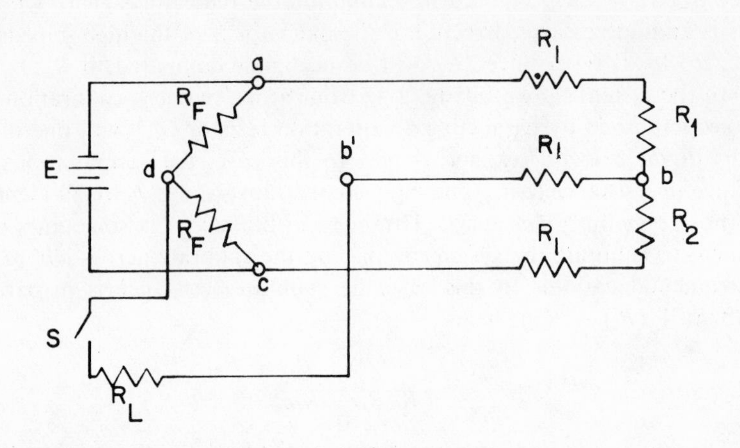

Fig. 2-48. Lead resistances in series with the active gages on a two-arm active bridge.

Here two gages (both active, or one active and one for temperature compensation) are at the test site, and the bridge is completed at the recorder. To investigate the effect of lead resistance on sensitivity for this case, it is necessary to return to the development of Eqs. (2-16) and (2-17). Thus

$$dE_{ab} = \frac{(R_2 + R_l)\, d(R_l + R_1)}{(R_2 + R_1 + 2R_l)^2} E,$$

and, treating R_l as a constant, we have

$$dE_{ab} = \frac{(R_2 + R_l)\, dR_1}{(R_2 + R_1 + 2R_l)^2} E.$$

Substituting

$$F = \frac{dR_1/R_1}{\epsilon},$$

we obtain

$$dE_{ab} = \frac{(R_2 + R_l)R_1F\epsilon}{(R_2 + R_1 + 2R_l)^2} E.$$

Hence, for this case the sensitivity equation comparable to Eq. (2-17) is

$$E_{bd} = \left[-\frac{(R_2 + R_l)R_1F_1\epsilon_1}{(R_1 + R_2 + 2R_l)^2} + \frac{(R_1 + R_l)R_2F_2\epsilon_2}{(R_1 + R_2 + 2R_l)^2} \right] E,$$

in which only two terms are shown, since, at most, only two gages (R_1 and R_2) will be active in this circuit. For the case in which $R_1 = R_2 = R$ and $F_1 = F_2 = F$,

$$\frac{E_{bd}}{\epsilon_{\text{net}}} = \frac{EF(R + R_l)R}{4(R + R_l)^2} = \frac{EFR}{4(R + R_l)}. \tag{2-34}$$

In this case the bridge voltage and the supply voltage are identical, but the total load resistance is $(R_L + R_l)$.

If the two-arm remote system is connected as shown in Fig. 2-49, the sensitivity [Eq. (2-34)] will be unchanged. The load resistance will be R_L.

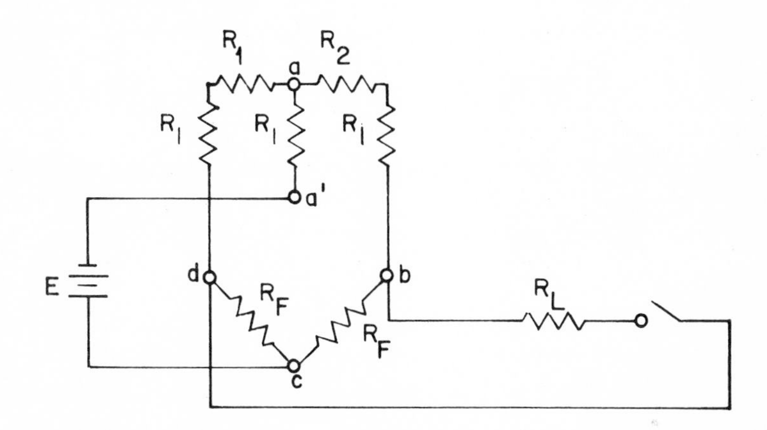

Fig. 2-49. Alternate circuit with lead resistances in series with the active gages on a two-arm bridge.

With either of these two-arm remote systems (Figs. 2-48 and 2-49), the remarks previously made concerning the difference between paralleling a calibrate resistor across the gage only (R) and across the gage plus the resistances of two leads ($R + 2R_l$) still apply.

With either of these two-arm remote systems, changes in lead-wire resistance due to temperature changes will be nearly compensating, since they occur in adjacent arms of the bridge except for changes in the one lead which is in series with either the supply voltage or the recording instrument. We assume that the leads all undergo the same resistance change—which will be the case of identical leads subjected to the same temperature change.

The last system to be considered for measuring strain at a point removed from the indicating equipment has only one arm remote. Here we must presume that the use of two gages in adjacent arms to accomplish temperature compensation is not contemplated, since gages at separated points could not be expected to perform this function. Indeed, this system is most commonly used in conjunction with a self-temperature-compensating strain gage.

The system shown in Fig. 2-50a is preferred over the system shown in Fig. 2-50b, since the latter circuit results in an unequal bridge for which initial balance is difficult to obtain, and since any change in lead resistance due to temperature change will be indistinguishable from strain.

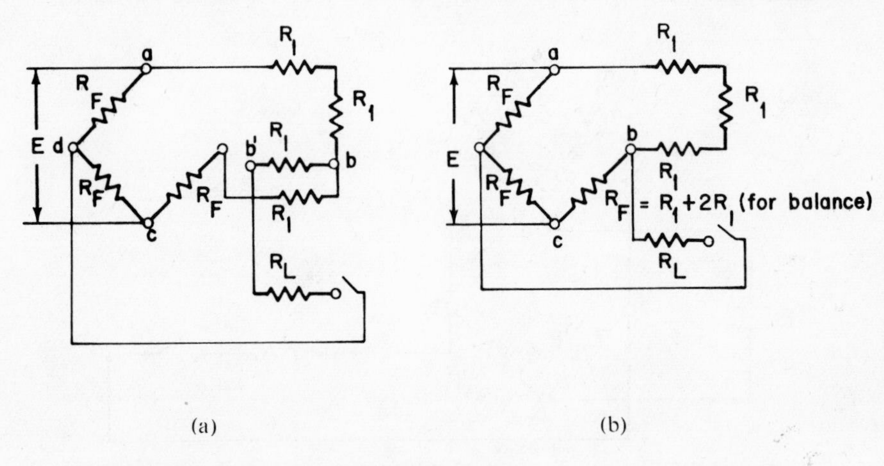

(a)

(b)

(a) Circuit employing 3-wire lead system
(b) Circuit with lead resistances in series with the active gage only.

Fig. 2-50. Two types of circuit for a single active gage.

The sensitivity equation for the circuit shown in Fig. 2-50a will be the same as for the two-arm remote system; i.e., Eq. (2-34). In the circuit shown in Fig. 2-50a, changes in lead resistance due to change in lead temperature affect only the magnitude of resistance in series with the indicator (or the supply voltage, if supply and indicator positions are reversed). The previous discussion on difference between calibrating at the gage (R_c across R_1 only) and calibrating at the instrument (R_c across $R_1 + 2R_l$) is still pertinent.

It is common to read or record from several gages, using a single instrument, by switching gages in and out of the system. Therefore, a few remarks on proper switching procedure are in order. The important consideration is that changes of resistance in the bridge arms due to any cause are interpreted by the system as strain. From this it follows that all elements which may undergo changes in resistance (such as switches and slip-ring contacts) should be kept out of the bridge arms. This can always be done when one is switching from one complete four-arm bridge to another, as shown in Fig. 2-51a, and it can sometimes be done when switching from one set of two active gages to another, as shown in Fig. 2-51b.

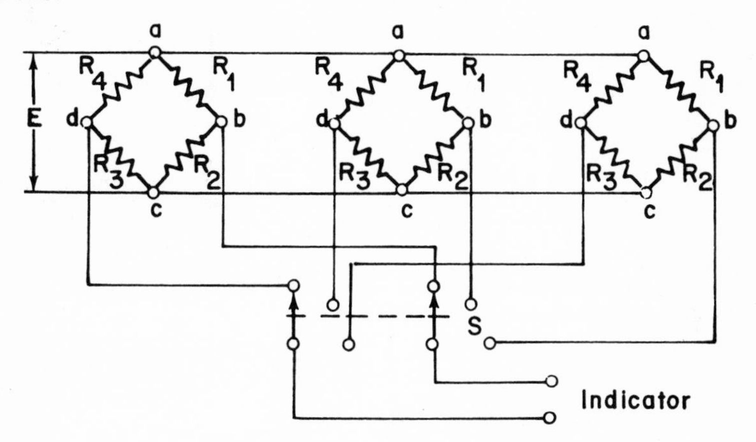

(a) All four arms of bridge switched

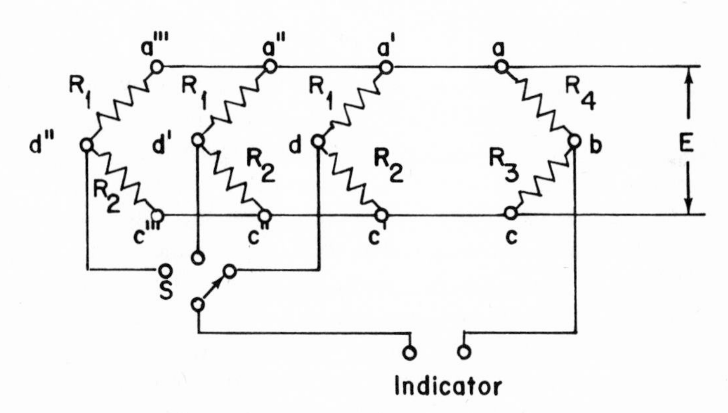

(b) Two arms of bridge switched

Fig. 2-51. Multiple strain-gage circuits with switch-contact resistances external to bridges.

Notice that in these systems any variation in switch contact resistance is felt only as a variation in load resistance. When one is switching from a single gage to another, the switch resistance is in series with the gage resistance (see Fig. 2-52). Therefore, switches of the highest quality are required. Remember, with a gage factor of 2 and a gage resistance of 120

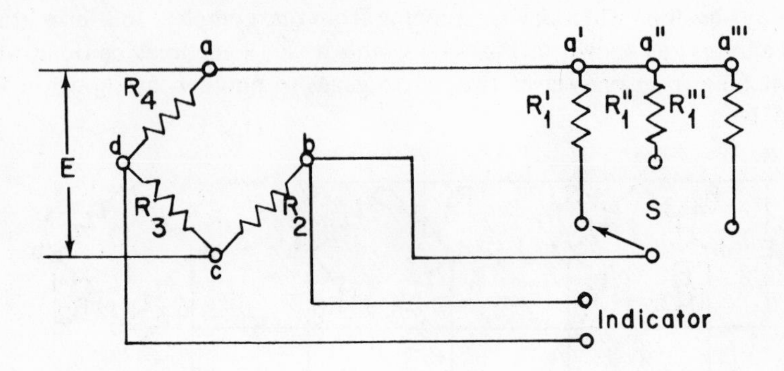

Fig. 2-52. Multiple strain-gage circuit with the switch-contact resistance in series with the active gage.

ohms, a change in contact resistance of 0.01 ohm would simulate a strain of

$$\epsilon_{\text{equivalent}} = \frac{\Delta R/R}{F} = \frac{0.01}{(2)(120)},$$

or

$$\epsilon_{\text{equivalent}} = 42 \ \mu\text{in./in.}$$

In addition to this, the circuit shown in Fig. 2-52 may be unsuitable because, as each cold gage is switched into the circuit, the output will drift due to resistance changes produced by gage heating.

When strain gages are mounted on rotating bodies, it is common to connect the gage or gages into the circuit, using slip-ring contacts. The effects of variation in slip-ring resistance are the same as for variations in switch resistances; hence, we reach the same conclusion: keep slip rings out of the bridge arms, if possible.

Slip rings may introduce undesirable high-frequency noise into the circuit even when they are placed in series with power and instrument leads. Several investigators have designed special circuits to minimize slip-ring noise. See Ref. [13], pp. 177–9, for a discussion of some of these special circuits.

2-2g Use of alternating current to power strain-gage circuits

Before we leave this discussion of basic strain-measuring circuits, the significant differences between DC (direct current)- and AC (alternating current)-powered circuits will be discussed. The bridge circuit shown in Fig. 2-53 is supplied with AC potential across the diagonal; the frequency of the supply (called the carrier) is usually between 60 and 10,000 cps.

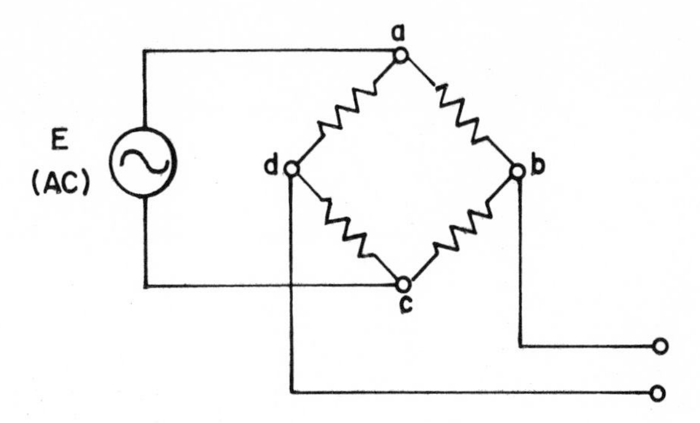

Fig. 2-53. An AC-excited bridge.

The frequency of this carrier voltage should be at least five times as high as the highest strain frequency that is to be measured. When the bridge is unbalanced by straining one or more of the gages, the amplitude of the AC potential across *bd* will be increased in proportion to the unbalance and hence to the applied strain. As has been developed previously for the DC bridge, an increase in the resistance of arm *ad* produces a higher voltage at point *d* than at point *b*. Conversely, a decrease in resistance of arm *ad* produces a higher voltage at point *b* than at point *d*. Thus, tension and compression strains (increasing and decreasing resistance) produce voltages of opposite sign at the bridge output terminals. The AC bridge is supplied with a voltage that is alternately positive and negative, with tension and compression strain both increasing the value of this AC voltage at the bridge output terminals. However, if we consider this AC voltage to be the difference between the voltage across *bc* and the voltage across *dc*, we find that an increase in the resistance of arm *ad* produces a resultant bridge voltage in phase with both the voltage across *dc* and that across *bc*, whereas a decrease in the resistance of arm *ad* produces a resultant bridge voltage out of phase with both voltage *dc* and voltage *bc* (see Fig. 2-54). Thus, tension and compression strains (increasing and decreasing resistance) produce AC voltage of opposite phase at the bridge output terminals.

The effect of unbalancing the bridge by straining is to amplitude-modulate an AC signal of carrier frequency; hence, the signal from the bridge can be amplified by an AC amplifier whether the applied strain is static or dynamic. It should be noted that the bridge output voltages are unsuitable for recording and interpretation into strain values for two

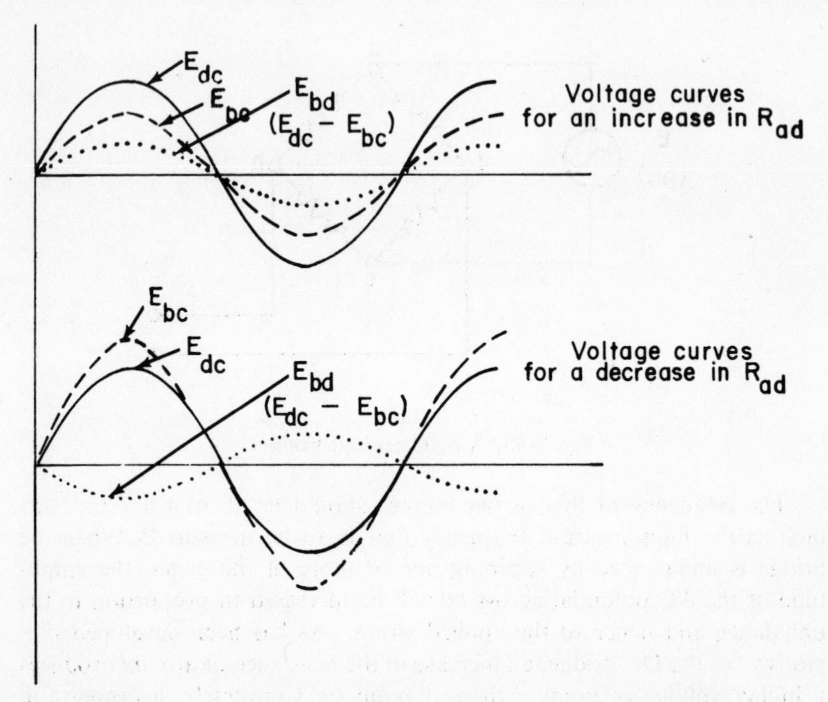

Fig. 2-54. Voltage phase relationships for an AC-excited bridge.

reasons: (1) presence of the carrier voltage tends to confuse interpretation of dynamic varying strains and necessitates higher frequency response indicators than would be necessary for the strain signals alone; (2) both tension and compression strains cause an increase in the amplitude of the carrier voltage at the bridge output terminals. These two objections to the carrier system can be eliminated in either of two methods. The first method, shown in Fig. 2-55, consists of rectifying and filtering the amplitude-modulated carrier signal after amplification, thus eliminating the carrier voltage.

Tension and compression strains can be detected by purposely unbalancing the strain-gage bridge to such a point that the maximum anticipated strain will not bring the bridge back to the balance point. It must be remembered that sensitivity adjustments of the amplifier change the zero point of the indicating instrument. The second and preferred method with laboratory equipment is to utilize a demodulator so that tension and compression strains can be detected without initially unbalancing the bridge. Figure 2-56 is a block diagram of a demodulator system.

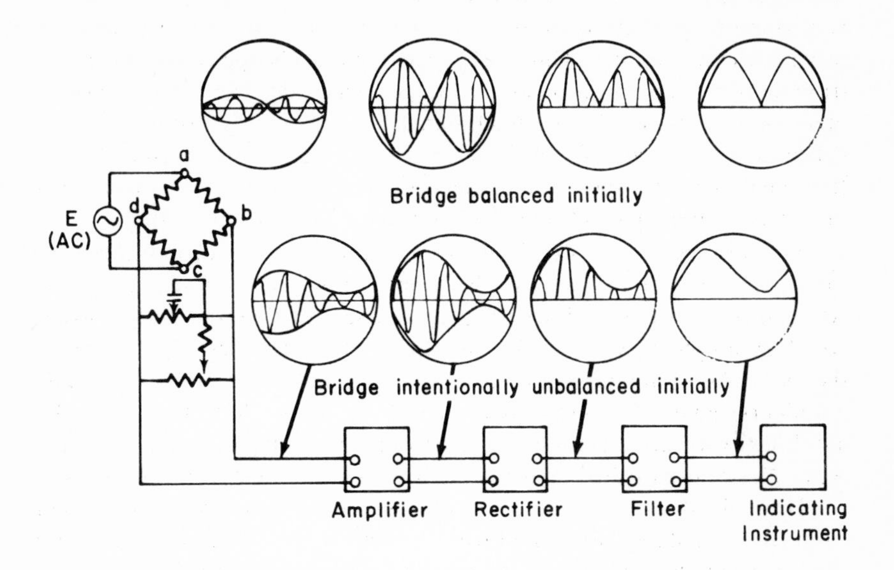

Fig. 2-55. An AC-excited bridge, associated instrumentation, and signals at several locations resulting from a sinusoidally varying strain.

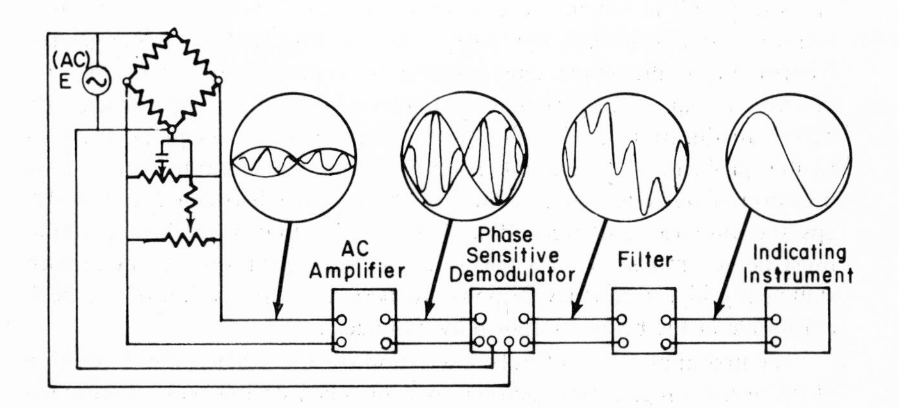

Fig. 2-56. An AC-excited bridge with a phase-sensitive demodulator and signals at various locations resulting from a sinusoidally varying strain.

The demodulator has the advantage that its output is of one polarity when the amplifier output is in phase with the original carrier voltage and is of opposite polarity when the amplifier output is out of phase with the original carrier voltage. Thus, the effective phase change caused by going from tension to compression on the bridge is easily detected. For measurement of varying strain, the final signal is used to drive some form of deflection-type indicator. In the case of static or slowing varying strains, the signal may be displayed on a deflection-type indicator for direct reading or as a simple indication of unbalance for use in a null system.

An example previously given (see Example 2-3, p. 86) indicates that the signal from the bridge is small; hence, amplification is required. The AC bridge system just described was devised so that the bridge signal could be amplified with an AC amplifier. This was desirable, since, in the past, AC amplifiers have been cheaper and more stable than DC amplifiers having the same gain. However, since 1955, high-gain DC amplifiers with good stability have become available, and as a result the trend in strain-indicator systems has been away from the AC bridge.

The difficulties encountered in the use of AC-powered bridges stem from the capacitance associated with the lead wires. When long leads are used, capacitance unbalance may make it impossible initially to balance the bridge with the equipment at hand or may unbalance the bridge to such an extent as to make the linear equations relating strain and electrical signal output invalid.

A special type of strain-gage bridge excitation utilizes voltage pulses as the bridge supply. Pulse excitation is useful in the solution of three types of problems which occur in strain-gage use (see Ref. [14]): (1) prevention of overheating of strain gages and/or base material, (2) sequential recording of multichannel gage installations on one indicator, (3) increase of gage output. The particular characteristics of the pulse voltage with regard to duration, peak value, and repetition rate depend on the particular problem at hand, but examples from the literature show pulse durations from 1 to 500 μsec with repetition rates between 2 and 40,000 cps and amplitudes between 10 and 200 v. Readout of the bridge output must be accomplished on a CRO, magnetic tape, or similar device with sufficiently high frequency response to permit determination of the peak amplitude of the bridge-output pulse voltage.

The first application of pulse excitation of strain gages, the prevention of the overheating, is particularly important when strain gages are mounted on very thin metallic sections or on plastics or other materials with very low values of thermal conductivity. In the case of gage use on plastics, gage currents supplied by most conventional commercial strain-gage equipment will result in gage overheating with resultant drift and, in addition, characteristic changes of the base material. In the case of gage use on thin metallic sections, the overheating affects gage stability, even though the base material may not be affected. Determination of the temperature conditions in the vicinity of the installed strain gage should be made with actual thermocouple measurements. Choice of the characteristics of the pulse-supply voltage would then be based on a temperature rise at the gage, which would permit accurate measurement of the strain at the gaged point without adverse effects on the material properties or excessive strain-gage drift.

The second application of pulse excitation of strain gages, the sequential recording of multichannel gage installations, is desirable for several reasons. First, it permits the channel-to-channel switching to be done at high voltages (bridge excitation voltage) rather than at low voltages (bridge output voltages). Second, since only one bridge at a time has voltage applied to it, cross talk between channels is eliminated. Finally, since the power supply need have only the current rating of a single strain-gage bridge, and no low-voltage-level switching is required, the cost of a multichannel system may be lower than for other types of systems.

The third application of pulse excitation of strain gages, the raising of bridge output, has become less important with the advent of high-gage-factor semiconductor gages, but applications may still exist where an appreciable increase in bridge output is desired and semiconductor-strain gages cannot be employed. With pulse excitation the output can be raised, since for a given power dissipation, the peak supply voltage can be raised.

2-3 References listed in Chapter 2

1. Kuczyski, G. C., "A Note on the Remarkable Stability of the Alloy Used in SR-4 Gages," *Testing Topics*, Vol. 9, No. 3, p. 8. Baldwin-Lima-Hamilton Corporation, Philadelphia, Pa. (1934).
2. Padgett, E. D. and W. V. Wright, "Silicon Piezoresistive Devices," Instrument Society of America, Paper Number NY60-42, New York (Sept. 26–30, 1960).
3. Sanchez, J. C. and W. V. Wright, "Recent Developments in Flexible Silicon Strain Gages," Instrument Society of America, Paper Number 37-SL61, St. Louis, Mo. (Jan. 17–19, 1961).
4. Sanchez, J. C. and W. V. Wright, "Recent Advances in Flexible Semiconductor Strain Gages," Instrument Society of America, Paper Number 46-LA61, Los Angeles, Calif. (Sept. 11–15, 1961).
5. McWhirter, M. and B. W. Duggin, "Minimizing Creep of Paper-Base SR-4 Strain Gages," *Proceedings of the Society for Experimental Stress Analysis*, Vol. 14, No. 2, pp. 149–54.
6. Pender, H. and K. McIlwain, eds., *Electrical Engineers' Handbook*, 3rd ed. New York: John Wiley and Sons, Inc., 1947.

7. Pohl, P., "Signal Conditioning for Semiconductors," *Instrument Society of America Journal*, Vol. 9, No. 6 (June, 1962), pp. 33–34.
8. Stein, P., "Parallel Balancing of Strain Gage Bridges," *Strain Gage Readings* **1**, **2**, Stein Engineering Services (June–July 1958), p. 35.
9. Hines, Frank F., "Effect of Mounting Surface Curvature on the Temperature Coefficient of Bonded Resistance Strain Gages," available from Baldwin-Lima-Hamilton Corporation.
10. Mason, W. P., "Use of Semiconductor Transducers and Esaki Diodes in Measuring Strains and Pressures," Instrument Society of America, Paper Number 44-LA-61 (Sept. 11–15, 1961).
11. Mason, W. P., J. J. Forst, and L. M. Tornillo, "Recent Development in Semiconductor Strain Transducers." Instrument Society of America, Paper Number NY60-15 (Sept. 26–30, 1960).
12. Hines, R. F. and L. J. Weymouth, "Practical Aspects of Temperature Effects on Resistance Strain Gages," available from Baldwin-Lima-Hamilton Corporation.
13. Perry, C. C. and H. R. Lissner, *The Strain Gage Primer*. New York: McGraw-Hill, 1955.
14. Stein, P., "The Pulse Excitation of Strain Gage Circuits. A State-of-the-Art Summary." *Strain Gage Readings* **5**, 5, Stein Engineering Services (Dec.–Jan. 1962–3), pp. 22–39.

2-4 Problems

2-1 A single strain gage is mounted on the center of the aluminum bar, as shown in Fig. 2-57. The bar is loaded with a constant moment section, and the curvature is obtained by reading the dial indicator shown. As the bar is loaded, gage resistance is measured by using a resistance-measuring bridge. From the data given, determine the gage factor for this gage.

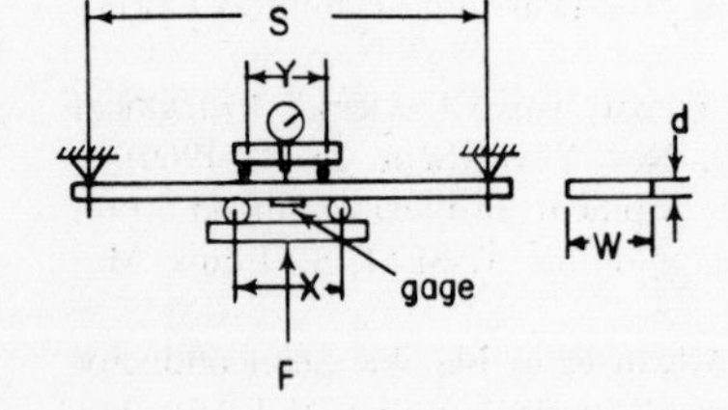

$d = 0.250$ in.
$W = 1.00$ in.
$S = 12.0$ in.
$X = 8.00$ in.
$Y = 6.00$ in.

R_{gage}, Ω	Dial Reading 0.001 in.
121.3	0
120.7	4
120.2	8
119.5	12

Fig. 2-57.

2-2 A single strain gage is mounted on a steel bar, as shown in Fig. 2-58. The bar is loaded as shown, and the deflection is measured by using a dial indicator. As the bar is bent, the gage resistance is measured by using a resistance-measuring bridge. From the data given, determine the gage factor for this gage. (*Note:* this is *not* a cantilever beam.)

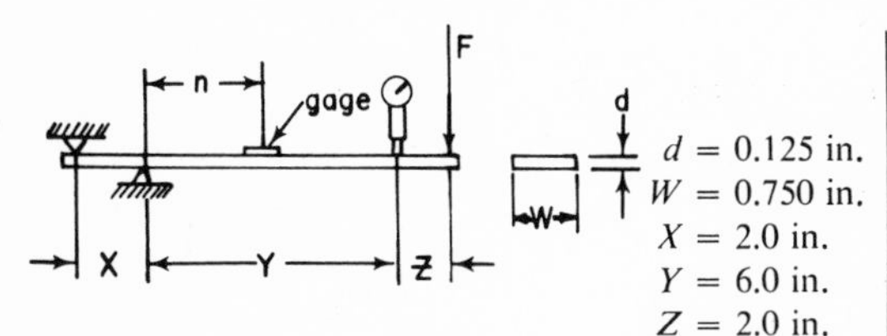

R_{gage}, Ω	Dial Reading 0.001 in.
503.1	0
503.4	50
503.6	100
504.0	150
504.3	200

Fig. 2-58.

2-3 (a) What change in resistance is produced by placing a 1,000,000-ohm (1 meg) resistor in parallel with a 120-ohm resistor (120 ohms is the nominal resistance of many strain gages)? (b) By placing a 500,000-ohm (500K) resistor in parallel with a 120-ohm resistor?

2-4 Four 120-ohm strain gages are connected in a bridge-type circuit, as shown in Fig. 2-59. The gage factor is 2.0. What strain is simulated by connecting a resistor in parallel with one gage?

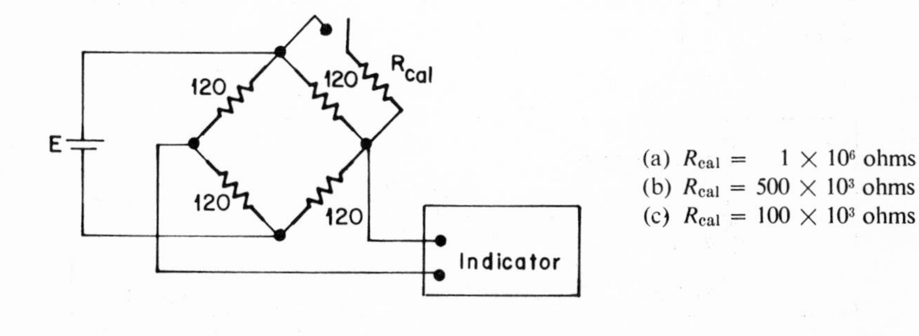

Fig. 2-59.

2-5 The loading frame shown in Prob. 2-1 is used, and a strain gage is again mounted at the center of the bar ($\frac{1}{4}$-in. thick). A precision resistance bridge was not available for measuring gage resistance, so the circuit shown in Fig. 2-60 was used. With the gage unstrained and the four-position switch open, the microammeter reads zero. The four-position switch is then moved to position *a*, as a result the microammeter is deflected. The bar is then strained until the microammeter returns to zero; the dial indicator is then read. This procedure is repeated and switch positions *b* and *c* are used. From the data given, find the gage factor.

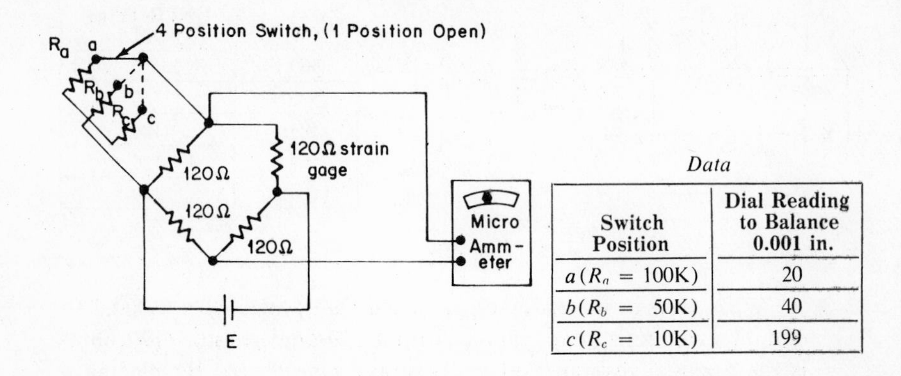

Data

Switch Position	Dial Reading to Balance 0.001 in.
$a(R_a = 100K)$	20
$b(R_b = 50K)$	40
$c(R_c = 10K)$	199

Fig. 2-60.

2-6 Two strain gages are mounted side by side on a metal surface and connected in series in a half-bridge circuit, as shown in Fig. 2-61. The gage factor is 3.5, and the resistance of each gage is 500 ohms. What strain is simulated by connecting a 100,000-ohm resistor as shown?

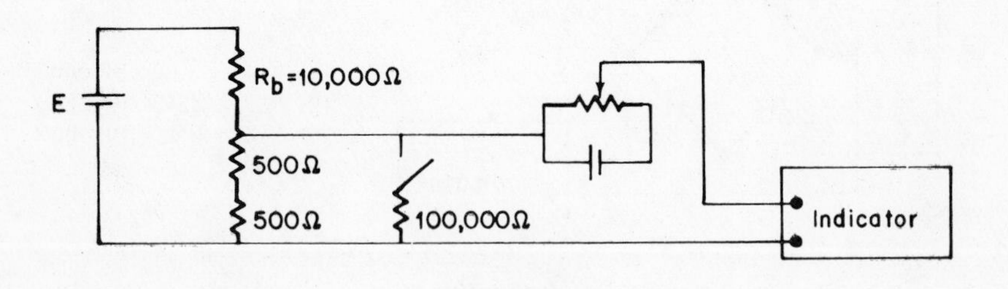

Fig. 2-61.

2-7 Figure 2-62 shows a four-arm bridge made up of 500-ohm strain gages. What potential (volts, DC) should be applied to the bridge if the current through each gage is to be 20 ma (1 ma = 0.001 amp)? With this voltage applied, what power must be dissipated by each gage?

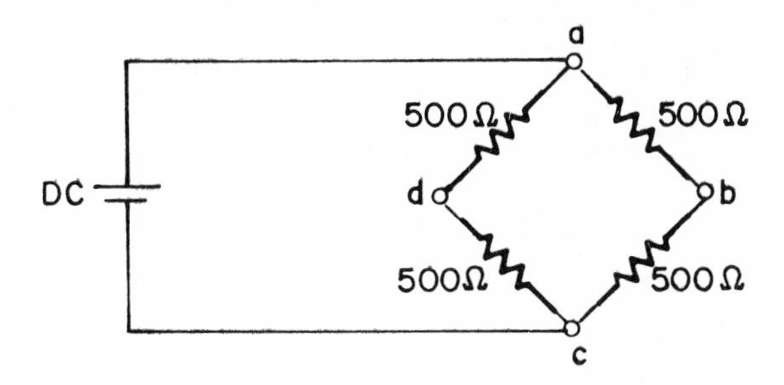

Fig. 2-62.

2-8 Figure 2-63 shows a potentiometer or half-bridge circuit used for measurement of transient strains. What value of resistance (R_b) should be used if the power dissipated by the strain gage is to be limited to 100×10^{-3} w?

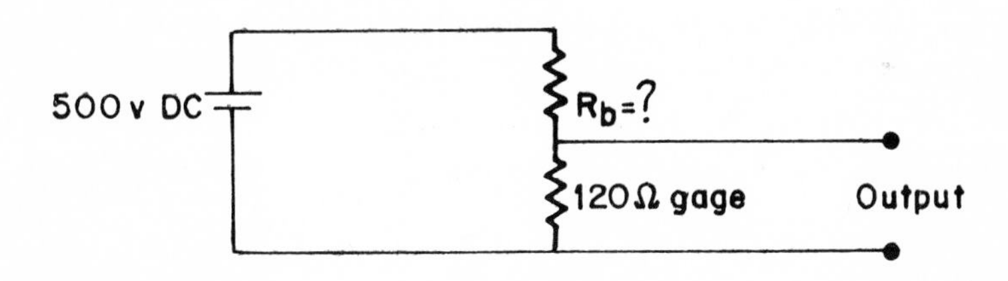

Fig. 2-63.

2-9 A DC bridge-type strain-measuring instrument is constructed as shown in Fig. 2-64. Any combination of strain gages and precision resistors can be connected at the binding posts (*a*, *b*, *c*, *d*). In this case the instrument is used as shown in (b), and the current to the bridge (measured at *A*) is 20 ma. When the active gage is subjected to a strain of 1000 μin./in., the recording galvanometer is deflected 30 units. (a) What would the galvanometer deflection be if the bridge current were increased to 30 ma (strain in one gage still 1000 μin./in.)? (b) What would the galvanometer deflection be for A = 20 ma, strain in one gage of 1000 μin./in. gage factor F = 3.5?

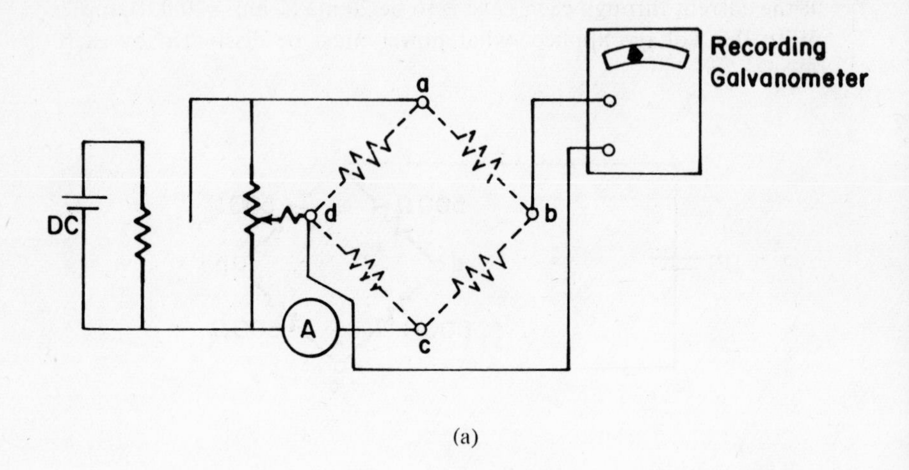

(a)

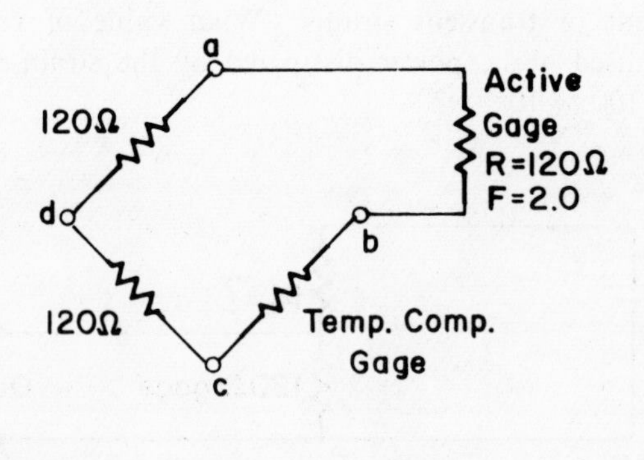

(b)

Fig. 2-64.

2-10 The measuring system shown in Prob. 2-9 is used. Gages are connected and strained as shown in Fig. 2-65. What is the galvanometer deflection for each case shown, if connecting a 100,000-ohm resistor across *ab* produces a deflection of 10 units? R gage $= 120\Omega$, $F = 2.0$.

2-11 Bonded-resistance strain gages are used in a Wheatstone bridge circuit to measure strain. The circuit and the placement of the gages

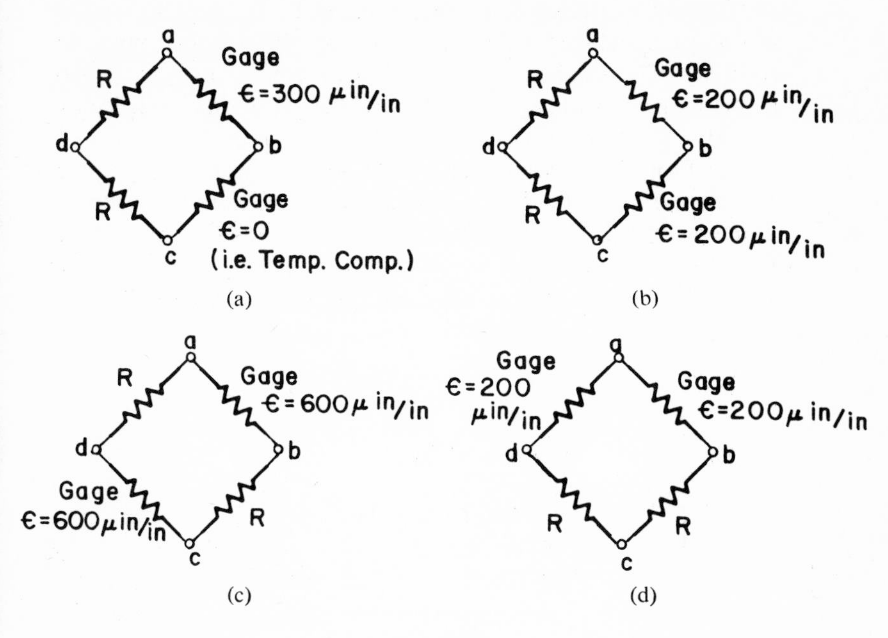

Fig. 2-65.

are shown in Fig. 2-66. (a) Find the proper DC voltage (E) if the current through the gages is to be limited to 15 ma. (b) When a

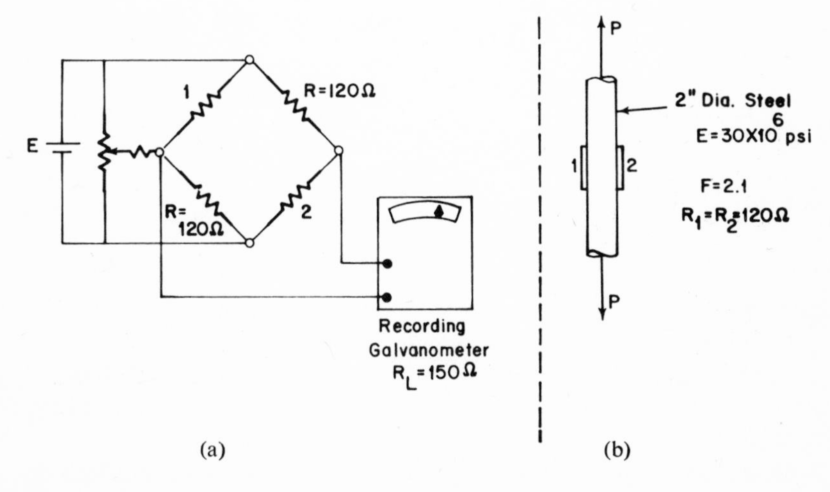

Fig. 2-66.

500,000-ohm resistance is placed in parallel with gage #1, the recording galvanometer is deflected one cm. What is the null-point sensitivity of this galvanometer in terms of: first, cm/ma; second, cm/in./in. per active gage? (c) What is the galvanometer deflection when $P = 2000$ lb?

2-12 Same as Prob. 2-11, except that a CRO is used as a recording instrument ($R_{CRO} \simeq \infty$). (a) When a 500,000-ohm resistance is placed in parallel with gage #1, the deflection of the oscilloscope trace is one in. What is the sensitivity of this CRO in terms of: first, in./mv; second, in./ (in./in.) per active gage? (b) What is the oscilloscope deflection when $P = 2000$ lb?

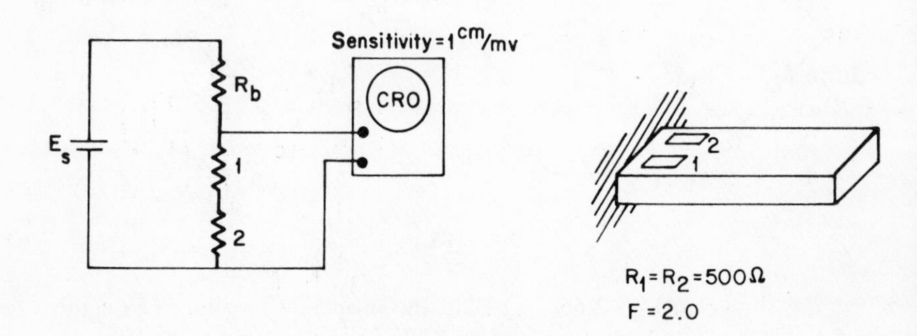

Fig. 2-67.

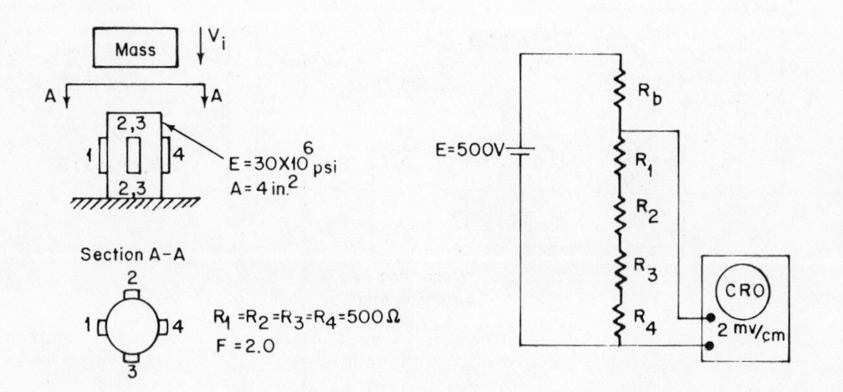

Fig. 2-68.

2-13 Two bonded-resistance strain gages are mounted on a vibrating beam and connected as shown in the Fig. 2-67. A DC voltage source is available which can be varied from 0 to 500 v. The maximum gage current is 15 ma. (a) R_b is selected as 2000 ohms. What value of E_s should be used? (b) With these values of R_b and E_s, what will the trace deflection be for strain of 1000 μin./in.? (c) If E_s is set at 500 v, what value should be used for R_b? (d) With these values of E_s and R_b, what will the trace deflection be when the strain is 1000 μin./in.?

2-14 Figure 2-68 shows the setup used to record the stresses produced by impact. (a) Find R_b if I is to be 10 ma. (b) Find the sensitivity of this circuit in cm/lb.

2-15 Figure 2-69 shows a bolt with strain gages mounted on the shank.

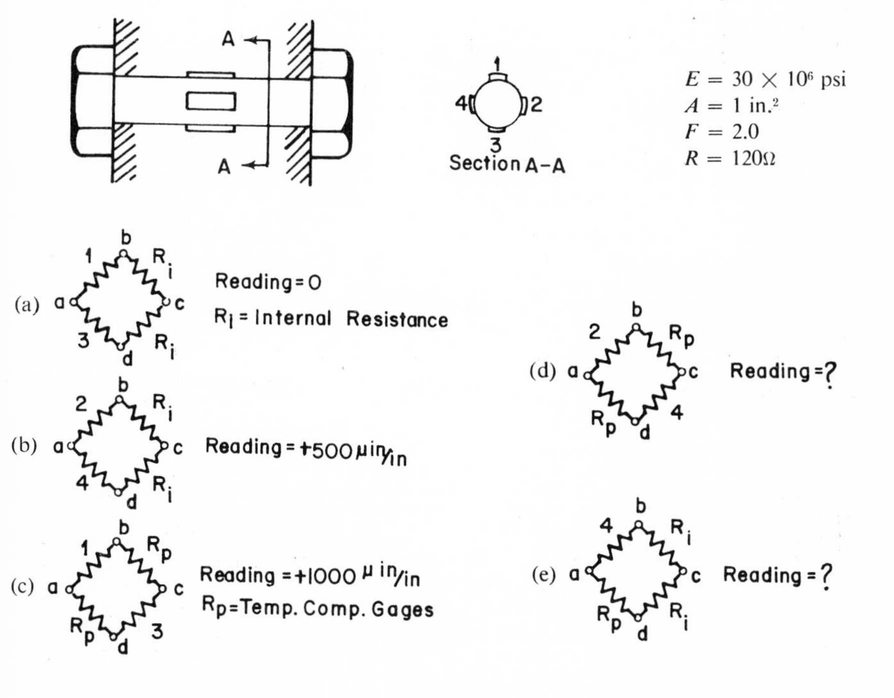

Fig. 2-69.

These gages are read on a static strain indicator. The gages are read while the various hookups shown (a), (b), (c) are used. (a) What is the magnitude of the stress in the bolt due to axial load? (b) What is the magnitude of the stress in the bolt due to flexure?

(c) What would the instrument read for the connections shown in (d) and (e)?

2-16 Figure 2-70 shows the circuit used to record from two gages which are located at some distance from the recording instrument. When R_{cal} is switched into the circuit, the indicator is deflected 16 units. When the force F is applied, the indicator is deflected 14 units. (a) What is the strain in the beam when the force F is applied? (b) What is the indicator sensitivity in units/mv?

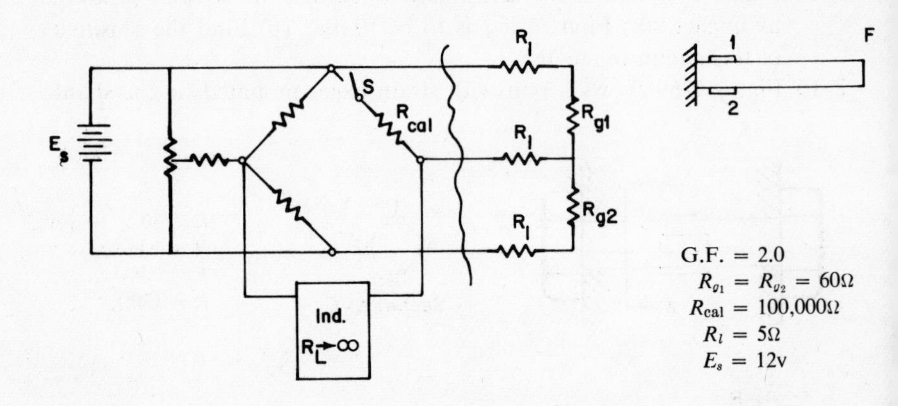

Fig. 2-70.

2-17 Figure 2-71 shows two gages mounted on a beam. They are connected in a bridge circuit as shown. The indicating galvanometer

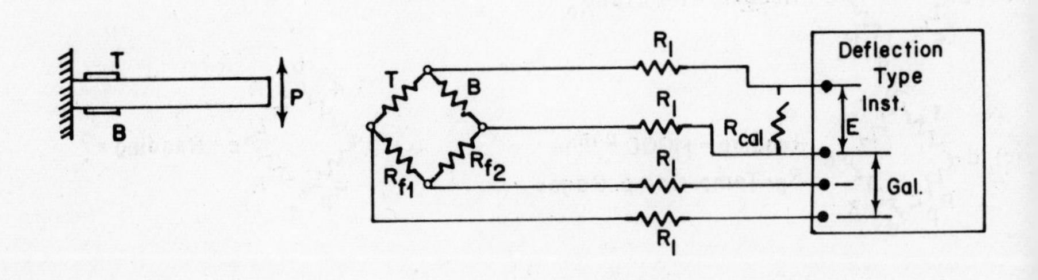

$$R_T = R_B = R_{f_1} = R_{f_2} = 120\Omega$$
$$F = 2.1$$
$$R_l = 3\Omega$$
$$R_{cal} = 100{,}000\Omega$$

Fig. 2-71.

is linear. When R_{cal} is inserted as shown, the galvanometer is deflected 26.4 units. When the beam is bent, the galvanometer is deflected 13.2 units. What is the strain in the beam?

2-18 Figure 2-72 shows four gages mounted on a gun barrel to measure the transient circumferential stresses developed when the gun is fired. (a) When the gages are connected as shown in (a), the scope trace moves two cm when the gun is fired. What is the circumfer-

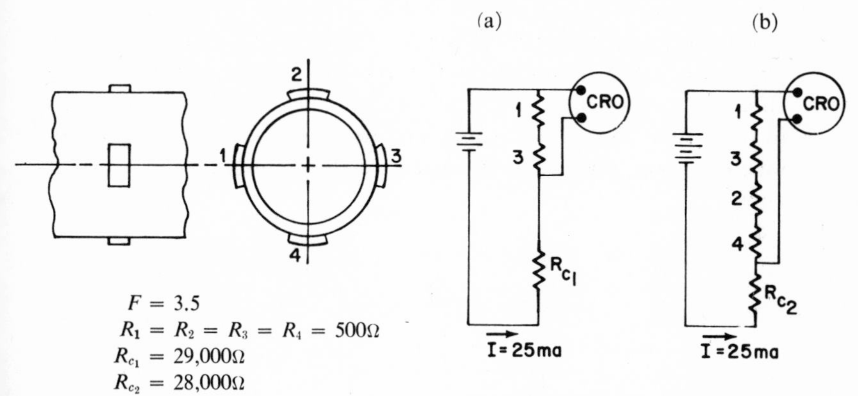

Fig. 2-72.

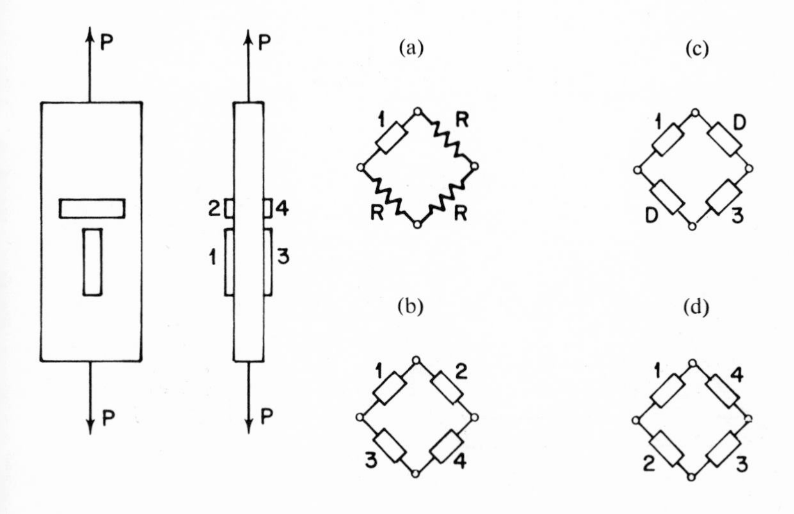

Fig. 2-73.

ential strain? (b) If the gages are connected as shown in (b) and the strain developed is the same as before, how far will the trace be deflected?

2-19 Figure 2-73 shows four gages mounted on a tensile test specimen; (a), (b), (c), and (d) show four possible circuit arrangements. How does the output of (b) compare with that of (a)? Of (c) with that of (a)? Of (d) with that of (a)? Give values of K: i.e., output from $b = (K)$ [Output from (a), etc.].

2-20 The solid steel cylinder shown in Fig. 2-74 is to be used as a force link to measure compressive loads. Eight electric resistance strain gages are to be mounted on the cylinder. Show how the gages should be mounted on the link and how they should be connected in the circuit: (a) if the gages are to be connected in a potentiometer circuit, and (b) if the gages are to be connected in a bridge circuit.

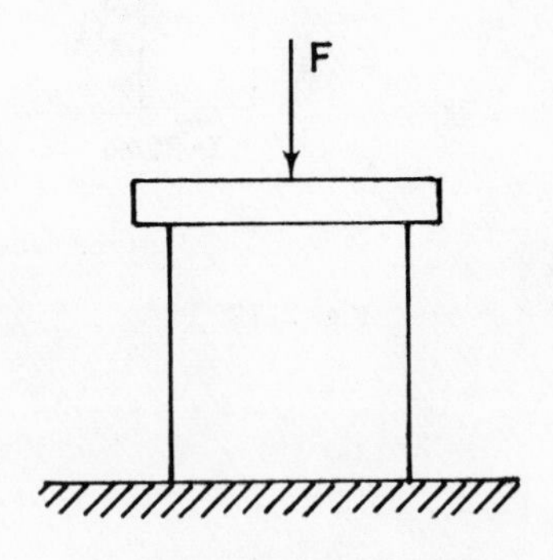

Fig. 2-74.

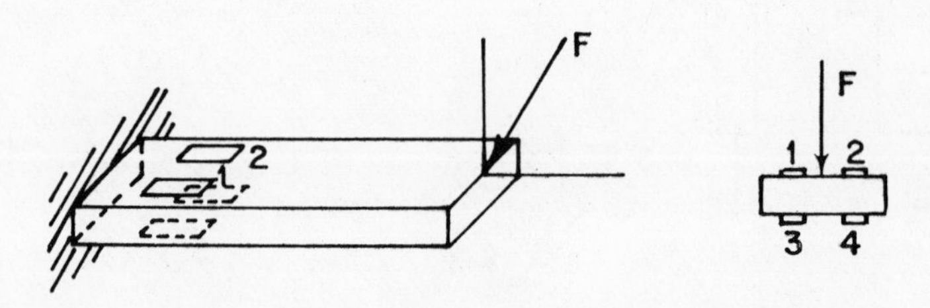

Fig. 2-75.

2-21 Four gages are mounted on a beam as shown in Fig. 2-75 below. Show how the gages should be connected in a bridge circuit so that they measure only the compressive strain produced by the axial component of the load.

2-22 Figure 2-76 shows a beam-column with gages mounted on it. (a) Show the gages connected in a bridge so that they measure only strain due to bending. (b) Show the gages connected in a bridge so that they measure only strain due to compression.

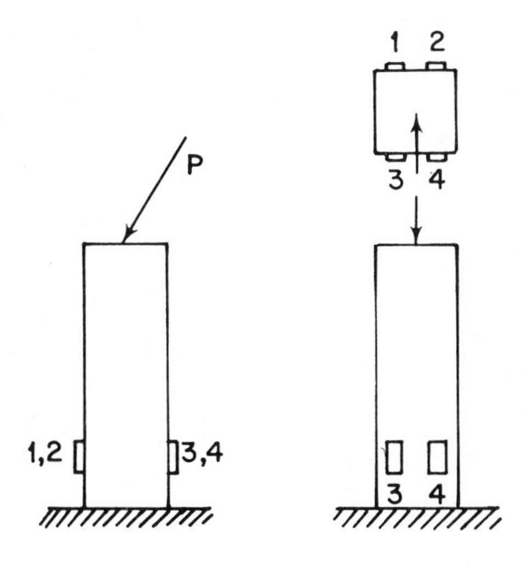

Fig. 2-76.

2-23 A tensile force link is to be made by mounting two gages back to back on a thin brass strip. See Fig. 2-77.

$$E_{\text{Brass}} = 15 \times 10^6 \text{ psi}; \qquad F_{\text{Max}} = 80 \text{ lb};$$
$$t = 0.025 \text{ in.}; \qquad I_{\text{Max}} = 25 \text{ ma thru a gage.}$$

The output from these gages is to be displayed on a CRO for which the maximum sensitivity is 28 mv/in. of trace deflection. The input impedance of the scope can be considered to be infinite. (a) Using four (two on the pull bar and two others to complete the bridge) 120-ohm gages having a gage factor of 2.0 in a bridge circuit, find: the bridge-supply voltage; the deflection of the scope trace at maximum load. (b) Same as (a), but 500-ohm gages are used and $F = 3.5$. (c) Same as (b), except that gages are mounted on a strip

0.010-in. thick (i.e., t = 0.010 in.), and I_{Max} is 10 ma. (*Note:* the thinner the piece on which the gages are mounted, the smaller the current must be to prevent overheating.)

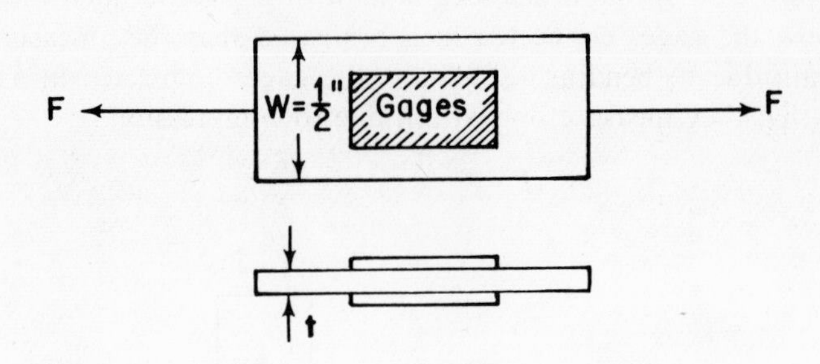

Fig. 2-77.

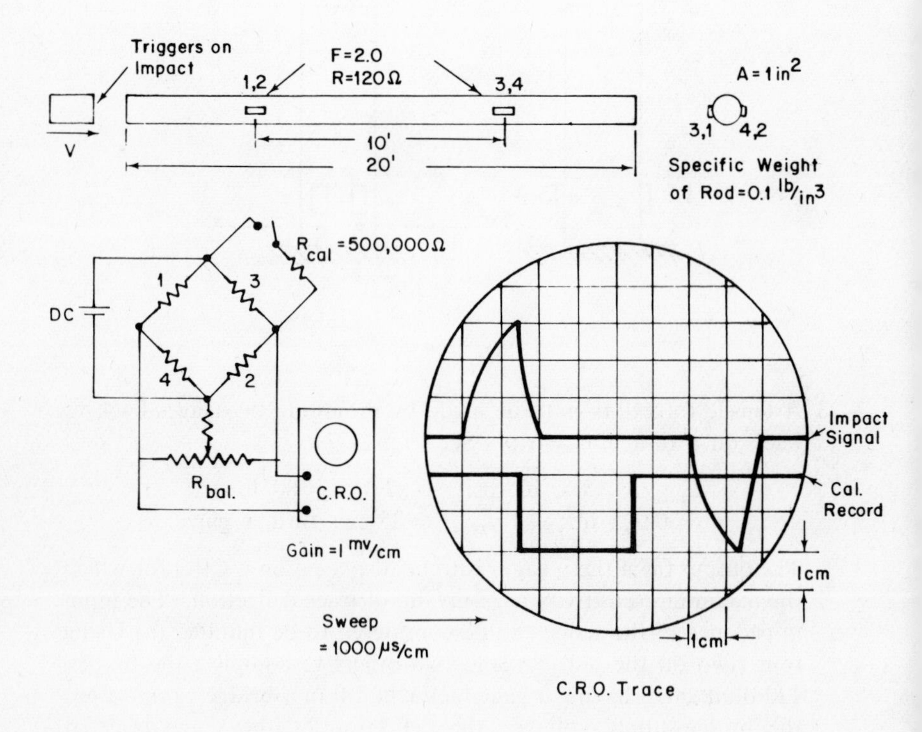

Fig. 2-78.

2-24 Four strain gages are mounted on a rod as shown in Fig. 2-78. The gages are connected to a CRO, as shown. Two traces are shown, one obtained when the rod was impacted on the left end, and one obtained when the circuit was calibrated. What is the magnitude of the stress produced by this impact?

2-25 Two 120-ohm, $F = 2.00$, strain gages are mounted, as shown in Fig. 2-79, on a one-in. diameter plastic rod 12 ft long. The rod is struck on the right end with a hammer, and the output signal is displayed on a CRO. A 100,000-ohm calibrate resistor is used, and its trace is shown. (a) What is the value of E for this material, if the rod weighs 30 lbs? (b) What is the magnitude of the peak strain?

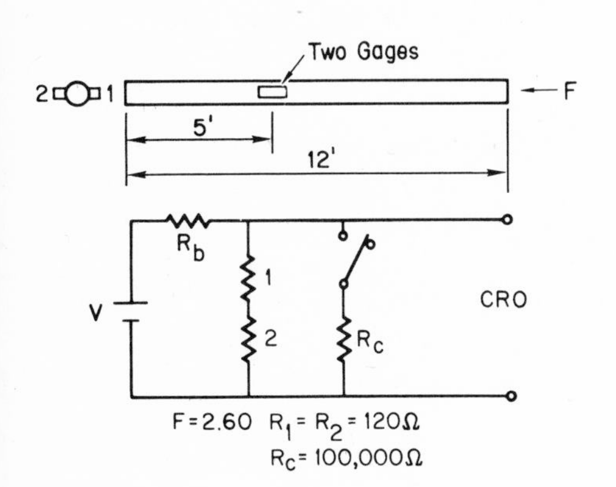

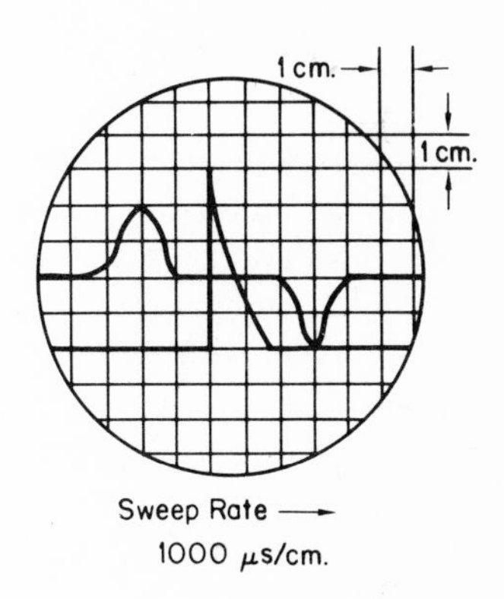

Fig. 2-79.

2-5 Suggested laboratory experiments

Experiment 2-1 Experimental determination of gage factor

EQUIPMENT NECESSARY

1. A selection of resistance-type strain gages mounted on a bar (or bars) which can be used as a beam in a situation in which the strain at the gage point can be determined from theory.
2. A suitable straining frame* and whatever instruments are necessary to measure quantities from which the strain at the gage point can be computed.

---

* A frame which puts the gage in a constant-moment section is recommended. In this case the strain can be computed from a measured value of curvature. See Prob. 2-1.

3. A suitable instrument or circuit for measuring change in gage resistance.*

PROCEDURE

For each gage furnished obtain data from which a plot of $\Delta R/R$ versus strain can be plotted.

REPORT

All necessary sketches and computations necessary to determine gage factor (F).

Experiment 2-2 The potentiometer or half-bridge circuit

EQUIPMENT NECESSARY

1. A resistance strain gage mounted near one end of a bar.
2. A motor-driven straining frame to produce a preselected strain value at a frequency which can be varied and measured; i.e., an eccentric or other cam driven by a variable-speed electric motor.
3. Additional resistors for making a potentiometer circuit.
4. A selection of precision resistors for calibration.
5. A high-voltage, low-ripple, DC power supply (several 45-volt dry cell batteries in series can be used).
6. A cathode ray oscilloscope which is capable of both AC- and DC-coupled input.

PROCEDURE

1. Make a potentiometer circuit (AC-coupled) in which $R_B = R_g$. Set the gage current (I_g) to a specified value and measure the signal produced by the standard deflection (frequency adjusted to give maximum signal).
2. Select a value of $R_B > R_g$. With the supply potential (E) set at the same value as in step 1, measure the signal produced by the standard deflection.
3. With this same R_B vary E until I_g is the same value used in step 1. Measure the signal produced by the standard deflection.

* If a resistance bridge of suitable resolution is not available (a five- or six-place bridge will be necessary, except when semiconductor gages are used), the following procedure is suggested. Wire the gage into an equal four-arm bridge. Produce a known $-\Delta R$ by connecting a calibration resistor in parallel, then rebalance the bridge by straining the gage. When balance is re-established, $|\Delta R|$ in the gage = $|\Delta R|$ produced by connection of the calibration resistor. See Prob. 2-5.

4. Using the circuit employed in step 3, find the frequency at which the output is reduced by 20 per cent. (An approximation, since signal will be read directly on CRO tube without photographing it.)
5. Starting with the circuit used in step 3, add a zeroing circuit, switch the CRO to DC-coupled input and measure the signal produced by the standard deflection. Calibrate the systems (units of deflection versus applied strain for a specified set of conditions).

REPORT

1. Show all sketches and computations necessary to reduce the data.
2. Compare measured results to theoretical results wherever possible.

Experiment 2-3 A single, four-arm bridge used in both a deflection and a null-type system

EQUIPMENT NECESSARY

1. Four resistance-type strain gages mounted near one end of a bar (two top, two bottom, back to back) which can be mounted and loaded as a cantiliver beam.
2. Additional mounted gages of the same type for completing the bridge when less than four active gages are used.
3. Clamps and selection of weights for loading the beam.
4. A galvanometer or other indicating device.
5. A selection of precision resistors to be used for calibration.
6. A ten-turn potentiometer fitted with a microdial so that a given setting can be recorded and repeated.

PROCEDURE

1. Connect the gages in a four-arm bridge and calibrate the indicating device (i.e., units of deflection versus strain for a specified set of conditions).
2. Calibrate the ten-turn potentiometer for use as a strain-reading dial (i.e., units of rotation versus strain for a specified set of conditions).
3. In turn, connect the gages so that they function with one active, two active, and four active. In each case apply the same standard load and read the strain using both deflection and null techniques.

REPORT

1. Show all sketches and computations necessary in reducing the data taken.

2. Show calibration curves obtained in steps 1 and 2 of procedure.
3. Present and discuss the results obtained in step 3 of procedure.

Experiment 2-4 Temperature-compensating gages and circuits

EQUIPMENT NECESSARY*

1. Several types of strain gages (including some of the self-temperature-compensating type). Three gages of each type are used: two mounted side by side on a plate so that they can be connected in a temperature-compensating circuit, and one mounted on a separate plate.
2. A variable-temperature chamber.
3. Thermocouple and potentiometer for measuring temperature at the gage location.
4. Switching system and strain indicator.

PROCEDURE

1. For each gage type available:
   a. Connect two gages in a temperature-compensating bridge. Record apparent strain versus temperature.
   b. Connect two gages so that the bridge is not temperature-compensated. Use a three-wire lead system. Record apparent strain versus temperature.
2. Using a self-temperature-compensated gage, connect so that the bridge is not temperature-compensated, and use a two-wire lead system.

REPORT

1. If the strain indicator will not record from any of the gages used directly, show sample calculations for reducing readings to strain.
2. Prepare three curve sheets:
   a. Apparent strain versus temperature for gages in a compensating bridge.
   b. Apparent strain versus temperature for gages not in a compensating bridge (three-wire lead system).
   c. For the self-temperature-compensated gage, apparent strain versus temperature for uncompensated bridge with three- and two-wire lead systems.

---

* The equipment arrangement used in the author's laboratory is shown in Fig. 2-80.

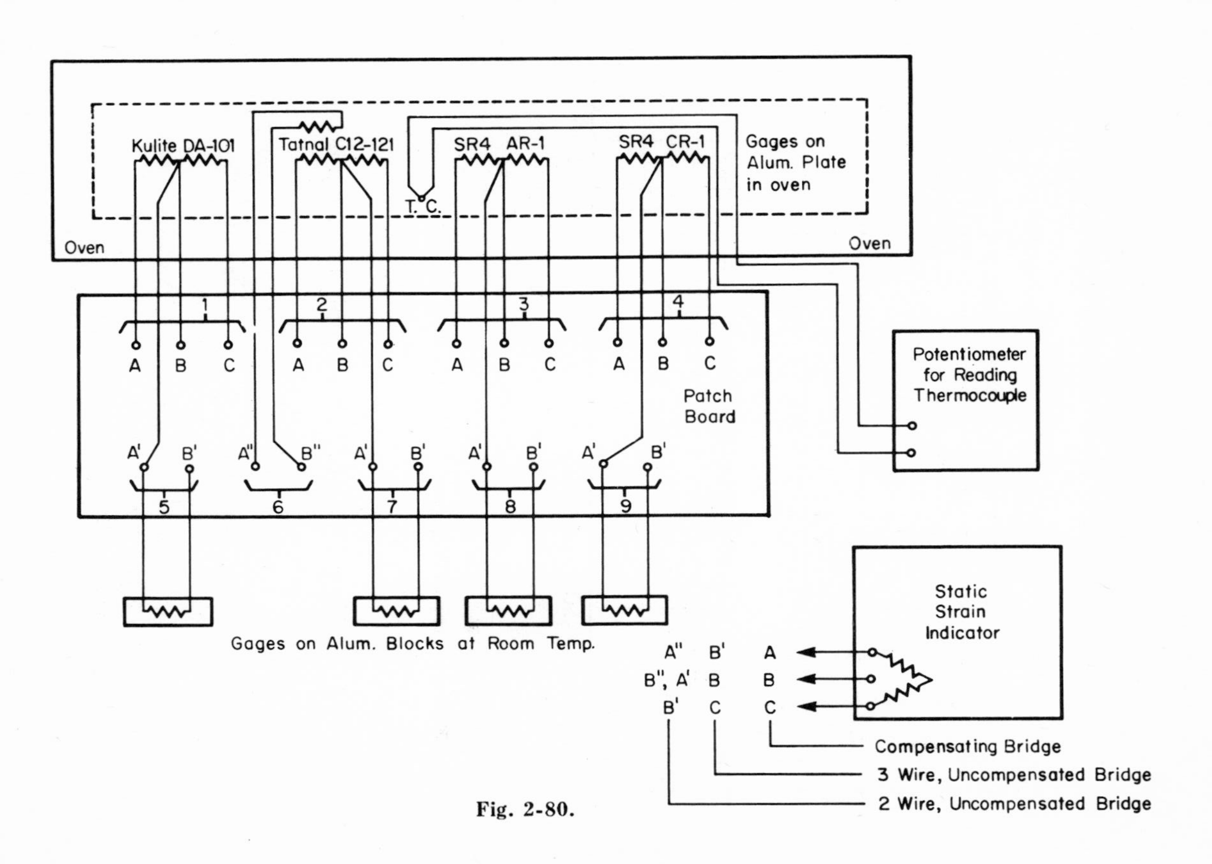
Kulite DA-101
Tatnal C12-121
SR4 AR-1
SR4 CR-1
Gages on Alum. Plate in oven
T. C.
Oven
Oven
1 2 3 4
A B C A B C A B C A B C
Patch Board
A' B' A'' B'' A' B' A' B' A' B'
5 6 7 8 9
Potentiometer for Reading Thermocouple
Static Strain Indicator
Gages on Alum. Blocks at Room Temp.
A'' B' A
B'', A' B B
B' C C
Compensating Bridge
3 Wire, Uncompensated Bridge
2 Wire, Uncompensated Bridge

Fig. 2-80.

3. For the self-temperature-compensated gage, compare your results with those published by the gage manufacturer.
4. Discuss the difference in the results obtained when two- and three-wire lead systems are used.

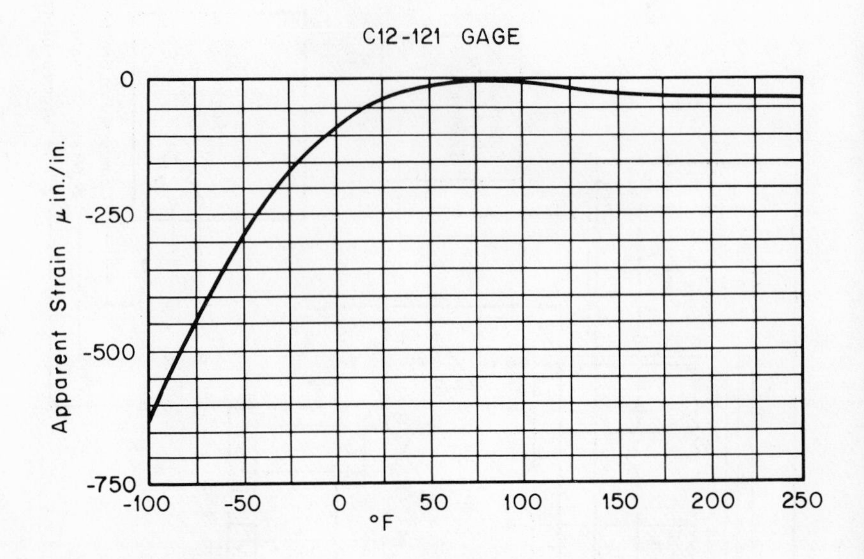

Fig. 2-81. Apparent strain versus temperature for a C12-121 strain gage.

Experiment 2-5 Measurement of transient strain signals

EQUIPMENT NECESSARY

1. Bonded-resistance strain gages mounted near the center of a long metal rod which will be impacted at one end.
2. Items 3, 4, 5, and 6 of Experiment 2-2 so that the gages may be connected in a half-bridge circuit.
3. A Polaroid-type oscilloscope camera.
4. Triggering circuit so that oscilloscope will sweep when rod is impacted.

PROCEDURE

1. Make up a potentiometer-type circuit.
2. Measure R_b, R_g, etc., as necessary.

3. Calibrate the circuit (be sure to note the direction of deflection associated with tensile and compressive strain).
4. Adjust the sweep speed so that the transient is visible both as it passes the gage going down the rod and as it returns after reflection at the opposite end. Photograph: (a) for free end; (b) for partially fixed end.

REPORT

1. Include traces of each photograph with appropriate *strain-time scales*.
2. What is the velocity of propogation of this disturbance in this rod?
3. What length (in inches) does this disturbance occupy at any instant?
4. What is the modulus of elasticity of the rod material?

CHAPTER 3

Indicating and Recording Equipment for Resistance Strain Gages

3-1 Introduction

There are numerous forms of systems used to read and record data from variable-resistance strain gages. Available systems range from small, portable, battery-powered instruments for reading a single gage ($300–1000) to systems with which the signals from up to 100 gages are broadcast simultaneously, received at a station miles from the test item, and recorded on magnetic tape ($100,000 or more). The record on the tape may then be displayed on a cathode ray oscilloscope for observation; it may be re-recorded on an oscillograph to produce a permanent visible record; it may be played into a computer for frequency and/or amplitude analysis; or any combination of these operations may be performed.

The number of specialized items of equipment available for use in reading or recording from strain-gage circuits is overwhelming, so much so that some kind of classification is necessary. We shall begin by classifying strain-gage systems according to the nature of the strain to be measured.

Section 3-2 deals with instruments used to read the output of a single strain-gage circuit in which the strain is static or slowly varying. Instruments for this use are generally available as a single item of equipment and are referred to as static-strain indicators.

In Sect. 3-2 we also discuss instruments used to record from several strain-gage circuits in which the strain is static or slowly varying. Instruments for this purpose are built up by assembling the circuits used in the single-channel indicators, together with suitable switching circuits and recording devices.

In Sect. 3-3 we deal with instruments used to record continuously from one or more strain-gage circuits in which the strain may be varying rapidly. Systems for the measurement of dynamic strain are generally built up by using appropriate circuits, power supplies, amplifiers, and recorders.

Whenever strains are to be measured at a point which cannot be wired to the location of the recording equipment, it is necessary to telemeter (broadcast) the signal from the gage location to the recording station. Equipment used to telemeter strain-gage signals is discussed in Sect. 3-4.

3-2 Indicators and multichannel recording equipment for static strains

3-2a Unbalanced bridge systems

The simplest type of static-strain indicator consists of a DC-powered bridge with a network for obtaining initial bridge balance, and an indicating device. Figure 3-1 shows such a system with a parallel balancing network.

As has already been pointed out, the open-circuit output (E_{bd}) of this circuit depends upon the bridge voltage (E) as well as upon gage factor, gage resistance, and strain. The indicated reading per unit of strain depends upon the open-circuit output (E_{bd}) and the indicator characteristics. As a disadvantage, the dependence of the final indication upon bridge voltage demands that the power supply be stable and easy to check. High-frequency oscillation of supply voltage will cause flutter of the indicator; long-term drift of supply voltage will cause progressive change of the system sensitivity. Either dry-cell batteries or commercially

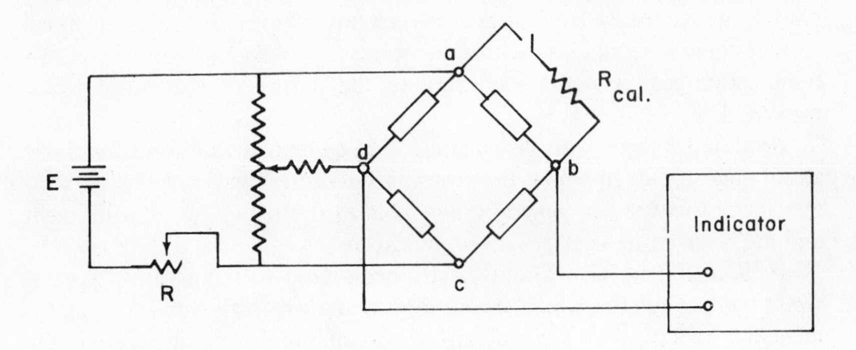

Fig. 3-1. A simple static-strain indicator circuit.

available stabilized DC supplies (which operate on 60 cycle AC) are suitable, provided the bridge voltage can be checked and set.

As an advantage, the dependence of the final indication upon bridge voltage permits the final reading to be calibrated in terms of strain. In a typical indicator of this type, a calibration resistor (R_{cal}) is paralleled across an active gage after the bridge is balanced; the bridge voltage (E_{ac}) is then adjusted by means of the variable resistor (R) to produce the indicator reading desired to correspond to the simulated strain. This calibration can be checked and adjusted at any time by reconnecting R_{cal}.

As has already been pointed out, the signal available to drive the indicator is ordinarily small, but galvanometers are available with sensitivities that will permit them to be deflected full scale by unamplified strain-gage signals. In the past, galvanometers of this sensitivity were very delicate instruments, requiring long periods to stabilize after being deflected by either electrical signal or mechanical shock. However, galvanometers are now available which have adequate sensitivity, are extremely rugged, and recover rapidly from electrical or mechanical shock.

Another approach to the problem of small signal is to insert an amplifier between the strain-gage bridge and the indicator. This has two advantages: (1) it permits less sensitive, more rugged, and cheaper (or expensive but more sophisticated, such as a digital voltmeter) indicators to be used; (2) it gives additional control over system sensitivity through the use of signal attenuators ahead of the amplifier. The disadvantages associated with the use of an amplifier are that it must be very stable (constant gain), since the gain affects the system sensitivity, and stable DC amplifiers are expensive.

Figure 3-2 is a photograph of an available strain indicator using the system just discussed, i.e., DC bridge supply, variable bridge voltage, variable attenuation, DC amplifier, and deflection-type indicator.

Fig. 3-2. Ellis BAM-1 bridge amplifier meter. (*Courtesy of Ellis Associates.*)

As we have already pointed out, an AC amplifier can be used in place of the DC amplifier if the bridge is AC-powered. In general, the advantages gained by using an AC amplifier (lower cost, ruggedness) are more than offset by disadvantages inherent in an AC bridge system (necessity of capacitor and inductive balance of the bridge, and additional equipment). The bridge may be powered with DC and the output amplified with an AC amplifier if the output is first chopped. See Fig. 3-3.

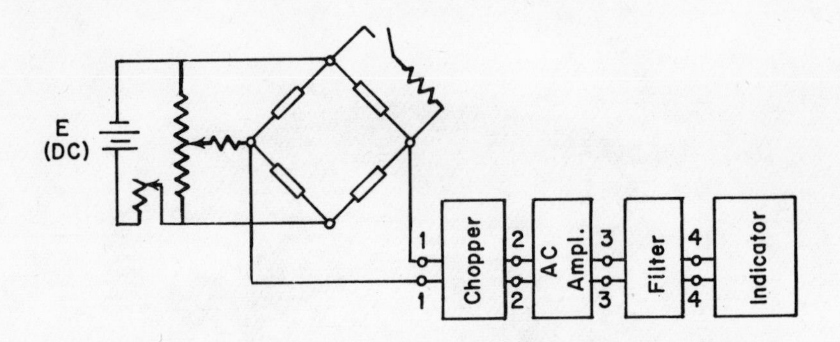

Fig. 3-3. Chopped output circuit.

The chopper is nothing more than a switch (electronic or mechanical) which alternates between the bridge output and a short circuit. The chopper output is a square wave even when the bridge output is a constant; therefore, the signal can be amplified with an AC amplifier. Figure 3-4 indicates the way in which this system operates by showing the signal

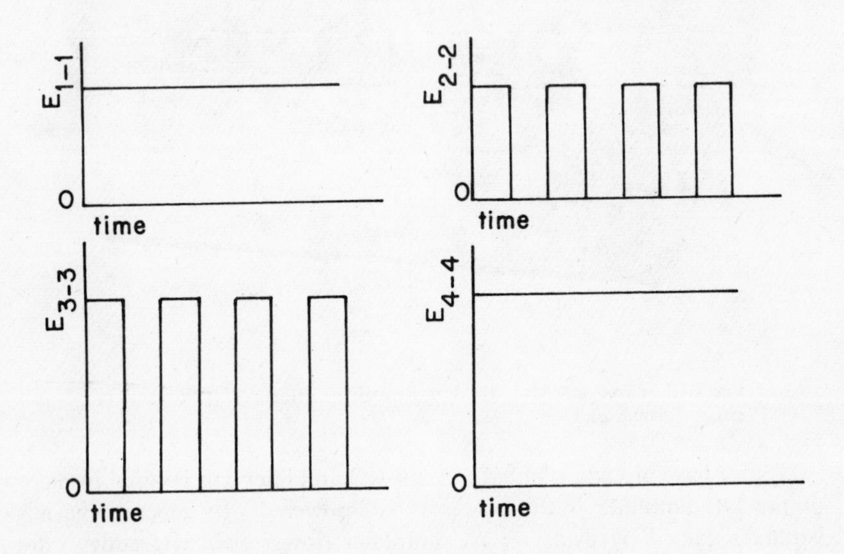

Fig. 3-4. Signals at various points in chopped output system. (Refer to Fig. 3-3.)

form at various points in the system (Fig. 3-3). Here again, the disadvantages tend to outweigh any advantage gained by eliminating the DC amplifier. Figure 3-5 is a photograph of an available strain indicator using a chopper and an AC amplifier.

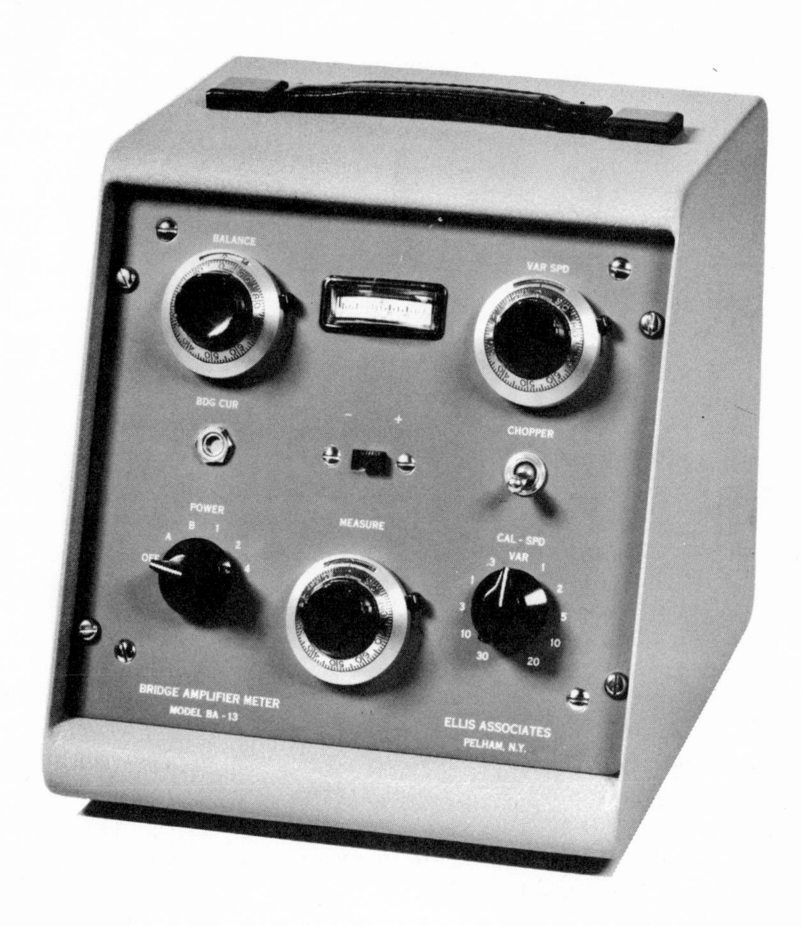

Fig. 3-5. Ellis BA-13 bridge amplifier meter. (*Courtesy of Ellis Associates.*)

We conclude that several forms of unbalanced bridge-type indicators are available. The chief limitation of this type of strain indicator is the limited reading resolution, which is fixed by the full-scale range of the indicator.

3-2b Balanced bridge systems

Another simple type of static-strain indicator consists of a DC-powered bridge, a network for obtaining initial bridge balance, a network for rebalancing the bridge after strain has occurred, and an indicator to establish when the bridge is in balance. Figure 3-6 shows such a system with a parallel-balancing network for initial bridge balance and a series-balancing network for rebalancing the bridge.*

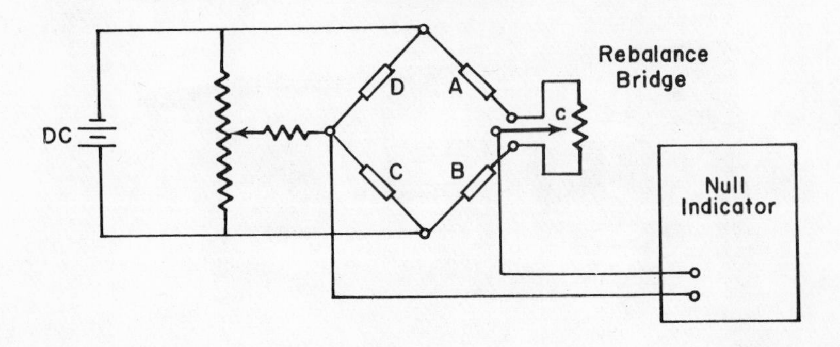

Fig. 3-6. Balanced bridge system.

In this case the strain is related to the amount of motion of c necessary to rebalance the bridge, and this relationship between strain and motion of c is independent of both bridge voltage and indicator impedance (load) and sensitivity.† This is the principal advantage of the balanced bridge system. Because of this independence of supply voltage and indicator characteristics the balanced-bridge-type indicator is especially well suited for measuring strains over long periods of time.

Other advantages of the balanced bridge system are (1) the bridge is always balanced—even when used to measure very large strains. (2) Hence, there is no possibility of errors due to nonlinearity of output. (3) A very high reading resolution is possible, since very finely divided balance circuits are possible.

The principal disadvantage of the balanced bridge system arises from the fact that the relationship between strain and motion of c is dependent

* Either parallel or series networks could be used for both functions, or, indeed, one network can perform both functions.

† Provided, of course, that there is sufficient sensitivity to establish the null or balance point with the required accuracy. A sensitive galvanometer may be used as an indicator, or an amplifier may be inserted between bridge and indicator.

upon gage factor and gage resistance and that there is no really good method for controlling this relationship because of its independence of supply voltage. Hence, this system must be calibrated (as by the use of parallel calibrate resistors) each time gage factor and/or gage resistance is changed.

Static-strain indicators utilizing the single balanced bridge just discussed are not commonly available from commercial sources. A model formerly available (Baldwin-Lima-Hamilton Corporation, SR-4 Control Box) utilized two strain gages mounted on opposite sides of a cantilever beam; the gages were connected in adjacent bridge arms, and the beam was bent to rebalance the bridge after it was unbalanced by strain in the other arms.

3-2c Reference bridge systems

The commonest type of static-strain indicator utilizes two Wheatstone-bridge circuits. Consider the system shown in Fig. 3-7. The gage bridge

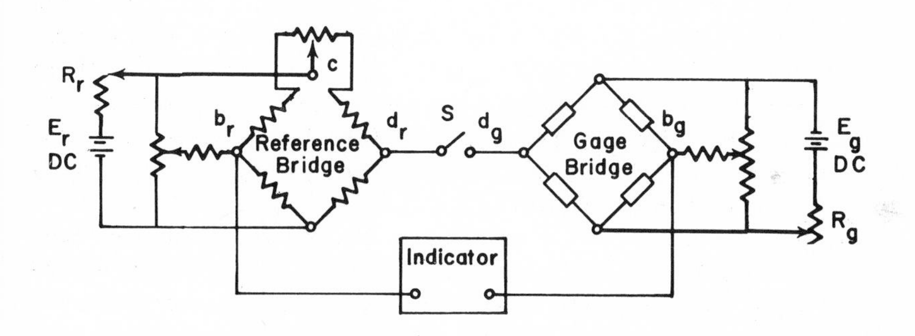

Fig. 3-7. Static-strain indicator utilizing two Wheatstone-bridge circuits.

is made up in the usual way and may be initially balanced, by using the parallel-balance network shown. While the gage bridge is being initially balanced, the switch S is open and the indicator is connected across the gage bridge diagonal ($b_g d_g$). The reference bridge is made up of fixed resistors, which need not be equal in magnitude to the gage resistors. The reference bridge is initially balanced by means of the parallel-balance network shown; while the reference bridge is being balanced, the switch S is open, and the indicator is connected across the reference bridge diagonal ($b_r d_r$).

For use, the switch S is closed, and the indicator is connected from $b_g b_r$, where it will measure the difference between any unbalance of the gage bridge and the reference bridge. When the gage bridge is unbalanced by straining, the indicator is deflected until the reference bridge is also unbalanced to the point at which $E_{b_r} = E_{b_g}$. The reference bridge may be unbalanced by means of the series network shown (the parallel network could also be used), and the motion of c, which is necessary to null (zero) the indicator, can be related to strain.

Notice that, although the indicator is nulled ($E_{b_r} = E_{b_g}$), *both bridges are unbalanced.*

This system has the following characteristics which lead to a number of advantages and disadvantages:

1. Because the strain is read when $E_{b_r} = E_{b_g}$, the system is independent of the indicator impedance (load) and sensitivity (again, we assume sufficient sensitivity to establish the null point with sufficient accuracy).
2. Because the individual bridges are unbalanced, the amount of motion of c necessary to make $E_{b_r} = E_{b_g}$ after the gage bridge has been unbalanced by straining can be controlled by varying the supply voltage to either bridge. Hence, either R_r or R_g may be used to set the system so that c can be calibrated and read directly in units of strain regardless of the gage factor of the gages used in the gage bridge. R_r is ordinarily used for this purpose (gage-factor control), since it can be calibrated in terms of gage factor, independent of gage resistance.
3. Since it has just been pointed out that the relationship between strain and motion of c can be controlled by controlling the bridge-supply voltages, it is obvious that the supply voltages must be stable or must vary in both bridges by the same amount (i.e., by the same percentage).

It is seen that this reference bridge system tends to combine the advantages and disadvantages of the balanced and unbalanced single-bridge systems. Calibration of motion of c in terms of strain and good resolution of reading is possible; however, zero shift and change in calibration can occur, due to variation in the supply voltages. Figure 3-8 is a photograph of a commercially available strain indicator which uses the system just discussed; i.e., Fig. 3-7.

As would be expected from our discussion of the single-bridge systems, it is possible to power the reference bridge system with an AC (or carrier) voltage. This is ordinarily accomplished by powering the two bridges (reference and gage) from independent but identical secondary transformer

Fig. 3-8. Hathaway RS-10 precision strain indicator.

coils which are supplied by the same primary coil. The reasons for, and the disadvantages associated with, using an AC supply are the same as previously discussed in connection with the single unbalanced bridge. Figure 3-9 is a photograph of a commercially available strain indicator which utilized an AC-powered reference bridge system.

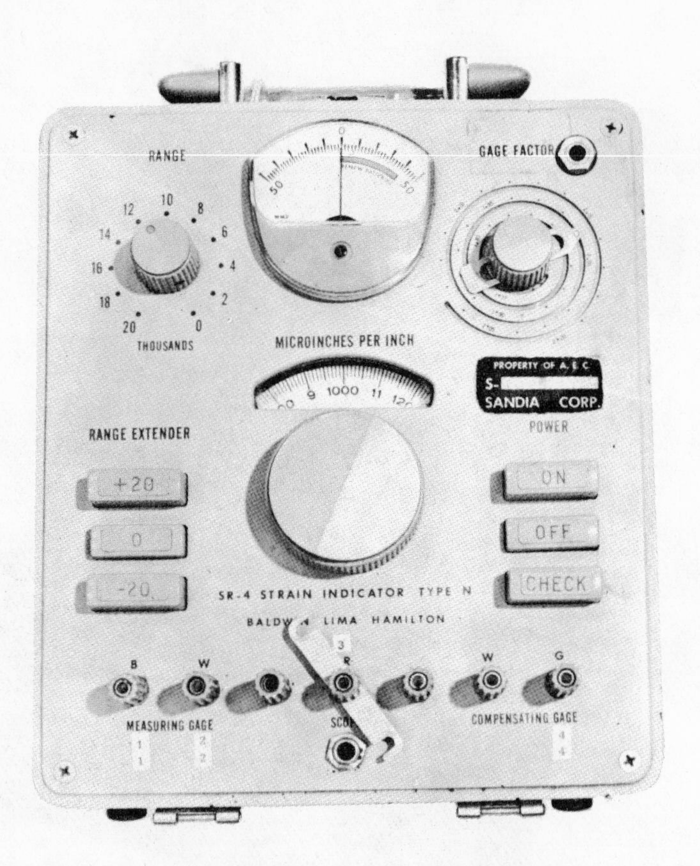

Fig. 3-9. **BLH type N strain indicator.**

It is possible to combine the reference bridge system with an indicating device to give direct visual indication of strain. Figure 3-10 shows an indicator of this type; the balancing dial (in reality, the unbalancing dial, since it unbalances the reference bridge by the same amount the gage bridge is unbalanced) is connected to and drives the digital readout. Some indicators (Model TC-22 Digital Strain Indicator, Instruments Division, Budd Company) of this type are self-balancing; i.e., when the gage bridge is unbalanced, a servo system drives the reference bridge control (*c* in Fig. 3-7) to unbalance the reference bridge by the same amount, and this amount in turn is indicated on the digital readout.

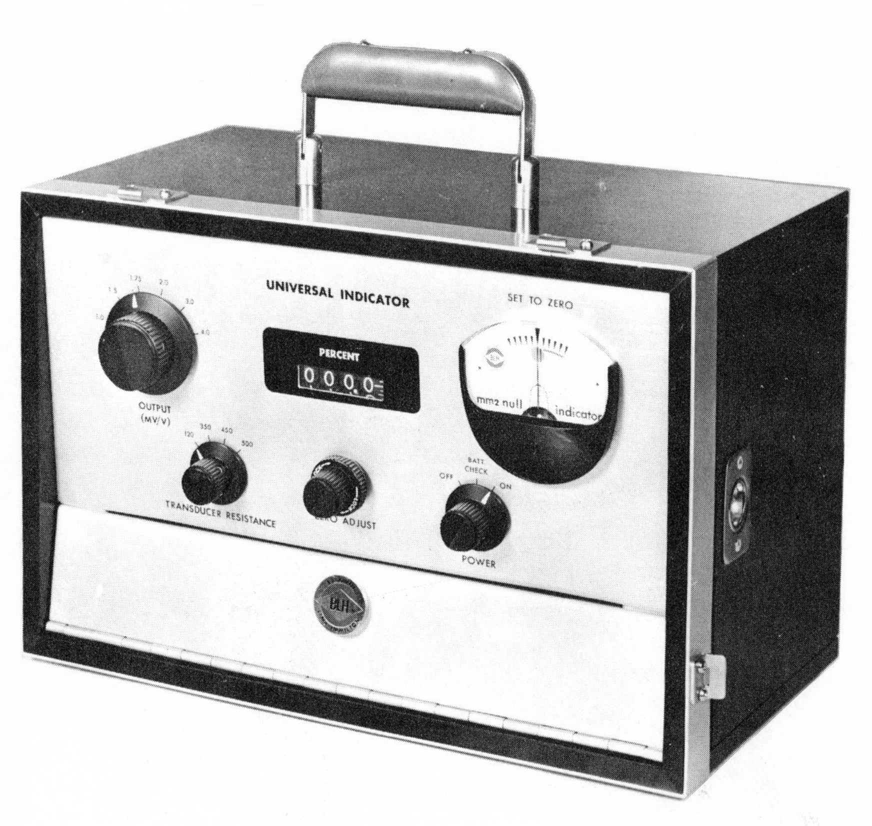

Fig. 3-10. BLH type 25-digital readout. (*Courtesy of Baldwin-Lima-Hamilton Corporation.*)

3-2d Constant-current strain indicators

All of the strain indicators described to this point are based on *constant-voltage* bridge circuits. As was pointed out in Sect. 2-2a, the potential output from a bridge circuit supplied with constant voltage is a nonlinear function of change in resistance in a single bridge arm, and this nonlinearity becomes significant with the magnitude of resistance change encountered in semiconductor strain gages. This nonlinearity of output directly affects the unbalanced bridge system and carries over into the balanced bridge and reference bridge systems, since the rebalancing network is ordinarily arranged to represent strain as a linear function of potential output. To overcome this difficulty and to incorporate gage factor controls that will permit direct reading in μin./in. of strains with gage factors as large as 100 or more, several *constant-current* indicators have been designed specifically for use with semiconductor gages. The basic circuit for constant-current indicators is the one shown in Fig. 2-28. If a deflection-type system is desired, a galvanometer is connected across the points marked "E_{out}" and the scale marked in units of strain. Since $E_{out} = I_1 \, \Delta R_1$ and ΔR_1 is the gage sensitivity (S) times strain (ϵ), $E_{out} = I_1 S \epsilon$. Therefore, I_1 can be adjusted to produce the same deflection (E_{out}) for a given strain (ϵ) regardless of the gage sensitivity (S); i.e., the gage current supply can be used for sensitivity control.

The indicator shown in Fig. 3-11 is of this basic type. The circuit used in this instrument is described in detail in Ref. [1].

Fig. 3-11. Semiconductor gage indicator. (*Courtesy of B & F Instruments, Inc.*)

A balanced constant-current system can be had by rebalancing (reducing E_{out} to zero) after strain has occurred; the strain is read from a calibrated control used to accomplish rebalance. The constant-current supply I_2 (see Fig. 2-28) may be calibrated and used for this purpose, the resistor R_2 may be calibrated and varied for this purpose, or an additional variable resistor may be added and calibrated for this purpose. This last method, which is shown in Fig. 3-12, has the advantage that R_2 can be a second strain gage used for temperature compensation. P. Pohl, Ref. [7] in Chap. 2, describes a constant-current, direct-reading strain indicator in detail.

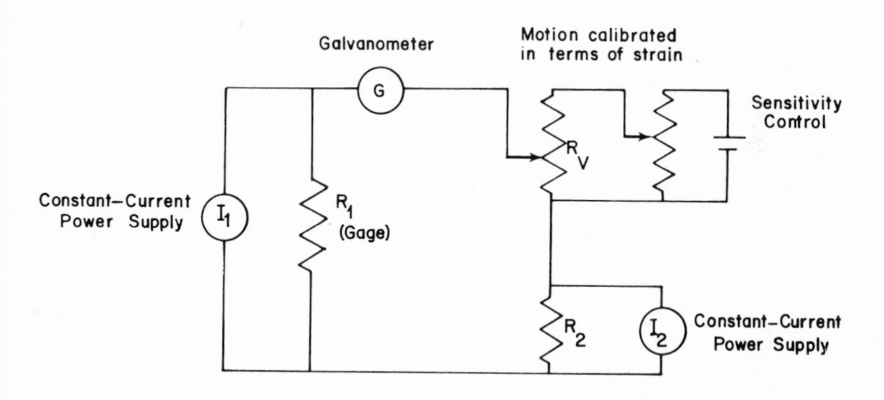

Fig. 3-12. Simplified constant-current, direct-reading strain indicator.

3-2e Multichannel recording systems

Any of the systems just discussed can be combined with suitable switching equipment to allow several gage points to be read and/or recorded. Although high switching and reading rates are possible and available, these systems are for use when static or slowly varying strains are read. Some systems record an individual point each second, but in a 100 channel system this means that each gage is read only once every 100 seconds.

One of the simplest systems for recording from several gages consists of several unbalanced bridges which can be switched in turn to a suitable recording device. Figure 3-13 shows such a system, in which a high-sensitivity recording oscillograph is used as a recorder. All of the remarks previously made about the unbalanced bridge (p. 80) and about switching circuits (p. 122) apply.

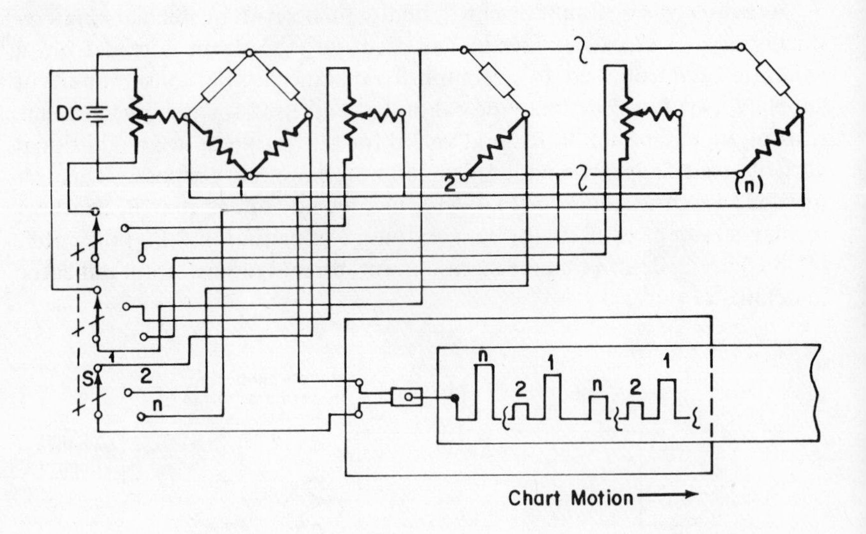

Fig. 3-13. Multichannel oscillograph recording system.

A balanced bridge or a reference bridge can also be used as the basis for a multichannel recording system. Figure 3-14 will serve as an example of this type of system, for which the following sequence of operational steps is typical:

After all bridges are connected, switch S goes to position 1, and bridge 1 is balanced by using the parallel-balance network $R_{bal(1)}$. (In some systems initial balancing is done automatically by a servo system.)

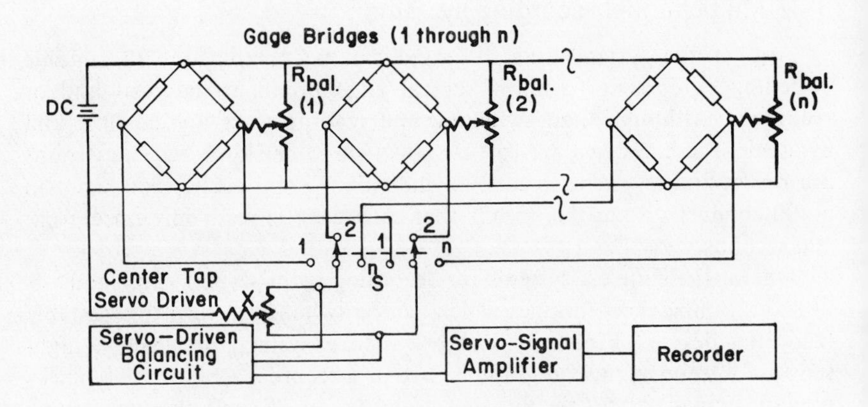

Fig. 3-14. Multichannel balanced-bridge recording system.

Switch S goes to positions 2, 3, etc., so that each bridge is balanced. The switch is returned to OFF, and the system is ready to record. To record, the switch goes to position 1, and the signal from the unbalanced bridge drives a servo system, which in turn rebalances the bridge (by motion of point X); and the amount of motion of X necessary to rebalance the bridge is sensed and recorded as a measure of strain.

In this case, gage-factor control is possible, since the gain of the servo-signal amplifier can be set to relate recorded signal to strain.

After each bridge is rebalanced and the strain is recorded, the switch goes on to the next bridge.

Output signal from a system of this type may be displayed on any number of different devices. Figure 3-15 shows a 100-channel system

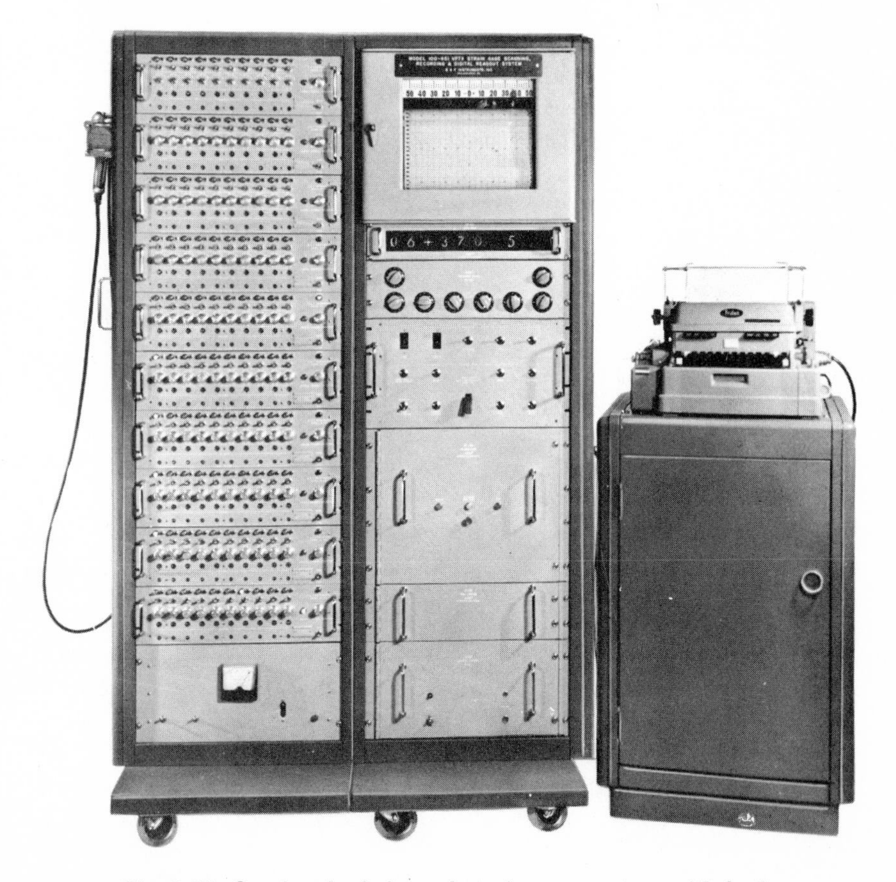

Fig. 3-15. One hundred-channel strain-gage system with both analog recording and digital readout. (*Courtesy of B & F Instruments, Inc.*)

which will permit strain readout on an electric typewriter, a paper-tape punch, a digital-lamp bank, or a chart recorder.

3-3 Equipment for recording dynamic strain

When the strain to be measured is varying rapidly, it becomes necessary to record the signal from the strain gage continuously. The system to be used will depend primarily upon the frequency of variation of the strain. Design of a dynamic strain-measuring system should be guided by the following basic principle: each part of the system must be chosen so that the system as a whole will faithfully measure the strain no matter how it varies with time.

Let us begin by investigating the frequency response of each item from the gage circuit to the signal recorder. (The bonded strain gage itself has a limited frequency response. This is discussed in Sect. 4-2k.)

The DC-powered bridge is preferred for dynamic work, because the frequency response of an AC-powered bridge is limited to a maximum of 20 per cent of the carrier frequency. This is obvious when it is remembered that in a carrier system the strain signal amplitude modulates

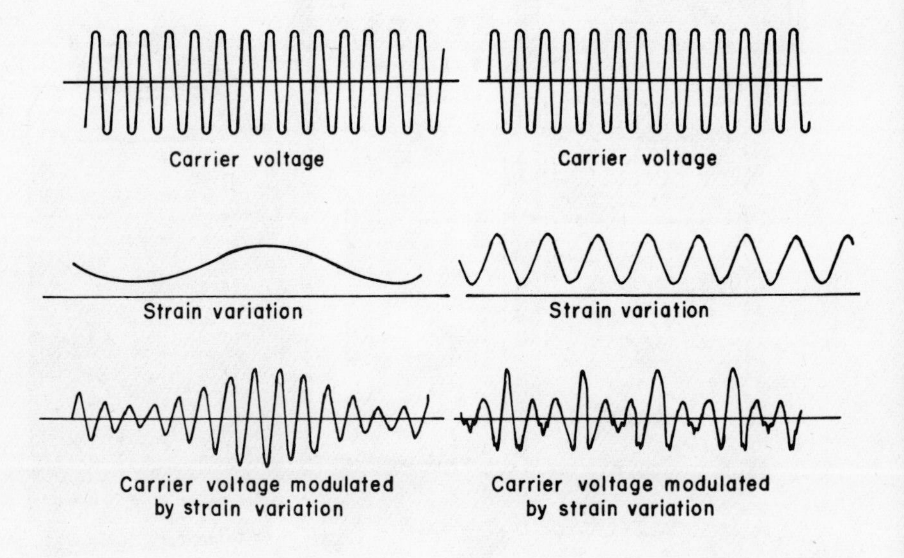

(a) Frequency of strain signal much less than frequency of carrier voltage. (b) Frequency of strain signal approaching frequency of carrier voltage.

Fig. 3-16. Modulated carrier signals.

the carrier wave—as the signal frequency approaches the carrier frequency, the shape of the strain signal becomes progressively less well defined (see Fig. 3-16).

Carrier frequencies as high as 10,000 cps are common and 50,000 cps have been used (Ref. [2]), but this frequency limitation inherent in AC-powered bridges cannot be continuously raised by raising carrier frequency, because of other electronic problems associated with the use of higher-frequency carriers.

Since the signal from strain-gage circuits is small, some amplification will be necessary in most cases. The exact type of amplifier will depend upon the type of recorder which it is to drive, but in general it should be capable of receiving signals in the millivolt range and of supplying a signal in the volt range. Two types of amplifiers are available: AC-coupled and DC-coupled. The gain characteristics of these two types are shown in Fig. 3-17. Even for the measurement of dynamic strain, the

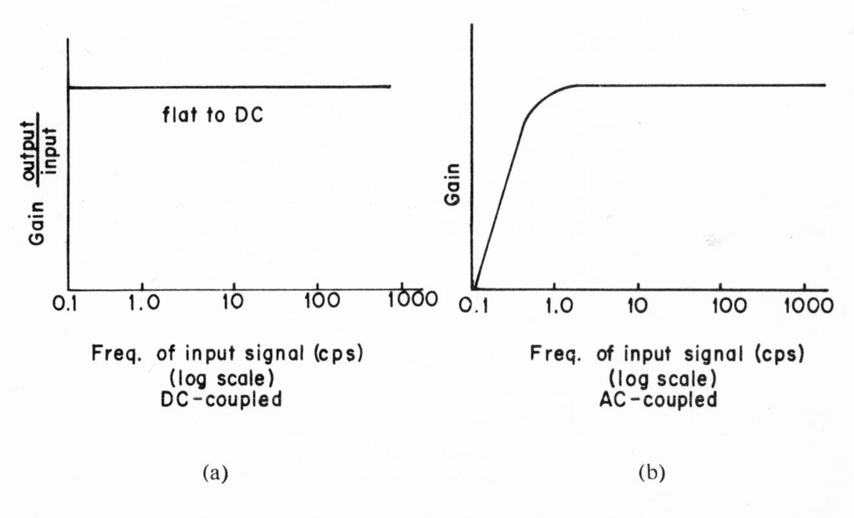

(a) (b)

Fig. 3-17. Gain characteristics of amplifiers.

DC-coupled amplifier is preferred, since it is generally not known what low-frequency components may exist in the signal to be measured. In addition, the usual calibration method (parallel resistor) simulates a static-strain signal.

The ability of this amplifier to function with high-frequency inputs is generally expressed by gain-versus-signal-frequency curves (see Fig. 3-18).

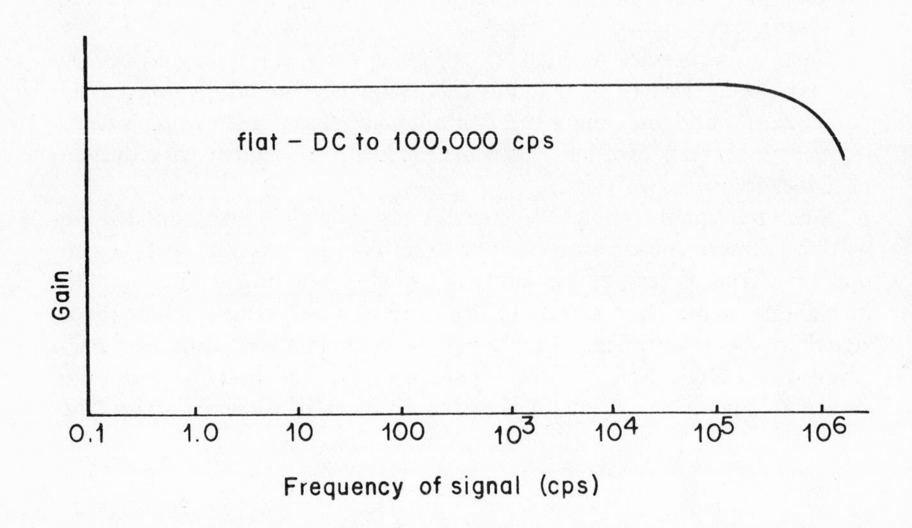

Fig. 3-18. Gain-versus-signal-frequency curve.

The amplifier is characterized by saying, "The gain is flat ±1.0 per cent to 100 K cps," or "The gain is down by not more than 3.0 db* at 300 K cps."

It is extremely important to realize that if the strain signal contains frequency components beyond the flat range of the amplifier, the signal will be distorted and no correction of the result is possible. Amplifiers for strain-gage work are discussed in some detail in Ref. [3].

The frequency response of a recorder is limited by two distinct considerations: first, the recorder must display the signal on a time base that permits resolution of the signal; second, the vibration characteristics of the recording mechanism must be such that all frequency components are reproduced without relative distortion.

An example will illustrate these two points: visualize a galvanometer-type pen motor recording on a strip chart, with a maximum chart speed of one inch per second (see Fig. 3-19). With an input signal of one cps, the record peaks will be separated by one inch. With an input signal of 1000 cps, the record will become a solid block, and no definition of the wave shape will be possible.

---

* Db for decibel; defined as 1 db = 20 $\log_{10} Q/Q_o$ in which Q/Q_o is the ratio of actual output to a reference output value.

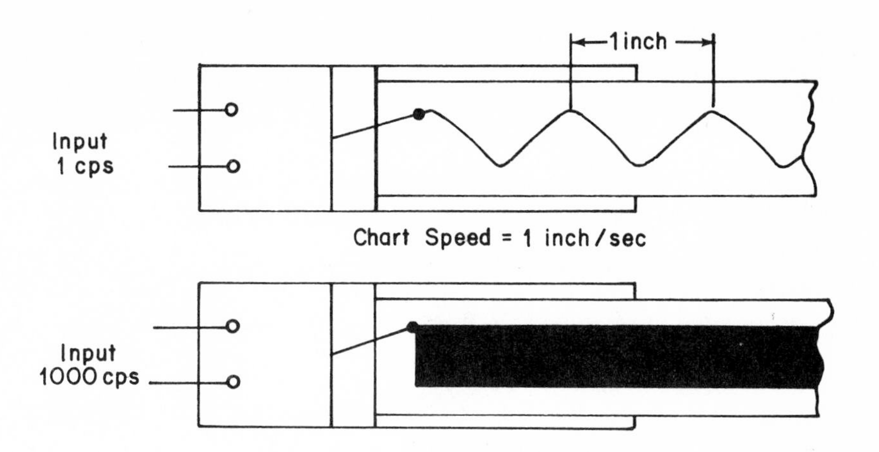

Fig. 3-19. Strip-chart recording.

Further imagine that the natural frequency of the pen in its mount is 100 cps. As the input signal approaches 100 cps, the pen motion will be characteristic of a vibrating system driven at resonance—the amount of mechanical amplification will be limited only by the damping present (see Fig. 3-20).

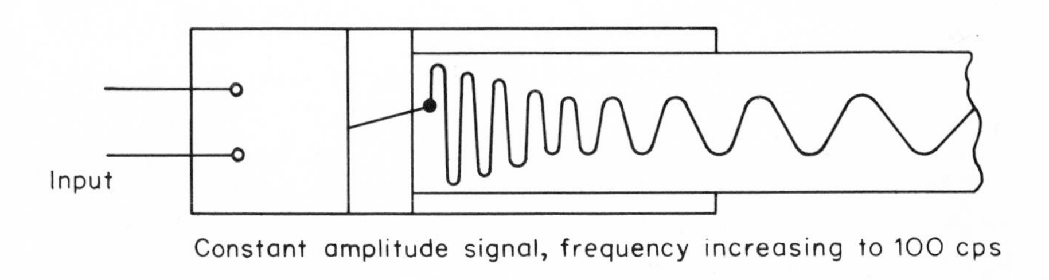

Fig. 3-20. Strip-chart recording signal of increasing frequency.

If a transient signal with a rapid rise is applied to the pen recorder, the pen will overshoot the maximum signal due to the mechanical inertia of the pen, thus giving a false peak strain. In considering the frequency limitations of recorders, a pen-and-strip-chart type has been used as an example, but the response of all recorders is limited by comparable considerations.

3-3a Recorders utilizing galvanometers

A galvanometer consists of a single metallic ribbon stretched between the poles of a permanent magnet (Bifilar type) or of a coil suspended between the poles of a permanent magnet (d'Arsonval or coil type). See Fig. 3-21.

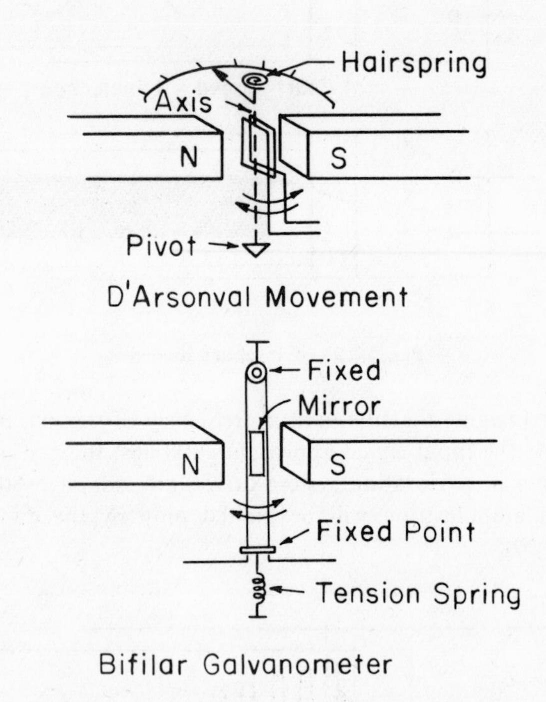

Fig. 3-21. Basic galvanometer movements.

When current flows through the single ribbon or through the coil, the ribbon or coil tends to twist, due to the interaction between the electrical and magnetic fields. The amount of element motion depends upon the magnitude of the current flow, the stiffness of the suspension, and the strength of the magnetic field. Since the latter two items are constant for a given galvanometer, the motion of the element can be related to current, and hence to strain, through the equations previously developed. Since galvanometers are low-impedance (low R_L) instruments, it is imperative, if they are connected directly to the output of a strain-gage circuit, that the load impedance be taken into account. If an amplifier is inserted between the strain-gage circuit and the galvanometer, the strain-gage-circuit load depends upon the input impedance of the amplifier.

In this case the amplifier must be capable of driving the low-impedance galvanometer.

To use the galvanometer as the basis of a recording device, the element motion must be recorded. In some cases this element carries a pen or a pointer which traces the record on a moving chart. Because of the large

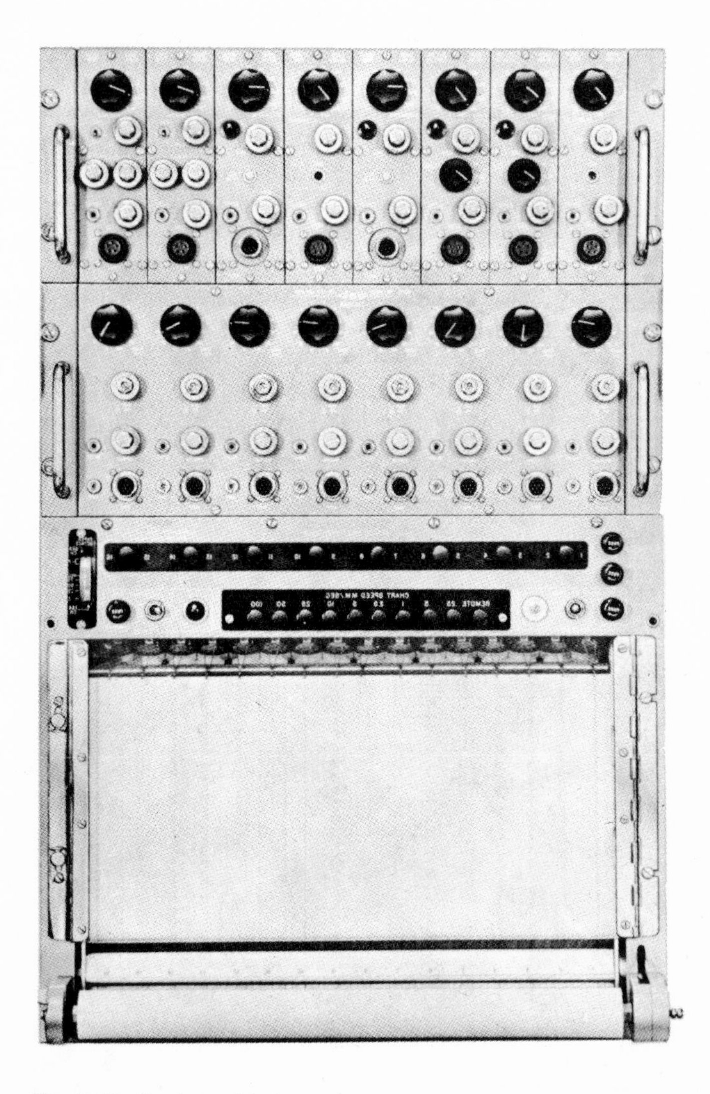

Fig. 3-22. Sanborn 16-channel pen recorder. (*Courtesy of Sanborn Co.*)

mechanical inertia of the pen, galvanometer recorders of this type are limited to recording strain signals with frequencies of less than 100 cps. The sensitivity of pen-type galvanometers is inherently low; hence, amplification of strain signals is almost always required. Figure 3-22 is a photograph of a complete 16-channel system containing 16 amplifiers and 16 pen-type galvanometers.

The record may be either ink or a dry line produced by a hot stylus on a special sensitized paper. The strain-gage circuit may be supplied with DC power, in which case DC amplifiers are used; or the system shown may provide AC (carrier) power to the gage circuit, in which case carrier amplifiers are used. Since the upper limit of frequency response of this type of recorder is inherently limited by the inertia of the galvanometer, it is very common to use it in conjunction with strain-gage circuits supplied with a rather low-frequency (1000-2000 cps) carrier.

The galvanometer element may be used for higher-frequency recording by mounting a mirror on the moving element and detecting and amplifying its motion, by using optical levers. Figure 3-23 is a diagrammatic sketch of such a system. Galvanometers of this type are available with sensitivity as high as 0.6 in. of trace deflection per microamp of signal with an 11.5 in. optical arm. Galvanometers of this type are also available with high natural frequency and sufficient damping so that they can be used to record signals with frequency components as high as 5000 cps.

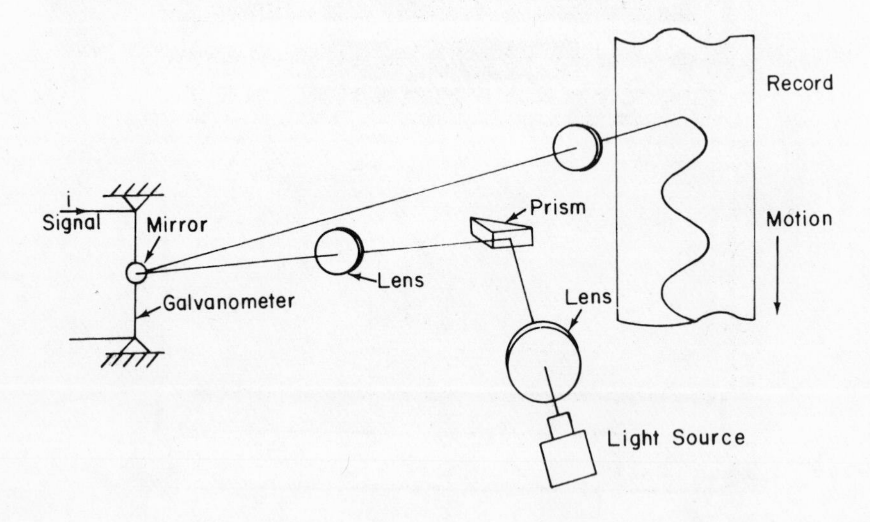

Fig. 3-23. Galvanometer recording system.

However, with all galvanometers, usable frequency response is inversely proportional to sensitivity. Since the natural frequency is increased by using a stiffer coil suspension, more driving current is required per unit of coil motion. As a result, those galvanometers that can be used to record from unamplified strain-gage circuits are limited to record frequencies of less than about ten cps. Those galvanometers which can adequately record higher frequencies require suitable signal amplification. If the strain-gage circuit is DC-powered, DC amplifiers must be used. If the strain-gage circuit is AC (carrier)-powered, a carrier amplifier system can be used. Because the upper limit of frequency response of this type of recorder has been limited to around 2000 cps by maximum record speed and galvanometer usable frequency, it has been common practice to use it with strain-gage circuits which are supplied by carrier frequencies of about 10,000 cps.

The record produced by oscillographs using the moving-mirror-type galvanometer is a trace on a light-sensitive paper or film which has been exposed by the mirror-reflected light spot. The film or paper may be

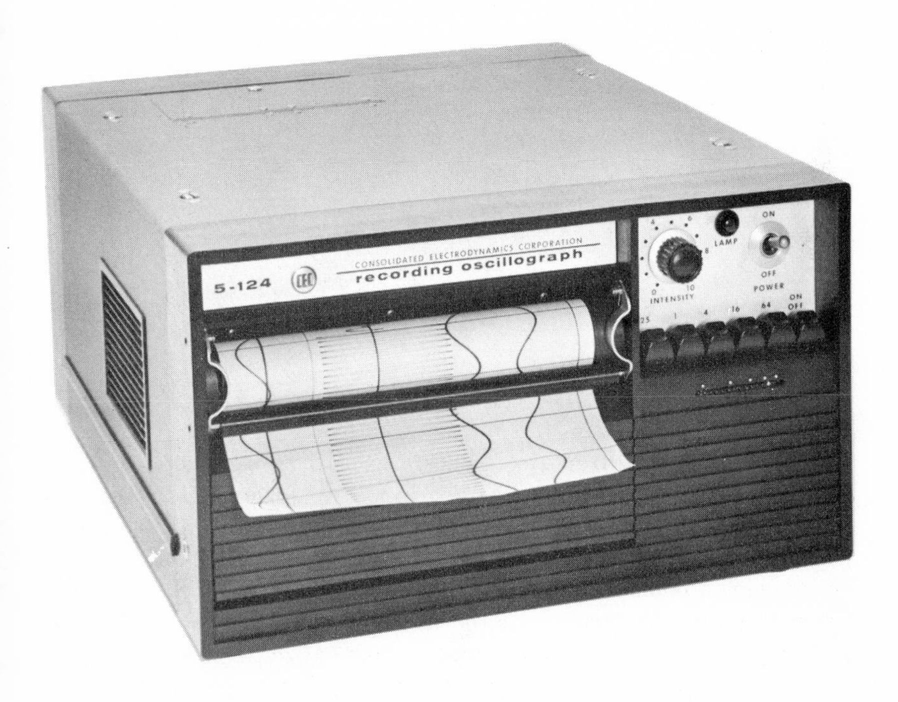

Fig. 3-24. CEC portable 18-channel oscillograph. (*Courtesy of CEC, Inc.*)

of the type that needs to be developed in darkness by the normal wet photographic process, or it may be of a sensitized type which is exposed only by the very intense light (mercury vapor light source is often used) used for the mirror-reflected spot and which is self-developing under normal daylight conditions. Figure 3-24 is a photograph of a portable 18-channel oscillograph which uses moving-mirror-type galvanometers. Galvanometers covering a wide range of sensitivities and frequency response are available and can be used interchangeably in this unit. The record is on sensitized paper which requires no developing.

3-3b Recorders utilizing cathode ray oscilloscopes

The principle of the cathode ray oscilloscope is shown in Fig. 3-25.

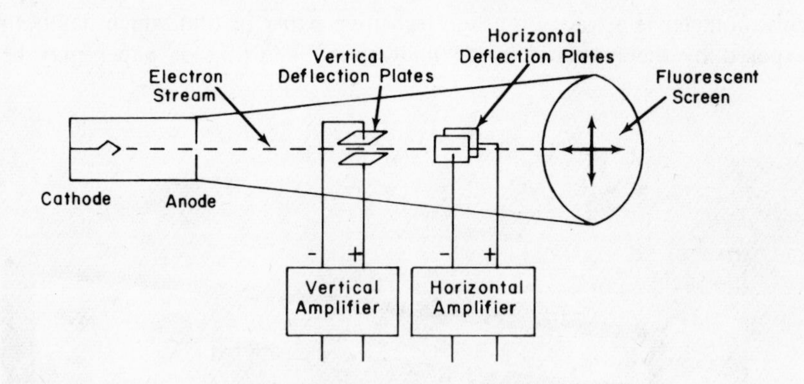

Fig. 3-25. Cathode ray oscilloscope.

Electrons are emitted from the heated cathode and are accelerated across the potential field between the cathode and the anode. These electrons, passing through the hole in the anode, stream in a straight line to the fluorescent tube unless they are deflected by an interposed electric field. By applying a potential across the vertical deflection plates, the light spot formed by electrons falling on the fluorescent screen can be deflected vertically. By applying a potential across the horizontal deflection plate, the light spot can be deflected horizontally.

As ordinarily used for recording strain-gage signals, the output from the strain-gage circuit is connected to the vertical amplifiers; therefore, vertical deflection is related to strain. The trace is driven horizontally by a sweep circuit which is contained in the oscilloscope. This sweep circuit allows the trace to be driven horizontally at a preselected rate; hence, the resultant display is a plot of strain versus time. (Sometimes it

Fig. 3-26. A cathode ray oscilloscope combined with a moving film camera.

is handy to display the output from one transducer vertically and the output from a second transducer horizontally. As an example, if a stress signal is displayed vertically and a strain signal is displayed horizontally, the result is the direct display of a stress-strain diagram.) Recording is accomplished by photographing the cathode ray screen.

The cathode ray oscilloscope has nearly zero inertia (even electrons have some mass); therefore, it is the basis for strain-recording systems when a frequency response from 2000 to 100,000 cps (in this case, the gage itself will put the upper limit on frequency response. See Sect. 4-2k) is required. Tape recorders also have capabilities above 2000 cps, the upper limit of frequency response of a tape recorder for instrumentation use is less than for a cathode ray oscilloscope system.

The potential that must be applied across the deflection plates per unit of trace deflection is large (10 to 50 v/in.), and amplification is ordinarily provided as part of the oscilloscope. For strain-gage work, the oscilloscope should have a sensitivity of at least one mv/cm of trace deflection. Although it is possible to use a less sensitive oscilloscope, together with preamplifiers, this is unhandy and makes the elimination of extraneous signal (noise) more difficult. The oscilloscope should have DC-coupled amplifiers so that the system can be calibrated by using parallel resistors and so that static and low-frequency strains can be recorded. The amplifiers should be flat to the frequency of the highest frequency in the signal to be recorded. The oscilloscope sweep circuit should cover a range that will permit display over a period as long as several seconds and as short as a few microseconds. Fortunately, oscilloscopes are available with all of these characteristics.

For recording over a considerable period of time, a cathode ray oscilloscope can be used with a moving film camera (Fig. 3-26). In this case, the strain signal drives the spot vertically, and the sweep circuit is turned off; the film moves horizontally past the screen, thus providing the time base.

Figure 3-27 is a photograph of a 16-channel cathode ray recorder. Each of the eight tubes contains two cathodes and two sets of deflection plates so that two independent signals can be displayed. A single strip of photographic paper, eight in. wide, is pulled across the tube screens at rates as high as 800 in./sec. Multichannel recording of transient strain signals can be made with drum cameras which provide film speeds as high as 6000 in./sec.

For recording transient strain signals it is more common to use open-shutter, fixed-film techniques. The sweep circuit is adjusted to sweep across the tube face in a time slightly longer than the expected time duration of the transient to be recorded. The scope is set to trigger (begin

Fig. 3-27. CEC 5-140 cathode ray recording oscillograph. (*Courtesy of CEC, Inc.*)

to sweep) just before the transient signal of interest occurs (this is easier to say than to do) and the camera shutter is opened. When the transient occurs, the film is exposed; the shutter is closed after the event. Figure 3-28 is a photograph of an oscilloscope fitted with a Polaroid Land-type camera (print in ten sec).

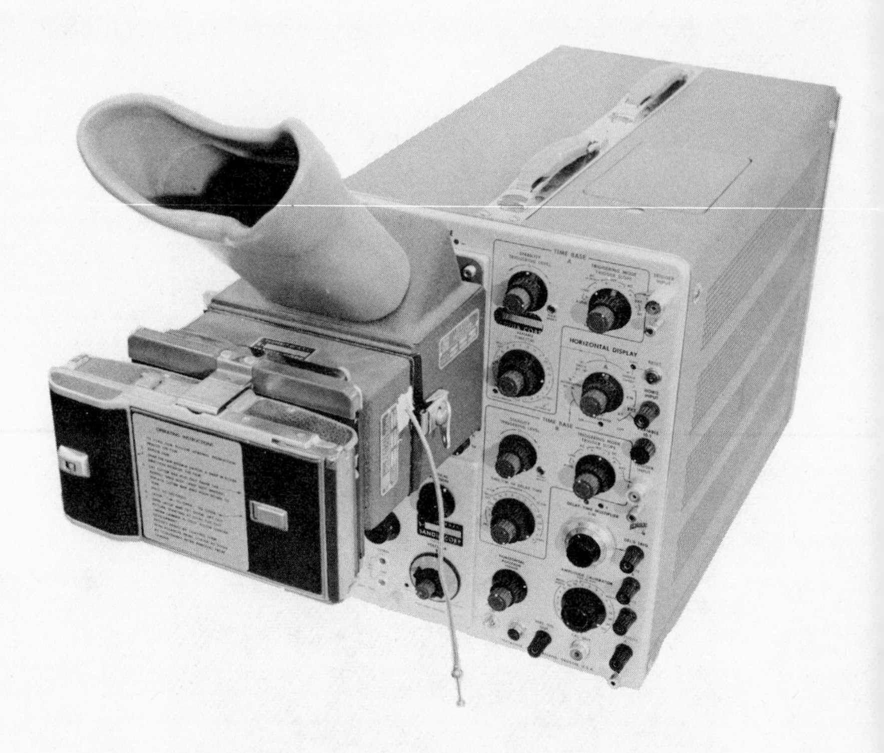

Fig. 3-28. Photograph of CRO with Polaroid still camera.

3-3c Magnetic tape recorders*

The magnetic recorder was invented in the late nineteenth century (patented in 1900, by V. Poulsen), and its use for recording audio signals is widespread and well known. However, the use of magnetic tape devices to record from instrumentation in general, and from strain gages in particular, dates from the early 1950's. Magnetic tape recording has some inherent advantages which would appear to insure that the use of this method will continue to grow rapidly. These advantages are as follows:

1. Magnetic tape recorders have a very wide range of frequency response. Presently they are used to record strain signals from DC up to 20,000 cps.

* For this material the authors have drawn on the article, "The Tape Recorder," by P. J. Weber, Ref. [4]. The material quoted directly from Ref. [4] is extensive and is indicated by using a smaller type-size and indenting both margins. Brackets are used to enclose added or changed material.

2. Magnetic tape recorders have a very wide dynamic range. Dynamic range is the ratio of maximum signal which can be recorded without distortion to the minimum signal which can be recorded and read at the same system gain. This is very important when the magnitude of strain which will be encountered is unknown. If the gain is set high (in anticipation of small signal) and the signal is unexpectedly large, most recorders will be overdriven and the record will be lost; or, if the gain is set low and the signal is unexpectedly small, the signal record will be indistinguishable from system noise. Tape records permit accurate and linear recording of signals which are less than one per cent of the preset full-scale signal.
3. Magnetic tape records are easy to store and the tape can be erased and reused.
4. Magnetic tape records preserve the signal information in electrical form. If visual observation of the signal were the only requirement in every case, this might be listed as a disadvantage; indeed, the signal on the tape must be re-recorded on some form of oscillograph for visual observation of the signal. But there are several other possibilities—a tape-recorded signal may be played into some form of computer for analysis, i.e., as a strain signal for frequency analysis.
5. The gain used to display various portions of the records can be varied after the test is completed. For example, if the strain signal is small in some portion of the record, this portion can be re-recorded on an oscillograph using a gain suitable to permit full-scale deflection.
6. The time base can be altered on playback. This is very useful, since it allows records of high-frequency strain to be displayed on an oscillograph with a lower frequency limitation. Consider taping a 600-cps signal with a tape speed of 60 in./sec. This will produce ten cycles per inch of tape. If this tape is rerun at six in./sec, the output signal will be 60 cps and can be recorded on an oscillograph with a 60-cps upper-frequency limit.

The principal disadvantage of the tape recorder appears to be its high cost—particularly when it is realized that the tape recorder is an intermediate link between the instrumentation and the final data presentation.

A magnetic tape recorder is made up of the items shown in Fig. 3-29. The exact functions of the record amplifier and the reproduce amplifier depend upon the type of recording process used, but in general they are more than amplifiers in the usual sense.

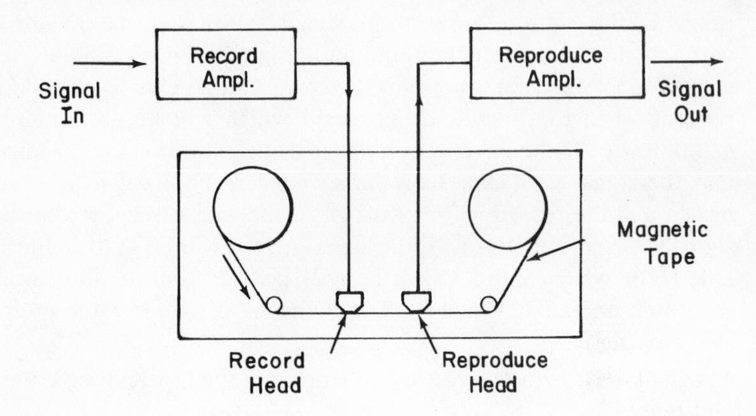

Fig. 3-29. Magnetic tape recorder.

Although there are four distinct recording processes in use, only one (frequency-modulation recording) is commonly used for instrumentation recording.* We shall begin by discussing the direct-recording process, since an understanding of this process is essential to an understanding of the others. We shall then discuss the frequency-modulation recording process and its use in strain-gage instrumentation. In the direct-recording process the input signal is amplified, mixed with a high-frequency bias,† and presented directly to the recording head as a varying electric current, i.

> The recording head consists of a magnetic core in the form of a closed ring having a short nonmagnetic gap in series with the magnetic path of the core. This is represented schematically in Fig. [3-30].
>
> The magnetic tape consists of a plastic base (such as acetate or Mylar‡) on the surface of which fine particles of magnetic material are dispersed uniformly. The magnetic surface of the tape contacts the magnetic head at the gap, in effect shunting the gap and completing the magnetic path in the head core. The signal current flows through a winding which links the magnetic core and produces magnetic flux, φ, whose magnitude is proportional to the recording current.
>
> $$\varphi = Ki.$$

* The four recording processes are (1) direct recording, (2) frequency-modulation recording, (3) pulse-duration-modulation recording, and (4) digital recording. For a discussion of all of these methods see Ref. [4].

† The function of the high-frequency bias is to eliminate distortion (see Ref. [4], p. 18), but an understanding of the refinement is not required at this point.

‡ Dupont trademark.

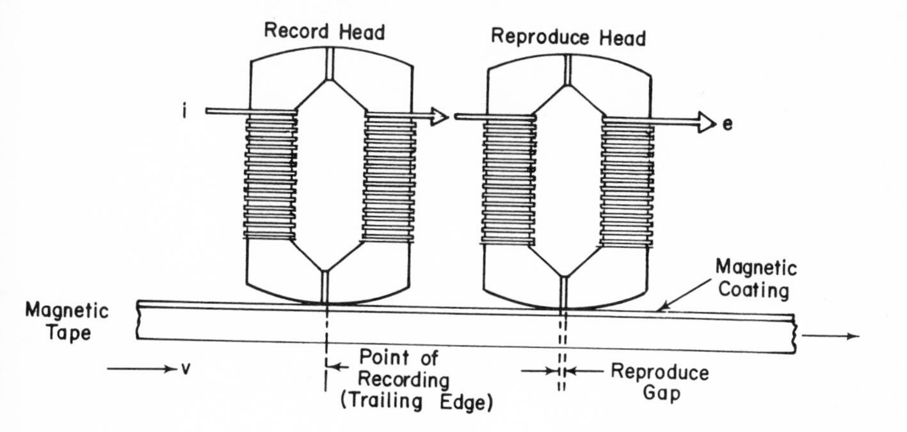

Fig. 3-30. The magnetic tape recording and reproducing system.

The tape is moving across the heads at a linear velocity of v. Any particle of the magnetic medium crossing the gap remains in a permanent state of magnetization which is proportional to the flux flowing through the head at the instant that particle passes out of the gap. Thus, the actual recording takes place at the trailing edge of the record gap.

If the signal to be recorded is sinusoidal, the intensity of magnetization on the tape will vary sinusoidally along the length of the tape. A wavelength of recorded signal along the tape will occur for each complete alternation of the input electrical signal. This wavelength will be directly proportional to the tape speed and inversely proportional to the frequency of the recorded signal.

$$\lambda = \frac{v}{f},$$

where λ = wavelength on tape (in.).

v = tape speed (in./sec).

f = frequency (cycles/sec) of electrical signal.

During playback, the magnetized surface of the tape passes the gap of a reproduce head, which is similar in construction to the record head. The portion of tape in contact with the gap is bridged by the magnetic core of the reproduce head, which causes magnetic lines of flux to flow through the core. The magnitude of this flux is a function of the average state of magnetization on that portion of the tape actually spanned by the gap at any given instant. As the tape passes by the reproduce gap, the amount of flux through the core varies with the varying state of magnetization on the tape and causes a voltage to be generated in the winding linking the core. It is important to note that the voltage generated is proportional not to the magnitude of the flux—but to its *rate of change*.

Thus, if flux is proportional to the recording current,

$$\phi = Ki = K \sin (2\pi ft),$$

the playback voltage from the reproduce head is

$$e = K' \frac{d\phi}{dt} = K'' \frac{d}{dt} \sin (2\pi ft)$$

$$= 2\pi K'' \times f \times \cos (2\pi ft).$$

From this, we can see that the playback voltage is dependent upon the frequency and for constant-current recording (recording current constant at all frequencies) the output voltage will vary in direct proportion to frequency.

Figure [3-31] illustrates the effect of frequency on the recording and reproduce characteristics and calls attention to two facts.

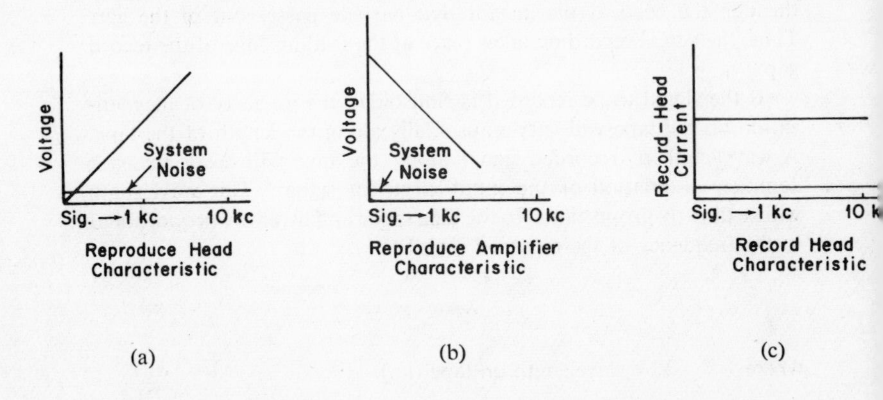

Fig. 3-31. Effect of frequency on recording and reproducing characteristics.

The first is that our reproduce amplifier must have a frequency response characteristic which is the inverse of the reproduce head characteristic, in order that an overall flat frequency response can be obtained. This is referred to as "playback equalization" and is illustrated in Fig. [3-32].

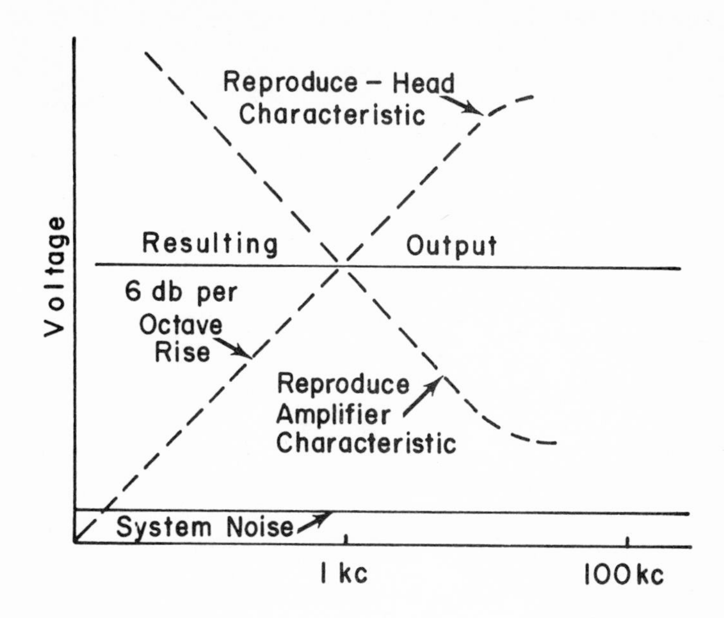

Fig. 3-32. Reproduce-amplifier output.

The second fact we observe is that as we go lower and lower in frequency, the output voltage from the reproduce head decreases until it approaches the inherent noise level of the system. At this point, it is impossible to recover the signal by equalization. This condition leads us to the first and principal limitation of the direct recording process: there is a *lower frequency limit*, below which it is impossible to record and play back successfully.

Let us now explore the high-frequency end of the recording spectrum. We will discover a limitation here which is fundamental to all recording processes. Figure [3-33a] illustrates the reproduction of a relatively long wavelength of recorded signal on the tape. As mentioned before, the average value of tape magnetization spanned by the gap is continually changing, resulting in an output voltage from the head. In Fig. [3-33b] we have a much shorter wave length, equal in length to the dimension of the gap itself.

Under this condition, the average magnetization in the gap is zero and does not change as the tape moves by. The output from the head is therefore zero, and is represented by point A in Fig. [3-34].

And as the frequency approaches that value at which the wavelength equals the gap width, the output from the reproduce head falls

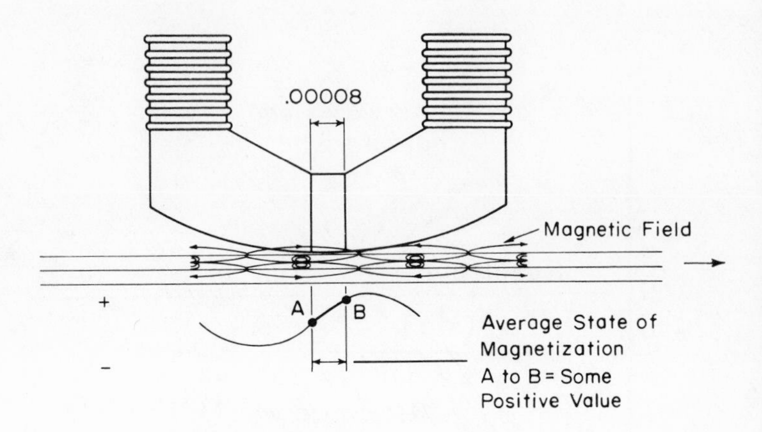

(a) Gap effect at low frequency

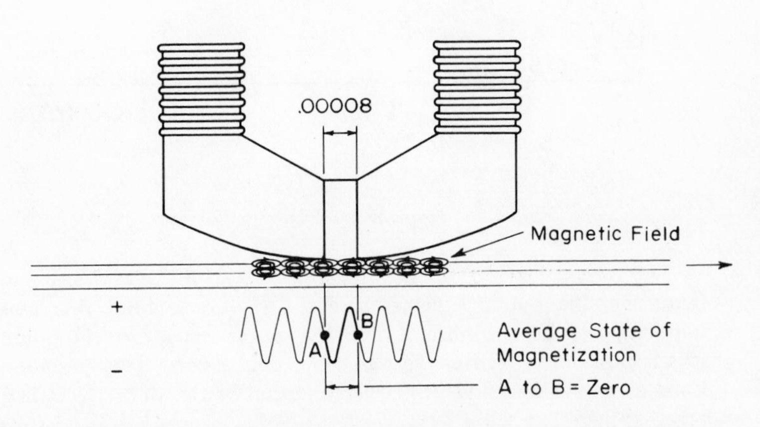

(b) Gap effect at high frequency

Fig. 3-33. Magnetic tape head gap effects.

off rapidly. Although the limitation on high-frequency response resulting from this "gap effect" cannot be eliminated, it can be improved in two ways, since

$$e \rightarrow 0 \quad \text{as } \lambda \rightarrow d, \quad \text{and} \quad \lambda = \frac{v}{f}.$$

We can record and play back higher frequencies by either reducing the size of the reproduce gap, or by increasing the tape speed. Either of these two alternatives, however, involves a compromise in some other desirable characteristic. If we reduce the gap size in an effort to get better resolution of high frequencies, the voltage output from

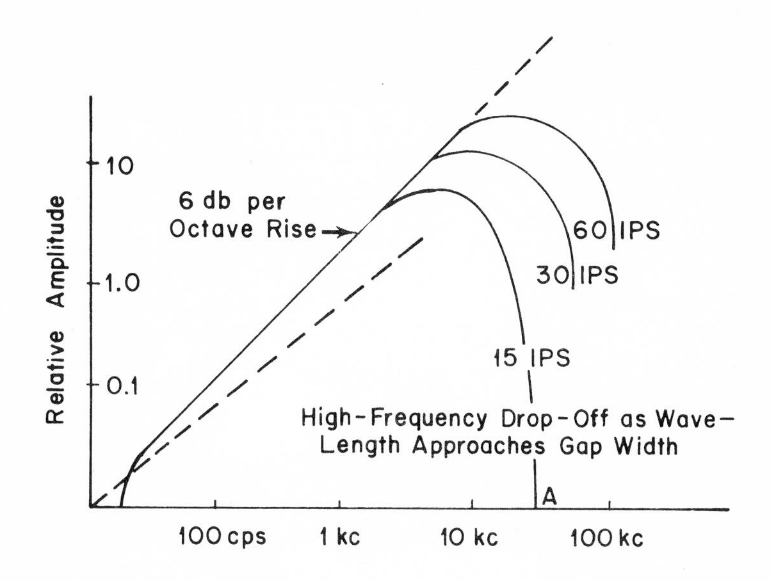

Fig. 3-34. Reproduce-head output.

the reproduce head will fall, as shown by the dotted curve in Fig. [3-34]. The result will be a deterioration in dynamic range or signal-to-noise ratio.

If, on the other hand, the tape speed is increased, head wear will be correspondingly increased and head life reduced.

Actual numerical values of those parameters which are in common use today are:

Tape speed	60 in./sec.
Gap width	0.00008 in.
Frequency response	250,000 cycles/sec at 60 in./sec or 4000 sine-wave cycles/in. of tape. This latter number can be taken as a figure of merit for the direct recording system and can be used as a basis of comparison with other recording systems.

The second major limitation of the direct recording process is one referred to as *amplitude instability*. This is a condition brought about by causes external to the recorder itself, namely, the surface condition of the magnetic tape medium. The effect manifests itself by instantaneous lapses or reduction in signal level, which are commonly referred to as "drop-outs."

Magnetic tape is manufactured in such a way that the magnetic (iron-oxide) particles are ground to a very small size and applied to the surface of the tape in as uniform a coating as possible. In spite of all reasonable precautions, the surface of the tape does not end up entirely smooth and homogeneous. Surface defects of various types occur. The most serious of these are "nodules" or clusters of oxide particles which form along the surface of the tape. As these nodules pass across the head, they cause the tape to be lifted away from the head and result in a drop in signal level. A similar drop in signal level will occur if a foreign particle of dust or dirt is permitted to find its way onto the surface of an otherwise perfect tape.

The effect is most serious at the shorter recorded wavelengths (high-frequency signals), ones which approach the size of the nodules or foreign particles. Figure [3-35] illustrates the magnitude of this effect.

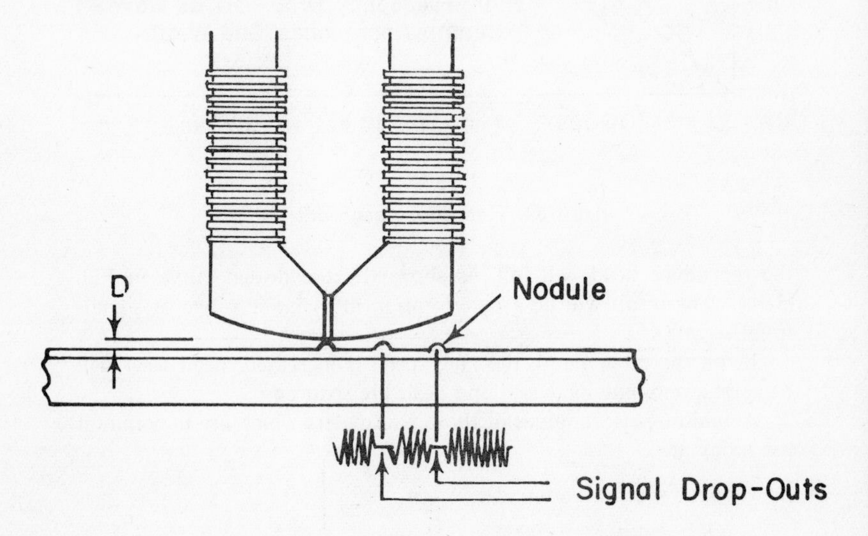

$$\text{Drop in playback level (in decibels)} = 54\,\frac{D}{\lambda}$$

where: D = Separation of tape from head

λ = Recorded wavelength on tape

Fig. 3-35. Effect of tape-surface imperfections.

The "drop-out" effect is relatively unimportant for audio recording, because the ear tends to integrate variations in signal level which occur instantaneously and, thus, is insensitive to them. For instrumentation recording, on the other hand, this effect might be intolerable, as for example if it is required to preserve accurately the waveshape of a transient phenomenon.

Having stated the two major limitations of the direct recording process, let us now mention its advantages. The direct recording process is the one having the widest frequency spectrum. Using practical tape speeds, signals can be recorded over a continuous range of frequencies from 50 cps to 250,000 cps. Other advantages are its wide dynamic range and its ability to handle moderate overloads gracefully, without sudden or drastic increases in distortion.

There is a way to overcome the two basic limitations of the direct recording process, which are the inability to record very low frequencies and the amplitude instability caused by tape drop-outs. This method employs a carrier frequency which is frequency-modulated by the signal to be recorded. Thus, a particular frequency is selected as the center frequency corresponding to zero input signal. A DC signal of positive polarity would deviate the carrier frequency a given percentage in one direction. A DC signal of negative polarity would deviate the carrier frequency an equal percentage in the opposite direction. An AC input signal would deviate the carrier alternately on both sides of center frequency, at a rate equal to the frequency of the input signal. Thus, all information presented to the tape is preserved in the frequency domain and normal amplitude instabilities will have little or no effect on the recording.

Figure [3-36] illustrates an elementary block diagram of the electronic coding employed in the frequency-modulation recording process and illustrates the relation between the input signal and the signal presented to the recording head.

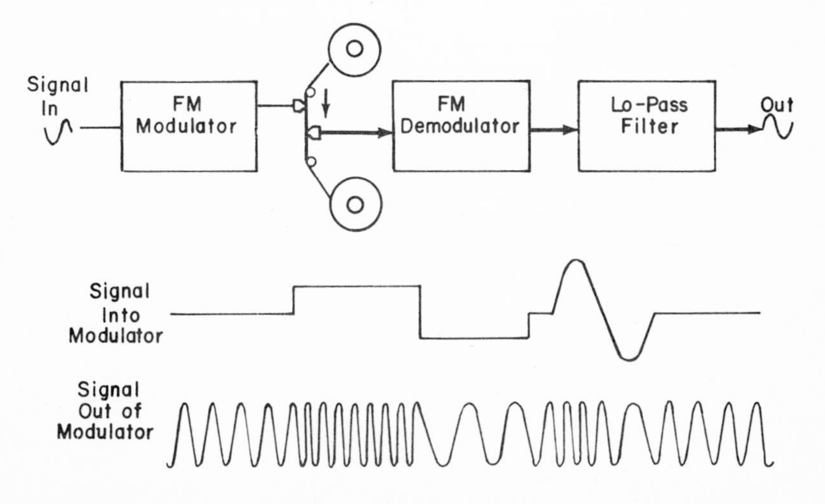

Fig. 3-36. Basic FM system.

On playback, the signal is demodulated and fed through a low-pass filter which removes the carrier and other unwanted frequencies generated in the modulation process.

The first widespread application of the FM recording technique was in *frequency-division multiplexing* where a number of individual carrier frequencies (F_1, F_2, F_3, ...) are each modulated by a separate input signal (f_1, f_2, f_3, ...) as illustrated in Fig. [3-37].

The resulting multiplicity of signals is then mixed linearly and the composite signal recorded using the direct recording process. Thus,

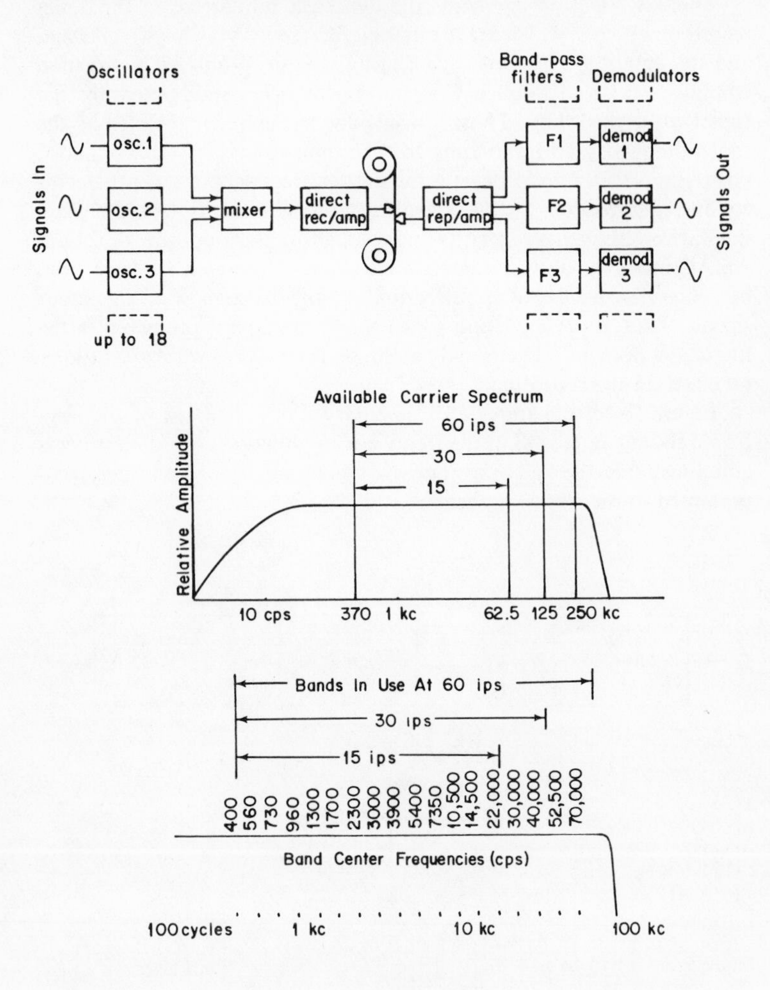

Fig. 3-37. Basic frequency-multiplexing narrow-deviation FM system.

the wide bandwidth and the linearity of the direct recording process are used to permit the simultaneous recording of many channels of signal information on one track of tape.

It is important to note that the FM recording process makes very stringent demands on the ability of the tape transport to move tape across the heads at a precisely uniform speed. Any speed variations introduced into the tape at its point of contact with the heads will cause an unwanted modulation of the carrier frequency and result in system noise. This is the limiting factor in the dynamic range and accuracy of the FM system.

This limitation, caused by speed variations (flutter and wow), is particularly acute in the frequency-multiplex scheme just described. In order to record a multiplicity of carriers in the available frequency spectrum, it is necessary to restrict the maximum frequency deviation of any one carrier. The frequency deviation commonly used has been ±7.5 per cent of center frequency. Thus, if a 7.5 per cent frequency deviation corresponds to a 100 per cent input signal, a 1 per cent deviation in frequency resulting from flutter or wow in the transport would appear as a

$$\frac{100}{7.5} = 13.3 \text{ per cent noise signal.}$$

We see then that any speed variation in the transport would be multiplied by a factor of 13.3.

Where it is desired to use the FM recording process over a wider total signal-frequency range, with a wider dynamic range and greater overall accuracy, a wide-deviation FM system can be used. Here only one channel of signal is recorded on a track of tape and the entire frequency bandwidth of the recorder is used for this signal, as shown in Fig. [3-38].

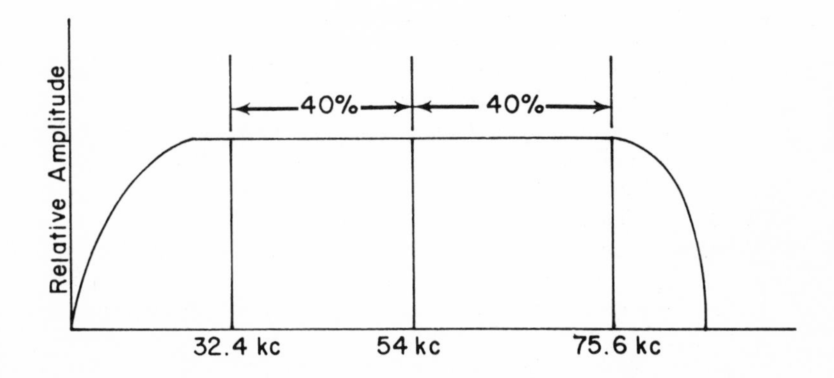

Fig. 3-38. Wide-deviation FM-carrier bandwidth.

It is possible to design modulators which will permit deviations of ±40 per cent of center frequency without sacrifice of linearity. In this case, a 1 per cent tape-speed error would only cause a

$$\frac{100}{40} = 2.5 \text{ per cent noise signal,}$$

giving an improvement of better than five times that of the narrow-deviation system first mentioned.

Actual values for the frequencies employed at a 60-ips tape speed are [given in Table 3-1]. Referring back to the block diagram in Fig.

Table 3-1

Input Signal	Modulator Frequency (at 60 ips)	Deviation
+1.4v DC	151.2 kc	+40%
0	108 kc	Center frequency
−1.4v DC	64.8 kc	−40%

[3-36], the low-pass filter following the demodulator would have a cut-off frequency approximately one-fifth that of the carrier frequency—permitting the recording of signals from DC to 20 kc at a 60-ips tape speed. This then gives a figure of merit for the frequency-modulation recording process of 333 sine-wave cycles per inch of tape (which can be compared with the 4000 cycles per inch of the direct recording process).

If it is not required to record frequencies as high as 20 kc, the tape speed can be reduced in direct proportion to the desired upper-frequency limit, with proportional increase in recording time. When this is done, the center frequency is scaled down in direct proportion to the tape speed, using the same ±40 per cent deviation. Thus, the wavelength recorded on the tape corresponding to a given DC signal voltage is the same, independent of tape speed. This makes it possible to record at one tape speed and reproduce at an entirely different tape speed, permitting time-base changes—one of the important applications of the FM recording process.

The advantages of the frequency-modulation recording process are: (1) its ability to record low frequencies down to DC; (2) its freedom from the effects of tape drop-outs; and (3) its excellent phase-shift versus frequency characteristics with the attendant ability of accurately preserving the wave form of a recorded signal. The disadvantages of the FM process—or the "price" we pay for the advantages are: (1) less efficient utilization of the tape, requiring approximately ten times the tape speed for a given upper-frequency limit; (2) the additional complexity of the electronic circuitry requiring modulators, demodulators, and low-pass filters; and (3) the requirement for a tape transport which is engineered and manufactured to high standards of precision.

The major applications for the FM recording process are:

1. The recording of low-frequency signal information, such as vibrations, noises, and underwater sounds for spectrum analysis.
2. The recording of transient phenomena, such as shock, blast, and ignition, where accuracy of waveshape is important. Short transients having rise times as short as 60 microseconds can be resolved with this process.
3. Changes in time base permitting a speed-up or slow-down of a given event; and permitting the frequency components of a given signal to be scaled up or down by large factors, up to 1000 times or more.

Since the input signal required by a magnetic tape recorder is in the volt range, the strain-gage signal must be amplified. Again, a DC bridge supply followed by DC amplifiers is recommended, although a carrier system could be used.

3-4 Telemetry systems

When strain gages and other transducers are used in situations where they cannot be wired to a stationary recording device, there are two possibilities: (1) The transducer may be wired to a portable recorder which moves with the transducer; portable oscillographs and tape recorders have been used extensively to record from strain gages during aircraft flight tests. (2) The transducer signal may be broadcast to a stationary recording station. This second method, which is called telemetering, is the only feasible method when the device being analyzed is not recovered.

In this brief discussion of telemetering we will draw upon the terminology and ideas developed in our discussion of tape recording. A typical FM-to-FM telemetering system is shown in block diagram form in Fig. 3-39.

The strain-gage circuit may be either DC or AC, but if an AC carrier is used, the output must be demodulated before the next function is performed. The output of the strain-gage circuit is used to frequency-modulate a subcarrier signal. Standardized subcarrier frequencies are those shown in Fig. 3-37. These modulators are usually set so that maximum input signals produce a frequency deviation of 7.5 per cent. Several

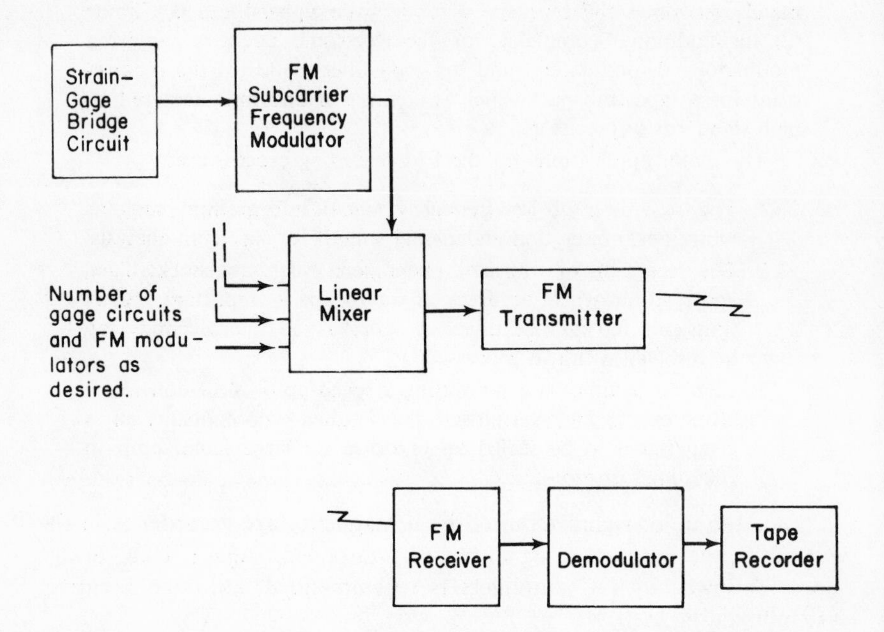

Fig. 3-39. FM-to-FM telemetering system.

frequency-modulated subcarriers are linearly mixed,* and this mixed signal is used to frequency-modulate the transmitted signal.

A wide range of transmission frequencies may be used, all in the megacycle region.† The transmitted signal is received by an FM receiver, demodulated (to remove the transmission frequency), and recorded. A tape recorder is ordinarily used because of the need for a frequency response higher than the frequency of the highest subcarrier.

Notice that the system just described is identical to the frequency-division multiplexing system discussed on p. 188 and shown in Fig. 3-37, except that an FM transmitter and an FM receiver have been inserted between the mixer and the tape recorder's direct-record amplifier. The recorded signal is filtered and demodulated as explained on p. 188, and the frequency limitations are those inherent in the frequency-division multiplexing.

* It is not practical to use all of the subcarrier frequencies shown in Fig. 3-37 simultaneously because of cross talk (signal on one channel interfering with adjacent channel), but as many as eight are commonly mixed.

† Holloman Air Force Base used approximately 800 megacycles to telemeter data from their rocket-sled test facility. Sandia Corporation uses approximately 200 megacycles for the same purpose.

If it is desired to telemeter signals having a wider frequency range than can be handled by frequency-division multiplexing, a direct-to-FM telemetering system is used. In this system the signal from a single strain-gage bridge is used to frequency-modulate the transmitter. The FM signal is received, demodulated, and recorded.

The frequency response of this system is essentially dependent on the frequency response of the recorder.

If a tape recorder is used, a direct-recording process is involved, since no carrier frequencies are used. Hence, all of the limitations of direct recording discussed on p. 184 apply. The demodulated signal may be recorded on a cathode ray oscilloscope by using moving film techniques.

3-5 References listed in Chapter 3

1. Frank, Eugene, "Strain Indicator for Semiconductor Gages," Instrument Society of America, Paper Number 58-LA-61.
2. Rohrbach, C., "A Strain Gage Bridge with 50 KCPS Carrier Frequency," *Archiv fur Technisches Messen* (May 1960), J-924-3, abstract in *Strain Gage Readings* 3, 4, Stein Engineering Services (Oct.–Nov. 1960), p. 61.
3. Bayne, R. T., "D. C. Amplifiers for Instrumentation," *Strain Gage Readings*, 2, 1, Stein Engineering Services (Apr.–May 1959), pp. 25–26.
4. Weber, Paul J., *The Tape Recorder*, second edition published by Ampex Corporation (1959).

3-6 Suggested laboratory experiments

Experiment 3-1 Characteristics of several strain indicators

EQUIPMENT NECESSARY

1. A mounted gage which can be subjected to a repeatable level of strain (gage on cantilever beam, clamp, weight, and hanger).
2. Sufficient additional gages or resistors so that either a full or half bridge can be constructed external to the indicator.
3. Small (5 to 10 ohms) resistors which can be series-connected in the leads to simulate long leads.
4. Calibrate resistors.
5. Various types of strain indicators.*

* This experiment can be conducted by using any, or all, of the strain indicators listed. If several of the types are available, the author has found it advantageous to conduct this experiment as a demonstration, giving particular emphasis to the basic differences in the several types and the effect these differences have on such items as linearity, calibration procedure, effect of lead resistance, etc.

a. Unbalanced bridge system (DC) (such as the Ellis Associates Model BAM-1).
b. Unbalanced bridge system (AC) (such as a Brush Development Co. "Universal Analyzer").
c. Reference bridge system (such as Hathaway strain indicator, DC, or BLH strain indicator, AC).

PROCEDURE

With each type of strain indicator:

1. Check the linearity of signal output with strain in a single bridge arm over the instruments full range. Use parallel resistors to simulate this strain. Note what percentage of change in R is represented by full-scale reading for the gage-factor settings available.
2. Using four arms remote, two arms remote, and one arm remote (use series resistors to simulate long leads), apply a standard strain signal and note the effect of lead resistance on output signal. Where possible, correct for this effect, using the gage-factor control.
3. Using four, two, and one arm remote, calibrate the deflection-type systems by placing calibrate resistors across a gage both at the gage location and at the instrument.
4. With the AC systems sample the signal at various points in the circuit, using a cathode ray oscilloscope. Determine the frequency of the AC supply and the method used to differentiate between positive and negative strains.

REPORT

Compare all experimental results to those predicted by theory.

CHAPTER 4

Some Special Problems Encountered in the Use of Resistance Strain Gages

4-1 Introduction

It often seems to the experimentalist that every problem encountered is "special" and every use of strain gages is "unusual." To a degree this is certainly true, and as a result it is impossible to devote a section to each of the problems that may be encountered which may require the use of strain gages. Indeed, the number of problems in which strain gages can profitably be used depends only upon the ingenuity of the investigator.

It will be our purpose here to survey the literature to uncover interesting and useful information concerning strain gages and their use. Much of this information results from the efforts of an experimentalist trying to solve his "special" problem at the moment, rather than from a systematic investigation designed to evaluate or improve strain gages and strain-gage techniques. The information uncovered which seems pertinent to a wide range of problems is discussed in Sect. 4-2.

Some additional problems which have been investigated by using strain gages are listed in Sect. 4-3. Although a brief abstract of the investigation is included here, the reader is directed to the references. These additional problems have been included primarily to stimulate the reader's imagination.*

4-2 Unusual environments and applications

4-2a Strain measurements over long time periods

The use of strain gages over long periods of time may be divided into two categories: (1) those tests in which the gage zero point can be reestablished when desired or at frequent intervals, and (2) those tests in which the gage zero point cannot be rechecked once the test has begun.

As an example of a test of the first type, consider the use of gages on the structural members of a static-load testing frame. The frame and gages may be in use for years, but at the beginning of each test the gage bridges may be balanced and at the end of each test the frame may be unloaded and checked for any drift or permanent strain. In situations of this type the actual test is of short duration, and no special problems are encountered.

As an example of a test of the second type, consider the use of gages on the structural members of a steel-frame building, the purpose being to check load distribution as the building progresses and after it is in use. In this case, readings will be compared to the original zero readings, and any shift in the zero reading will produce an unknown error. Clearly, in this type of test it is imperative that only strain produces change in indicator readings.

A number of factors assume increased importance in this second type of test:

1. *Temperature compensation.* Since, in general, temperatures may vary over long periods of time, it is extremely important that temperature compensation be as perfect as possible. If temperature

* The "Review and Digest of the Current Literature" published in each issue of *Strain Gage Readings* (Stein Engineering Services, Phoenix 18, Ariz.) and the index issues of the *Proceedings of the Society for Experimental Stress Analysis* were invaluable in preparing this material.

compensation is imperfect, then readings interpreted as varying strain may only represent a variation in temperature.

2. *Bond stability* (*mechanical and electrical*). Any shrinkage, swelling, or creep of the bond or any change in the conductivity of the bond will produce a signal which is indistinguishable from that produced by strain in the surface under test. Several things can contribute to lack of bond stability. If the bond is not completely cured before the gage is placed in service, then curing continues during service, with associated dimensional and electrical changes and, hence, false signals. Proper curing of strain-gage bond for long-term tests is extremely important.

   The formation of the bond produced by cyanoacrylic cement (Eastman 910) is generally considered to be completed in a very short period of time (minutes), and no elevated temperature cure is needed.

   The bonds produced by cellulose-nitrate cements (Duco) and by various epoxy cements form over extended periods of time; the time required for the bond to become stable depends upon the cure temperature used. In general, we may say that the cure times suggested by the manufacturers (often for "normal" or short-time tests) are not adequate for installation of gages to be used in long-term tests. Investigators have often noted that when gages are bonded with cellulose nitrate and air-dried for 24 to 72 hours, the gage output drifts excessively at high strains (say 1000 μin./in. or more). As a result, Bakelite-backed gages bonded with Bakelite cement were used for long-time tests, even under indoor conditions. However, M. McWhirter and B. W. Duggin, Ref. [5], Chap. 2, demonstrated that if a cellulose-nitrate bond is properly cured, the resultant gage installation is capable of measuring strains as high as 2900 μin./in. (tension or compression) over a 63-day period with only one per cent drift. The curing procedure used by McWhirter and Duggin to mount paper-backed gages with SR-4 cement may be summarized as follows:

   a. Air-dry for two hours.
   b. Place in oven and heat slowly to 140°F.
   c. Hold in oven at 140°F until the gage-to-specimen resistance reaches 10,000 megohms (12 to 24 hours).
   d. Heat to 160°F for one hour and *waterproof*.

   It is important to note that gage-to-specimen resistance is significant not only because it must be constant for electrical stability but also because it is an indication of bond cure and, hence, mechanical stability as well. As a cellulose-nitrate bond cures, the gage-to-specimen resistance increases.

So many different epoxy bonds are available that no specific cure-time information can be given, but for long-term tests the cure time is important. Unless an evaluation test (similar to the one by McWhirter and Duggin) is available for the specific epoxy being used, the user must make his own evaluation. In general, a short post-cure (taking the gage to temperatures higher than it will see in service) and strain cycling (to a value higher than will be reached in service, if possible) will improve gage stability.

If the bond is attacked by foreign substances during the test, it may become unstable. Moisture invariably acts to make a bond electrically unstable and, hence, must be excluded. Proven methods for moistureproofing strain gages are discussed in Sect. 4-2b. If the bond is attacked by nuclear radiation, it will become unstable. The information currently available on the effect of radiation on strain-gage elements and bonds is presented in Sect. 4-2c. All bonding materials become unstable at elevated temperatures. This cause of bond instability is discussed in Sect. 4-2d, below. All three of these last-mentioned problems (moisture, radiation, and high temperature) are important in all kinds of tests. However, they require particular attention in long-time tests, since the adverse effects produced by all three generally increase with time. Hence, an amount of moisture, radiation intensity, and temperature excess that might be tolerated in a short test may completely invalidate the results obtained from a long-term test.

3. *Instrument stability.* Numerous factors acting on the strain-gage circuit and indicating device can produce signals that are unrelated to strain. These factors have the most adverse effect on the results of long-term tests. Since long-time tests are by nature static tests, static strain indicators are most often used to obtain gage readings. Both single and reference bridge systems are widely used as null indicators, and both AC and DC are utilized to power the bridge. The normal procedure is to balance the bridge at the beginning of the test and then to compute gage readings at all later times by comparing the new balance point to the original balance point. Change in balance point produced by changes other than strain is referred to as zero shift, and any such shift will result in an erroneous gage reading unless it is detected and accounted for. Let us examine the factors that may contribute to zero shift.

   a. Change in resistance of any of the elements that make up the complete bridge (or bridges, in the reference bridge system) may cause zero shift. In general, the bridge is completed by using resistors other than strain gages, and since these resistors are temperature-sensitive it is imperative that they be held at constant temperature or that they be connected so as to be compensating. Most commercial indicators are designed so that normal temperature changes at the indicator will produce only negligible drift. However, extreme temperature or rapid temperature fluctuations at the indicator location can produce instability. Changes of resistance in lead wires that are not compensating will cause zero drift. Such changes can be produced by changes in lead-wire temperature; or, in the case of AC-powered bridges, the change in lead impedance (total AC resistance) is very sensitive to change in lead capacitance produced by moisture.

b. In AC-powered bridges the balance point may vary with supply voltage, and, hence, zero drift accompanies supply-voltage variation. On first thought, this statement seems incompatible with our knowledge of balanced bridge indicators. The point to be emphasized here is that most commercial indicators which utilize AC bridge power are not in a true state of balance when the indicator galvanometer shows zero; hence, the value established as the "balance" point is dependent on bridge voltage.

Since there is a possibility of indicator zero shift in long-term tests, it is imperative that each system be investigated *before* testing is begun, and that steps be taken to prevent, or correct for, any drift that is present. After everything possible has been done to minimize zero drift, either of two procedures can be used to measure and correct for drift. One method involves mounting two gages side by side for complete temperature compensation on a base that will be unstrained. These "reference" gages are connected to the indicator and read at the beginning of the test and each time thereafter that the active gages are read. Any change in the reading (balance point) obtained from the reference gage is taken as indicator zero drift, and the active gage readings are corrected accordingly. A second method for determining indicator zero drift does not require reference gages, but does require that two readings be taken from each active gage at every time of interest. This method is based on the fact that resistance changes in adjacent bridge arms produce a bridge unbalance of opposite sense. Before the test is begun, the active gage pair (A and T) is connected in position 1 (see Fig. 4-1a), and the bridge is balanced at point 1 (see Fig. 4-1b); the gage pair is

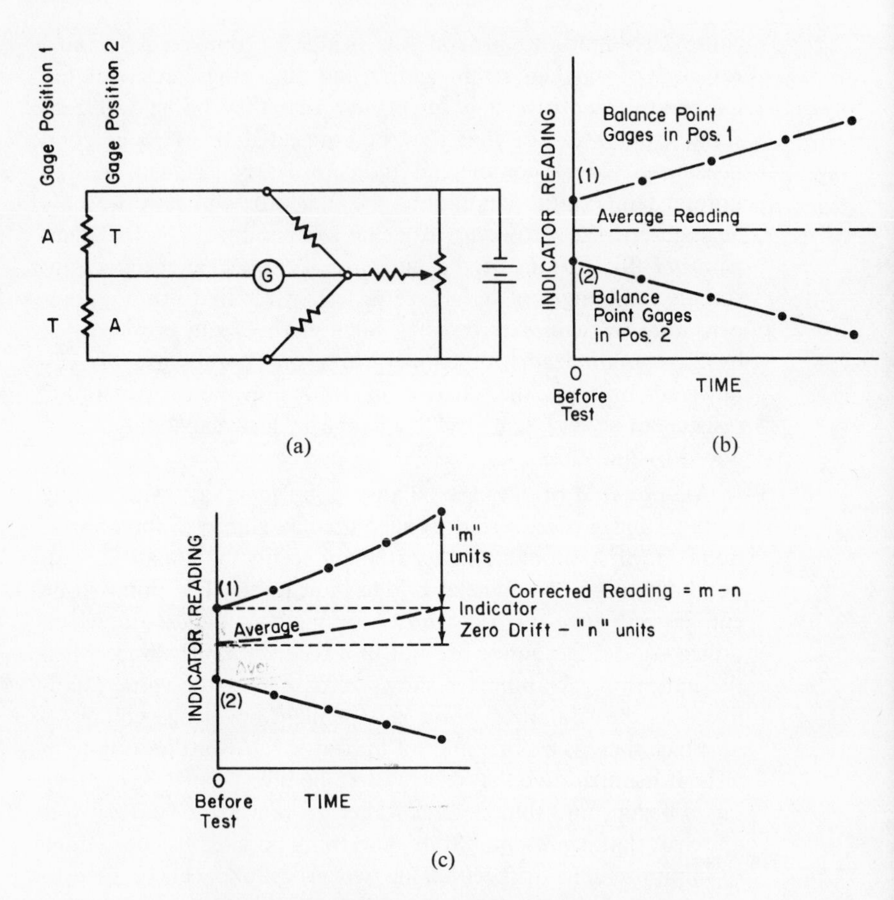

Fig. 4-1. Strain indicator zero drift correction.

then connected in position 2 and the bridge is balanced at point 2. (Points 1 and 2 will, in general, be different because of small differences in the initial resistance of gages *A* and *T*.) As the test progresses, the gages are read in both positions. If the strain signal is such that the reading obtained with the gages in position 1 is increasing, then the reading obtained with the gages in position 2 should be decreasing. If at any time the increase in reading position 1 is just equal to the decrease in reading position 2 (i.e., the average reading remains constant), as indicated in Fig. 4-1b, then no indicator zero drift is indicated. Indicator zero drift is indicated by a change in the average value of the readings taken for the two gage positions. This condition is indicated in Fig. 4-1c, and the correction is made as shown.

4-2b Moistureproofing strain gages

Moisture acts to reduce the gage-to-surface resistance and/or partially to short-circuit sections of the gage itself. In either case the effect of moisture is to place a resistance path in parallel with the strain gage, thereby producing a change in resistance equivalent to strain. To understand the importance of this effect it must be remembered that the change in resistance associated with strain is very small.

As pointed out in the last section, moistureproofing may be necessary in long-time tests even under normal indoor conditions. Moistureproofing will always be necessary in outdoor tests and when the gages are used at locations in continuous or intermittent contact with liquid. In these cases the degree of moistureproofing required will be dependent upon the conditions of service and how long the gages will be in service.

Before we discuss specific moistureproofing techniques and the results obtainable, some general rules of procedure are in order.

1. The bond should be *completely* cured before the moistureproofing agent is applied. This is especially important when the bond is formed by the evaporation of a solvent (Duco). Moistureproofing too soon may prevent formation of a good bond.
2. Moistureproofing is best applied to a heated (150° to 450°F, depending on the temperature limitations associated with the gage and with the moistureproofing) gage and test surface so that no surface moisture will be trapped beneath the moistureproofing.
3. The identical moistureproofing treatment should be used on the active and the temperature-compensating gages. Since the moistureproofing material is also an insulating material, this is necessary for temperature compensation.
4. The moistureproofing agent must be chosen to function over the entire temperature range of interest. Nitrate rubber (B. F. Goodrich A-178-B) has been used to cryogenic temperatures to moistureproof gages from liquefied gases; silicone varnishes and lacquers will function between $-50°$ and 250°F; epoxy resins will provide moistureproofing to temperatures in excess of 500°F. Petroleum waxes and grease generally melt above 200°F and become brittle and crack below 0°F.
5. If the gage is mounted on a substance that will be penetrated by moisture (wood and concrete), it must be moistureproofed on the bonded side.

Any of the moistureproofing kits available from the gage suppliers can be used to moistureproof gages for protection against high humidity and/or water splash (rain). Budd Type GW-1 silicone compound has been successfully used for both indoor and outdoor, long-time, gage installations. Important points in the moistureproofing procedure are

1. The area around the gage must be cleaned to remove excess bonding agent. Sanding, followed by a solvent swab, is recommended. It is imperative that moistureproofing adhere to both gage and surrounding surface to form a continuous and sealed gage cover.
2. The moistureproofing must adhere to the lead wires; therefore, the lead wires should be cleaned in the area where they will project through the moistureproofing.

One of the simplest and most rapid methods of moistureproofing which is suitable when the gages are totally immersed was reported by F. E. Wells [1]. This method, which is outlined below, is suitable for use with paper-backed gages.

1. Thoroughly clean the area around the gage with special care to remove all glue runners.
2. Cover the gage and harness wire junction with an excess of soft wax (such as Di-Jell*).
3. Place a piece of thin aluminum foil over the Di-Jell. Press the foil into intimate contact with the wax. Work the wax from the center out to eject all air until Di-Jell is extruded all the way around.
4. Using a small putty knife, or similar tool, press the foil edge down until a $\frac{1}{8}$ to $\frac{1}{4}$-in. border of the foil is pressed into intimate contact with the specimen, with the thinnest possible film of wax between.
5. Thoroughly clean, with a solvent-soaked gauze, the top of the foil, the lead wire, and the adjacent area, so that all exposed wax is removed.
6. Cover the entire assembly with Epoxylite 222,† or a comparable material.

E. L. Kimbel [2] reports underwater use of paper-backed gages, bonded to a metal surface with Duco cement. The gages were moistureproofed by complete immersion in transformer oil or multiple layers of stiffened neutral vaseline. H. O. Meyer [3] reports moistureproofing gages to be submerged in salt water by covering the gage location with a plastic dome. A water-absorbing agent (such as silica gel) was placed inside the sealed dome to absorb any residual humidity in the gage vicinity. A. E. Newton and R. E. Karcher [4] used stainless steel bellows to cover strain gages that were immersed in hot water. R. I. Barker and J. B. Murtland [5]

---

* Di-Jell 171 is available from the Associated Wax Refining Company, 300 Fourth Avenue, New York 10, N.Y.

† Epoxylite 222 is available from the Epoxylite Corporation, 812 Truck Way, Montebello, Calif.

describe a sealed mechanical cover which they have used to moistureproof and physically to protect strain gages mounted on the inside of a steel tunnel liner.

Moistureproofed, paper-backed gages have been used successfully on the outside of submarine pressure hulls during deep submergence tests. P. M. Palermo [6] outlines several moistureproofing methods that were used in these tests; they involve covering the gages with rubber patches, neoprene compound, or Okonite tape. The reader is referred to Palermo's paper for the full details, since, as he points out, "No waterproofing method is any better than the technique that is used to apply it."

Mills Dean [7] describes some moistureproofing methods that provide considerable protection from turbulent water flow, underwater explosion, particle abrasion, and direct mechanical shock.

Several investigators have measured strains on concrete and wood and have reported difficulty due to moisture penetration from below the gage. For long-time tests on wood and concrete, or for short-duration tests at high humidity, paper-backed gages bonded with a cellulose-nitrate cement and moistureproofed on top are not adequate. Use of epoxy or phenol cements offers some improvement, as does the insertion of metal foil or shim stock between the gage and the test surface. Strain has been successfully measured within concrete by inclusion of a strain-gaged load cell; see Ref. [8]. In this case the load cell is itself moistureproofed. Gages of this type (for embedment in concrete) are commercially available.*

4-2c Strain gages subjected to nuclear radiation

Strain gages may be exposed to nuclear radiation when they are used in either of two ways. In some cases, when it is desired to test an item mechanically after it has been irradiated, it is advantageous to mount any strain gages required in the test before irradiation, since mounting gages by using remote manipulators may prove difficult. In this case it is feasible to zero the gage bridges after irradiation but before the mechanical tests begin. The question of interest is whether or not the irradiation has affected the gage bond and/or gage factor.

In other cases it is desired to use strain gages to make measurements during the irradiation process. In this case, any zero shift produced by irradiation also becomes important.

The use of bonded resistance strain gages in radiation environments has been suspect since the first studies on radiation damage of materials were undertaken. These early studies showed that organic material (hence,

* Baldwin-Lima-Hamilton Corporation, Constantan wire grid Valore-Brass foil envelope.

most strain gage bonds) are affected by modest amounts of radiation; the radiation produces dimensional changes, as well as changes in mechanical and electrical properties. These studies also showed that the mechanism of conduction in metals is affected by radiation; hence, the effect of radiation on gage factor was open to question.

Early studies by J. R. Hume [9] on strain gages which were backed and bonded with organic materials (cellulose-nitrate, epoxy, or phenol) confirmed that in a radiation environment a continual zero shift occurred, with eventual complete electrical breakdown of the gage bond. Fortunately, early radiation damage studies also showed that ceramics are less affected than organics, and so a second type of gage was suggested—the strippable-backed gages, bonded with ceramic cements which had been developed for high-temperature service.

R. C. Smith and N. J. Readler [10] of the U. S. Naval Research Laboratory have conducted evaluation studies of ceramic bonded gages in neutron and gamma-ray environments. In the first studies, Smith and Readler used both Nichrome V and Constantan gages bonded with ceramic cement. The gages were mounted on cantilever beams which could be inserted in the beam hole of a material-testing reactor. The results of these tests may be summarized very briefly as follows:

1. The gage-to-specimen resistance decreased continuously during the irradiation (from 1000 megohms to 0.01 megohm in 150 hours) when the integrated fast neutron flux reached a value of approximately 2.5×10^{17} neutrons/cm^2. Beyond this point the gage-to-specimen resistance was erratic, and the gage readings were meaningless.
2. During this irradiation period the resistance of the individual Nichrome V gages increased by approximately one per cent, while the resistance of the individual Constantan gages decreased by less than half of one per cent.
3. When the gages were connected in compensating bridge circuits (two gages in adjacent arms subjected to identical environments), the rate of bridge unbalance was reduced but not eliminated. The rate of unbalance observed represented the equivalent of a few microinches per inch per hour of test.

   It is concluded that short-time tests can be conducted any time during irradiation until gage-to-specimen resistance breakdowns. Results of long-time tests will be more difficult to interpret because of the difficulty in obtaining complete compensation. It must be remembered that the studies just referred to were conducted in a location at which the flux level was 10^{13} thermal neutrons/cm^2/sec and 10^{11} fast neutrons/cm^2/sec. In areas outside but adjacent to reactors, the flux level may be three or four orders of magnitude less than this and, hence, strain gages could be used in correspondingly longer tests. However, in some reactors the flux level is several orders of magnitude higher than in these studies, and in these the permissible test time would be very short.

Like all semiconductor devices, semiconductor gages are affected by radiation damage. Enough radiation damage will result in both change in gage resistance and change in gage factor. However, one gage manufacturer* reports that their silicon semiconductor gages "will tolerate a total radiation flux of at least 10^{14} particles/cm^2 with energies greater than 1 Mev before changes in gage factor or gage resistance occur."

Experience with strain gages in radiation environments has also indicated that special attention must be paid to solder joints and lead wires, since they, too, are affected. Since many solders undergo pronounced resistance changes with radiation, welded connections are recommended.

4-2d Strain measurements at high temperatures

The number of instances in which it is desired to measure strain at elevated temperature has been growing at an ever-increasing rate. As a result, development work in the area of strain gages for elevated temperature service has been intensified. The present state of the art may be summarized as follows:

WITH METAL GAGES

1. For temperatures as high as 350°F, phenol-resin (Bakelite)-backed gages bonded with either Bakelite or high-temperature epoxy cement are suitable. Although bonding and temperature compensation require considerable attention to details, the necessary procedures are well worked out. The procedures require only reasonable skill. Problems such as change in gage factor, breakdown of electrical resistance between gage and specimen, and metallurgical changes that produce sudden and/or irreversible resistance changes are not encountered at temperatures below 350°F.
2. It is possible to evaluate static strains with good accuracy at temperatures as high as 600°F. In this region (350° to 600°F) the task involves more than mounting a gage and reading strains, even when the gage is correctly mounted. The mounting techniques used in

* Micro Systems Incorporated; material quoted taken from company literature.

this temperature range differ from those used below 350°F, but several suitable methods have been developed. The characteristics of the gage element and circuit must be well understood, and readings taken must be "corrected" to account for such factors as gage resistance change and gage factor change.

3. Above temperatures of 600°F, *accurate* measurement of static strain is very difficult. Gage-mounting techniques have been developed which adequately bond gages for static measurements at temperatures as high as 1200°F. But above 700°F, changes in the gage element itself tend to become so large that the reduction of readings to strain values becomes questionable. Three methods of approach to this problem appear possible.

   a. By thoroughly evaluating the gage to establish the effect of temperature on gage factor, specific resistance, etc., necessary corrections can be applied to the data.
   b. By accomplishing complete compensation, signals that are not strain-related can be canceled.
   c. By developing a strain-sensitive material that is electrically stable in the temperature range of interest, the problem can be eliminated.

   All of these three approaches have been, and are being, tried, but without complete success.
4. Above 1200°F, mechanical and electrical breakdown of the gage bond complicates the problems already mentioned. However, some dynamic tests have been conducted at temperatures as high as 1500°F.

Ambient to 350°F

Gages for use in this region are generally constructed by using the copper-nickel alloys (Advance,* Constantan, Cupron) commonly used for ambient temperature gages. These alloys are suitable for use in this region because they do not become electrically unstable until somewhat above 450°F. These alloys are preferred for the same properties that have made them popular for ambient temperature service: reasonable gage factor ($\sim$2), which remains constant to large strains and which is unaffected by temperature (increases slightly—one-half of one per cent per 100°F); low temperature coefficient of resistance, and one that can be controlled to produce a self-temperature-compensated gage.

Gages are available on Bakelite (phenolic and cellulose fiber matrix) for use to 350°F. These may be bonded with either phenol or a suitable

* SR-4, Bakelite-type wire gages.

epoxy cement. In general, epoxy bonds are equal to the phenol bonds and are much easier to make, because they require less contact pressure during curing. The 350°F limit is fixed by the Bakelite base.

350 to 600°F

It is possible to extend the use of copper-nickel alloy elements up to the temperature at which the electrical resistance of the gage element becomes unstable (450° to 600°F, depending on the exact alloy and its treatment). This is accomplished by providing a gage carrier which remains stable at higher temperatures than does Bakelite. Gages are available on a phenol-resin and glass-fiber base (SR-4, Bakelite-type foil gages) which can be used to 450°F with a suitable epoxy cement (EPY-400, Mithra 200, etc.). Strippable gages and free-filament gages made of copper-nickel alloys may be imbedded directly in high-temperature organic cements (filled epoxies, phenols, and epoxy-phenol combinations) to produce installations for use at the temperature limit of the gage element itself. The phenol-resin and glass-fiber-based gage just mentioned is available premounted, with phenol cement, on a 0.005 in.-thick stainless steel shim stock (SR-4 Bakelite weldable gages). This gage is installed by welding to the test surface.

Above 600°F it is necessary to use a different alloy for the gage element, and a different bonding agent. The gages and bonds discussed in the next section, for use above 600°F, are widely used in work between 350° and 600°F. However, because of the disadvantages (to be discussed), it is advisable to use copper-nickel alloy gages and organic cements whenever they are adequate.

Above 600°F

Since the copper-nickel alloys become unstable at or below 600°F, other materials must be used. Chrome-nickel alloys (Nichrome V*) are most often used because, although they do suffer changes in temperature coefficient of resistance, gage factor, and specific resistance, at temperatures between 600° and 2000°F the material tends to be self-stabilizing; i.e., at a constant temperature these changes stop, or at least the rate of change decreases with time. Nichrome V has the advantages of a gage factor of 2.2 and high specific resistance, but it suffers from several disadvantages. The gage factor decreases with both increasing strain and increasing temperature (ten per cent or more between ambient and 1000°F), and the temperature coefficient of resistance is larger than that of any other common gage material. Karma (T. M. Driver-Harris Co.), which is basically a chrome-nickel alloy modified with aluminum and iron, has

* Trade-mark of Driver-Harris Co.

an even higher specific resistance and a lower temperature coefficient of resistance than does Nichrome V, but it lacks the stability (drift of properties at constant temperature) of Nichrome V.

Because of changes in specific resistance, in temperature coefficient of resistance, and in gage factor that occurs with changes in temperature, readings taken above 600°F are difficult to interpret. The curves shown in Fig. 4-2a indicate that the necessary corrections are large and are dependent on past temperature service history. In addition, even for the most stable gage alloys, constant temperature zero drift of single active gage circuits equal to 50μin./in./hr or more is common at temperatures above 800°F (see Fig. 4-2b). Under certain favorable conditions, two gage-compensating circuits can be used to reduce this zero drift, but perfect compensation at high temperatures is almost impossible because of slight gage differences as well as small temperature differences.

Zero drift becomes less important as the test time is reduced, and consequently dynamic tests at still higher temperatures are possible. However, in dynamic tests and in longer tests where the circuit is well compensated, the fact that gage factor changes with both temperature and strain level complicates interpretation (see Fig. 4-2c).

At this point we may conclude that above 600°F the measurement of strain is complicated by the strain-sensitive element itself. In addition, gage bonding becomes more difficult, and special techniques are necessary even to use the available gage alloys to their maximum capabilities. If it is agreed (and it is not) that existing gage alloys are suitable for measuring dynamic strains at temperatures above 1200°F, then we may say that bonding methods impose the upper temperature limit on strain measurements.

The most common method for mounting gages to be used above 600°F is to imbed the gage element in a ceramic cement (metallic oxides with a phosphoric acid binder for chemical setting or refractory materials which are flowed in place). Ceramic cements designed specifically for strain-gage bonding are commercially available.* The upper usable temperature limit of all ceramic cements is fixed by their tendency toward decreasing resistance with increasing temperature. Taking one megohm gage-to-specimen resistance as the minimum requirement, we find that most of the commercially available ceramic cements are limited to use below 1200°F. If this criterion is ignored, most of these cements may be, and have been, used in dynamic test work at temperatures as high as 1500°F.

Detailed instructions for using these commercially available ceramic cements are furnished by the manufacturers, but at best their use is

* Budd—Type H. Allen P-1 and PBX—Robert A. Allen Co., Mechanicsville, N.Y. Brimor U-529—Morganite, Inc., Long Island City 1, N.Y.

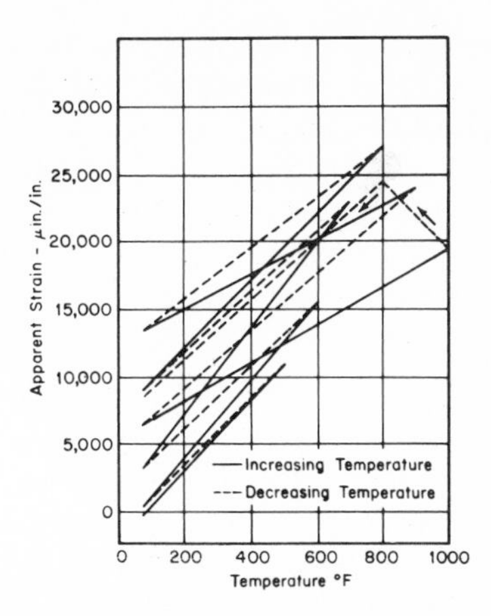

(a) Typical temperature coefficient slope change and zero shift with increasing temperature. Nickel-chrome alloys—Nichrome V

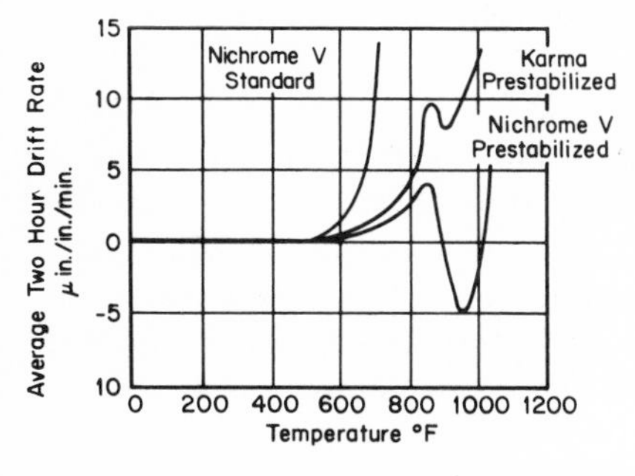

(b) Typical zero drift at constant temperature. Nickel-chrome alloys

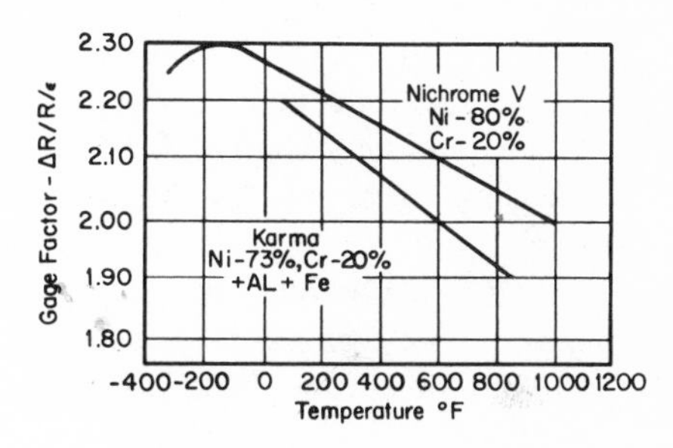

(c) Typical gage factor versus temperature characteristics. Nickel-chrome alloys

Fig. 4-2. Gage-wire characteristic changes at elevated temperatures. (*Courtesy of Baldwin-Lima-Hamilton Corporation.*)

difficult and time-consuming, requiring favorable conditions not often available in the field. In general, the methods used are chemical setting and heat curing. A gage-mounting method utilizing a molten oxide spray has been developed at Rolls-Royce.* The process† utilizes oxide rods, which are melted by oxyacetylene flame; the atomized molten oxide is sprayed on the pre-positioned gage to bond it in place. Boeing Airplane

* This method was described by D. A. Drew and reported in *Strain Gage Readings* 1, 5 (Dec. 1958—Jan. 1959), p. 27.

† Norton Rokide process, Norton Grinding Wheel Co., Ltd., England.

Company has developed the flame spraying of both the insulating base and the gage element. The flame-sprayed aluminum oxide coating, 0.012 to 0.018 in. thick, serves as the insulating base. A 0.020-in. thick phosphor-bronze stencil is used to obtain the desired pattern of the flame-sprayed metallic grid. The grid thickness can be varied between 0.003 and 0.005 in., depending on the desired resistance. Gage fusing at about 2000°F was found to be necessary in order to obtain accuracies of three per cent up to 1000°F. Good bonding and thermal-stability characteristics up to 2200°F were obtained through the use of laminar base coatings; see Ref. [11].

Gage elements made of high-temperature alloys (Nichrome V, Karma, etc.) and formed specifically for mounting in ceramic cements are available. Foil gages for this purpose are available either on a plastic backing which can be stripped away after the gage is placed in a ceramic cement (strippable gage) or as completely free filaments (free-handling gages). Wire gages for this purpose are available either as completely free filaments or as a single strand of strain-sensitive wire which has been precoated with a ceramic cement.

To facilitate mounting gages in the field, they have sometimes been bonded to steel shim stock with ceramic cement in the laboratory, and the shim stock in turn has been welded to the test surface at the test site. Prebonded gages of this type are commercially available. The need for a bonding cement has been completely eliminated in weldable gages. These gages utilize a one-piece, etched wire filament in a swagged stainless-steel tube. The filament is surrounded by tightly packed metallic oxide insulation. The gage is mounted by welding the stainless-steel tube to the test surface. In this case the gage element characteristics alone establish the upper temperature limit.

WITH SEMICONDUCTOR GAGES

The bonding problems associated with higher temperature are the same when semiconductor gages are used as when metal gages are used. In general, however, the semiconductor strain-sensitive element is more affected by temperature than is the metal element. Specifically, the change in resistance (ΔR) or the change in resistance per unit of resistance ($\Delta R/R$) is greater per unit of temperature change with semiconductors than with metal gages. However, it must be remembered that the apparent, or false, strain signal produced is $\Delta R/S$ or $\Delta R/R/F$, and since the sensitivity (S) or gage factor (F) of semiconductors is large, the apparent strain per unit temperature may be the same order as with metal gages. A greater problem is the fact that with semiconductor gages the gage factor or sensitivity is affected by temperature. Figure 4-3 shows a typical plot of

F versus temperature. This effect is approximately ten times as great with semiconductors as with metal gages. It must be remembered that normal temperature-compensation techniques do not correct for this change in gage factor with temperature.

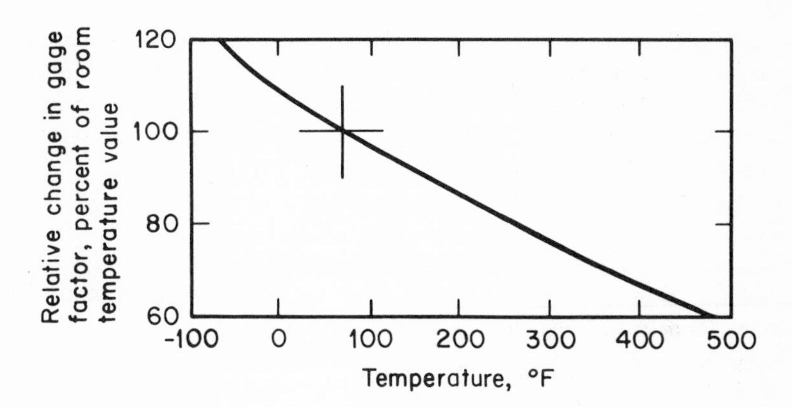

Fig. 4-3. Gage factor versus temperature for a semiconductor gage. (*Courtesy of ISA: see Ref.* [4] *at the end of Chap. 2.*)

The fact that semiconductor elements have a very low coefficient of expansion compared to the coefficient of expansion of most of the materials on which they are mounted introduces an additional temperature-related problem.* At high temperatures the strain introduced by differential expansion between the test item and the gage may be so large that only limited usable strain range remains for the measurement of additional stress-induced strains. This is important, since the operating strain range of semiconductor gages is less than with metal gages even at room temperature; see Sect. 2-2b.

LEAD-WIRE PROBLEMS AT HIGH TEMPERATURE

Lead-wire materials undergo the same type of resistance changes at high temperatures as do the strain-sensitive elements. Hence, it is imperative that materials with good temperature stability be used for leads. Nichrome V is widely used for this purpose, but during the first few temperature cycles even this basically stable material will undergo permanent resistance changes that could be confused with strain. Temperature cycling of the complete installation, gage and leads, is, therefore, advisable.

* The coefficient of expansion of silicon is 1.3×10^{-6} in./in./°F.

The change in lead resistance during tests will generally be large. This is the case not only because large changes in temperature may be involved, but also because the more stable materials often have large temperature coefficients of resistance. For this reason it is imperative that the leads be temperature-compensating, i.e., that a three-wire lead system be used, even if a single active gage is used.

In high-temperature work the lead resistance is often large enough to effectively desensitize the gage, because the necessary lead materials tend to have higher values of resistance than do the copper leads used in ambient-temperature work. This desensitization may be accounted for by computing an effective gage factor as:

$$F_{\text{Effective}} = \frac{R_g}{R_g + R_l} F$$

in which $F_{\text{Effective}}$ is the gage factor to be used in computing strain. This takes the effect of lead resistance into account.

F is the gage factor given by the manufacturer.

R_g is the gage resistance.

R_l is the lead resistance in series with the active gage.

Since a thermocouple is produced at every point where two dissimilar metals are joined, we realize that two thermocouples may be formed when the lead wires are joined to the two ends of the gage elements.

These two thermocouples produce voltages which are opposed; hence, the net effect is due to the difference in temperature between the two ends of the element. Surprisingly enough, in high-temperature work there may be a significant temperature difference across the width of the gage, and, therefore, this problem must be considered. If the lead wire used is the same as the gage element, then no thermocouples exist.* (A common case is Nichrome V lead wire used with a Nichrome V gage.) If this is not practical, then the lead should be chosen to give the least thermal emf in contact with the gage element. Constantan produces a strong electromotive force (emf) in contact with most gage materials and, therefore, should only be used for leads when the gage element is also Constantan.

As already mentioned, Nichrome V is often used for high-temperature leads because of its greater stability and the elimination of thermoelectric effect when used with Nichrome V gages. Its principal drawback is its high resistance, which desensitizes the gage.

* Because of difference in heat treatment, cold work, and impurity elements between gage material and leads, some thermoelectric effect is possible, but using the same alloy will minimize the output.

Lead wires may be soft-soldered, provided that the resistance of the soldered joint remains stable up to the operating temperature. In general, for use at temperatures up to 350°F, gage leads are soldered. For use at higher temperatures, gage leads are ordinarily welded to the gage elements.

Nickel- and stainless-steel-clad copper lead wires are available which are stable to temperatures as high as 1200°F and which have much lower resistance than a similar Nichrome lead. Unfortunately, these clad-copper materials have a higher temperature coefficient of resistance than does Nichrome V.

The insulation of lead wires also poses special problems in high-temperature work. In general, the lead-wire insulation should be capable of use to as high a temperature as is the gage itself. Teflon is suitable as lead insulation for temperatures as high as 500°F, silicon-impregnated Fiberglas may be used to 600°F, and Fiberglas braid may be used to 800° or 900°F. Above 800° or 900°F, ceramic insulation is necessary. Bare leads may be enclosed in ceramic tubes and the tubes held in place with spot-welded metal straps, or bare leads may be coated with the same ceramic cement used to bond the gage. Gage leads should not be bonded to the test surface, however, since errors are introduced if the leads produce strain-induced resistance changes.

SELECTED BIBLIOGRAPHY ON HIGH-TEMPERATURE STRAIN MEASUREMENTS

Group I: Techniques

1. Gorton, R. E., "Development and Use of High-Temperature Strain Gages," *Proceedings of the Society for Experimental Stress Analysis*, 9, 1 (1951), pp. 163–76.
2. Hauser, R. L., "Techniques for Installation of High-Temperature Foil Strain Gages," *Strain Gage Readings*, 2, 6 (Feb.–Mar. 1960), pp. 41–44.
3. Teague, E. D., "The Rokide Process for Mounting Resistance Strain Gages," *Proceedings of the Annual Conference of the Stress Analysis Group of the Institute of Physics* (Sept. 1959), Birmingham, England.
4. Beyer, F. R. and J. O. Smith, "Evaluation of High-Temperature Strain Gages for the Enrico Firmi Reactor Vessel," *Experimental Mechanics*, 2, 3 (Mar. 1962), pp. 81–88.
5. Brewer, G. A. and J. D. Ingham, "Measurement of Thermal Stresses Within an Experimental Nuclear Reactor Vessel Head," *Experimental Mechanics*, 2, 1 (Jan. 1962), pp. 9–14.

Group II: Evaluation

1. Pitts, J. W. and D. G. Moore, *Development of High-Temperature Strain Gages*, NBS Monograph 26 (Mar. 17, 1961).
2. Brosius, G. F. and D. Hartley, "Evaluation of High-Temperature Strain Gages," "*Proceedings of the Society for Experimental Stress Analysis*, 17, 1 (1959), pp. 67–84.
3. Day, E. E., "Performance of Foil-Type High-Temperature Strain Gages Up to 700°F," *Proceedings of the Society for Experimental Stress Analysis*, 16, 1 (1958), pp. 97–108.

4. *High-Temperature Cement Evaluation, Phase I—Electrical Properties*, Baldwin-Lima-Hamilton Corporation, Electronic Instrumentation Division, Technical Data Bulletin 4310-9 (Jan. 1, 1960).

4-2e Strain measurements at low temperatures

At present, there is considerable interest in the measurement of strains at temperatures approaching absolute zero, and all indications point toward increasing interest in the future.

Gage evaluation has not been as extensively reported at very low temperatures as it has at very high temperatures, but several gage alloys and most of the common bonds have been tested at temperatures of −320°F or less.

As is the case in any application where temperature varies, it is imperative to separate resistance changes produced by strain from those produced by temperature change. The use of compensating gages has been possible in most of the low temperatures reported, and the usual compensating techniques have proved to be satisfactory. In studies which were specifically designed to evaluate strain-gage alloys, it has been found that the most-used alloys are stable in the low-temperature range; both gage factor and temperature coefficient of resistance vary with temperature, but the effect is reversible and the values are constant at constant temperature. From this it would appear that, when the use of a compensating-gage circuit is not possible, the data may be corrected for temperature effect. C. R. Harris and J. E. Davis [12] report on the use of a self-temperature-compensating strain gage from room temperature to −320°F. They indicate that a universally self-temperature-compensating gage (resistance thermometer in series with gage grid, BLH Type FNH-50-12E) can be adjusted to read true strain at any desired lower temperature, but with various amounts of error at other temperatures.

Most investigators agree that the gage factor of the copper-nickel alloys decreases with decreasing temperature. E. W. Kammer [13] reports that the gage factor of annealed Constantan wire is 1.7 at 4.2°K (−452.2°F), which suggests that at this temperature the resistance change is wholly a dimensional effect ($F = 1 + 2\mu$); i.e., the resistivity does not change with strain. Kammer points out that this is not the usual case, and refers to another alloy which has the same or increased gage factor at low temperatures. In the case of Constantan, cold-working raises the gage factor obtained at low temperatures.

Cellulose-nitrate and epoxy cements have been successfully used to bond paper-backed gages for low-temperature service. R. M. McClintock and D. A. Van Gundy [14] report using paper-backed gages at 76°K bonded with cellulose-nitrate and epoxies. Strains as high as 5000μin./in.

were recorded before the cellulose-nitrate bonds failed, and strains as high as 10,000 μin./in. were recorded before the epoxy bonds failed.

One low-temperature limitation common to all organic cements is the fact that they oxidize rapidly and may be explosive in direct contact with liquid oxygen. For this reason, ceramic cements have been used in this particular low-temperature application.

4-2f Magnetic effects

When a ferromagnetic material is used as a strain-gage element [isoelastic wire gages by Baldwin-Lima-Hamilton (C-type) are the only commercially available gages of this type], two possible sources of false strain are introduced.

The presence of a magnetic field will cause a change in resistance of the element (magnetoresistive effect) and, hence, a false strain signal. The magnitude of the false strain which will be induced in a given gage depends upon the strength of the magnetic field, the state of strain in the element, and the orientation of the element in the magnetic field. The curves shown in Fig. 4-4 are taken from a paper by J. Gunn and E. Billinghurst [15], who investigated this effect in conjunction with strain-gage work on the University of California Bevatron. I. Vigness [16] shows that, with proper conditioning, isoelastic wire gages generate a voltage signal when strained. This false strain signal is also a magnetic effect. Vigness suggests that when the gage wire is conditioned by carrying a current, the magnetic domains within the wire are aligned in a preferred direction by the magnetic field associated with the current. When the state of strain is changed, the magnetic field associated with the conditioned wire will be changed and a voltage is generated. Self-generated voltages approaching one mv have been observed in isoelastic wire gages being used to measure transient strains.

One semiconductor gage manufacturer (Micro Systems, Incorporated) checked for magnetoresistive effects by bonding its gages to an aluminum cantilever beam, which was placed successively in each of the three orthogonal positions with respect to a 9000 Gauss magnetic field. Observations of zero shift and gage factor at 500 μin./in. showed no measurable change within the resolution of the test equipment (one μin./in.).

4-2g Strain measurements at high pressures

When strain gages are used on surfaces which are subjected to pressure, several precautions are necessary.

First, it is important that the surface be smooth. If surface irregularities are present, the applied pressure will tend to contour the gage to the irregularities; in the extreme case this may rupture the gage grid, and in any case it will produce erratic and false readings.

Second, a compensating gage subjected to the same pressure environment as the active gage should be used. This is good practice, since it is the most convenient way to assure temperature compensation and it tends to provide compensation for resistance changes due to the effect of pressure on the grid and bond. When the data is being reduced, it is important to account for the fact that the compensating gage is subjected

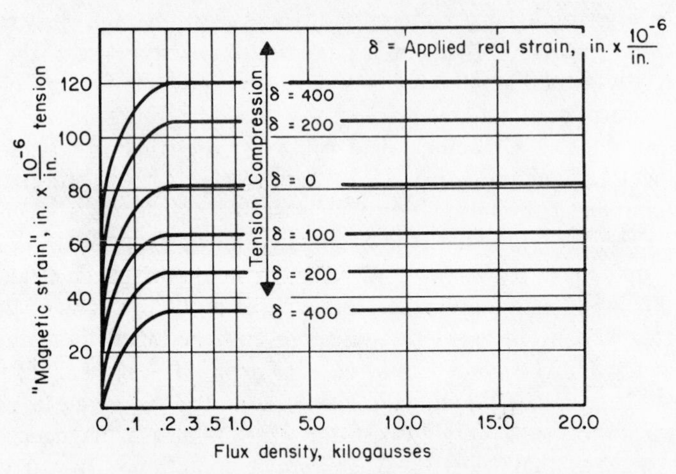

(a) Magnetoresistive effect in Elinvar plotted as an effective "magnetic strain," for fields parallel to gage.

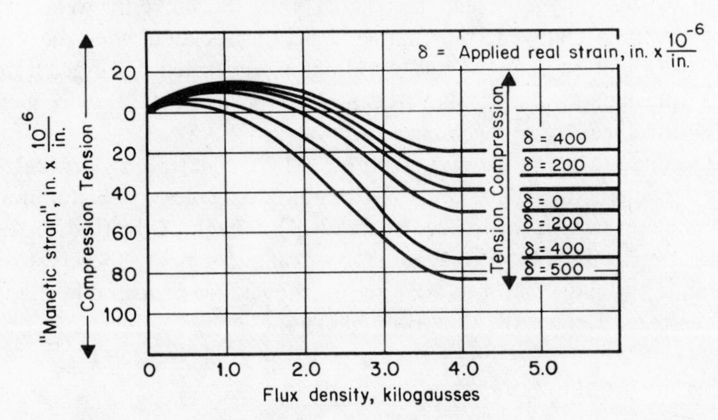

(b) Magnetoresistive effect in Elinvar plotted as a "magnetic strain," for field perpendicular to gage wires.

Fig. 4-4. Magnetic field effect on strain gages. (*Courtesy of Control Engineering, Ref.* [15].)

to strain which is dependent on the bulk modulus and the applied pressure. This can easily be computed as

$$\epsilon_x = \frac{S_x}{E} - \frac{\mu}{E}(S_y + S_z),$$

and for the case of hydrostatic pressure ($S_x = S_y = S_z = -$ applied pressure P)

$$\epsilon = -\frac{1 - 2\mu}{E}P.$$

Third, only flat-grid-type gages (wire or foil) are suitable when pressure is applied to the gage surface. The wrap-around type of gage gives erratic output and considerable zero shift under this condition.

M. C. Steele and L. C. Eichberger [17] have evaluated foil-type gages subjected to pressures as high as 20,000 psi. Taking the precautions noted above, they find that any unaccounted-for pressure effect is small and linear—between $\frac{1}{2}$ and $3\frac{1}{2}$ μin./in./1000 psi.

J. P. Guerard and G. F. Weissmann [18] have evaluated paper-backed wire gages subjected to 12,000 psi. Again, taking the precautions noted, they find that any unaccounted-for pressure effects are of the same magnitude as indication errors ($< 25\mu$in./in. in the worst case).

More recently, J. C. Gerdeen [19] has evaluated foil gages subjected to pressures as high as 35,000 psi. He placed gaged metal samples with various curvature radii under hydrostatic pressure with the compensating gages remaining at ambient conditions. Cynoacrylate contact cement was found to give the most easily reproducible results of any of the four cements tested. Unaccounted-for pressure effects were found to be approximately linear and between six μin./in./1000 psi for flat specimens and three μin./in./1000 psi for specimens with a radii of 0.19 in.

4-2h Measurement of strains on low-modulus materials and/or on thin sections

When strain gages are bonded to the surface of materials which have either a very low modulus of elasticity or a small cross section, the local stiffening effect of the gage may be of great importance. Not only is the recorded strain less than the value of strain which would exist if the gage were not present, but the distribution of strain near the gage is altered.

One approach to the problem of using strain gages on a material having a low elastic modulus is to determine a corrected gage factor. The gage factor determined will be lower than the value given by the manufacturer if the gage reinforces the material on which it is mounted—the greater the reinforcing, the lower the gage factor. (The gage factor given by the manufacturer is determined with the gage mounted on steel, for which the reinforcing effect is negligible.) Several investigators have found that the common paper-backed gages with a gage factor of approximately 2 will have an effective gage factor of near 1.7 when bonded on a low modulus plastic [$E < 500{,}000$ psi) with cellulose-nitrate cement [20, 21]. M. M. Frocht [22] points out that in this application the effect of gage heating on the bond and plastic properties near the gage point is very important.

Use of an "effective gage factor" when a gage is bonded to a low-modulus material may not be a suitable solution to the reinforcing problem, however. First of all, the effective gage factor will strictly apply only if the dimensions of the specimen of interest and the specimen used in the determination of effective gage factor are identical. Second, use of an effective gage factor does not account for the fact that the strain distribution is altered by the gage's presence.

Some guides as to when gage reinforcing will be significant can be established from a knowledge of gage-bond stiffness, i.e., the force required to strain a gage and its bond. Evaluation of gage stiffness has been undertaken both experimentally [23] and theoretically [24], but this value is available for only a few gage types. The experimental approach consists of bonding two gages back-to-back and subjecting them to a tensile test. From the force-strain data the gage stiffness can be computed.

Since

$$E_g = \frac{S}{\epsilon} = \frac{F}{A_g \epsilon},$$

we may write

$$(AE)_g = \frac{F}{\epsilon},$$

in which E = effective modulus of elasticity of the entire gage (grid, back, and bond).

A = the cross-sectional area of the equivalent homogeneous gage.

The importance of this product $(EA)_g$, which is the gage stiffness, can best be illustrated by an example.

Example 4-1. Consider a tensile specimen having a rectangular cross section of A_s. The force required to produce a unit strain is

$$\frac{F_s}{\epsilon_s} = A_s E_s, \tag{4-1}$$

in which the subscript s is used to denote the specimen. Now if we mount a gage on each edge of this specimen, and assume that at the cross section where the gages are mounted the strain is uniform (ϵ of gages = ϵ in the specimen), the force required to produce a unit strain may be determined as follows: since

$$\epsilon_g = \epsilon_s,$$

$$\epsilon_g = \epsilon_s = \frac{F_g}{(EA)_g} = \frac{F_s}{E_s A_s}, \tag{4-2}$$

in which the subscript g denotes the gages. The total force applied is equal to the sum of the resistive forces developed by the specimen and by the gages; i.e.,

$$F_{\text{Total}} = F_g + F_s;$$

substituting Eq. (4-2) into this expression gives

$$\frac{F_{\text{Total}}}{\epsilon_s} = (EA)_g + E_s A_s. \tag{4-3}$$

The ratio of force required to produce a given strain with gages in place to the force required when no gages are present is

$$R = \frac{\left(\frac{F}{\epsilon}\right)_{\text{with gages}}}{\left(\frac{F}{\epsilon}\right)_{\text{without gages}}} = \frac{(EA)_g + E_s A_s}{E_s A_s} = \frac{(EA)_g}{E_s A_s} + 1. \tag{4-4}$$

This ratio is a measure of the stiffening or reinforcing effect of the gages. The value of this effect, and hence the possible error introduced in strain measurement, is obviously dependent upon

$$\frac{(EA)_g}{E_s A_s}.$$

Reference [23] finds the stiffness $(EA)_g$ of a type A-1 gage, trimmed to a width of 0.375 in. and bonded with nitrocellulose cement, to be

$$(EA)_g = 1040 \text{ lb/in./in.}$$

Then, if two such gages are bonded on opposite sides of a specimen,

$$(EA)_{g_{\text{Total}}} = 2080 \text{ lb/in./in.}$$

With this value, Eq. (4-4) can be solved for various materials having various thicknesses. The results of such a computation appear in Table 4-1.

Table 4-1. The reinforcing effect of two Type A-1, SR-4 gages bonded with cellulose-nitrate to the opposite sides of tensile specimens of various materials and sizes.

Material	E_s (psi)	Specimen size (in. × in.)	Reinforcing effect $= \dfrac{(F/\epsilon)_{\text{with gages}}}{(F/\epsilon)_{\text{without gages}}}$
Rubber or	1,000	$1 \times \frac{3}{8}$	6.55
rubberlike	5,000	$1 \times \frac{3}{8}$	2.11
Plastic	200,000	$1 \times \frac{3}{8}$	1.03
	200,000	$\frac{1}{8} \times \frac{3}{8}$	1.22
Aluminum	10×10^6	$\frac{1}{16} \times \frac{3}{8}$	1.01

The values given in the table point out that although gages can be mounted on very thin metal sections without introducing any appreciable reinforcing effect, the reinforcing effect may be large when they are mounted on thin plastic sections or on rubberlike materials of any size.

The assumption that the strain is uniform through the cross sections at which the gages are applied is certainly an oversimplification, even for tensile loading. The localized stiffening of the surface will, in fact, produce distortion of the strain pattern within the specimen, and this distortion will be more complex when the shape of the specimen and/or the type of loading becomes more complex. The distortion of the strain pattern in the vicinity of the gages makes the entire problem of gage reinforcing more difficult, because the distortion makes it more difficult to apply any meaningful correction factor to values of strain measured by the gages.

How the total stiffening effect of the type A-1, SR-4 gage is divided between the wire grid, which is the strain-sensitive element, and the material which joins that grid to the strained surface was also investigated. The total cross-sectional area of the six lengths of one mil wire in the grid is

$$A_W = \frac{(6)(\pi)(0.001)^2}{4} = 4.71 \times 10^{-6} \text{ in.}^2$$

If the modulus of elasticity of the grid wire (Advance) is taken as

$$E_W = 26 \times 10^6 \text{ psi},$$

then the force required to strain the grid is

$$\frac{F_W}{\epsilon} = A_W E_W = 122 \text{ lb/in./in.},$$

in which the subscript W denotes the grid wire. Comparison of this value with the value of F/ϵ for the type A-1 gage as a whole shows that the wire grid accounts for only $\frac{122}{1040}$, or 12 per cent of the total stiffening effect of the gage.

This suggests that when strain gages are used on low-modulus materials or thin sections, the use of an unbacked gage will reduce the reinforcing. Several investigators* have used strippable-backed foil gages in low modulus plastics without introducing measurable reinforcing.

When strain gages are mounted on thin sections which are subjected to bending, there are two sources of error. First, the distance from the neutral surface to the strain-sensitive grid is greater than the distance to the specimen surface at which strain is desired; hence, the reading tends to be too large. Second, the gage reinforces the thin section; hence, the reading tends to be too small. These factors tend to cancel, but the net effect depends upon both bond thickness and reinforcing effect. In general, the thinner the glue line, the better, since both effects are reduced.

4-2i Measurement of large strains

The range of strain over which bonded resistance strain gages will function properly is dependent on several factors and, therefore, is different for each different gage type, and for the same gage with different bonds. The following factors will be considered in order:

1. Influence of strain magnitude on gage factor. It is desirable to have a constant gage factor. As we pointed out on p. 53, for those gage alloys which have a gage factor of approximately 2, the gage factor is unchanged by strains even in the plastic region (up to 15 per cent) (see Ref. [1], listed at the end of Chap. 2). Also, as was pointed out on p. 96, semiconductor gages tend to show progressive changes in gage factor, or sensitivity, with strain. See Fig. 2-25 on p. 95, and Fig. 4-5.
2. Effect of grid material and form. Elements of annealed wire or foil will function to higher strains than will elements of the same

* See Sect. 4-2m.

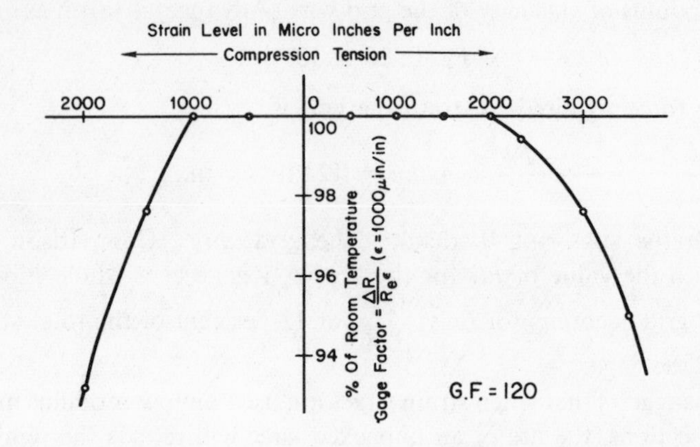

Fig. 4-5. Strain sensitivity versus strain level for a Bakelite-backed semiconductor strain gage. (*Courtesy of ISA, Ref.* [25].)

material but with a lesser degree of anneal. Foil gages will, in general, function to higher strains than will flat-wire grids, and flat-wire grids will function to higher strains than will helically wound wire grids. A large gage will function to larger strains than will a smaller gage of the same material. Most semiconductor gages will not function at tensile strains in excess of 5000 μin./in. and hence will not be considered further for the measurement of large strains.

3. Effect of backing and bonding material. The organic bases and bonds will function at higher strains than will the ceramic cements. But, since the elasticity of the organics is affected by temperature, the allowable strain decreases with decreasing temperatures when organic bonds are used.
4. Effect of lead-wire connection. The manner in which the gage is connected to the lead wires has a tremendous influence on the magnitude of strain to which the gage installation will function. This factor is too often overlooked and, as a result, the maximum gage capability is often not realized. The main lead wires should be securely fastened to the test specimen at a point very near the gage tabs, and an intermediate lead of smaller size should be used to connect this fixed point to the gage tab. The use of strain-gage wiring terminals is excellent practice.

When properly bonded and wired, epoxy- and Bakelite-backed wire-wound gages of the flat-grid type and of $\frac{1}{4}$-in. gage length or greater will measure strains as large as $1\frac{1}{2}$ to 2 per cent (15,000 to 20,000 μin./in.)

Epoxy- and Bakelite-backed foil gages will measure strains as large as 3 to 4 per cent (30,000 to 40,000 μin./in.).

The heat-curing epoxies appear to be the best for bonding either the epoxy or the Bakelite gages. Cyanocrylate (Eastman 910) bonding is *not* recommended when large strains are expected. Although a fresh bond of this type may be good for 2 or 3 per cent strain, an aged bond (48 hours or more) may not be capable of more than 0.5 per cent strain.

Because of the brittle nature of ceramic cements, gages bonded with ceramics have a useful strain range of approximately 0.5 per cent. Cellulose-nitrate and epoxies become so brittle at low temperatures that the useful strain range of gages so bonded is reduced to approximately 0.5 per cent at −320°F.

Flat-grid, wire-wound gages are available on a special flexible paper backing which will measure strains up to 10 per cent (BLH. post-yield gages, Type PA). These gages have an intermediate-sized, flexible lead inserted between the grid wire and the standard lead. These gages must be bonded with a special flexible cement.

Epoxy-backed foil gages which have been processed to permit measurement of strains as high as 15 per cent are also available (Budd, high-elongation gage, Type HE).

Many investigators have devised special methods to use bonded resistance gages to measure very high strains. The most common method utilizes what is known as a "clip" or U-gage. Figure 4-6a shows such a gage, which was designed by one of the authors. Figure 4-6b shows the calibration curve for this gage. J. A. Hurry and R. P. Wooley [26] describe an interesting bonded resistance gage for measuring large strains in low-modulus materials. This gage consists of a rubber tube three to six in. long with an inside diameter of four- to eight-thousandths of an inch, filled with mercury. Electrical connections are made to the mercury column by means of copper wires, which also seal the ends of the tube. The filled tube is formed into a flat grid and bonded to the test specimen with a flexible cement. Hurry and Wooley report a linear change in resistance over a range of strain from −25 to +100 per cent, and no zero shift after several thousand cycles from 0 to +50 per cent strain.

4-2j Measurement of cyclic strains

When strain gages are used to measure varying and repeated strains, the fatigue life of the strain-gage installation becomes important. Special care must be exercised in gage selection, in gage bonding, and in lead attachment, if the gage installation is to perform satisfactorily.

It was formerly felt that helically wound wire gages and "Isoelastic" wire gages had superior fatigue life [27]. However, more recent research

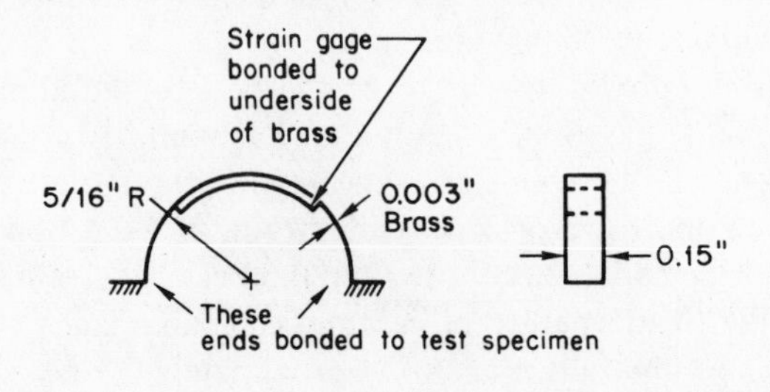

(a) U-gage

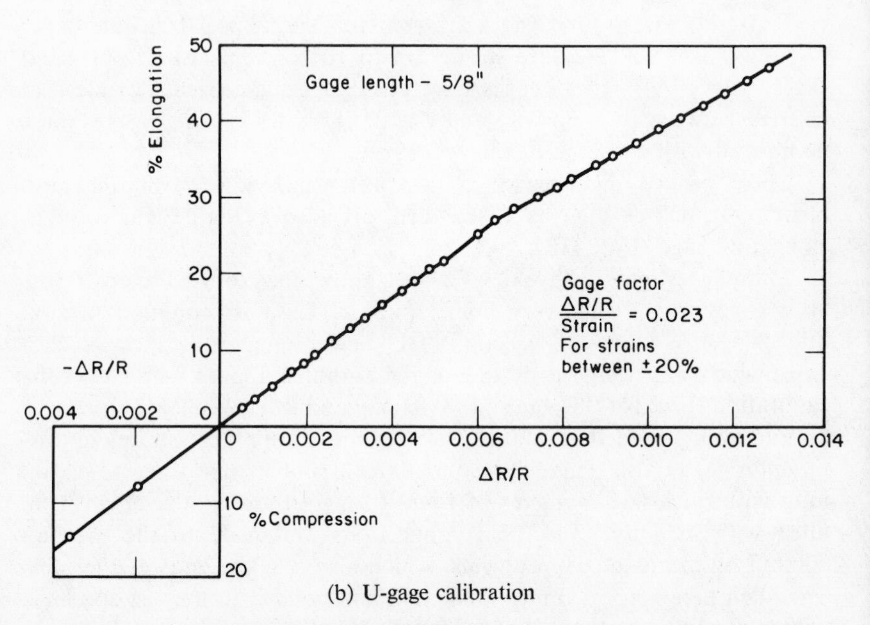

(b) U-gage calibration

Fig. 4-6. U-gage with calibration curve.

shows that Constantan gages in the form of either flat-wire grid or foil can be mounted so as to have a fatigue life greater than either helically wound gages or "Isoelastic" wire gages; therefore, these two types, which have other disadvantages (see pp. 58-59), need not be considered for vibration environments. A special form of wire gage which incorporates a link of intermediate-size wire between the filament wire and the larger lead wire is available (BLH Dual-Lead Gage, Type AD) but, here again, recent tests have shown that other "standard" gages have as great or greater fatigue life.

Flat-grid, wire, and foil metal gages on paper backing and bonded with cellulose-nitrate cement have been strain-cycled ($\pm 1000\mu$in./in.) for 1,250,000 cycles without failure.* Bakelite-backed foil metal gages bonded with Bakelite cement have been strain-cycled (± 1500 μin./in.) for 2,650,-000 cycles without failure.† Epoxy-backed foil metal gages bonded with epoxy cements are capable of more than 3,000,000 cycles at ± 1500 μin./in., according to one manufacturer. One manufacturer (Micro Systems, Incorporated) of semiconductor gages reports that tests on epoxy-backed semiconductor gages at strain levels of 500, 1000, and 1500 μin./in. indicate fatigue life in excess of five million cycles. At a strain level of 500 μin./in. the time to failure was in excess of 200 million cycles.

Unfortunately, little information is available on the fatigue life of high-temperature gage installation using ceramic cements.

It is generally agreed that as the magnitude of repeated strain increases from 1500 μin./in., the fatigue life is reduced very rapidly. Peter Stein [28] makes the following suggestion: "When it is necessary to monitor high strains which occur more often than the strain gage to be used is likely to withstand, the following procedure has proven helpful: mount a second strain gage near the one subjected to high strains, but mount the second one in a low-strain region. Utilize the life of the first gage to establish an effective strain ratio between the two gages. Subsequently use this ratio and the readings from the low-strain gage (which will live "forever") to monitor the strains at the failed gage location."

It is well established that connection of the lead wires is the most critical step in the installation of a gage for cyclic strain service. The use of small (for example, No. 37 copper), solid wires between the main lead wires and the gage is imperative. These small wires must contain a flex loop, and the main lead wires must be securely anchored at their junction with the smaller wires.

4-2k Measurement of transient strains

Bonded resistance strain gages are probably more used in shock and impact studies than is any other type of transducer. This is true not only because magnitudes of strain produced in these environments are important, but also because the bonded resistance gage, with its small volume and low mass, is ideally suited for use in these environments.

---

* Technical Data 4310-7, Baldwin-Lima-Hamilton Corporation, Electronics and Instrumentation Division, Waltham, Mass. (May 1, 1959).

† Technical Data 4310-8, Baldwin-Lima-Hamilton Corporation, Electronics and Instrumentation Division, Waltham, Mass. (May 1, 1959).

There are, however, several special factors to be considered when bonded gages are used to measure transient strains. The importance of response time of circuit components and recording rates of recording equipment has been discussed in Chap. 3. In many cases the readout circuitry and recording equipment place the limitation on the transient strain pulses that can be accurately recorded. The shorter the strain pulse rise time and duration, the better the system response required.

However, the strain-gage installation itself imposes some limitations on the measurement of transients. First, the gage and/or bond must not fail when subjected to the strain transient. Elevated temperature-curing epoxy bonds have been found to be best for use in shock and impact environments. Cyanocrylate (Eastman 910) is not recommended for large strain transients, and the ceramic cements will stand the least mechanical shock of all.

Second, the transfer of strain from the specimen surface to the gage grid may be different in the dynamic case from what it is in the static case; hence, the "dynamic" gage factor may be different from the "static" gage factor. This suspicion arises since it is well-known that the properties (modulus, limit of linear deformation, etc.) of plastics, such as those interposed between specimen surface and gage grid, are affected by the rate of straining. J. I. Nisbet, J. N. Brennan, and H. I. Tarpley [29] investigated this effect, using paper-backed gages bonded with cellulose-nitrate and epoxy cements. In the frequency range of 2,000 to 20,000 cps, the dynamic gage factor differed by less than five per cent from the static gage factor. But some discrepancies were noted, and the investigators suggest that dynamic response may be very sensitive to bond thickness, thicker bonds producing lower dynamic gage factors.

Third, the ratio of the gage length to the physical length of the strain pulse influences the signal produced. Consideration of a strain pulse propagating past a gage location will show that as the length of the strain pulse is reduced to approach the length of the strain gage element, the output signal is progressively distorted. Figure 4-7, which shows a rectangular pulse passing a gage, illustrates the point. The output-pulse duration exceeds the time required for the strain transient to pass a point by an amount equal to ($2l/c$), in which (l) is the gage length and (c) is the velocity of propagation. In this simple example only the pulse shape is distorted; the magnitude is not. In some cases, where the input is not of constant magnitude or is shorter than the gage length, this averaging of the input over the gage length will distort the magnitude as well as the shape. G. Murphy, A. Hausrath, and P. Peterson [30] consider this effect in more detail. Peter Stein [31] analyzes a sinusoidal pulse and shows that if the error in the amplitude of the peak strain is to be no greater

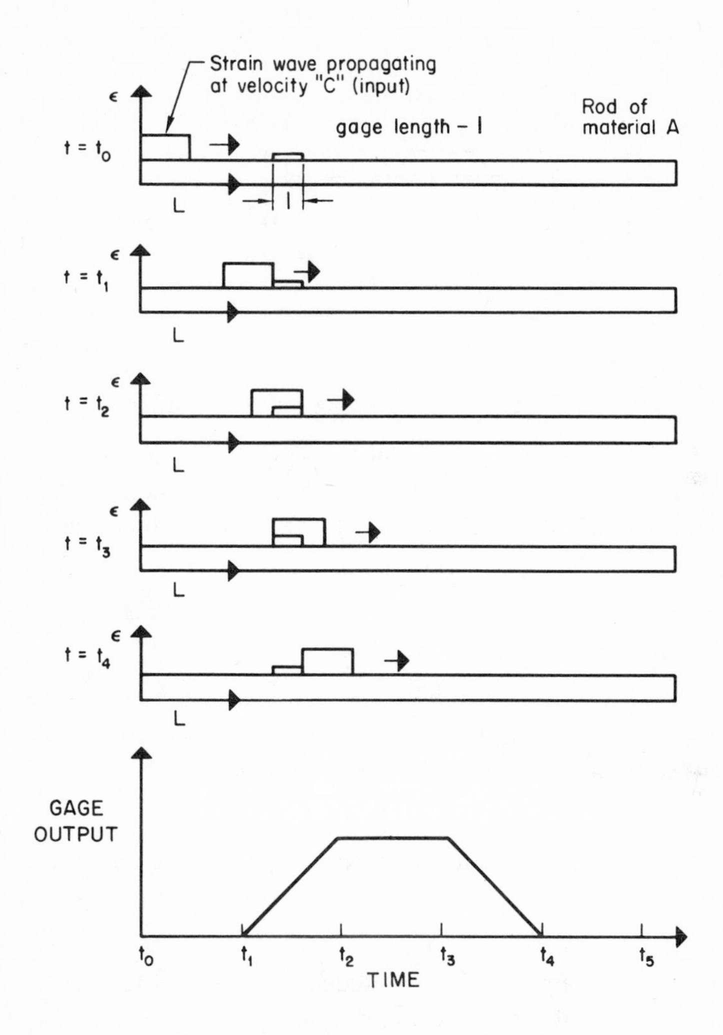

Fig. 4-7. Effect of gage length on signal.

than one per cent, the gage length can be no greater than one-twentieth of the wavelength.

4-21 Thermal-stress studies

Thermally induced stresses are those stresses produced by restraint of thermal expansion (plus or minus). The restraint may be external, internal, or any combination of the two. As an example of thermal stress produced by external restraint, consider a tube mounted between two relatively rigid walls (see Fig. 4-8).

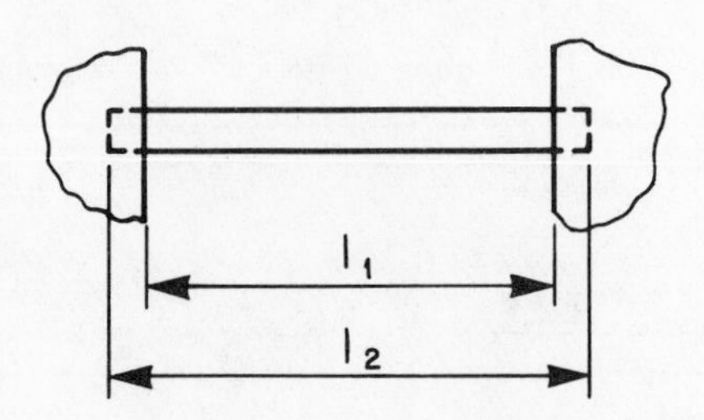

Fig. 4-8. Thermal stress due to external restraint.

If the tube were free to expand, the tube length would be l_2 at some higher temperature T_2. Since the walls prevent expansion, the actual tube length at temperature T_2 will be l_1, and the induced strain will be

$$\epsilon_t = \frac{l_1 - l_2}{l_1}.$$

If the restraint is complete, we may write

$$l_1 - l_2 = -\alpha \, \Delta T l_1,$$

in which (α) is the coefficient of linear expansion of the tube, and (ΔT) is the temperature change. Hence, for complete restraint,

$$\epsilon_t = -\alpha \, \Delta T.$$

For partial restraint the thermally induced strain will be the change in length per unit of original length (ξ) minus ($\alpha \, \Delta T$); i.e.,

$$\epsilon_t = \xi - \alpha \, \Delta T. \tag{4-5}$$

As an example of thermal stress produced by internal restraint, consider a free tube heated at one end (see Fig. 4-9). At temperature (T_1) the diameter of the entire tube is d_1. If a section on the left end is heated to a temperature T_2, the tube will attempt to expand to a diameter (d_2) equal to

$$d_2 = d_1 + d_1 \alpha \, \Delta T.$$

Now, in the area of the temperature interface the material will be subjected to thermally induced stress. To the left of the interface the material is compressed because of the restraint offered to free expansion by the material on the right. To the right of the temperature interface the strain situation is reversed.

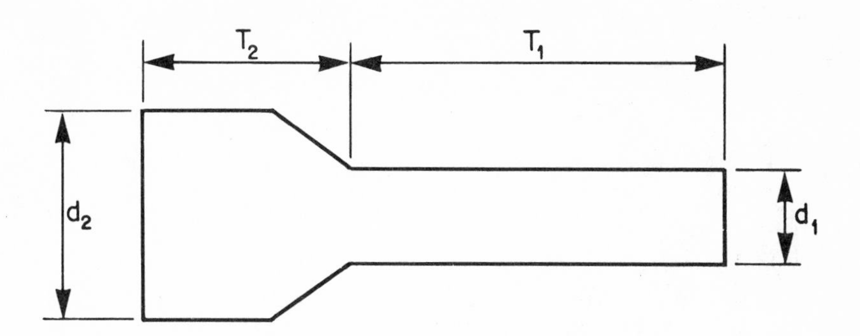

Fig. 4-9. Thermal stress due to internal restraint.

In either case, external or internal restraint, the thermal strain is

$$\epsilon_t = \xi - \alpha\,\Delta T. \tag{4-5}$$

In the elastic region the thermally induced stress is related to the thermally induced strain by the usual equations. For the uniaxial stress case,

$$\sigma_t = E\epsilon_t, \tag{4-6}$$

or

$$\sigma_t = E(\xi - \alpha\,\Delta T). \tag{4-6a}$$

For the biaxial stress case

$$\sigma_{tx} = \frac{E}{1-\mu^2}(\epsilon_{tx} + \mu\epsilon_{ty}), \qquad (4\text{-}7)$$

and

$$\sigma_{ty} = \frac{E}{1-\mu^2}(\epsilon_{ty} + \mu\epsilon_{tx}), \qquad (4\text{-}7)$$

or

$$\sigma_{tx} = \frac{E}{1-\mu^2}(\xi_x + \mu\xi_y) - \frac{E\alpha\,\Delta T}{1-\mu}, \qquad (4\text{-}7a)$$

and

$$\sigma_{ty} = \frac{E}{1-\mu^2}(\xi_y + \mu\xi_x) - \frac{E\alpha\,\Delta T}{1-\mu}. \qquad (4\text{-}7a)$$

Two possibilities suggest themselves for reducing strain-gage readings to thermal-stress values.

First, if the gage is temperature-compensated, either by means of a compensating gage in the circuit or by use of a self-compensating gage, the reading obtained is the quantity $(\xi - \alpha\,\Delta T)$. This follows from the fact that when a perfectly temperature-compensated gage is mounted on material which undergoes free expansion ($\xi = \alpha\,\Delta T$), the output (Q_g) is zero; i.e., for

$$\xi = \alpha\,\Delta T,$$

$$Q_g = (\xi - \alpha\,\Delta T) = 0.$$

This would certainly seem to be the most direct approach to the evaluation of thermal stresses; however, it has limited application for the following reasons:

1. There are no "perfect" self-temperature-compensated gages. All give some output under the influence of free expansion; over a wide temperature range the output is considerable, and without simultaneous temperature measurements at the gage point, estimates of error and/or corrections are impossible.
2. Under certain conditions it is possible to set up a nearly perfect temperature-compensated circuit by using an active and a compensating gage. However, when high-temperature gradients and rapidly changing temperatures are involved, it is almost impossible to mount a compensating gage subject only to free expansion in such a way that it will follow the temperature excursions of the active gage point. Unfortunately, the thermal stress problems of interest are the ones involving high-temperature gradients and rapidly changing temperatures.

The second method for reducing strain-gage readings to thermal-stress values involves the simultaneous measurement of strain and temperature at a point. In general, when a strain gage is mounted on a specimen which undergoes a change in temperature, the gage output can be expressed as

$$Q_g \simeq \Delta R_\xi + \Delta R_T.$$

That is, the output is due to the sum of the strain-produced resistance change (ΔR_ξ) and the temperature-produced resistance change (ΔR_T). The temperature-produced resistance change includes the effect of temperature on the specific resistance and the effect of the differential coefficient of expansion between the gage and the specimen. We may think of the reading obtained from any strain gage as the sum of two parts: the total strain (ξ), and some increment (I) which is dependent upon the temperature, the gage type, and the material on which it is mounted.

$$Q_g = \xi + I. \tag{4-8}$$

If we mount a gage on a material which is subjected to free expansion, the total strain (ξ) is $\alpha\,\Delta T$, and hence for this case

$$Q_{g_{\text{free expansion}}} = \alpha\,\Delta T + I. \tag{4-8a}$$

The same type of gage, mounted on the same kind of material at the same temperature but used under actual test conditions, will give a reading which is

$$Q_{g_{\text{test}}} = \xi + I. \tag{4-8b}$$

Subtracting Eq. (4-8a) from Eq. (4-8b), we obtain

$$Q_{g_{\text{test}}} - Q_{g_{\text{free expansion}}} = \xi - \alpha \, \Delta T, \tag{4-9}$$

which can be substituted in Eqs. (4-6a) and (4-7a) to obtain thermal stress.

When this method is used, the experimental procedure is as follows: A gage (or gages) of the type to be used is (or are) mounted on a coupon of the test-specimen material. The coupon is heated and/or cooled, and data are taken to plot $Q_{g_{\text{free expansion}}}$ versus T (see Fig. 4-10).

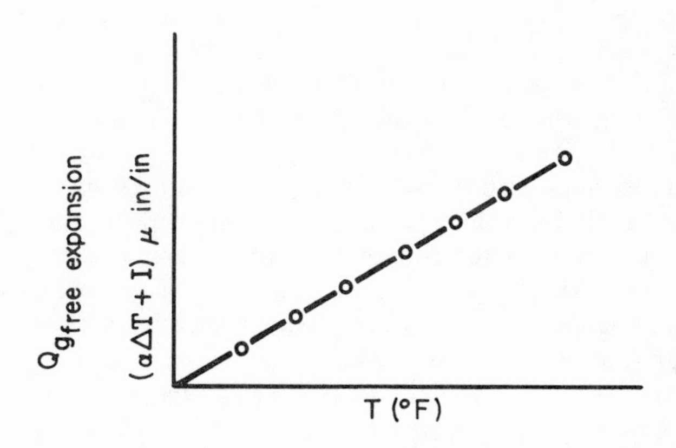

Fig. 4-10. Free-expansion correction curve.

The actual test specimen is instrumented at each point with a strain gage and thermocouple, and during the test the strain gage and thermocouple are read simultaneously. The data are reduced by entering the $Q_{g_{\text{free expansion}}}$ versus T curve for each temperature recorded during the test and subtracting the value $Q_{g_{\text{free expansion}}}$ from the gage reading obtained at that temperature during the test $\left(Q_{g_{\text{test}}}\right)$. The result is the desired value of thermal strain ($\epsilon_t = \xi - \alpha \, \Delta T$). The thermal stress is computed from Eqs. (4-6) and (4-7), and this value of (ϵ_t) is used. Properly selected self-temperature-compensated gages are the best suited even for use with this method, since they function to keep the correction factor $\left(Q_{g_{\text{free expansion}}}\right)$ small and, therefore, improve the resolution of the method. The knowledge of temperature variation and distribution which is inherently obtained in this method is invaluable for comparison with theory and/or for locating interesting and unexpected features of the test environment.

If radiant-heating conditions are encountered, the temperature of the gage may exceed the temperature of the specimen by as much as 300°F. Thus, it is important to measure the actual temperature of the strain gage as well as the temperature of the specimen. M. F. Andreika [32] presents detailed instructions for strain-gage instrumentation of thermal stresses during radiant heating conditions.

4-2m Measurement of strains at interior points

Strain gages of all types have been used almost exclusively to measure strains on surfaces. In the case of the mechanical, optical, and electrical gage types which preceded the development of bonded resistance gages, the limitation was physical. The very size of these other gage types precluded the possibility of embedding them in a solid without altering the strain pattern which was to be investigated. In addition, it is certainly true that in most cases it can be shown that the maximum strains occur at a surface.

There are some problems, however, in which strains at interior points are of considerable interest. The strain distribution throughout a solid body may be of interest for confirmation of theory; or the maximum strains may occur at interior points, as in the case of thermal stress due to absorbed radiation heating. In such cases the possibility of embedding resistance strain gages is also of interest.

As yet, no method has been developed for embedding strain gages in metal prototypes, but they have been used in concrete and in models constructed from suitable plastics.

As used in concrete, the gages are bonded to an element which is then a force link. This force link is included at the point of interest in place of parent material; often it replaces a particle of aggregate. Gages of this type are commercially available and special-purpose types have been designed by several investigators. Y. C. Loh [33] discusses the design, calibration, embedding, and use of gages in concrete to measure both static and dynamic strains. Loh gives special attention to the errors introduced by the fact that the gaged element does not perfectly match the material in which it is included. He shows that with careful design these errors can be made negligibly small.

The use of resistance strain gages and plastic models to study interior strains is different, in that the gage is included with a minimum of foreign material. R. I. Brasier [34] succeeded in locating one mil Advance wire gages in a model of a large pressure vessel. The only foreign material was the wire itself (no backing or bonding), and a photoelastic analysis showed that the presence of the wire did not alter the strain pattern.

Work at one of the author's laboratories has shown that free-filament gages and Bakelite-backed foil gages can also be embedded in certain plastics without altering the strain pattern [21]. These commercially available gages have been embedded and used in several investigations [35]. Gages have been arranged in the form of a six-element rosette (see Fig. 4-11) and embedded in a plastic model to study the most general three-dimensional problem.* See Ref. [36].

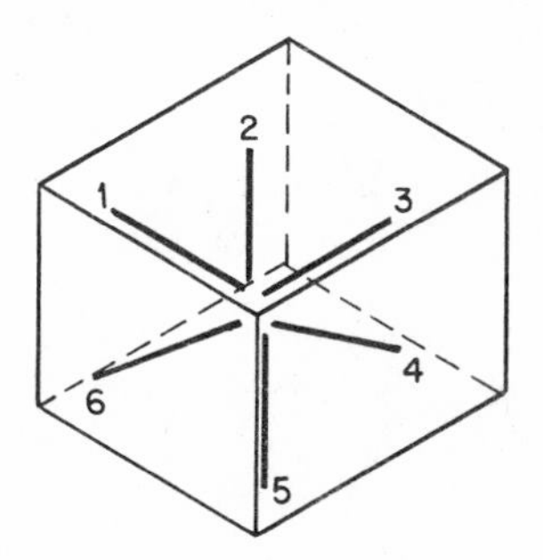

Fig. 4-11. Six-element rosette.

4-3 Additional special problems (abstracts and references)

4-3a Use of strain gages on nonmetallic materials

Strain gages have been used predominantly to measure strain in metals, but the following group of abstracts shows that they can be used successfully on a great many materials.

1. "Suitable Cement for Strain Gages on *Glass* at −320°F," J. Gunn. A letter to the editor appearing in *Strain Gage Readings*, 1, 4 (Oct.–Nov. 1958), p. 52. Gages were mounted on optical glass with Sauerisin No. 1 cement and used in tests at room temperature and at −320°F. After testing, the gages were removed without damaging the optical surface.

2. "Strain Gages on *Pavement*," F. H. Scrivner. Communications by the author to P. Stein, reported in *Strain Gage Readings*, 1, 6 (Feb.–Mar. 1959), p. 31.

* The "most general three-dimensional problem" is the problem in which both magnitudes and directions of principal stresses are unknown.

The gages we use are manufactured by Baldwin-Lima-Hamilton Corporation and were developed especially for this project. They are Constantan Foil Epoxy-Backed gages of 6 in. effective length, $\frac{3}{4}$ in. effective width, and 750-ohm nominal resistance. The Gage Factor is 2.10 plus or minus 1 per cent.

Each gage, on receipt at the project, is further processed as follows:

a. One side of a 3″ × 7$\frac{1}{4}$″ piece of 0.001-inch brass shim stock is coated with an epoxy resin containing the following:

Epi-Rez 510	100 parts by weight
Versamid 125	25 parts by weight
Tetra Ethylene Pentamine	7$\frac{1}{2}$ parts by weight

b. Both sides of the gage are coated with this epoxy, and the gage is centered on the shim stock with the foil upward.
c. Both sides of a 7″ × 1″ strip of linen tracing cloth are coated with this epoxy, and the cloth is placed over the gage so as to insulate the foil.
d. The shim stock, previously creased, is now folded over the gage, and the assembled gage is held under light pressure overnight while the epoxy cures.

Gages are mounted in the field as follows:

a. An area of pavement slightly larger than the gage is ground to a smooth finish.
b. The area is scrubbed with water.
c. The area is dried about 3 hours by infrared heat lamps.
d. The area is scrubbed with carbon tetrachloride.
e. The area is coated with epoxy of the composition described above.
f. The gage is pressed into the epoxy, then held down lightly by a rubber-covered board weighted by a brick, for a 2-hour curing period.
g. The rubber-covered board is removed and the top of the gage is coated with epoxy, which is allowed to cure for 2 hours.
h. A thin coat of Di-Jell 171 (a waterproofing agent) is applied over the gage.
i. A thick coat of Product 2300 (a waterproofing agent) is applied over the Di-Jell 171.
j. Shielded microphone cable, with polyethylene insulation and vinyl plastic jacket (Alpha No. 1710 or No. 1715) is then soldered to the leads.
k. The soldered joint is wrapped with electrician's tape and coated in the same way as the gage. Cables are led underground to a junction box 11 feet from the pavement edge.

Over 500 gages, mounted as described, have thus far withstood freezing, thawing, wetting and drying, and are seldom damaged by traffic, although they are mounted on the surface of the pavement along the free edge, and are frequently run over by test trucks.

> Gages mounted on concrete beams were subjected to freezing (−20°F) and thawing (140°F) water cycles in the Portland Cement Laboratories at Skokie, Illinois, at frequent intervals for several months without detectable change.

The foregoing is quoted from Mr. Scrivner's letter as published in *Strain Gage Readings.*

3. "A Method for Determining Stresses in *Concrete Reinforcement* During Long Term Tests," G. C. Rouse, U. S. Department of Interior, Bureau of Reclamation Tech. Memo 655 (Sept. 1958). Abstracted in *Strain Gage Readings*, 1, 6 (Feb.–Mar. 1959), p. 41.

> The special gage developed for field installation to reinforcing rods consisted of an SR-4 Bakelite gage bonded to fine mesh wire cloth which in turn can be soldered to shim stock. In either case, the prefabricated gage is installed to the test specimen by soldering the gage assembly in place. Various solders are investigated and tested for stability. Solders, in general, are found to exhibit both growth or shrinkage with time, depending on their respective constituents. Types Cerrotru and Cerrocast solders were found to be more stable than other soft solders.

A more complete abstract, from which this is quoted, appears in *Strain Gage Readings.*

4. "Strain Gage Technique of Dynamic Measurement on *Ice*," D. B. Clark. Available in PB ·146971 microfilm or photocopy from Library of Congress. Abstracted in *Strain Gage Readings*, **4**, 1 (Apr.–May 1961), p. 27.

> A technique for applying resistance strain gages to ice samples for dynamic strain measurement was developed. To provide the necessary high impedance between gages and ice, a coating material was sought for the strain gages. Baldwin type A-5-1 gages with the felt protective strip removed were dipped in several different coating materials, immersed in a sea-water tank and allowed to soak. The impedance was measured at various time intervals. ZEROK 110, styrene-butadiene copolymer, was chosen as the best coating. A 1000-megohm resistance was maintained from instant of immersion to beyond 1 hour afterwards, dropping to 10 megohms after overnight immersion. Before applying the coated gages to ice, it was necessary to face the gage front and back with a thin absorbent paper (lens tissue) so that a "glue line" of fresh water could be formed between the gage and the ice sample. The tissue was cemented to the coated gage with acetone, sparingly applied to the paper and with a slight, well-distributed pressure from a sponge.
>
> Applying the gages to the ice samples was easier if the sample temperature was reduced below its freezing point. The gage, after soaking in distilled water, is placed upon the ice in the desired orientation, and

compressed with a thin rectangular slice of sea sponge which has been wet in distilled water. The gage and sponge are allowed to freeze to the ice surface. If application without sponge is desired, a piece of dry ice can be used to build up a layer of ice over the gage by successive application of water drops followed by freezing with dry ice.

A more complete abstract, from which this is quoted, appears in *Strain Gage Readings.*

5. "Bonded Wire Strain Gage Techniques for *Polymethyl Methacrylate Plastics*," A. G. H. Dietz and W. H. Campbell, *Proc. S. E. S. A.*, 5, 1 (1947), p. 59–62. This paper deals with a search for cement that will satisfactorily bond gages to plastic without changing the plastic chemically or mechanically. This paper (and the discussion of it by W. J. Eney) is an excellent example of the care and thought required to extend properly the use of strain gages to new materials.

4-3b Use of strain gages in medical research

In medical research, strain gages have been used both to make special transducers, such as a tooth-sized force link (see 1, below), and to study directly the state of strain in some part of the human body.

1. "Measurement of the Forces of Chewing With Resistance Transducers of Molar Size Without Interference With Articulation," C. Rohrbach and K. Eichner. Abstracted from the *German Dentists Journal* by P. Stein in *Strain Gage Readings*, 1, 2 (June–July 1958), p. 22.

The rather stringent specifications on size, toxicity, and waterproofing which attend the design of a force transducer to replace missing teeth for purposes of measuring chewing forces are solved in a particularly ingenious manner. Initially, a thin piece of paper is cut into an oblong shape, and fine, strain-sensitive (copper-nickel alloy) resistance wire is wound spirally around the "card" and glued down (cement is given in the paper). The strip is then formed into an almost-circle after attachment of the lead wires to the ends of the wound card. A larger strip of paper is formed into a cylinder to act as a mold, and placed around the strain-sensitive winding. The mold is then filled with an elastic plastic and allowed to cure. Steel cover-plates are inserted at the top and bottom to transmit the pressures. The transducer is complete! Strains of up to 2500 micro-inches per inch are attained at full load with amazing linearity and repeatability. Recordings are shown for chewing forces involved in chewing zwieback and a special kind of bread.

Quoted from the more complete abstract by P. Stein in *Strain Gage Readings.*

2. "A Study of the Mechanical Behavior of the Skull and Its Contents When Subjected to Injuring Blows," H. R. Lissner and E. I. Gurdjean. *Proc. S. E. S. A.*, 3, 2 (1946), pp. 40–46.

Applications of experimental stress analysis to problems in the field of medicine are discussed. The Stresscoat method was used to determine the tensile strain patterns resulting from blows administered to various regions of the skulls of animals, living and dead, and to human skulls. Applications of fixed amounts of energy to various portions of the human skull indicated that the tensile deformations at the base of the skull due to blows at the back were far more severe than those caused by frontal blows. By the use of SR-4 strain gages cemented to the skulls of living anesthetized dogs, the time of maximum deformation was found to be 0.0005 second and equilibrium was reached in 0.005 second after the blow. Records of pressure waves through the brain and cerebrospinal fluid were obtained by means of pressure plugs screwed into the skull. The pressure plugs operate on the principle that the electrical resistance of an electrolyte changes with changes in pressure. Maximum pressure was reached $\frac{1}{1400}$ second after the start of the blow.

Quoted from the author's synopsis.

3. "Two Devices for Measuring the Forces Acting on the Human Body During Walking," D. M. Cunningham and G. W. Brown. *Proc. S. E. S. A.*, 9, 2 (1952), pp. 75–90.

Forces acting on the leg during walking were measured by two means: a load-measuring pylon which was substituted for the shank of a prothesis and a force plate which measured the floor reactions on a normal or artificial foot.

Quoted from the author's introduction.

4. "Development of a Physiological Pressure Transducer System for Recording Under Severe Accelerative or Decelerative Forces," L. J. Rossbach. Presented at 30th Annual Meeting of the Aero Medical Association, Los Angeles, Calif. (1959). Abstracted in *Strain Gage Readings*, 2, 3 (Aug.–Sept. 1958), p. 33.

A miniature, deposited-film strain gage pressure transducer has been developed. The system is aimed at the sensing of an equivalent of zero to 50 cm of mercury with less than ± 3 per cent full-scale error, with a response time of one millisecond; furthermore, it should be unaffected by accelerations or decelerations of up to 200 g's.

The pressure transducer consists primarily of a small, thin-walled cylinder approximately 10 mm in length and 3 mm in diameter having a spirally wound evaporated film strain gage on its circumference, a blunt nose on the forward end, and the catheter attached to the aft end. In this configuration, the transducer will measure difference in pressure between its outer surface within the lumen and the inner surface exposed to atmospheric pressure via the catheter.

Quoted from a more complete abstract in *Strain Gage Readings*.

4-3c Use of strain gages to measure residual stresses

The theory of residual stresses is rather involved, and relationship between measured quantities and stresses is complicated by several factors. Several experimental methods in addition to strain gages have been used to study residual stresses, among which are brittle coatings and X-ray techniques. The use of strain gages for this purpose is of interest because it involves mounting the gage on a stressed surface and then deducing the stress magnitude by unloading.

1. "Residual Stresses and Fatigue Studies," O. J. Horger, H. R. Neifert, and R. R. Regan, *Proc. S. E. S. A.*, 1, 1 (1943), pp. 10–18.

Residual stresses were determined on three shafts which were all quenched in water at 1525°F, but drawn at three different tempering temperatures. A new and greatly simplified procedure was used for measuring the changes in diameter and length of the cylinders following each successive boring-out operation (Sachs method). Six wire-resistant-type strain gages were cemented on each cylinder as a means of measuring the changes in strain. When the cylinder reached the boring-out stage at which 90 per cent of the original cross-section area was removed, then this thin cylinder was slit longitudinally. This procedure permitted a determination of the remaining residual tangential stresses which are usually obtained by extrapolation of the deformation curves from the boring-out method.

Quoted from the authors' synopsis.

2. "A Method for the Determination of Residual Stresses," C. Riparbelli. *Proc. S. E. S. A.*, 8, 1 (1950), pp. 173–96.

In brief, the method consists of introducing a circular discontinuity in the surface of a body possessing residual stress, and measuring by means of electric strain gages the resulting stresses occurring in the vicinity of the hole. Since the stress distribution around a circular hole in an otherwise uniform stress field has a well-known solution, the initial stress in a body can be calculated from measurements of the stress concentration about a circular hole placed in the body.

With the use of electric strain gages, adequate sensitivity may be obtained with holes as small as $\frac{1}{8}$-inch diameter. Hence, the method can be considered nondestructive with respect to large statically loaded structures.

Quoted from the author's introduction.

4-3d Use of strain gages in the construction of transducers

Ever since bonded resistance strain gages were introduced, there has been a continuous flow of strain-gage-based transducers. They range from simple gaged pull bars for axial-force measurement, through six-component wind-tunnel balances, to strain-gage accelerometers and pressure pickups. The abstracts below will serve as an introduction to a particularly fruitful field of strain-gage use.

1. "Electric Strain Gage Tool Dynamometers," E. G. Loewen, E. R. Marshall, and M. C. Shaw. *Proc. S. E. S. A.*, 8, 2 (1951), pp. 1–16.

In this paper a number of dynamometers utilizing electric strain gages are described. The machining operations involved in this discussion include: planing, drilling, grinding and turning. The bridge circuits used with each of the dynamometers are described as well as the mechanical aspects of each unit. Design details of the load measuring elements employed are given in considerable detail. Some of the advantages and disadvantages of the several measuring instruments that are available for use with complete strain gage bridges are presented.

Quoted from authors' abstract.

2. "A Diaphragm-Type Gage for Measuring Low Pressures in Fluids," E. Wenk, Jr. *Proc. S. E. S. A.*, 8, 2 (1951), pp. 90–96.

An instrument consisting primarily of a thin metallic diaphragm and electrical strain gages adhered thereto was developed at the David Taylor Model Basin for measuring low pressures in fluids. The design and construction of the instrument, and operating characteristics, such as sensitivity, accuracy, and response to rapidly varying pressures, are described.

Quoted from the author's abstract.

3. "A Bonded Wire Strain Gage Type Accelerometer," E. W. Kammer. *Proc. S. E. S. A.*, 6, 2 (1948), pp. 53–60.

An accelerometer is described in which a mass, when accelerated, causes axial strains to develop in a thin-walled duraluminum cylinder. Bonded wire strain gages are placed on this cylinder to measure these strains. The design considerations, sensitivity, useful range of acceleration, and calibration methods for this instrument are discussed.

Quoted from the author's abstract.

4-4 References listed in Chapter 4

1. Wells, F. E., "A Rapid Method of Waterproofing Bonded Wire Strain Gages," *Proceedings of the Society for Experimental Stress Analysis*, Vol. 15, No. 2 (1958), pp. 107–10.
2. Kimbel, E. L., "A Method of Effecting SR-4 Strain Gage Operation Under Water," *Proceedings of the Society for Experimental Stress Analysis*, Vol. 3, No. 2 (1946), pp. 53–54.
3. Meyer, H. O., "A Method of Waterproofing Electrical Strain Gages," letter to the editor in *Proceedings of the Society for Experimental Stress Analysis*, Vol. 10, No. 1 (1952), pp. 243–45.
4. Newton, A. E. and R. E. Karcher, "Load Sensing Under Thirty Feet of Hot Water," *Proceedings of the Society for Experimental Stress Analysis*, Vol. 17, No. 1 (1959), pp. 135–42.
5. Barker, R. I. and J. B. Murtland, "Protection of Underwater SR-4 Strain Gage Installations on Tunnel Liner of a Hydroelectric Development," *Proceedings of the Society for Experimental Stress Analysis*, Vol. 14, No. 2 (1957), pp. 131–38.
6. Palermo, P. M., "Methods of Waterproofing SR-4 Strain Gages," *Proceedings of the Society for Experimental Stress Analysis*, Vol. 13, No. 2 (1956), pp. 79–88.
7. Dean, Mills, III, "Strain Gage Waterproofing Methods and Installation of Gages on Propeller Strut of U.S.S. Saratoga," *Proceedings of the Society for Experimental Stress Analysis*, Vol. 16, No. 1 (1958), pp. 137–50.
8. Loh, Y. C., "Internal Stress Gauges for Cementitious Materials," *Proceedings of the Society for Experimental Stress Analysis*, Vol. 11, No. 2 (1954), pp. 13–28.
9. Hume, J. R., *Strain Measurement in a Nuclear Radiation Environment*, unpublished report, Mechanical Engineering Department, The University of New Mexico (1956).
10. Smith, R. C. and N. J. Readler, "Transducers for Strain Measurement in Intense Radiation Fields," *Proceedings of the Society for Experimental Stress Analysis*, Vol. 16, No. 2 (1956), pp. 73–80. Also Readler, N. J. and R. C. Smith, "Effect of Radiation Upon Ceramic-Bonded Strain Gages," N.R.L. Report 5450, Naval Research Laboratory, Washington, D.C. (Apr. 1960).
11. Leszynski, S. T., "The Development of Flame-Sprayed Sensors," Instrument Society of America, Paper Number 22-TC-61.
12. Harris, C. R. and J. E. Davis, "A New Strain Gage for Use at Cryogenic Temperatures," Baldwin-Lima-Hamilton Corporation, Electronics and Instrumentation Division, Waltham, Mass., Technical Data Bulletin 4320-7.
13. Kammer, E. W., "Low-Temperature Gage Factors" *Stresses and Strains*, Vol. 7, No. 2 (Nov. 1959). Reprinted in *Strain Gage Readings*, Vol. 2, No. 6 (Feb.–Mar. 1960), p. 51.
14. McClintock, R. M. and D. A. Van Gundy, "Adhesives at Low Temperatures," Laboratory Note 54-5, NBS-AEC, Cryogenic Engineering Laboratory, Boulder, Colo. (June 28, 1954).
15. Gunn, J. and E. Billinghurst, "Magnetic Fields Affect Strain Gages," *Control Engr.*, Vol. 4, No. 8 (Aug. 1957), pp. 109–11.
16. Vigness, I., "Magnetostrictive Effects in Wire Strain Gages," *Proceedings of the Society for Experimental Stress Analysis*, Vol. 14, No. 2 (1957), pp. 139–48.
17. Steele, M. C. and L. C. Eichberger, "The Use of Foil Gages to Measure Large Strains Under High Fluid Pressures," *Proceedings of the Society for Experimental Stress Analysis*, Vol. 13, No. 1 (1955), pp. 151–8.

18. Guerard J. P. and G. F. Weissmann, "Effect of Hydrostatic Pressure on SR-4 Strain Gages," *Proceedings of the Society for Experimental Stress Analysis*, Vol. 16, No. 1 (1958), pp. 151–6.
19. Gerdeen, J. C., "Effects of Pressure on Small Foil Strain Gages," *Experimental Mechanics*, Vol. 3, No. 3 (Mar. 1963), p. 73–80.
20. Clark, Austin B., "Static and Dynamic Calibration of a Photoelastic Model Material, CR-39," N.R.L. Report 4779, Naval Research Laboratory, Washington, D.C. (June 7, 1956).
21. Dove, R. C., R. I. Brasier, and W. E. Baker, "Selection of Gages for Strain Measurement at Interior Points," *Experimental Mechanics*, Vol. 2, No. 6 (June 1962), pp. 189–90.
22. Frocht, M. M., D. Landsberg, and B. C. Wang, "The Effect of Gage Current on Strain Measurements," *Proceedings of the Society for Experimental Stress Analysis*, Vol. 16, No. 2 (1959), pp. 69–72.
23. Dove, R. C., "Strain Measurement Errors in Materials of Low Modulus," *Transactions of the American Society of Civil Engineers*, 81 (Sept. 1955).
24. Jones, E. and K. R. Maslen, "The Physical Characteristics of Wire Resistance Strain Gauges," Her Majesty's Stationery Office, Aeronautical Research Council, Reports and Memoranda, No. 2661 (Nov. 1948). Reported in *Strain Gage Readings*, Vol. 1, No. 3 (Aug.–Sept. 1958).
25. Dorsey, James, "Bakelite Backed Semiconductor Strain Gages," Instrument Society of America, Paper Number 146-LA-61. Los Angeles, Calif. (Sept. 11–15, 1961).
26. Hurry, J. A. and R. P. Wooley, "A New High-Range Strain Gage," *Testing Topics*, Vol. 8, No. 2 (Apr., May, June, 1953), pp. 6–7, Baldwin-Lima-Hamilton Corporation, Philadelphia, Pa.
27. Stephens, R. W., "Fatigue Life of SR-4 Strain Gages," *Testing Topics*, Vol. 8, No. 3 (July, Aug., Sept., 1953), p. 1, Baldwin-Lima-Hamilton Corporation, Philadelphia, Pa.
28. Stein, Peter, "Fatigue Life of Strain Gages," *Strain Gage Readings*, Vol. 1, No. 3 (Aug.–Sept., 1958), pp. 21–24.
29. Nisbet, J. I., J. N. Brennan, and H. I. Tarpley, "High-Frequency Strain Gauge and Accelerometer Calibration," *Journal of Acoustical Society of America*, Vol. 32, No. 1 (Jan. 1960), pp. 71–75.
30. Murphy, G., A. Hausrath, III, and P. Peterson, "Response of Resistance Strain Gages to Dynamic Strains," *Proceedings of 9th International Congress of Applied Mechanics* (1957).
31. Stein, Peter, "The Frequency Response of a Strain Gage," *Strain Gage Readings*, Vol. 3 (June–July 1960), pp. 9–16.
32. Andreika, M. F., "Stress Determination With Bakelite Backed Strain Gages Under Transient Heating Conditions," Instrument Society of America, Conference Preprint Number 23-TC-61.
33. Loh, Y. C., "Internal Stress Gauges for Cementitious Materials," *Proceedings of the Society for Experimental Stress Analysis*, Vol. 11, No. 2 (1954), pp. 13–28.
34. Brasier, R. I. and R. C. Dove, "Use of Electrical-Resistance Strain Elements in Three-Dimensional Stress Analysis," *Experimental Mechanics*, Vol. 1, No. 6 (June 1961), pp. 186–91.
35. Baker, W. E. and R. C. Dove, "Measurement of Internal Strains in a Bar Subjected to Longitudinal Impact," *Experimental Mechanics*, Vol. 2, No. 10 (Oct. 1962), pp. 307–11.
36. Baker, W. E. and R. C. Dove, "Construction and Evaluation of a Three Dimensional Strain Rosette," *Experimental Mechanics*, Vol. 3, No. 9 (Sept. 1963), pp. 201–6.

CHAPTER 5

Reduction of Strain-Gage Data

5-1 Introduction

This section presents methods for reducing and analyzing strain-gage readings. The usual requirement is that the state of stress at a point be determined from strain-gage readings. This implies the use of an appropriate theory relating strains to stresses; hence, the validity of the final results depends upon the validity of any relationships used in reducing the data.

The following discussion will deal specifically with the reduction of data from electric resistance strain gages, but many of the remarks can be applied to the reduction of strain-gage data in general. The discussion will be limited to those cases where the material on which the gage is mounted behaves in accordance with the linear theory of elasticity throughout the range of strain being investigated. Evaluation of stresses from measured strains beyond the elastic limit is uncertain, not because of an inability to measure plastic strains, but rather because of the lack of a valid theory relating stresses to strains in this region. Some work is being done in this area; see Refs. [1] and [2].

5-2 Effect of transverse sensitivity

In electrical resistance strain-gage work the gage factor (F) is defined as

$$F = \frac{\Delta R/R}{\epsilon} \tag{2-1}$$

Inspection of Fig. 5-1 will call attention to the fact that, because of

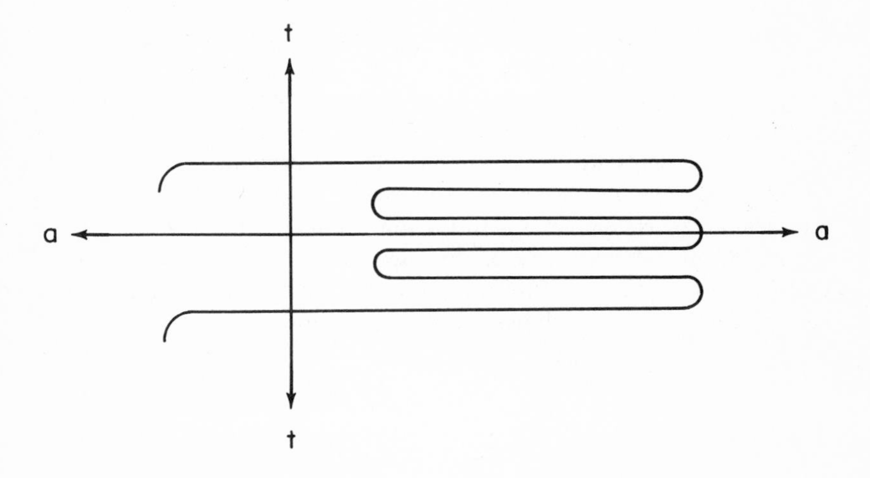

Fig. 5-1. Strain gage in biaxial strain field.

the way in which the gage is constructed, the actual change in resistance (ΔR) is due not only to the strain along the gage axis (ϵ_a) but to the strain perpendicular to the gage axis (ϵ_t) as well. Therefore, we may write

$$\frac{\Delta R}{R} = F_a\epsilon_a + F_t\epsilon_t, \tag{5-1}$$

in which ΔR is the total change in resistance experienced by the gage grid.

R is the total grid resistance.

F_a is the factor relating the strain in the a direction to the change in resistance of that part of the gage grid which is oriented in the a direction.

F_t is the factor relating the strain in the t direction to the change in resistance of that part of the gage grid which is oriented in the t direction.

If $F_t = 0$, then Eq. (5-1) reduces to $\Delta R/R = F_a \epsilon_a$, the previous definition of gage factor. The questions of interest are (1) What is the value of F_t? (2) If F_t is not equal to zero, how is the analysis of strain gage data affected?

First, it would appear that the sensitivity of the gage to transverse strain (F_t) would be zero if no part of the grid is oriented in the transverse (or t) direction. This suggests a gage utilizing a single length of strain-sensitive element. This is generally impractical with wire gages because of the low gage resistance per unit of gage length. Some semiconductor gages are made this way, and they are found to have a value of F_t/F_a of less than one per cent. A more practical method for making F_t approach zero is to make the resistance of that part of the gage grid in the transverse direction so small compared to the resistance of that part of the grid in the longitudinal direction that any change in the resistance of the transverse elements will be negligible. This is partially accomplished in foil gages by making the transverse element lengths of very large cross-sectional areas as compared with the longitudinal element lengths.

Second, if the sensitivity of the gage to transverse strain (F_t) is not equal to zero, the effect of this output on the analysis of the gage reading can be determined as follows: Figure 5-2 shows a co-ordinate system

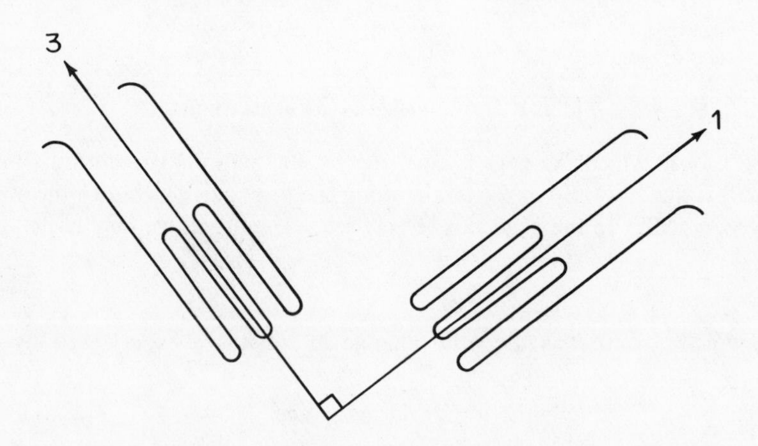

Fig. 5-2. Strain gages in biaxial stress field.

laid out on the surface of a member subjected to a general biaxial stress field. If gages (identical gages, since in the following both gages must have the same values of F_a and F_t) are mounted with their axes in the 1 and 3 directions, the output of the two gages may be expressed as

$$\left(\frac{\Delta R}{R}\right)_1 = F_a\epsilon_1 + F_t\epsilon_3 \tag{5-1a}$$

and

$$\left(\frac{\Delta R}{R}\right)_3 = F_a\epsilon_3 + F_t\epsilon_1. \tag{5-1b}$$

Multiplying Eq. (5-1a) by F_a and Eq. (5-1b) by F_t, subtracting Eq. (5-1b) from Eq. (5-1a) and rearranging, we have

$$\epsilon_1 = \frac{F_a}{F_a^2 - F_t^2}\left(\frac{\Delta R}{R}\right)_1 - \frac{F_t}{F_a^2 - F_t^2}\left(\frac{\Delta R}{R}\right)_3, \tag{5-2}$$

which may be written as

$$\epsilon_1 = \frac{1}{F_G}\left(\frac{\Delta R}{R}\right)_1 - \frac{K}{F_G}\left(\frac{\Delta R}{R}\right)_3, \tag{5-2a}$$

in which

$$F_G = \frac{F_a^2 - F_t^2}{F_a}$$

is defined as the gage factor for a general stress field, and $K = F_t/F_a$ is the transverse sensitivity of the gage.

Equation (5-2a) is important because it shows that to obtain the actual, or true, strain in any given direction, it is necessary to obtain readings from *two gages*, one mounted in the direction of the desired strain and one mounted perpendicular to the direction of the desired strain.

The question now arises as to whether the gage factor (F) which is furnished by the manufacturer with single element gages is the value of F_G used in the above equation. *The answer is "No."* Single-element gages are calibrated, and gage factor is determined, in a uniaxial stress field in which the strain perpendicular to the gage axis (ϵ_t) is $-\mu_o\epsilon_a$, where μ_o is the Poisson's ratio of the material on which the gage is mounted, and ϵ_a is the strain in the direction of the gage axis. For this specific condition the output (in terms of $\Delta R/R$) is expressed by the manufacturer as

$$\frac{\Delta R}{R} = F_u\epsilon_a, \tag{5-3}$$

in which the manufacturer's gage factor has been written as F_u to indicate clearly that this gage factor was determined in a uniaxial stress field. In general, the output can be expressed by Eq. (5-1), and for this specific case

$$\frac{\Delta R}{R} = F_a \epsilon_a - F_t (\mu_o \epsilon_a), \tag{5-4}$$

since

$$\epsilon_t = -\mu_o \epsilon_a.$$

Equating Eqs. (5-3) and (5-4) gives

$$F_u = F_a - \mu_o F_t, \tag{5-5}$$

or

$$F_u = (1 - \mu_o K) F_a. \tag{5-5a}$$

Since the general gage factor and cross sensitivity are defined as

$$F_G = \frac{F_a^2 - F_t^2}{F_a} \quad \text{and} \quad K = \frac{F_t}{F_a},$$

by substituting in Eq. (5-5a) we may write

$$F_G = \frac{(1 - K^2)}{(1 - \mu_o K)} F_u. \tag{5-6}$$

Equation (5-6) shows how the gage factor given by the manufacturer for a single-element gage (F_u) is related to the general gage factor (F_G) which must be used in Eq. (5-2a). The difference between the two values depends upon the values of K and μ_o.

Only one manufacturer gives the value of μ_o (Baldwin-Lima-Hamilton Corporation, $\mu_o = 0.285$) for the specimens on which the gages are mounted for calibration, but it is safe to assume that all manufacturers use metal specimens for which μ_o is approximately 0.3.

Values of K are tabulated in Table 5-1. Experimental methods for determining K are discussed in Appendix A to this chapter. Substituting a value of K of 0.07 (apparently near the maximum for commercially available types) and a value of μ_o of 0.30 into Eq. (5-6) gives

$$F_G = \frac{(1 - 0.0049)}{1 - (0.30)(0.07)} F_u$$

$$F_G = 1.016\, F_u$$

$$F_G \simeq F_u.$$

We conclude that when a single-element strain gage is used in a biaxial stress field, the manufacturer's gage factor (F_u) may be used instead of F_G, unless the greatest precision is required and warranted.

However, this does not mean that the reading obtained from a single gage used in a biaxial stress field can be related to strain. Equation (5-2a) shows that this is not possible. We can now determine the magnitude of error resulting from the use of a single-element strain gage in a biaxial stress field. When a single-element gage is used in a biaxial stress field, the error that results in taking the gage reading as the true strain can be expressed as follows:

$$\text{Error in } \epsilon_1 = \frac{Q_1 - \epsilon_1}{\epsilon_1}, \tag{5-7}$$

in which Q_1 is the reading obtained from a gage with axis in the 1 direction (see Fig. 5-2).

ϵ_1 is the true strain in the 1 direction.

From our previous work [Eqs. (2-1) and (5-1) and $K = F_t/F_a$], we may substitute

$$Q_1 = \frac{F_a\epsilon_1 + F_t\epsilon_3}{F} = \frac{F_a}{F}(\epsilon_1 + K\epsilon_3).$$

If the manufacturer's gage factor (F_u) is used to obtain the reading Q_1, we may substitute

$$F_u = (1 - \mu_o K)F_a, \tag{5-5a}$$

which gives

$$\text{Error in } \epsilon_1 = \frac{K}{1 - \mu_o K}\left(\mu_o + \frac{\epsilon_3}{\epsilon_1}\right),$$

or

$$\text{Error in } \epsilon_1 = K\left(\mu_o + \frac{\epsilon_3}{\epsilon_1}\right). \tag{5-7a}$$

If the reading Q_1 is obtained by using the general gage factor, we may substitute

$$F_G = \frac{1 - K^2}{1 - \mu_o K}F_u, \tag{5-6}$$

or, combining with Eq. (5-5a), we obtain

$$F_G = (1 - K^2)F_a.$$

This gives

$$\text{Error in } \epsilon_1 = \frac{K\left(K + \frac{\epsilon_3}{\epsilon_1}\right)}{1 - K^2}$$

or

$$\text{Error in } \epsilon_1 = K\left(K + \frac{\epsilon_3}{\epsilon_1}\right). \tag{5-7b}$$

Table 5-1. Transverse sensitivity coefficient for several strain gages

Paper-Backed Wire Gages

Gage Type*	Transverse Sensitivity Coefficient (K)	Gage Type	Transverse Sensitivity Coefficient (K)
A-1	2.0%‡	A-14	−0.8%‡
A-2†	1.8%	A-16	−0.3%
A-3	2.0%‡	A-18	−2.0%‡
A-5	3.5%‡	A-12-4	1.0%‡
A-5-1†	3.5%	A-15	−0.8%‡
A-6	1.8%‡	A-19	−1.2%
A-7	−1.0%‡	A-21	2.8%
AF-7†	0.9%	C-1	1.8%‡
AF-7-1	0.9%	C-3	1.8%‡
A-7-2†	−1.0%‡	C-5	4.0%‡
A-8	−2.0%‡	C-5-1	4.0%‡
A-8-2†	−2.0%‡	C-7	−1.0%‡
A-9	0 ‡	C-7-5	−1.0%‡
A-9-6	0	C-8	−2.0%‡
A-12	1.0%‡	C-10	−0.8%‡
A-12-2†	0.5%	C-11	−2.0%‡
A-13	−0.8%‡	C-14	−0.8%‡
A-13-1	−0.5%	C-19	−1.4%

Bakelite-Backed Wire Gages

Gage Type*	Transverse Sensitivity Coefficient (K)	Gage Type	Transverse Sensitivity Coefficient (K)
AB-1	1.6%	ABF-7	1.6%
AB-3	1.7%	ABF-7-2	1.3%
AB-5	2.4%	ABF-11	0.8%
AB-7	−0.7%	ABF-13	0.8%
AB-7-1	−0.6%	ABF-19	2.9%
AB-7-5	−0.6%	ABF-32	6.7%
AB-7-6	−0.7%	ABFX-11	4.2%
AB-8-1	−0.9%	CB-1	2.2%
AB-11	−0.8%	CB-1-1†	2.2%
AB-11-1	−0.8%	CB-5	2.6%
AB-11-5†	−0.8%	CB-7	0.5%
AB-13	−0.4%	CB-10	0.4%
AB-14	−0.4%	CB-11	0
AB-19	−0.4%	CB-11-1	0
AB-19-1	−0.4%	CB-19	1.2%
AB-19-2	−0.4%	CBD-10	0.3%
AB-19-5	−0.4%	EB-1D+	1.2%
AB-20	−0.2%	EBF-7D+	1.3%
AB-32	−2.3%	EBF-13D+	1.0%
ABF-1	0.4%	EBFX-13D+	0.9%

* All gages are BLH types. † Semi-standard gages. ‡ Taken from Ref. [3]; all others from Ref. [4].

Table 5-1 (cont.)

Foil Gages and Special-Purpose Gages

Gage Type*	Transverse Sensitivity Coefficient (*K*)	Gage Type	Transverse Sensitivity Coefficient (*K*)
FA-600-75	−0.2%	FAB-50-12	−1.1%
FA-100-12	0	FAB-25-12	0.1%
FA-50-12	0.6%	FAB-12-12	−0.6%
FA-25-12	0.8%	FAB-06-12	0.7%
FA-12-12	1.0%	FAB-03-12	3.0%
FA-06-12	1.6%	FAB-50-35	−1.4%
FA-03-12	3.9%	FAB-25-35	−0.3%
FA-50-35	0.2%	AS-9	0.2%
FA-25-35	0.5%	AS-9-1†	0.2%
FAP-50-12	0.2%	ES-9S†	0.2%
FAP-25-12	0.2%	PA-3	3.7%
FAP-12-12	0.4%	PA-5	4.6%
FAP-06-12	1.2%	PA-7	1.9%
FAP-03-12	3.6%	PA-8	2.9%
FAP-50-35	−0.2%	FNB-50-12E	−2.9%
FAP-25-35	−0.1%		

* All gages are BLH types. † Semi-standard gages. ‡ Taken from Ref. [3]; all others from Ref. [4].

Equations (5-7a) and (5-7b) indicate that when the reading of a single-element gage is interpreted as strain, the error is dependent on the transverse sensitivity of the gage (K) and on the ratio of the strain perpendicular to the gage axis to the strain along the gage axis.

Since in a biaxial stress field the maximum (u) and minimum (v) strain axes are perpendicular to each other, it is apparent that for a given value of K the maximum error will result when the gage is placed parallel to the axis of minimum strain (i.e., $\epsilon_1 = \epsilon_v$; $\epsilon_3 = \epsilon_u$).

Table 5-1 indicates that values of K range between −0.029 and +0.067 for standard gage types. Hence, considerable error may result from random placement of a single-element gage in a biaxial stress field; see Table 5-2.

Even when a surface has been Stresscoated and tested to determine the direction of the maximum principal stress, error is involved in the use of a single-element strain gage. Stresscoat cracks indicate the direction of the maximum tensile strain (perpendicular to the Stresscoat cracks). If a strain gage is mounted so that the gage axis is parallel to the axis of maximum tensile strain, the error in taking the strain gage reading as the maximum tensile strain may still have any value between

$$\frac{K(\mu_o + 1)}{1 - \mu_o K}$$

Table 5-2. Error in strains and stresses resulting from use of uniaxial methods in biaxial stress fields*

True strain in No. 1 direction (ϵ_1)	True strain ⊥ to No. 1 direction (ϵ_3)	Per cent error in strain when strain is evaluated as $Q_1 = \frac{\Delta R/R}{F_u}$	Per cent error in stress when stress is evaluated as Q_1E
ϵ_1	$+1\epsilon_1$	+4.0	−33.3
ϵ_1	$+\frac{1}{2}\epsilon_1$	+2.5	−23.8
ϵ_1	0	+1.0	−11.1
ϵ_1	$-\frac{1}{3}\epsilon_1$	0	0
ϵ_1	$-1\epsilon_1$	−2.0	+33.1
ϵ_1	$-2\epsilon_1$	−5.1	+66.2
ϵ_1	$-3\epsilon_1$	−8.1	∞
ϵ_1	$-4\epsilon_1$	−11.1	−366.2
ϵ_1	$-5\epsilon_1$	−14.1	−233.1
ϵ_1	$-10\epsilon_1$	−29.3	−138.1

* Values given are based on the following constants:
$K = 0.03$.
$\mu_o = 0.285$.
$\mu = \frac{1}{3}$.

and approximately 180 per cent. This follows from the fact that, since Stresscoat cracks under the influence of the largest *tensile* strain,* the ratio of ϵ_3/ϵ_1 may have any value from unity to 0.0240/0.0004. The maximum value of the ratio ϵ_3/ϵ_1 is fixed as the ratio of the maximum flaking sensitivity divided by the minimum threshold sensitivity. Unfortunately, the magnitude of this error is unknown, since ϵ_3 remains unknown, and hence no correction is possible.

Application of the theory of elasticity to a biaxial stress field gives the following relationships between mutually perpendicular stresses and strains; see Ref. [6], p. 63.

$$S_1 = \frac{E}{1 - \mu^2}(\epsilon_1 + \mu\epsilon_3), \tag{5-8}$$

and

$$S_3 = \frac{E}{1 - \mu^2}(\epsilon_3 + \mu\epsilon_1), \tag{5-9}$$

in which E is the modulus of elasticity and μ is Poisson's ratio of the material. If a single-element strain-gage reading is used in an attempt to evaluate the normal stress along the gage axis by using the uniaxial expression

$$S_1 = \epsilon_1 E, \tag{5-10}$$

* The maximum-tensile-stress law of failure is only a first approximation of the failure phenomena of Stresscoat; see Ref. [5], p. 339.

the resulting error can be expressed as follows:

$$\text{Error in } S_1 = \frac{\epsilon_1 E - S_1}{S_1}. \tag{5-11}$$

Since the true stress in the 1 direction (S_1) may be expressed in terms of the strains in the 1 and 3 directions by using Eq. (5-8), substitution yields

$$\text{Error in } S_1 = \frac{\epsilon_1 E - \dfrac{E}{1-\mu^2}(\epsilon_1 + \mu\epsilon_3)}{\dfrac{E}{1-\mu^2}(\epsilon_1 + \mu\epsilon_3)}. \tag{5-11a}$$

Table 5-2 also indicates the magnitude of the errors made in evaluating stress when a single-element gage reading and uniaxial theory are used in a biaxial stress field.

5-3 Computing stresses from measured strains

Application of the theory of elasticity at a free surface (biaxial stress state) gives the following important stress-strain relationships (see Ref. [6], p. 41):

$$\epsilon_a = \epsilon_x \cos^2\theta + \epsilon_y \sin^2\theta - \frac{\epsilon_{xy}}{2}\sin 2\theta, \tag{5-12}$$

$$\epsilon_t = \epsilon_x \sin^2\theta + \epsilon_y \cos^2\theta + \frac{\epsilon_{xy}}{2}\sin 2\theta, \tag{5-13}$$

$$\epsilon_u = \frac{\epsilon_x + \epsilon_y}{2} + \frac{1}{2}\sqrt{(\epsilon_x - \epsilon_y)^2 + \epsilon_{xy}^2}, \tag{5-14}$$

$$\epsilon_v = \frac{\epsilon_x + \epsilon_y}{2} - \frac{1}{2}\sqrt{(\epsilon_x - \epsilon_y)^2 + \epsilon_{xy}^2}, \tag{5-15}$$

$$\tan 2\alpha = \frac{-\epsilon_{xy}}{\epsilon_x - \epsilon_y}, \tag{5-16}$$

$$S_u = \frac{E}{1-\mu^2}(\epsilon_u + \mu\epsilon_v), \quad \text{and} \quad S_v = \frac{E}{1-\mu^2}(\epsilon_v + \mu\epsilon_u), \tag{5-17}$$

in which ϵ = strain in in./in. Single subscripts denote normal strains; the direction of the normal strain corresponds to the direction of the subscript axis in Fig. 5-3. Double subscripts denote shearing strains.

S = stress in lb/in². Subscripts as for strains.

θ = the angle between the x and the a directions.

ϵ_u, S_u = the subscript u is reserved to denote the direction of the maximum normal (principal) strain or stress.

ϵ_v, S_v = the subscript v is reserved to denote the direction of the minimum normal (principal) strain or stress. The v direction is always at an angle of 90 deg to the n direction.

α = the angle that the principal stresses (or strains) make with the x axis.

With these four equations, the principal (i.e., maximum and minimum) stresses at a point can be evaluated from three normal strains at that same point.

5-3a Rectangular rosettes

We shall illustrate, using a rectangular rosette (see Fig. 5-4), i.e., three gages with axes spaced at 45-deg intervals.

Assume that the strains in the 1, 2, and 3 directions are known. Application of Eq. (5-12) to the 2 direction yields

$$\epsilon_2 = \epsilon_1 \cos^2 45° + \epsilon_3 \sin^2 45° - \frac{\epsilon_{13}}{2} \sin (2 \times 45)°, \tag{5-12a}$$

or

$$\epsilon_{13} = \epsilon_1 + \epsilon_3 - 2\epsilon_2. \tag{5-12b}$$

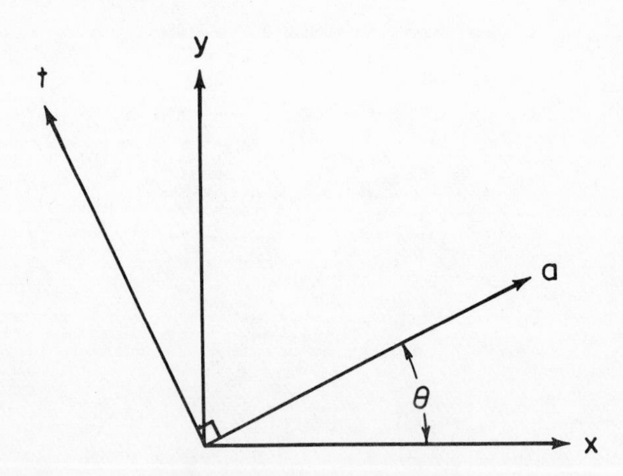

Fig. 5-3. Strain-axis designation.

Substitution of this result into Eq. (5-14) gives

$$\epsilon_{u,v} = \frac{\epsilon_1 + \epsilon_3}{2} \pm \frac{1}{2}\sqrt{(\epsilon_1 - \epsilon_3)^2 + (\epsilon_1 + \epsilon_3 - 2\epsilon_2)^2}, \tag{5-14a}$$

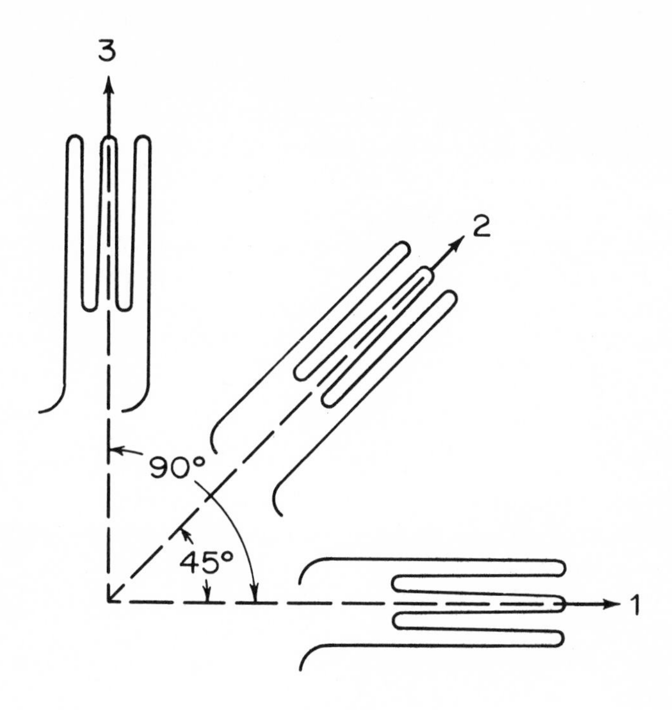

Fig. 5-4. Rectangular rosette.

which may be rewritten as

$$\epsilon_{u,v} = \frac{\epsilon_1 + \epsilon_3}{2} \pm \frac{1}{\sqrt{2}}\sqrt{(\epsilon_1 - \epsilon_2)^2 + (\epsilon_2 - \epsilon_3)^2}, \qquad (5\text{-}14b)$$

or

$$\epsilon_{u,v} = \frac{\Sigma_{13}}{2} \pm \frac{1}{\sqrt{2}}\sqrt{\Delta_{12}^2 + \Delta_{23}^2}, \qquad (5\text{-}14c)$$

in which $\Sigma_{13} = \epsilon_1 + \epsilon_3.$

$\Delta_{12} = \epsilon_1 - \epsilon_2.$

$\Delta_{23} = \epsilon_2 - \epsilon_3.$

Substitution of this result in Eq. (5-17) gives

$$S_u = \frac{E}{1 - \mu^2}\left(\frac{\Sigma_{13}}{2} + \frac{\sqrt{\Delta_{12}^2 + \Delta_{23}^2}}{\sqrt{2}} + \mu\frac{\Sigma_{13}}{2} - \mu\frac{\sqrt{\Delta_{12}^2 + \Delta_{23}^2}}{\sqrt{2}}\right), \qquad (5\text{-}17a)$$

which may be rewritten as

$$S_u = \frac{E}{2(1 - \mu)}\,\Sigma_{13} + \frac{E}{\sqrt{2}(1 + \mu)}\sqrt{\Delta_{12}^2 + \Delta_{23}^2}. \qquad (5\text{-}17b)$$

Likewise,

$$S_v = \frac{E}{2(1-\mu)}\Sigma_{13} - \frac{E}{\sqrt{2}(1+\mu)}\sqrt{\Delta_{12}^2 + \Delta_{23}^2}. \qquad (5\text{-}17c)$$

Since in the practical case the strains in the 1, 2, and 3 directions will be known only through the use of strain gages, we must consider how these strains are related to strain gage readings in the 1, 2, and 3 directions. For the commercially available three-element rectangular rosette gages, the manufacturer gives the following relationships between true strains (ϵ_1, ϵ_2, ϵ_3) and the readings obtained from the individual gage elements (Q_1, Q_2, Q_3):

$$\begin{aligned} \epsilon_1 &= Q_1 - KQ_3, \\ \epsilon_2 &= (1+K)Q_2 - K(Q_1 + Q_3), \\ \epsilon_3 &= Q_3 - KQ_1, \end{aligned} \qquad (5\text{-}18)$$

in which the readings (Q_1, Q_2, Q_3) are obtained by using the gage factor given by the manufacturer, and K is the transverse sensitivity [sometimes given by the manufacturer in terms of an auxiliary gage factor (b). $K = 1/b$]. To show how Eqs. (5-18) were arrived at, we shall refer to Fig. 5-5 and Eq. (5-2a).

Using the same approach and manipulations as were used to develop Eq. (5-2a), we may write

$$\epsilon_1 = \frac{\left(\frac{\Delta R}{R}\right)_1}{F_G} - \frac{K}{F_G}\left(\frac{\Delta R}{R}\right)_3, \qquad (5\text{-}2a)$$

$$\epsilon_3 = \frac{\left(\frac{\Delta R}{R}\right)_3}{F_G} - \frac{K}{F_G}\left(\frac{\Delta R}{R}\right)_1, \qquad (5\text{-}2b)$$

$$\epsilon_2 = \frac{\left(\frac{\Delta R}{R}\right)_2}{F_G} - \frac{K}{F_G}\left(\frac{\Delta R}{R}\right)_4, \qquad (5\text{-}2c)$$

$$\epsilon_4 = \frac{\left(\frac{\Delta R}{R}\right)_4}{F_G} - \frac{K}{F_G}\left(\frac{\Delta R}{R}\right)_2. \qquad (5\text{-}2d)$$

For a rectangular rosette gage the manufacturer gives the gage factor F_G; hence, using this factor, we see that the gage reading taken on any element (Q_n) is

$$\frac{\left(\frac{\Delta R}{R}\right)_n}{F_G}.$$

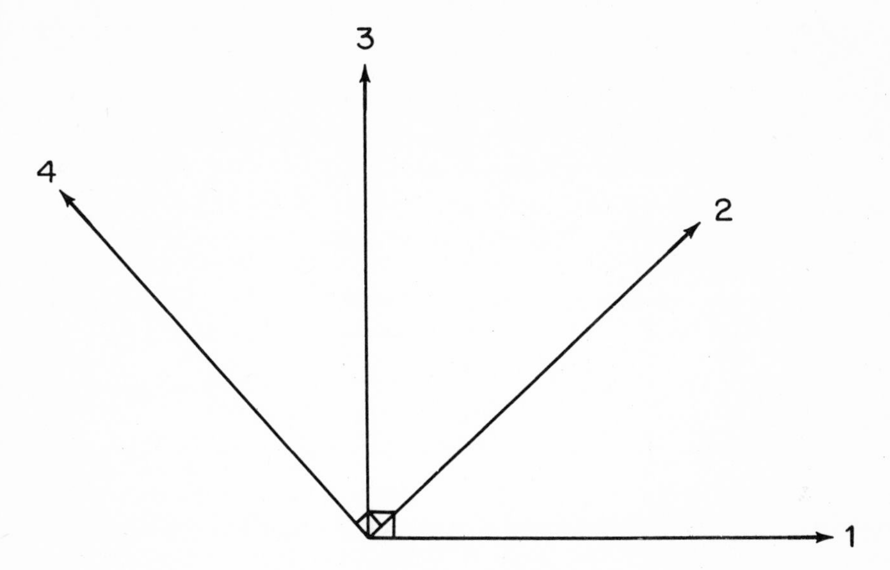

Fig. 5-5. Strain-axis designations.

The above equations then become

$$\epsilon_1 = Q_1 - KQ_3, \tag{5-2e}$$

$$\epsilon_3 = Q_3 - KQ_1, \tag{5-2f}$$

$$\epsilon_2 = Q_2 - KQ_4, \tag{5-2g}$$

$$\epsilon_4 = Q_4 - KQ_2. \tag{5-2h}$$

From elastic theory (the sum of the strains at a point in perpendicular directions is a constant), we have

$$\epsilon_1 + \epsilon_3 = \epsilon_2 + \epsilon_4, \tag{5-19}$$

or

$$\epsilon_4 = \epsilon_1 + \epsilon_3 - \epsilon_2, \tag{5-19a}$$

which allows us to eliminate ϵ_4 and Q_4 from the above equation. Thus

$$\epsilon_4 = \epsilon_1 + \epsilon_3 - \epsilon_2 = Q_4 - KQ_2, \tag{5-20}$$

$$\epsilon_2 = Q_2 - KQ_4 = Q_2 - K(\epsilon_1 + \epsilon_3 - \epsilon_2 + KQ_2), \tag{5-21}$$

$$\epsilon_2 = Q_2 - K[(Q_1 - KQ_3) + (Q_3 - KQ_1) - \epsilon_2 + KQ_2], \tag{5-22}$$

$$\epsilon_2 - K\epsilon_2 = Q_2 - K^2Q_2 - KQ_1 + K^2Q_1 + K^2Q_3 - KQ_3, \tag{5-22a}$$

$$\epsilon_2(1 - K) = Q_2(1 - K^2) - K(Q_1 + Q_3)(1 - K), \tag{5-22b}$$

$$\epsilon_2 = (1 + K)Q_2 - K(Q_1 + Q_3). \tag{5-22c}$$

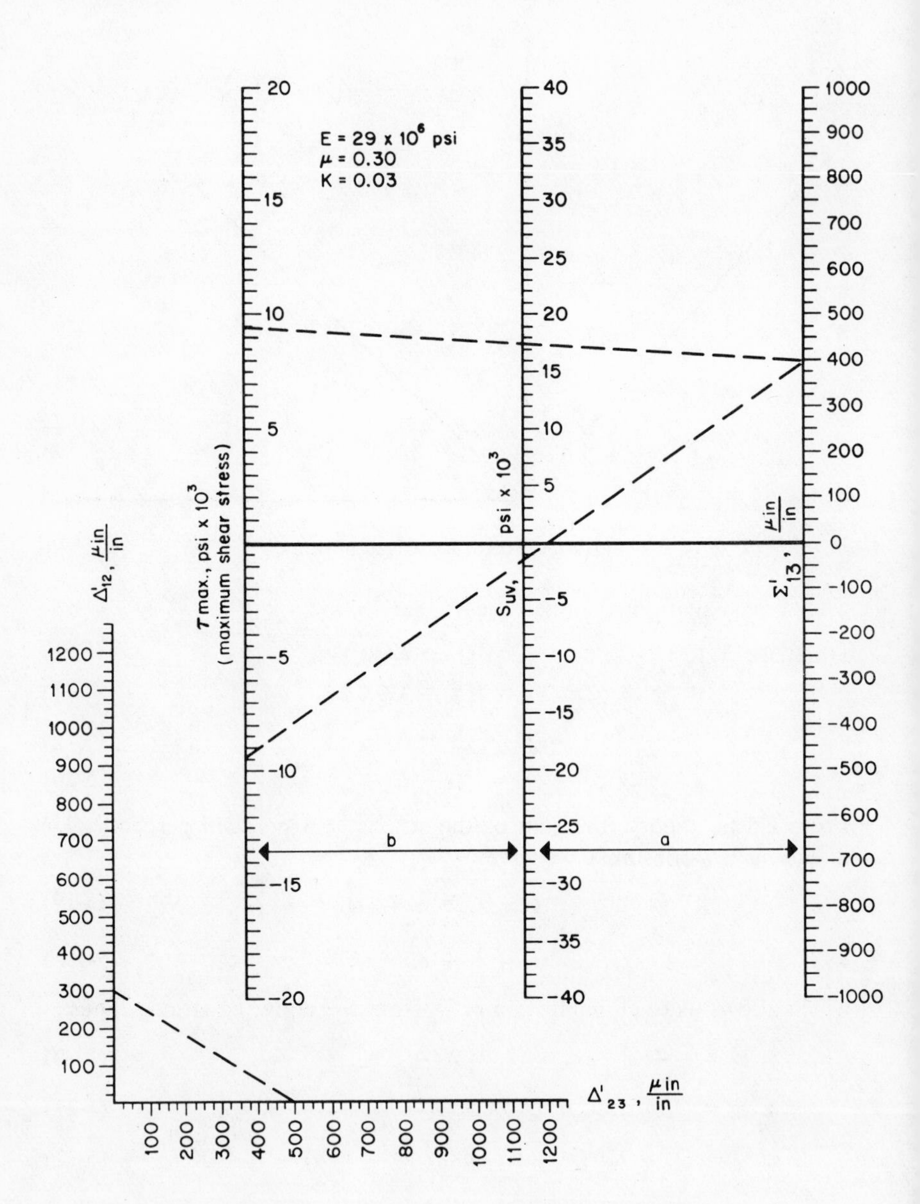

Fig. 5-6. Nomograph for rectangular rosette.

When Eqs. (5-18) are substituted in Eqs. (5-17b) and (5-17c), the principal stresses appear as functions of the three strain-gage readings.

$$S_{u,v} = \frac{E(1-K)}{2(1-\mu)}\Sigma'_{13} \pm \frac{E(1+K)}{\sqrt{2}(1+\mu)}\sqrt{\Delta'^2_{12} + \Delta'^2_{23}}, \qquad \text{(5-17d)}$$

or

$$S_{u,v} = A\,\Sigma'_{13} \pm B\sqrt{\Delta'^2_{12} + \Delta'^2_{23}}, \qquad \text{(5-17e)}$$

in which

$$\Sigma'_{13} = Q_1 + Q_3.$$

$$\Delta'_{12} = Q_1 - Q_2.$$

$$\Delta'_{23} = Q_2 - Q_3.$$

$$A = \frac{E(1-K)}{2(1-\mu)}.$$

$$B = \frac{E(1+K)}{\sqrt{2}(1+\mu)}.$$

Although this result could have been written in numerous other forms, this particular form was chosen because it lends itself well to solution by nomography. Figure 5-6 shows a nomograph for the solution of this equation. An example will indicate the usefulness of the nomograph.

Example 5-1. (Refer to Fig. 5-6.)

A rectangular rosette is mounted on a surface, and the gage readings taken are

$$Q_1 = +600\ \mu\text{in./in.}$$

$$Q_2 = +300\ \mu\text{in./in.}$$

$$Q_3 = -200\ \mu\text{in./in.}$$

The material is steel ($E = 29 \times 10^6$ psi, $\mu = 0.30$), and the gage has a transverse sensitivity of three per cent ($K = 0.03$).

We begin the solution by computing

$$\Sigma'_{13} = Q_1 + Q_3 = +400\ \mu\text{in./in.}$$

$$\Delta'_{12} = Q_1 - Q_2 = +300\ \mu\text{in./in.}$$

$$\Delta'_{23} = Q_2 - Q_3 = +500\ \mu\text{in./in.}$$

These values are located on the nomograph as shown. The length fixed by joining Δ'_{12} and Δ'_{23} is marked on the τ_{max} scale. This is the maximum shear stress and is laid off on both sides of zero, since in Eq. (5-17e) the maximum shear stress (second term) may have either sign.

Each point so located on the τ_{max} scale is connected with the value of Σ'_{13} on the Σ'_{13} scale, and the intersections of these two lines with the $S_{u,v}$ scale give the values of the principal stresses.
In this case we read

$$S_u = +17{,}500 \text{ psi}$$

and

$$S_v = -1500 \text{ psi.}$$

The answers obtained by substitution in and solution of Eq. (5-17e) are.

$$S_u = +17{,}500 \text{ psi,}$$

$$S_v = -1460 \text{ psi.}$$

Each nomograph must be constructed for the particular values of E and μ associated with a given material and a particular value of K for a given gage type.

The steps in the construction of this nomograph are as follows:

1. The scales for the Δ'_{12} and Δ'_{23} are the same and may be of any value compatible with the range desired and the size of the sheet.
2. The scale for the τ_{max} axis is chosen so that

$$\tau_{max} = B\sqrt{(\Delta'_{12})^2 + (\Delta'_{23})^2}.$$

This scale is easily established by making one length unit on the τ_{max} scale equal to B times the value of one length unit on the Δ'_{12} (or Δ'_{23}) scale. B is computed as

$$\frac{E(1 + K)}{\sqrt{2}\,(1 + \mu)}.$$

3. The scale for the Σ'_{13} axis is chosen arbitrarily, within the limitations imposed by the size of the sheet and the range desired.
4. The $S_{u,v}$ axis is located so that

$$\frac{a}{b} = \frac{\tau_{max} \text{ scale (psi/unit length)}}{(A \times \Sigma'_{13} \text{ scale) (psi/unit length)}}$$

A is computed as

$$\frac{E(1 - K)}{2(1 + \mu)}.$$

(See Fig. 5-6 for the definitions of a and b.)

5. The $S_{u,v}$ scale is equal to the τ_{max} scale plus the product of A times Σ'_{13} scale; i.e., one unit length on the $S_{u,v}$ axis is equal to the value

of one unit length on the τ_{max} axis plus A times the value of one unit length on the Σ'_{13} axis.

Other nomographs for the evaluation of principal stresses from three normal strains are to be found in the literature (see Refs. [7], [8], and [9]), but they must be entered with true strain (ϵ), *not* with strain-gage reading (Q).

The directions of the principal stresses may be evaluated with the aid of Eq. (5-16). Again, for a rectangular rosette: substitution of Eq. (5-12b) in Eq. (5-16) gives

$$\tan 2\alpha = \frac{-(\epsilon_1 + \epsilon_3) + 2\epsilon_2}{\epsilon_1 - \epsilon_3}, \qquad (5\text{-}23)$$

which may be rewritten as

$$\tan 2\alpha = \frac{-(\epsilon_1 - \epsilon_2) + (\epsilon_2 - \epsilon_3)}{(\epsilon_1 - \epsilon_2) + (\epsilon_2 - \epsilon_3)}, \qquad (5\text{-}23a)$$

or

$$\tan 2\alpha = \frac{\Delta_{23} - \Delta_{12}}{\Delta_{23} + \Delta_{12}}. \qquad (5\text{-}23b)$$

This is the same as

$$\tan 2\alpha = \frac{\Delta'_{23} - \Delta'_{12}}{\Delta'_{23} + \Delta'_{12}}, \qquad (5\text{-}24)$$

as we can show by substituting values of Q for ϵ, using Eqs. (5-18). This expression for the angle between the principal stress axis and the number 1 axis in a rectangular rosette has been arranged to involve the same terms (Δ'_{12}, Δ'_{23}) as were used in the expression for the magnitudes of the principal stresses. Figure 5-7 is a chart for the evaluation of α from values of Δ'_{12} and Δ'_{23}. The numbers given in the previous example may be used to illustrate the use in Fig. 5-7.

Projecting to the right from $\Delta'_{23} = 500$, until the Δ'_{12} of 300 value is intersected, and then projecting down to the abscissa, we read

$$\alpha = +7^\circ$$

(i.e., the u axis is 7° counterclockwise from the 1 axis).

Solution of Eq. (5-24) gives $\alpha = +7.02^\circ$.

Notice that Eq. (5-24) (and hence Fig. 5-7) is independent of gage constants and material properties. Therefore, Fig. 5-7 can be used to solve for principal stress directions for any *rectangular* rosette used on any material.

Standard computer programs are now available for the solution of principal stresses (magnitudes and directions) from strain-rosette data, and anyone having access to computer facilities should investigate this possibility.

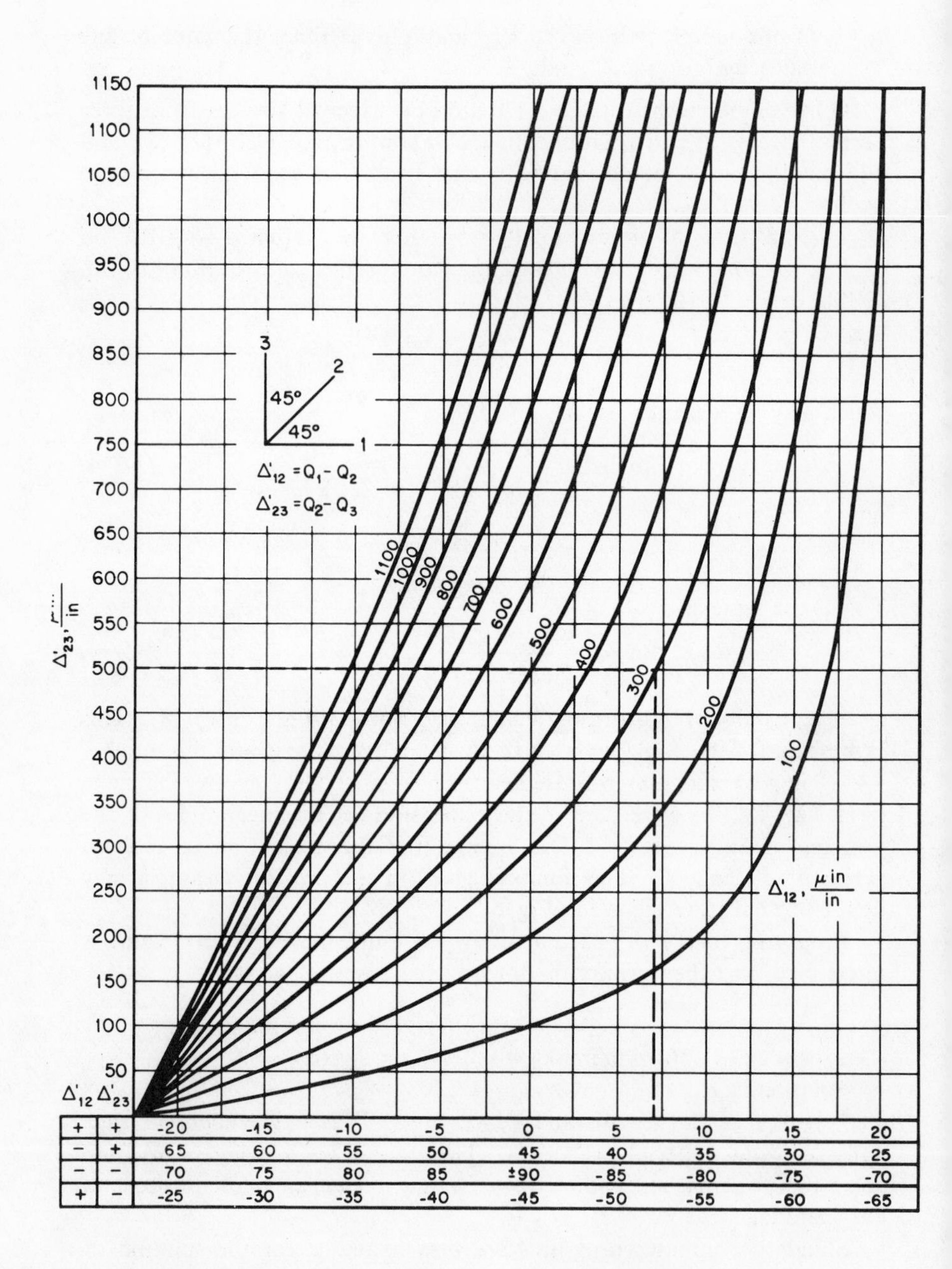

Fig. 5-7. Nomograph for angle between principal stress axis and gage axis.

5-3b Delta rosettes

Actually, principal stresses can be evaluated from normal strains in any three directions, but the only other rosette form in common use is the delta rosette (see Fig. 5-8).

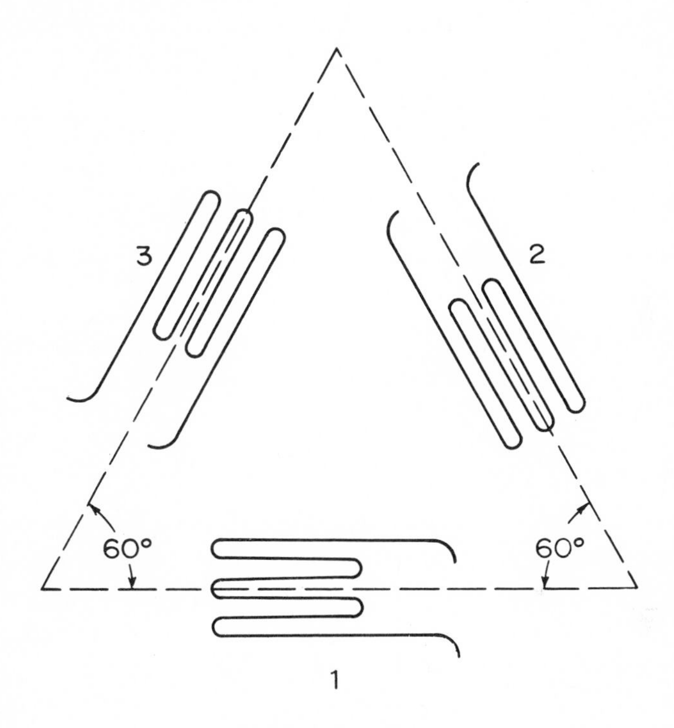

Fig. 5-8. Delta rosette.

In this case, Eqs. (5-12) through (5-17) are again solved for S_u, S_v, and α in terms of the measured strains (ϵ_1, ϵ_2, ϵ_3); for those gages having measurable cross sensitivity, the relationships between gage readings and true strain similar to Eq. (5-18) are given by the manufacturer. Since the method of analysis is similar to that just completed for the rectangular rosette, only the results for the delta rosette will be given here.*

$$\begin{aligned} \epsilon_1 &= Q_1 - K'(Q_2 + Q_3), \\ \epsilon_2 &= Q_2 - K'(Q_1 + Q_3), \\ \epsilon_3 &= Q_3 - K'(Q_1 + Q_2), \end{aligned} \tag{5-25}$$

* For this derivation, see Ref. [3].

$$S_{u,v} = \frac{E(1 - 2K')}{3(1 - \mu)} \Sigma'_{123} \pm \frac{\sqrt{2}}{3} \frac{E(1 + K')}{(1 + \mu)} \sqrt{(\Delta'_{12})^2 + (\Delta'_{23})^2 + (\Delta'_{31})^2}, \quad (5\text{-}17f)$$

$$\alpha = \frac{1}{2} \tan^{-1} \frac{\sqrt{3}(\Delta'_{12} + \Delta'_{31})}{\Delta'_{12} - \Delta'_{31}}, \quad (5\text{-}24a)$$

in which $\Sigma'_{123} = Q_1 + Q_2 + Q_3$.

$\Delta'_{12} = Q_1 - Q_2$.

$\Delta'_{23} = Q_2 - Q_3$.

$\Delta'_{31} = Q_3 - Q_1$.

Q = reading obtained by using the gage factor given by the manufacturer for the delta rosette (F_D).

Note: $F_D = \dfrac{F_a^2 - F_t^2}{F_a + \frac{1}{3}F_t}$ (see Ref. [3]).

K' = the appropriate transverse sensitivity for the delta rosette given by the manufacturer.

Note: $K' = \dfrac{\frac{2}{3}F_t}{F_a + \frac{1}{3}F_t}$ or

$K' = \dfrac{\frac{2}{3}K}{1 + \frac{1}{3}K}$ where $K = \dfrac{F_t}{F_a}$.

Nomographs utilizing gage readings (Q_1, Q_2, Q_3) may be made for the solution of these equations. Nomographs utilizing true strains (ϵ_1, ϵ_2, ϵ_3) are available in the literature (Refs. [8] and [9]).

5-3c Two-element, 90-degree rosettes

In the case where the directions of the principal stresses are known, as from symmetry or as when the strain-gage test is preceded by a Stress-coat test, a biaxial strain gage [two strain-gage elements 90 deg apart (see Fig. 5-9)] can be used. In this case the 1 and 3 elements are oriented in the u and v directions.

For commercially available biaxial gages the manufacturer gives the proper gage factor (F_G) and the cross sensitivity (K). Substitution of Eq. (5-18) in Eq. (5-17) gives

$$S_u = \frac{E}{1 - \mu^2}(Q_1 - KQ_3 + \mu Q_3 - \mu K Q_1), \quad (5\text{-}26)$$

or

$$S_u = CQ_1 + DQ_3, \quad (5\text{-}27)$$

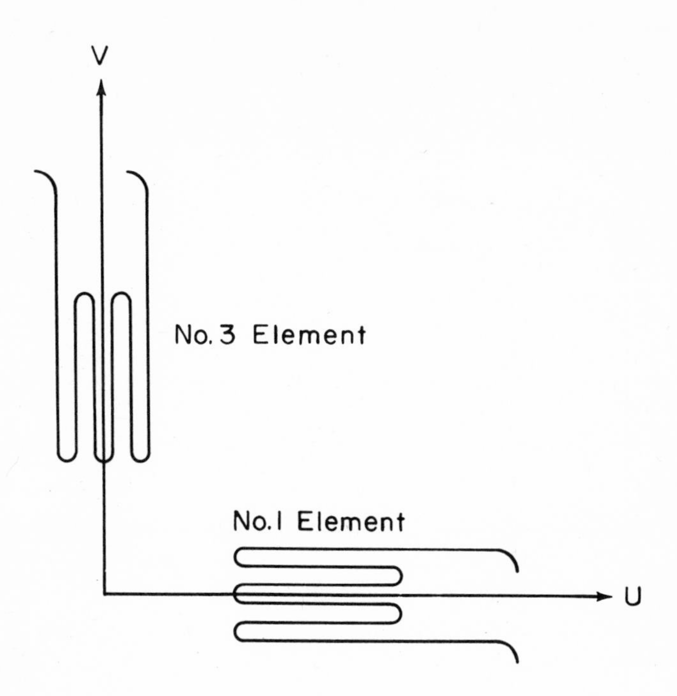

Fig. 5-9. Biaxial strain gage and principal strain-axis designations.

in which
$$C = \frac{E(1 - K\mu)}{1 - \mu^2}.$$
$$D = \frac{E(\mu - K)}{1 - \mu^2}.$$

Likewise,
$$S_v = CQ_3 + DQ_1. \tag{5-27a}$$

Figure 5-10 shows a nomograph for the solution of Eq. (5-27); an example will illustrate its use.

Example 5-2. Two gages are mounted parallel to the principal stress axes on steel ($E = 29 \times 10^6$ psi, $\mu = 0.3$). The gages, which have a transverse sensitivity of three per cent ($K = 0.03$), give readings of
$$Q_1 = +600 \ \mu\text{in./in.}$$
and
$$Q_3 = -200 \ \mu\text{in./in.}$$

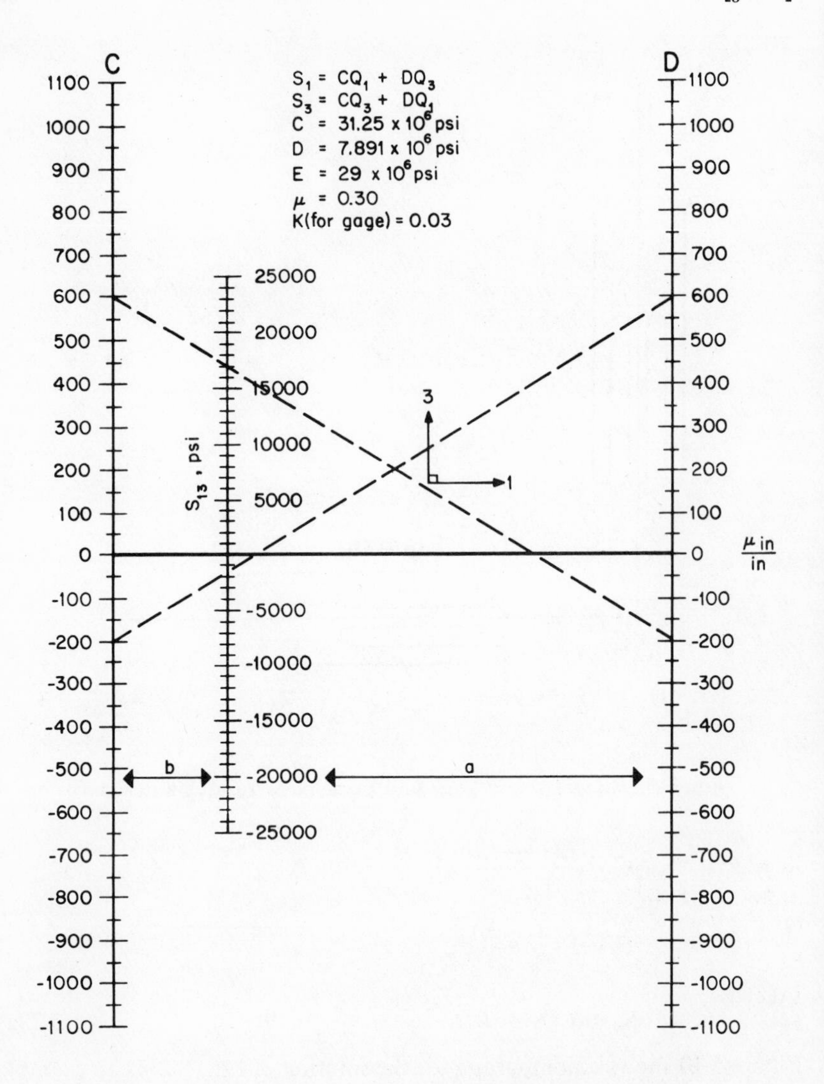

Fig. 5-10. Nomograph for solution of biaxial strain gages.

Joining the value of Q_1 (600) on the C axis to the value of Q_3 (-200) on the D axis, we read S_1 as

$$S_1 = 17{,}000 \text{ psi.}$$

Joining the value of Q_3 (-200) on the C axis to the value of Q_1 ($+600$) on the D axis, we read S_3 as

$$S_3 = -1500 \text{ psi.}$$

Substitution into and solution of Eq. (5-27) give

$$S_1 = S_u = 17{,}175 \text{ psi},$$

$$S_3 = S_v = -1525 \text{ psi}.$$

A nomograph must be constructed for each new set of material properties (E and μ) and gage transverse sensitivity (K). The construction steps are as follows [refer to Fig. (5-10)]:

1. The scales on the C and D axes are the same and are arbitrary within the limitation of the range desired and the sheet size.
2. The $S_{1,3}$ axis is located so that

$$\frac{a}{b} = \frac{C}{D},$$

in which

$$C = \frac{E(1 - K\mu)}{1 - \mu^2}.$$

$$D = \frac{E(\mu - K)}{1 - \mu^2}.$$

See Fig. 5-10 for location of a and b.

3. The $S_{1,3}$ scale is equal to $(C + D)$ times the scale chosen for the C (or D) axis; i.e., one unit length on the $S_{1,3}$ axis is equal to $(C + D)$ times the value of one unit length on the C (or D) axis.

In the case of biaxial gages there are other possible methods of solution. The four terms (CQ_1, DQ_3, CQ_3, DQ_1) can easily be obtained directly by proper adjustment of the output gain in the gage circuits. In this case solution for S_u and S_v requires only addition of measured quantities.

5-3d Rosettes made from single-element gages

Two- or three-element rosettes may be constructed by using two or three single-element strain gages oriented along the rosette axis. But, as previously pointed out, the manufacturers calibrate all single-element gages in a uniaxial stress field, and hence the effect on gage output of transverse strain due to the Poisson effect has been eliminated in the calibration. Since this is not desired when a single-element gage is to be used as an element in a rosette, the gage factor for the single-element gage given by the manufacturer (F_u) should be converted to the appropriate rosette gage factor, i.e., the gage factor used when readings are related to strains by using Eqs. (5-18) and (5-25).

For rectangular rosettes and two-element, 90-deg rosettes the correct gage factor is F_G, which is related to F_u by Eq. (5-6);

$$F_G = \frac{(1 - K^2)}{(1 - \mu_o K)} F_u. \tag{5-6}$$

For delta rosettes the correct gage factor is F_D, which can be related to F_u by the same type of calculation used to develop Eq. (5-6):

$$F_D = \frac{(1 - K^2)}{(1 - \mu_o K)\left(1 + \frac{K}{3}\right)} F_u. \tag{5-28}$$

It will be observed that the difference between F_u and F_G and between F_u and F_D is small *and* is constant, i.e., not a function of the nature of the strain field. This means that, except when the maximum of precision is warranted, it is permissible to use the manufacturer's gage factor (F_u) when single-element gages are mounted and used as rosettes. However, this is entirely different from using a single-element gage alone in a biaxial stress field to determine either stress or strain (see Table 5-2).

5-3e Stress gages

Under certain conditions the direction of the maximum principal stress is known. In this case, it is possible to evaluate the magnitude of the maximum principal stress by using only one single-element strain gage. If the x and y directions (Fig. 5-3) are replaced by u and v directions, Eqs. (5-12) and (5-13) become

$$\epsilon_a = \epsilon_u \cos^2 \theta + \epsilon_v \sin^2 \theta \tag{5-12c}$$

and

$$\epsilon_t = \epsilon_u \sin^2 \theta + \epsilon_v \cos^2 \theta, \tag{5-13a}$$

since the shearing strain on the principal planes (ϵ_{uv}) is known to be equal to zero.

We proceed as follows to determine at what angle (θ) a single-element gage should be placed so that the gage reading (Q_a) will be zero for any stress applied in the v direction. For a given stress (S_v) in the v direction, $\epsilon_v \equiv \epsilon_v$ and $\epsilon_u = -\mu\epsilon_v$. As before,

$$\epsilon_a = Q_a - KQ_t, \tag{5-18a}$$

$$\epsilon_t = Q_t - KQ_a. \tag{5-18b}$$

If these values are substituted into Eqs. (5-12c) and (5-13a) and Q_a is set equal to zero, the result is

$$\frac{\sin^2 \theta}{\cos^2 \theta} = \frac{\mu - K}{1 - K\mu}, \tag{5-29}$$

or

$$\tan^2\theta = \frac{\mu - K}{1 - K\mu} \tag{5-29a}$$

That is, if a single-element strain gage is oriented at an angle

$$\theta = \tan^{-1}\sqrt{\frac{\mu - K}{1 - K\mu}}$$

with respect to the u axis, it is completely insensitive to stress in the v direction. With the gage oriented at this angle θ, the gage reading can be related to a stress in the u direction as follows: substituting

$$\tan^2\theta = \frac{(\mu - K)}{(1 - K\mu)}, \tag{5-29a}$$

$$\epsilon_u = Q_u - KQ_v,$$

$$\epsilon_v = Q_v - KQ_u \tag{5-18c}$$

$$\epsilon_a = Q_a - KQ_t,$$

and

$$\epsilon_t = Q_t - KQ_a$$

into Eqs. (5-12c) and (5-13a), we obtain

$$Q_a = \frac{(1 - \mu K)}{(1 + \mu)(1 - K)}\left[Q_u + Q_v\frac{(\mu - K)}{(1 - \mu K)}\right]. \tag{5-30}$$

Writing

$$S_u = \frac{E}{1 - \mu^2}(\epsilon_u + \mu\epsilon_v) \tag{5-17}$$

and substituting

$$\epsilon_u = Q_u - KQ_v \tag{5-18c}$$

and

$$\epsilon_v = Q_v - KQ_u \tag{5-18c}$$

gives

$$S_u = \frac{E}{1 - \mu^2}[Q_u(1 - \mu K) + Q_v(\mu - K)], \tag{5-17g}$$

which may be rewritten as

$$S_u = \frac{E(1 - \mu K)}{1 - \mu^2}\left[Q_u + \frac{Q_v(\mu - K)}{(1 - \mu K)}\right]. \tag{5-17h}$$

Substitution for the bracketed term in Eq. (5-17h) in terms of Eq. (5-30) gives

$$S_u = \frac{E(1 - K)}{(1 - \mu)}Q_a. \tag{5-31}$$

In using this expression the following fact must be remembered: since the relationship between true strain and gage readings ($\epsilon_a = Q_a - KQ_t$) was applied, Eq. (5-31) is strictly valid only when the gage output is read by using a gage factor of F_G. As previously explained, the appropriate gage factor F_G can be evaluated as

$$F_G = \frac{(1 - K^2)}{(1 - \mu_o K)} F_u. \tag{5-6}$$

This use of a single-element strain gage to determine the magnitude of the maximum stress was originally proposed by C. C. Perry (Ref. [9], p. 147). However, in his treatment of the subject Perry neglected the transverse sensitivity of the gage (K taken as equal to zero). With $K = 0$, Perry finds

$$\theta = \tan^{-1} \sqrt{\mu} \tag{5-32}$$

and

$$S_u = \frac{E}{1 - \mu} Q_a. \tag{5-33}$$

The error introduced by this omission is indeed small—approximately equal (in percentage) to the value of the transverse sensitivity (K). H. R. Lissner and Perry analyzed this omission and the effect of misalignment of the gage, i.e., $\theta \neq \tan^{-1} \sqrt{\mu}$ (see Ref. [10]).

Under some conditions it is desired to know the stress in a given direction even when it is not known that this direction is a principal stress direction. In this case it is always possible to obtain the stress in the desired direction (say S_x) by mounting two gages, one in the x direction and one in the y direction, taking two readings (Q_x and Q_y), and solving for S_x, using Eq. (5-27) in the form*

$$S_x = CQ_x + DQ_y. \tag{5-27a}$$

Another method for solving this same problem, which was suggested by S. B. Williams (Ref. [11]), has led to development of the "stress gage" (see Fig. 5-11).

Consider a gage in which the active element consists of equal lengths along the a and a' axis (see Fig. 5-12).

The sum of the strain in the a and a' directions is independent of the shear strain (ϵ_{xy}), as can be seen by writing Eqs. (5-12) for ϵ_a and ϵ_a' and adding. Therefore, we can write

$$\epsilon_a + \epsilon_{a'} = 2\epsilon_x \cos^2 \theta + 2\epsilon_y \sin^2 \theta \tag{5-34}$$

and, in the same manner,

$$\epsilon_t + \epsilon_{t'} = 2\epsilon_x \sin^2 \theta + 2\epsilon_y \cos^2 \theta. \tag{5-35}$$

---

* Equation (5-27) may be written in terms of x and y as well as u and v because the two expressions used to derive Eq. (5-27), namely, Eqs. (5-17) and (5-18), are valid for any perpendicular axes.

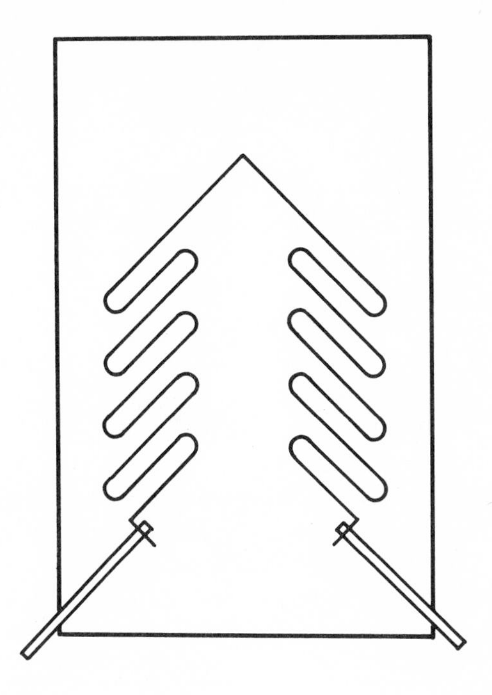

Fig. 5-11. Stress gage.

The same method of analysis as was used in connection with Eqs. (5-12c) and (5-13a) can be used to show that if

$$\theta = \tan^{-1}\sqrt{\frac{\mu - K}{1 - K\mu}},$$

then the stress in the x direction (S_x) is

$$S_x = \frac{E(1 - K)}{(1 - \mu)} Q_{a-a'}. \tag{5-36}$$

Here again, the gage reading ($Q_{a-a'}$) must be obtained by using F_G. It is apparent that a stress gage may be constructed by using two single-element gages which are mounted at $+\theta$ and $-\theta$ from the desired stress axis and wired in series.

Figure 5-13 shows another style of commercially available gage which functions to measure stress regardless of the nature of the stress field. When it is used in the conventional manner, i.e., to measure strain in a given direction, only one element is used. Thus, to measure the strain

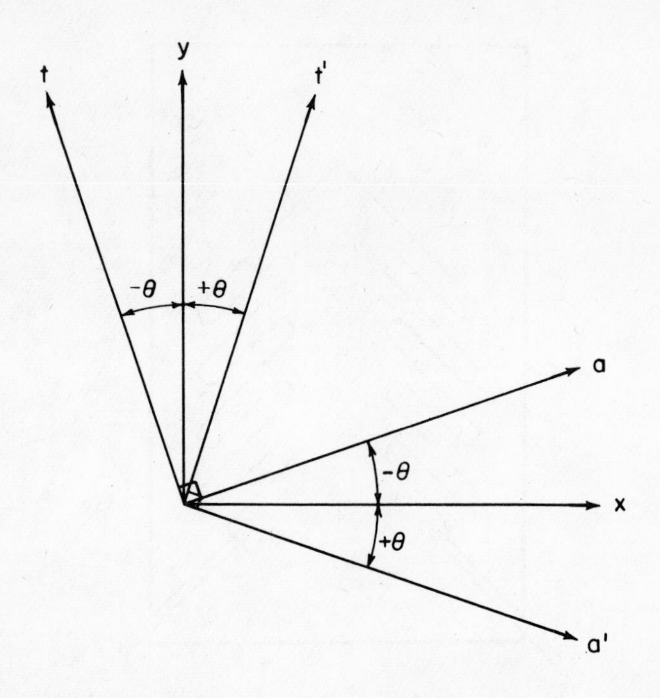

Fig. 5-12. Stress gage axis designations.

parallel to the *a-a* axis, leads 1 and 3 are connected (see Fig. 5-13). To measure the strain parallel to the *t-t* axis, leads 1 and 2 are connected. To obtain a signal proportional to the *stress* parallel to the *a-a* axis, the two elements are connected in series (leads 2 and 3). Brief analysis will establish how and under what conditions this gage functions to solve Eq. (5-27).

The stress parallel to the *a-a* axis is

$$S_a = \frac{E}{1 - \mu^2} (\epsilon_a + \mu\epsilon_t). \tag{5-8}$$

If we neglect the transverse sensitivity of the individual elements, this may be written as

$$S_a = \frac{E}{1 - \mu^2} \left(\frac{\Delta R_a / R_a}{F_a} + \mu \frac{\Delta R_t / R_t}{F_t} \right), \tag{5-37}$$

since the strain along each axis can be written in terms of the element's gage factor.

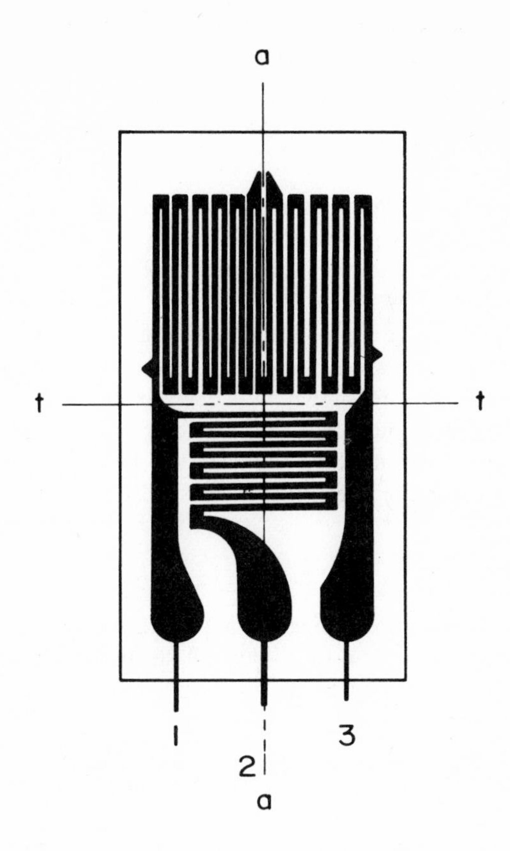

Fig. 5-13. Foil stress-strain gage.

Now for

$$R_t = \mu R_a \quad \text{and} \quad F_a = F_t,$$

where R_a is the resistance of the *a-a* oriented element, R_t is the resistance of the *t-t* oriented element, and F is gage factor of the individual element, Eq. (5-37) becomes

$$S_a = \frac{E}{(1 - \mu^2)F_a}\left(\frac{\Delta R_a + \Delta R_t}{R_a}\right), \tag{5-37a}$$

or

$$S_a = \frac{E}{(1 - \mu)F_a}\frac{\Delta R_T}{R_T}, \tag{5-37b}$$

in which

$$\Delta R_T = \Delta R_a + \Delta R_t.$$

$$R_T = R_a + R_t.$$

If we define the gage factor for the two elements used in series as

$$F_c = (1 - \mu)F_a, \tag{5-38}$$

Eq. (5-37) can be written as

$$S_a = E\frac{\Delta R_T/R_T}{F_c}; \tag{5-37c}$$

i.e., S_a is the product of modulus E and the reading taken with the two elements in series and a gage factor of F_c set on the indicator.

Remember that the transverse sensitivity of the individual elements has been neglected. How much error this will produce depends on the value of the ratio ϵ_t/ϵ_a. It is possible to design a gage of this type and to take into account the transverse sensitivity of the individual element; the necessary computations are shown in Appendix B. However, as F. F. Hines (Ref. [12]) points out, uncertainty of the exact value of Poisson's ratio (μ) of the material on which the gage will be used probably makes this refinement unwarranted even if it is physically possible.

5-4 Summary

When one is working in a general biaxial stress field (i.e., direction of principal stresses unknown), a three-element strain rosette must be used. From three gage readings both the magnitudes and the orientations of the principal stresses can be established.

When one is working in a biaxial stress field, in which the directions of the principal stresses are known, a two-element rosette gage should be used if both principal stress magnitudes are desired.

When one is working in a biaxial stress field in which the directions of the principal stresses are known, either of the two (but not both) principal stresses may be evaluated from a single gage reading. The gage element axis (a) should be placed at an angle θ from the axis of the desired principal strain, where

$$\theta = \tan^{-1}\sqrt{\frac{(\mu - K)}{(1 - K\mu)}}.$$

The desired principal stress (say S_u) is then evaluated as

$$S_u = \frac{E(1 - K)}{(1 - \mu)}Q_a. \tag{5-31}$$

When one is working in a biaxial stress field and it is desired to obtain the stress in a direction that is not known to be a principal direction, any of three methods may be used.

1. A two-element, 90-deg rosette may be used and the desired stress computed from the two gage readings.

2. A "stress gage" (Fig. 5-11) may be used.
3. A "stress-strain gage" (Fig. 5-13) may be used.

5-5 Appendix A (Methods for determining transverse sensitivity)

The transverse sensitivity of bonded, resistance-type strain gages is defined as the change in resistance of the gage due to strain perpendicular to the gage axis divided by change in resistance due to strain parallel to the gage axis. Thus

$$K = \frac{F_t}{F_a},$$

in which
$$F_t = \frac{\Delta R/R}{\epsilon_t}. \qquad \text{(A-1)}$$

$$F_a = \frac{\Delta R/R}{\epsilon_a}. \qquad \text{(A-1a)}$$

The measurement of transverse sensitivity requires that the gage be mounted in a field for which ϵ_t and ϵ_a are known. There are several possibilities:

1. In a uniaxial stress field the strain perpendicular to the maximum principal stress axis is known to be equal to the Poisson's strain. See Fig. 5-14. If two identical gages are mounted as shown, K may be computed from their readings.

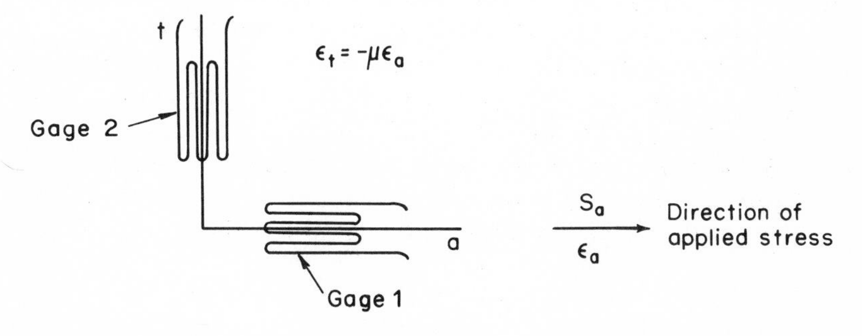

Fig. 5-14.

Thus

$$\left(\frac{\Delta R}{R}\right)_1 = F_a\epsilon_a + F_t\epsilon_t = F_a\epsilon_a - \mu F_t\epsilon_a = \epsilon_a(F_a - \mu F_t), \qquad \text{(A-2)}$$

$$\left(\frac{\Delta R}{R}\right)_2 = \epsilon_a(F_t - \mu F_a). \qquad \text{(A-2a)}$$

Solving for F_t and F_a, we obtain

$$F_t = \frac{\left(\frac{\Delta R}{R}\right)_2 + \mu\left(\frac{\Delta R}{R}\right)_1}{\epsilon_a(1 - \mu^2)}$$

and

$$F_a = \frac{\left(\frac{\Delta R}{R}\right)_1 + \mu\left(\frac{\Delta R}{R}\right)_2}{\epsilon_a(1 - \mu^2)}. \tag{A-3a}$$

Finally,

$$K = \frac{F_t}{F_a} = \frac{\left(\frac{\Delta R}{R}\right)_2 + \mu\left(\frac{\Delta R}{R}\right)_1}{\left(\frac{\Delta R}{R}\right)_1 + \mu\left(\frac{\Delta R}{R}\right)_2}$$

or

$$K = \frac{\mu + X}{1 + \mu X}, \tag{A-4}$$

in which
$$X = \frac{\left(\frac{\Delta R}{R}\right)_2}{\left(\frac{\Delta R}{R}\right)_1}.$$

The difficulty with this method is that the value obtained for K is very dependent on the precision with which μ is known, and surprisingly little is known concerning exact values for μ.

For example, if the value for K is three per cent, and if the value for Poisson's ratio of the test material is 0.285, the ratio of the gage readings, X, will be -0.257 [found by solving Eq. (A-4)]. Assume now that K is to be determined and that -0.257 is read from the gages. If a value of μ which is one per cent in error is assumed, i.e., 0.288, the resulting error in K will be

$$\text{Per cent error} = \frac{0.03 - \dfrac{\mu + X}{1 + \mu X}}{0.03} \times 100$$

$$= 1 - \left[\frac{\dfrac{0.288 - 0.257}{1 + (0.288)(-0.257)}}{0.03}\right] \times 100$$

$$= -11 \text{ per cent.}$$

Because of this large magnification between the error in μ and the error in K, it is necessary that μ be known with great accuracy before this method can be used. Consequently, this method is inadequate for most purposes.

2. The strain in the two directions of interest (a and t) may be measured, but this measurement must be made in such a way that it is independent of any unknown or questionable transverse sensitivity of the measuring transducer (bonded strain gages with unknown or doubtful transverse sensitivity cannot be used). The National Bureau of Standards has used Tuckerman optical gages for this purpose (see Ref. [13]).

   An adequate method for determining the transverse sensitivity of a gage by strain measurement involves mounting two gages with known K's and two gages of unknown K's side by side along the principal axes (u, v) in a uniaxial stress field. The transverse sensitivity of the test gages can be found from the strain readings on the gages as follows: the readings on the test gages (i.e., K unknown) are given by

$$\left(\frac{\Delta R}{R}\right)_u = F_a\epsilon_u + F_t\epsilon_v \tag{A-2b}$$

and

$$\left(\frac{\Delta R}{R}\right)_v = F_a\epsilon_v + F_t\epsilon_u. \tag{A-2c}$$

Solving both equations simultaneously for F_t and F_a, we have

$$F_a = \frac{\epsilon_v\left(\frac{\Delta R}{R}\right)_v - \epsilon_u\left(\frac{\Delta R}{R}\right)_u}{\epsilon_v^2 - \epsilon_u^2}$$

and

$$F_t = \frac{\epsilon_u\left(\frac{\Delta R}{R}\right)_v - \epsilon_v\left(\frac{\Delta R}{R}\right)_u}{\epsilon_u^2 - \epsilon_v^2}.$$

Then

$$K = \frac{F_t}{F_a} = \frac{\dfrac{\epsilon_u\left(\frac{\Delta R}{R}\right)_v - \epsilon_v\left(\frac{\Delta R}{R}\right)_u}{\epsilon_u^2 - \epsilon_v^2}}{\dfrac{\epsilon_v\left(\frac{\Delta R}{R}\right)_v - \epsilon_u\left(\frac{\Delta R}{R}\right)_u}{\epsilon_v^2 - \epsilon_u^2}} = \frac{\epsilon_v - X\epsilon_u}{X\epsilon_v - \epsilon_u}, \tag{A-5}$$

where $$X = \frac{\left(\frac{\Delta R}{R}\right)_v}{\left(\frac{\Delta R}{R}\right)_u}.$$

The readings on the reference gage (i.e., known transverse sensitivity) are given by the same expressions, Eqs. (A-2b) and (A-2c). Solving these expressions simultaneously for ϵ_u and ϵ_v, and letting an asterisk indicate properties and readings from the reference gage, we obtain

$$\epsilon_u^* = \frac{K^*\left(\frac{\Delta R}{R}\right)_v^* - \left(\frac{\Delta R}{R}\right)_u^*}{F_a^*\,(K^{*2} - 1)} \tag{A-6a}$$

and

$$\epsilon_v^* = \frac{\left(\frac{\Delta R}{R}\right)_v^* - K^*\left(\frac{\Delta R}{R}\right)_u^*}{F_a^*\,(1 - K^{*2})}, \tag{A-6b}$$

where K^* is the known transverse sensitivity of the reference gage.

If the gages are mounted carefully in the stress field so that they both encounter the same strains, we may substitute these expressions for ϵ_u and ϵ_v in the previous expression (A-5) for K, thus obtaining an expression involving only ratios of readings and K factors. That is,

$$\epsilon_v = \epsilon_v^* \qquad \text{and} \qquad \epsilon_u = \epsilon_u^*,$$

and substituting Eqs. (A-6) in Eq. (A-5), we obtain

$$K = \frac{(K^* - X^*) - X(K^*X^* - 1)}{X(K^* - X^*) - (K^*X^* - 1)}, \tag{A-7}$$

where K^* = known cross sensitivity.

$$X^* = \frac{\left(\frac{\Delta R}{R}\right)_v^*}{\left(\frac{\Delta R}{R}\right)_u^*}$$ = ratio of readings of the reference gages in the u and v directions.

$$X = \frac{\left(\frac{\Delta R}{R}\right)_v}{\left(\frac{\Delta R}{R}\right)_u}.$$

The above expression may be used to find K for a gage accurately, provided that reference gages are available. Care must be taken to assure that both gages are mounted on the principal stress axis and that both encounter the same strains. It can be shown that the value of Poisson's ratio for the material upon which the gages are mounted has little effect upon the accuracy of K.

The important factor to be considered when this method is used is the error involved in the value of K^*. This error will also appear in the result obtained for K of the test gage. If the known gage has a very low K^*, whereas the test gage has a somewhat higher value of K, this error will be minimized. For example, if $K^* = 0.03$, $K = 0.01$, and $\mu = 0.333$, the ratio of readings from the known gage, X^*, would be -0.306, and the ratio of readings from the test gage, X, would be -0.324. Using these values for X and X^* and assuming a ten per cent error in K^* (i.e., $K^* = 0.033$), we find that solution of Eq. (A-7) gives

$$K = \frac{(0.033 + 0.306) + (0.324)\ [(0.033)(-0.306) - 1]}{(-0.324)(0.033 + 0.306) - [(0.033)(-0.306) - 1]} = 0.0122.$$

The resultant error in the measured K due to a ten per cent error in K^* is

$$\text{Per cent error} = \frac{0.0122 - 0.01}{0.01} \times 100 = 22 \text{ per cent.}$$

However, if $K^* = 0.0015$ and $K = 0.01$, a ten per cent error in K^* will result in a four per cent error in K; if $K^* = 0.0015$ and $K = 0.04$, a ten per cent error in K^* will result in a one per cent error in K. The value of 0.0015 was chosen for K^* because the FAP-50-12 strain gage has this value (see Table 5-1).

We conclude that this method can be used accurately to find the transverse sensitivity of a gage if the transverse sensitivity of the standard is known and is sufficiently low. The lower the value of K^*/K, the greater will be the accuracy of K. It should also be noted that if the unknown gage has zero cross sensitivity, an infinite error will result in its determination by this method, since some value for K will be obtained. However, this method is superior to either methods 1 or 3 cited in this section.

3. In a uniaxial stress field an axis (q) can be located along which the strain is zero. See Fig. 5-15. Referring to Eq. (5-12) on p. 251, we can write

$$\epsilon_a = \epsilon_u \cos^2 \theta + \epsilon_v \sin^2 \theta - \frac{\epsilon_{uv}}{2} \sin^2 \theta,$$

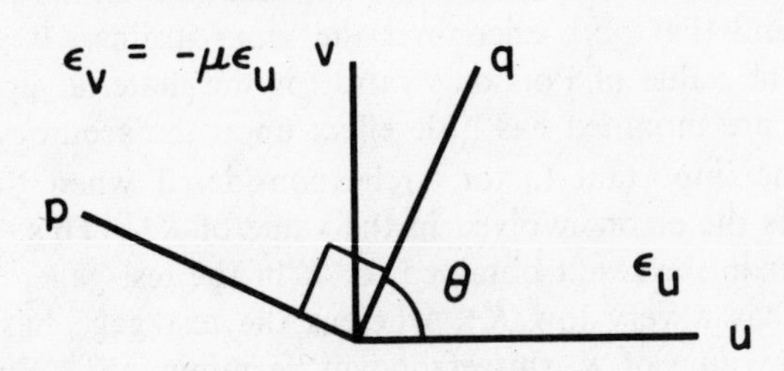

Fig. 5-15.

but $\epsilon_v = -\mu\epsilon_u$, since this is a uniaxial stress field, and $\epsilon_{uv} = 0$, since u and v are principal directions. Hence

$$\epsilon_q = \epsilon_u (\cos^2 \theta - \mu \sin^2 \theta).$$

If

$$\frac{\cos^2 \theta}{\sin^2 \theta} = \mu, \qquad \text{or} \qquad \tan \theta = \sqrt{\frac{1}{\mu}}, \tag{A-8}$$

then $\epsilon_q = 0$.

By mounting two identical gages in the p and q directions we can compute K from their readings. Thus

$$\left(\frac{\Delta R}{R}\right)_q = 0 + F_t\epsilon_p \tag{A-2d}$$

and

$$\left(\frac{\Delta R}{R}\right)_p = F_a\epsilon_p + 0; \tag{A-2e}$$

dividing the first by the second, we obtain

$$K = \frac{F_t}{F_a} = \frac{\left(\frac{\Delta R}{R}\right)_q}{\left(\frac{\Delta R}{R}\right)_p}. \tag{A-9}$$

Here, again, the value of K is dependent upon the precision with which μ is known and, in addition, upon the precision with which the gages can be mounted after θ is computed from μ. A five per cent error in μ results in a change of less than one deg from the correct θ. Since it would be difficult to mount the gages within a tolerance of ± 1 deg, errors in K resulting from inaccurate gage mounting, rather than inaccuracies in μ, will be investigated.

If the gages are not mounted precisely in the p and q directions, $\epsilon_q \neq 0$, and the readings from the gages are given by

$$\left(\frac{\Delta R}{R}\right)_q = F_a\epsilon_q + F_t\epsilon_p \tag{A-2f}$$

and

$$\left(\frac{\Delta R}{R}\right)_p = F_a\epsilon_p + F_t\epsilon_q. \tag{A-2g}$$

Solving both equations simultaneously for F_a and F_t yields

$$F_t = \frac{\left(\frac{\Delta R}{R}\right)_p - \frac{\epsilon_p}{\epsilon_q}\left(\frac{\Delta R}{R}\right)_q}{\left(\epsilon_q - \frac{\epsilon_p^2}{\epsilon_q}\right)}$$

and

$$F_a = \frac{\left(\frac{\Delta R}{R}\right)_p - \frac{\epsilon_q}{\epsilon_p}\left(\frac{\Delta R}{R}\right)_q}{\left(\epsilon_q - \frac{\epsilon_q^2}{\epsilon_p}\right)}.$$

Dividing the first by the second, we obtain

$$K = \frac{F_t}{F_a} = \frac{\epsilon_p X - \epsilon_q}{\epsilon_p - \epsilon_q X}, \tag{A-10}$$

where $X = (\Delta R/R)_q/(\Delta R/R)_p$
and

$$\begin{aligned}\epsilon_q &= \epsilon_u \cos^2\phi + \epsilon_v \sin^2\phi \\ &= \epsilon_u(\cos^2\phi - \mu \sin^2\phi),\end{aligned}$$

since $\epsilon_v = -u\epsilon_u$ in a uniaxial stress field.

Similarly,

$$\epsilon_p = \epsilon_u(\sin^2\phi - \mu\cos^2\phi).$$

In this case ϕ is used to denote the angle from the u axis to the q direction, since it is not the value required to make

$$\epsilon_q = 0 \qquad \text{(i.e., } \phi \neq \theta).$$

Since

$$\frac{(\Delta R/R)_q}{(\Delta R/R)_p} = X$$

represents the erroneous K, the expression for the error is

$$\text{Per cent error} = \frac{X - K}{K} \times 100.$$

For example, using Eq. (A-8) we determine that for $K = 3$ per cent and $\mu = 0.285$ the gages should be mounted 61.9 deg and 151.9 deg.

If the gages had been mounted in error by one degree (at 60.9 deg and 150.9 deg), a greatly inaccurate value of K would have resulted. That is,

$$\begin{aligned}\epsilon_q &= \epsilon_x(\cos^2 60.9° - 0.285 \sin^2 60.9°) \\ &= 0.018\epsilon_u, \\ \epsilon_p &= \epsilon_x(\sin^2 60.9° - 0.285 \cos^2 60.9°) \\ &= 0.697\epsilon_u, \\ X &= 0.0558 \qquad \text{[Eq. (A-10) is solved for } X\text{]},\end{aligned}$$

$$\text{Per cent error} = \frac{0.0558 - 0.03}{0.03} \times 100 = 86 \text{ per cent.}$$

The example illustrates the impracticability of this method for determining K.

5-6 Appendix B (Stress-strain gage corrected for transverse sensitivity of the individual elements)

On page 270 it was pointed out that, if the transverse sensitivity of the individual elements of a stress-strain gage is neglected, then making $R_t = \mu R_a$ will result in gage output proportional to S_a.

If the cross-sensitivity of the individual elements is considered, then stress is related to gage reading as shown by Eq. (5-27).

$$S_a = \frac{E}{1 - \mu^2}\left[(1 - K_t\mu)\frac{\Delta R_a}{R_a F_a} + (\mu - K_a)\frac{\Delta R_t}{R_t F_t}\right].$$

If we require that

$$R_t F_t = R_a F_a \frac{(\mu - K_a)}{(1 - K_t\mu)},$$

this reduces to

$$S_a = \frac{E}{(1 - \mu^2)} \times \frac{[F_t(1 - K_t\mu) + F_a(\mu - K_a)]}{F_t F_a} \times \frac{\Delta R_T}{R_T},$$

in which $\Delta R_T = \Delta R_a + \Delta R_t,$
and

$$R_T = R_a + R_t.$$

This result can be rewritten as

$$S_a = \frac{E}{F_c}\frac{\Delta R_T}{R_T},$$

in which

$$F_c = \frac{(1 - \mu^2)F_t F_a}{F_t(1 - K_t\mu) + F_a(\mu - K_a)}.$$

5-7 References listed in Chapter 5

1. Twynman, J., "The Interpretation into Stresses of Post-Yield Strains up to Two Percent," *Proceedings of the Society for Experimental Stress Analysis*, Vol. 6, No. 1, pp. 131–7.
2. Ades, C. S., "Reduction of Strain Rosettes in the Plastic Range," *Experimental Mechanics*, Vol. 2, No. 11 (Nov. 1962), pp. 345–52.
3. Baumberger, R. and F. Hines, "Practical Reduction Formulas for Use on Bonded Wire Strain Gages in Two-Dimensional Stress Fields," *Proceedings of the Society for Experimental Stress Analysis*, Vol. 2, No. 1 (1944), pp. 113–47.
4. Wu, Charles T., "Transverse Sensitivity of Bonded Strain Gages," *Experimental Mechanics*, Vol. 2, No. 11 (Nov. 1962), pp. 338–44.
5. Durelli, Phillips, and Tsao, *Analysis of Stress and Strain.* New York: McGraw-Hill, 1958.
6. Murphy, Glenn, *Advanced Mechanics of Materials.* New York: McGraw-Hill, 1946.
7. Grossman, N. A., "Nomographic Rosette Computer," *Proceedings of the Society for Experimental Stress Analysis*, Vol. 4, No. 1, pp. 27–35.
8. Hewson, T. A., "A Nomographic Solution to the Strain Rosette Equation," *Proceedings of the Society for Experimental Stress Analysis*, Vol. 4, No. 1, pp. 9–26.
9. Perry, C. C. and H. R. Lissner, *The Strain Gage Primer.* New York: McGraw-Hill, 1955, Chapter 7.
10. Lissner, H. R. and C. C. Perry, "Conventional Wire Strain Gage Used as a Principal Stress Gage," *Proceedings of the Society for Experimental Stress Analysis*, Vol. 13, No. 1, pp. 25–32.
11. Williams, S. B., "The Dyadic Gage," *Proceedings of the Society for Experimental Stress Analysis*, Vol. 1, No. 2, pp. 43–55.
12. Hines, F. F., "The Stress-Strain Gage," Memo by Baldwin-Lima-Hamilton Corporation, Waltham 54, Mass.
13. Campbell, W. R., "Performance Tests of Wire Strain Gages: IV - Axial and Transverse Sensitivities," NACA Tech. Note No. 1042 (June 1946).

5-8 Problems

5-1 Three gages are mounted as shown in Fig. 5-16. The gage factor given by the manufacturer is 2.00. With this factor set on a null balance strain indicator, the readings taken were as shown. (a) What is the true strain in #3 direction? (b) Find the magnitude and direction of the principal stresses. Show on sketch.

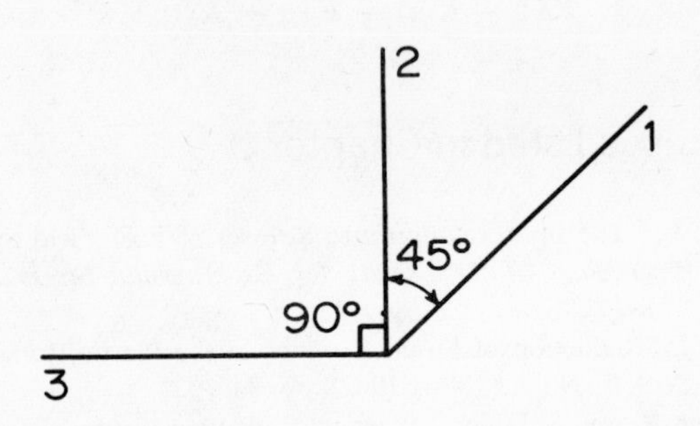

$E_1 = 10 \times 10^6$ psi
$\mu = 0.3$
$K = 0.03$
$F = 2.00$

$Q_1 = 130$ μin./in.
$Q_2 = -70$ μin./in.
$Q_3 = 700$ μin./in.

Fig. 5-16.

5-2 From the results of a Stresscoat test on a 17ST part the directions of principal stress are known. A single strain gage is to be used to determine the principal stress at a given point. $F_u = 1.98$, $K = 0.035$, $E = 10.5 \times 10^6$ psi, $\mu = 0.33$. (a) Find the angle at which the gage must be mounted. Show on a sketch, relating the gage axis to the Stresscoat cracks. (b) The gage is read on a standard indicator with the gage factor control set at 1.98. The reading obtained was 800 μin./in. What is the principal stress?

5-3 Two gages are mounted on steel at right angles to form a biaxial strain gage. $F_u = 3.5$, $K = 0.03$, $E = 29 \times 10^6$ psi, and $\mu = 0.285$. With the gage factor set at 3.5, gage (1) reads 700 μin./in. and gage (2) reads 300 μin./in. Find the stresses in the (1) and (2) directions.

5-4 A rectangular rosette is mounted on steel ($E = 29 \times 10^6$ psi; $\mu = 0.285$). The gage factors given by the manufacturer are $F = 2.09$, $K = 0.02$. The gage readings taken were:

$R_1 = 750$ μin./in.
$R_2 = 1000$ μin./in.
$R_3 = -200$ μin./in.

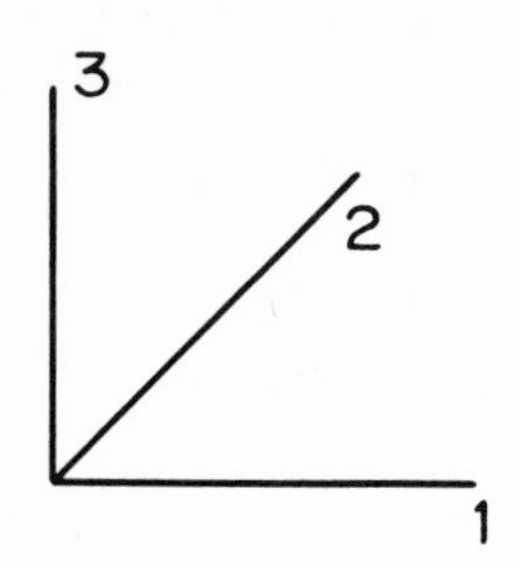

Fig. 5-17.

Find the principal stress magnitude and directions.
Show on a sketch.

5-5 Three gages are mounted as shown on a steel plate ($E = 30 \times 10^6$; $\mu = 0.3$). The gage factor given on the package was $F = 1.83$ and the cross sensitivity of this type is known to be -0.02. The strain indicator was read with the gage factor control set at 1.83. Readings obtained were:

$$R_a = -1000 \ \mu\text{in./in.}$$
$$R_b = -1000 \ \mu\text{in./in.}$$
$$R_c = -1000 \ \mu\text{in./in.}$$

Find S_u, S_v, α.

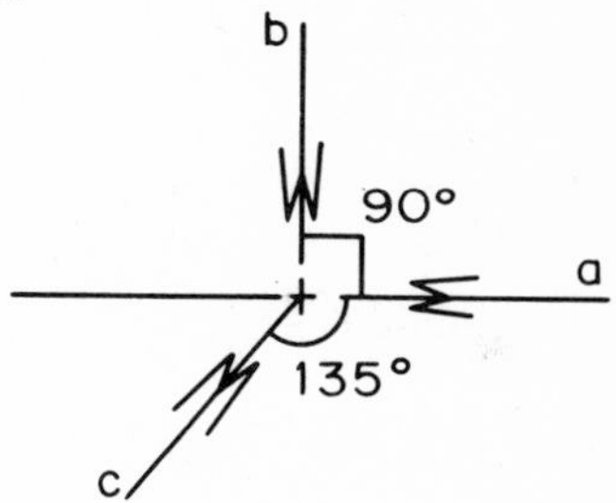

Fig. 5-18.

5-6 From the results of a Stresscoat test on S. S. 304 ($E = 30 \times 10^6$ psi, $\mu = 0.30$) directions of principal stress are known. A single strain gage is to be used to determine the principal stress at a given point. $F_u = 2.00$ and cross sensitivity is $+0.04$. (a) Find the angle at which the gage must be mounted. Show on a sketch, relating the gage axis to the Stresscoat cracks. (b) The gage is read on a standard indicator with the gage factor control set at 2.00. The reading obtained was 1000 μin./in. What is the principal stress?

5-7 Three gages are mounted on steel as shown in Fig. 5-19. The gage factor given by the manufacturer is 2.00. With this factor set on a null balance strain indicator, the readings taken were as shown.

(a) What is the true strain in #3 direction? (b) Find the magnitude and direction of the principal stresses. Show on sketch.

$R_1 = 500\ \mu\text{in./in.}$
$R_2 = -70\ \mu\text{in./in.}$
$R_3 = 700\ \mu\text{in./in.}$
$E = 30 \times 10^6$ psi
$\mu = 0.285$
$K = 0.02$

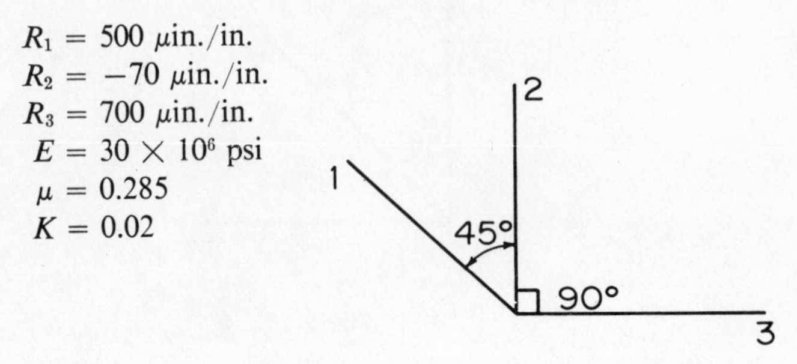

Fig. 5-19.

5-8 A circular plate is loaded at the center point and supported at four points as shown in the Fig. 5-20. $E_{\text{plate}} = 10 \times 10^6$ psi, $\mu_{\text{plate}} = \frac{1}{3}$. The gage, mounted as shown, has the following characteristics:

$F = 60$ (calibrated in a uniaxial stress field on a material having a Poisson's ratio of 0.3),

$K = 0.10$.

With the strain-indicator gage factor control set at 2.0, the reading obtained was 30,000 μin./in. What is the stress along the $y-y$ axis (i.e., the gage axis)?

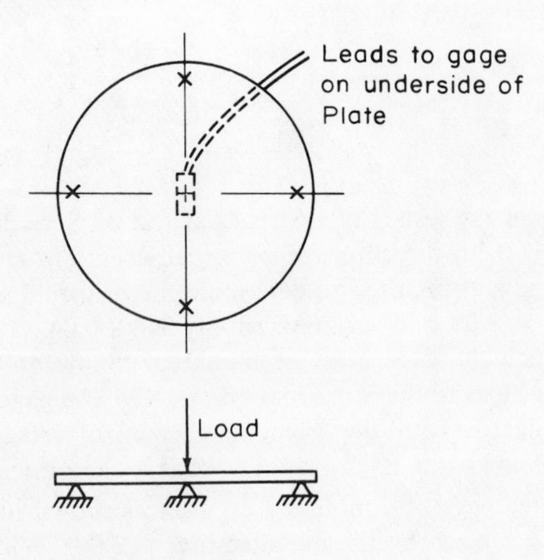

Fig. 5-20.

5-9 When strain gages are mounted on a surface to which a pressure is applied, the stress situation is no longer biaxial. For this case, develop the equations necessary to relate the three strain readings from a rectangular rosette to principal stress magnitudes and directions.

5-9 Suggested laboratory experiments

Experiment 5-1 Computation of stresses from strains in a biaxial stress field

EQUIPMENT NECESSARY

1. A flat-plate tensile specimen containing a centrally located hole. Biaxial strain gages have been bonded at several points with the gage axis aligned with known principal stress directions. Three-element rosettes have been bonded at several locations where the principal stress directions are not known.
2. A tensile test machine.
3. A static strain indicator for reading the strain gages.
4. A switching unit or plug-in panel so that all gages can be read on the same strain indicator.

PROCEDURE

1. Compute the maximum load that can be applied if the maximum stress is not to exceed 80 per cent of the proportional limit of the material.
2. Load the plate to this maximum value in a series of several equally spaced steps. Read all gages at each load level.

REPORT

1. Plot all data to check linearity of strain with load.
2. At each gaged location compute the principal stress magnitudes and directions.
3. Compare the results obtained to those predicted by elastic theory.

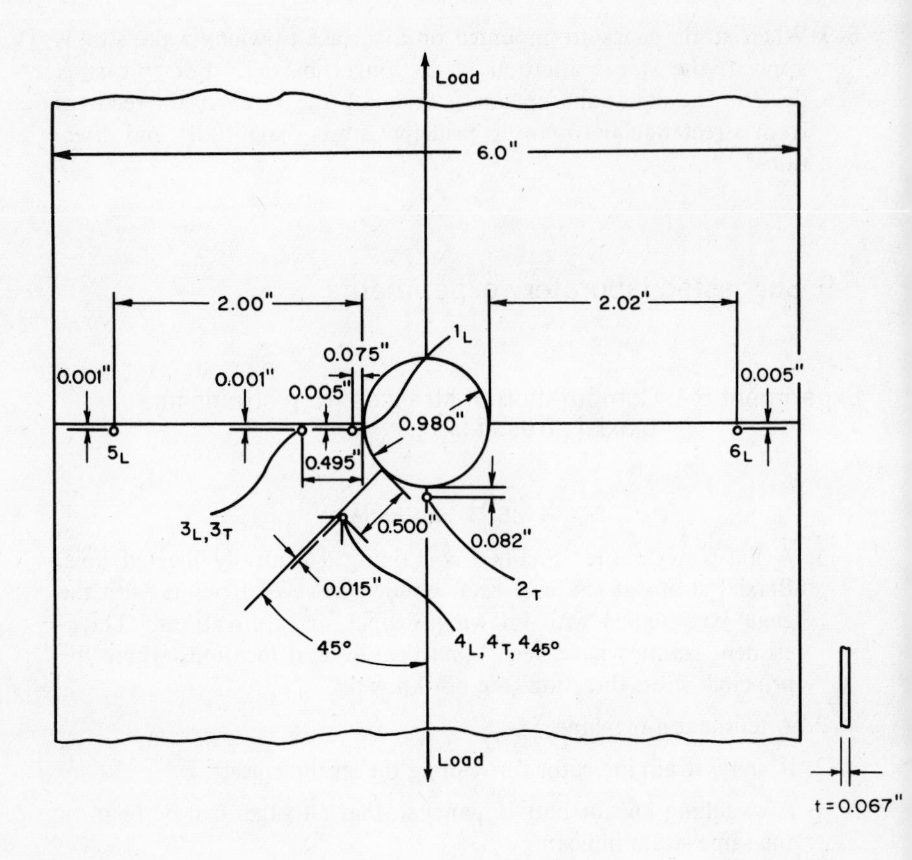

Material Properties: $E = 6.7 \times 10^6$ psi
$\mu = 0.3$ (Magnesium)
$S_{YP} = 20{,}000$ psi

Gage Information: 1_L, 2_T − FAB − 06 − 12, $R = 119.5 \pm 0.5$, $F = 2.12 \pm 1\%$
3_L, 3_T − FABX − 12 − 12, $R = 121.1 \pm 0.5$, $F = 2.08 \pm 1\%$
4_L, 4_T, $4_{45°}$ − FABR − 12 − 12, $R = 120.5 \pm 0.5$, $F = 2.12 \pm 1\%$
5_L, 6_L − A8, $R = 120.0 \pm 3$, $F = 1.83 \pm 2\%$
Dummy Gages − FAB − 12 − 12, $R = 121.0 \pm 0.5$, $F = 2.12 \pm 1\%$

Fig. 5-21.

CHAPTER 6

Stress Analysis by Photoelasticity

6-1 Introduction

The photoelastic method for experimental stress analysis depends upon the relationship between the state of stress in a transparent material and the way in which that material transmits polarized light. The experimentally determined quantity is an observed optical pattern; the observed optical pattern is related to the state of stress by using both optical theory and the theory of elasticity. In addition, in many cases a model is used, and then the state of stress in the model must be related to the state of stress in the prototype by using appropriate model theory. Hence, as was the case in stress analysis by strain measurement, the method is not 100 per cent experimental.

The photoelastic method is like the moiré-fringe and brittle-coating methods discussed in Chap. 1, in that it is a whole-field method. But like the other whole-field methods, it yields only certain kinds of stress information, usually not enough to define completely the state of stress at any point.

The photoelastic effect was first noted by Sir David Brewster in the early 1800's, but its application to stress analysis was not made until the early 1900's. Professor E. G. Coker and L. N. G. Filon [1] published the first extensive analysis of photoelasticity as a method of experimental stress analysis in 1931.

The history of photoelasticity since 1930 has been one of ups and downs. Through the 1930's, photoelasticity was "the" method of experimental stress analysis. Attention was directed to improvement of the optical apparatus (the photoelastic polariscope and its attachments), to the development of better transparent model materials, and to the solution of many two-dimensional problems. Of necessity the problems solved were two-dimensional. The models were cut from sheet stock, and all stresses were in the plane of the sheet; however, there were a host of important and interesting problems of this type in 1930, and photoelasticity offered the most precise method for solution. See Refs. [2], [3], [4], and [5].

During the 1940's the photoelastic method did not receive the attention to which it had grown accustomed, primarily because of the tremendous renewal of interest in strain measurement following the introduction of the bonded resistance strain gage in 1941. However, many people interested in photoelasticity have continued to work to improve and extend the method. G. Oppel [6] and M. Hetényi ([7], [8], and [9]) showed how photoelasticity could be used to study three-dimensional models. D. C. Drucker and R. D. Mindlin [10] offered new and improved methods of analysis. M. M. Frocht [11] has been active in improving and applying the method.

During the 1950's and 1960's the photoelastic method was extended in several areas. Applying the principle suggested by Mesnager in 1930, both F. Zandman [12], working in France, and a group working with Drucker [13] at Brown University succeeded in applying plastic coatings to parts and in using photoelasticity to study surface strain. G. Gerard and A. C. Gilbert ([14] and [15]) extended the photoelastic method to the study of thermal stresses. Several investigators have combined high-speed photography and the photoelastic method to study transient stresses.

We shall proceed by discussing the following items in order: (1) optical theory, (2) stress-optical relationships, (3) equipment and models, (4) static stress analysis, (5) dynamic stress analysis, and (6) thermal stress analysis. In Chap. 7 we shall discuss (1) surface-coating techniques and (2) photoelastic strain gages.

6-2 Optical theory

A brief review of certain of the concepts concerning the wave nature of light will aid in establishing the necessary optical fundamentals.

If we depict visible light as electromagnetic wave motion, the intensity of light as a function of time is expressed as

$$x = X \sin \omega t, \tag{6-1}$$

in which x is the intensity of light (amplitude) at any time.

X is the maximum intensity.

ω is the circular frequency of the radiation.

Color is associated with the frequency of the radiation (ω). Hence, monochromatic light is light of a single frequency (ω), whereas white light is a mixture of radiations of various frequencies.

Light which originates at a point (such as a glowing filament), propagates radially in all directions and, hence, is spherically divergent. A lens may be employed to collimate light; that is, to convert spherically divergent light to parallel rays which propagate without convergence or divergence. Likewise, a lens may be employed to focus collimated light (parallel rays) to a point. See Fig. 6-1.

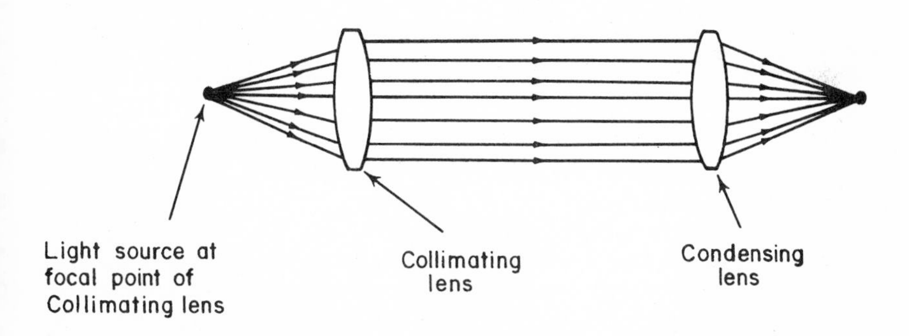

Fig. 6-1. Collimation of light.

The velocity with which light propagates is dependent upon the material through which it is passing and, as we shall see later, the velocity of propagation of light waves passing through the same material at the same point may be different if the waves vibrate in different planes.

Unpolarized light consists of wave motion in an infinite number of planes. Polarized light consists of light waves, which vibrate in parallel planes. Hence, a polarizing element is one which transmits only wave motion which is vibrating in a selected plane. See Fig. 6-2.

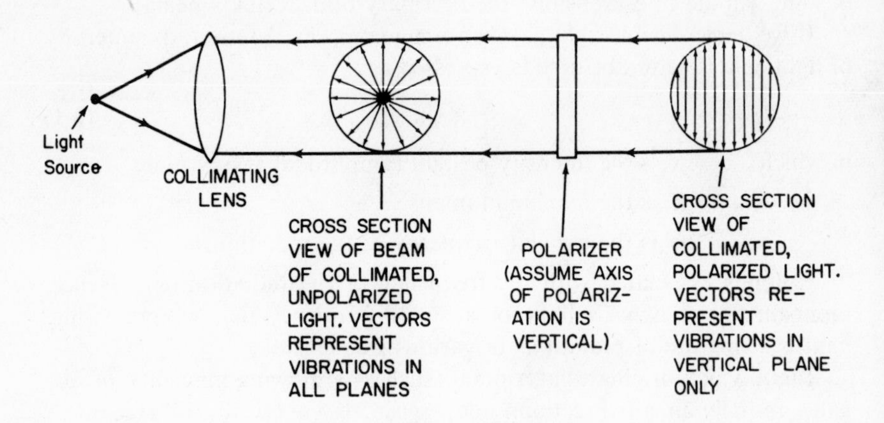

Fig. 6-2. Polarization of light.

The way in which polarized light is transmitted through a series of polarizing elements is illustrated in Fig. 6-3. Since a polarizing element transmits only waves vibrating in planes parallel to the element's polarizing axis, the amount of polarized light transmitted by the second polarizing element is that component of the incident light which is parallel to the element's polarizing axis.

Certain transparent materials are doubly refracting. These materials transmit only light vibrating in selected planes (i.e., they polarize light in several planes, and, in general, the velocity of transmission is not the same in the several selected planes). In photoelastic work we are primarily interested in doubly refracting materials which have two polarizing axes oriented at right angles to each other. How plane polarized light is transmitted through this type of doubly refracting material is shown in Fig. 6-4. The items of equipment shown in the figure make up the basic instrument used in the photoelastic method. This instrument is called a "plane polariscope," and in the figure shown the polarizer and the analyzer are said to be crossed; i.e., their polarizing axes are perpendicular. The final equation which expresses the amount of polarized light transmitted by a doubly refracting material and a second polarizing element (called the analyzer) is of great importance.

$$x_{\text{transmitted}} = \frac{X}{2} \sin 2\theta \, [\sin \omega(t + dt) - \sin \omega t]. \tag{6-2}$$

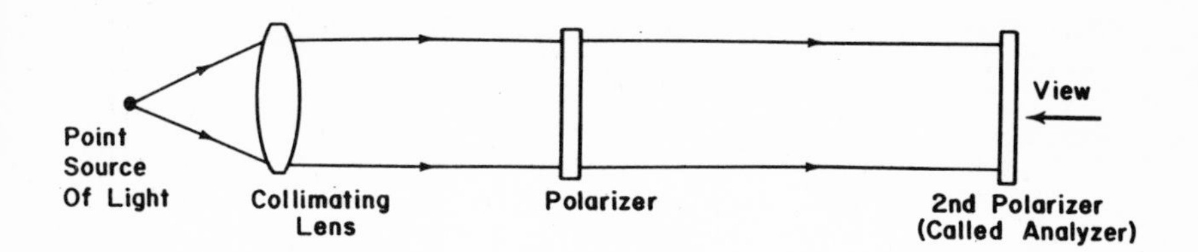

(a) Arrangement of polariscope elements

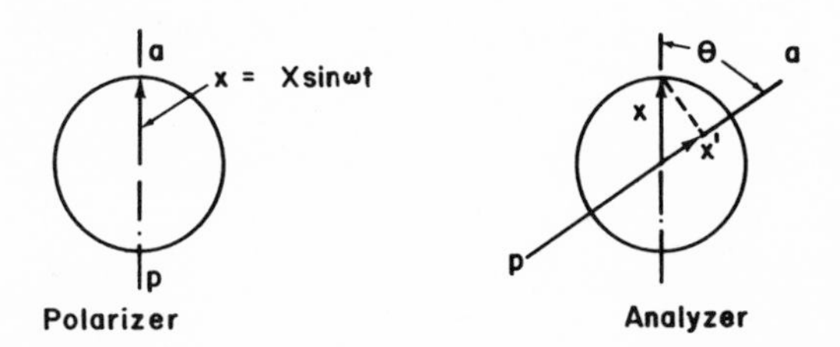

(b) Orientation of light vectors passing through polariscope elements

Vectors shown are defined as follows:

In the polarizer: ap = axis of polarization of polarizer.

$x = X \sin \omega t$ = the light vector passed by the polarizer.

In the analyzer:

ap = axis of polarization of analyzer.

θ = angle by which ap of analyzer is rotated from ap of polarizer.

$x' = X \sin \omega t \cos \theta$ = light vector passed by analyzer.

Fig. 6-3. Transmission of plane polarized light.

Examination of Fig. 6-4 and the equations given reveals that, if the doubly refracting material is removed, no light will be transmitted; i.e., a dark-field arrangement. Examination of Eq. (6-2) reveals that, with the doubly refracting material in the field, the light transmitted will be zero through all points at which either of two conditions are fulfilled.

First, when $\theta = 0$ or any multiple of 90 deg, $\sin 2\theta = 0$ and, hence, $x_t = 0$. This means that no light will be transmitted through points in the doubly refracting material at which one of the doubly refracting axes is aligned with the axis of polarization.

Second, when $[\sin \omega(t + dt) = \sin \omega t]$ for all values of t, then $x_t = 0$. Since the sines of angles separated by 360 deg are identical, this condition is fulfilled when

$$\sin (\omega t + \omega\, dt) = \sin (\omega t + 2\pi n)$$

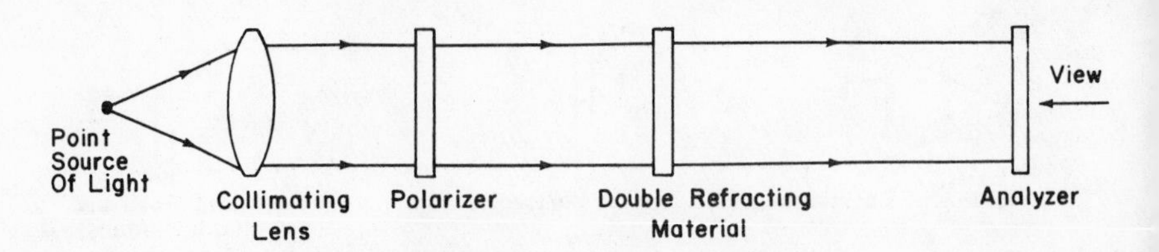

(a) Arrangement of polariscope elements

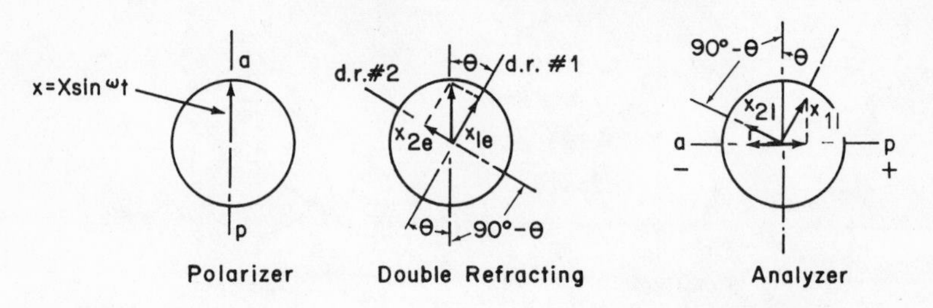

(b) Orientation of light vectors passing through polariscope elements

Vectors shown are defined as follows:

In the polarizer:

$$x = X \sin \omega t = \text{incident polarized light.}$$

In the double refracting material:

d.r. #1 = #1 transmission axis in double refracting material.

d.r. #2 = #2 transmission axis.

$x_{1e} = X \sin \omega t \cos \theta$ = the light vector entering the d.r. #1 axis.

$x_{2e} = X \sin \omega t \sin \theta$ = the light vector entering the d.r. #2 axis.

In the analyzer:

$x_{1l} = x_{1e} = X \sin \omega t \cos \theta$ = the light leaving the d.r. #1 axis and falling on the analyzer.

$x_{2l} = X \sin \omega(t + dt) \sin \theta$ = the light leaving the d.r. #2 axis and falling on the analyzer. It is out of phase with x_{1l} by dt. The light transmitted through the analyzer is $x_t = x_{1l} \sin \theta - x_{2l} \cos \theta$, or $x_t = \dfrac{X}{2} \sin 2\theta\,[\sin \omega(t + dt) - \sin \omega t]$.

Fig. 6-4. Plane polariscope.

in which n is any integer (0, 1, 2, 3, etc.).* Hence, $x_t = 0$ when $dt = 2\pi n/\omega$. This means that no light of a given ω (hence, no color) will be transmitted through points in the doubly refracting material at which

* Although $\sin(\omega t + \omega\, dt) = \sin \omega t$ when $\omega t + \omega\, dt = m\pi - \omega t$, since $\sin(\pi - \theta) = \sin \theta$, this condition is not fulfilled for all values of t. (Note $m = 1, 3, 5$, etc.)

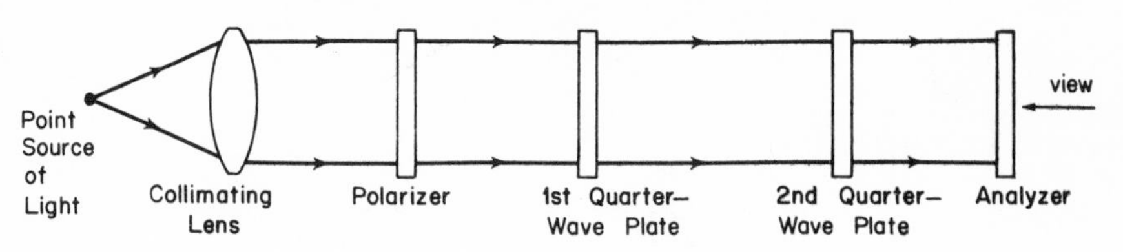

(a) Arrangement of polariscope elements

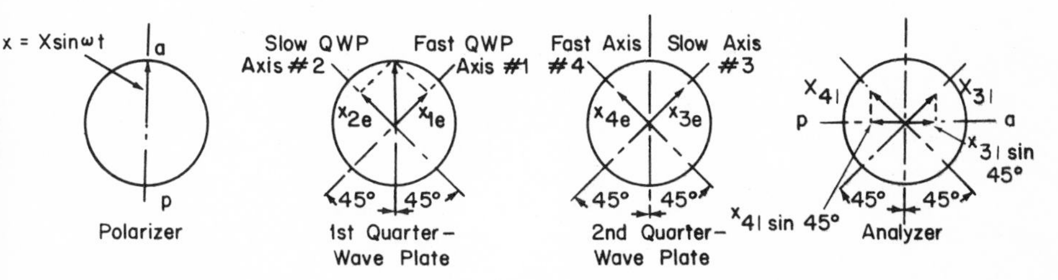

(b) Orientation of light vectors passing through polariscope elements

Vectors shown are defined as follows:
In the polarizer:

$$x = X \sin \omega t = \text{incident polarized light.}$$

In the first quarter-wave plate:

$x_{1e} = X \sin \omega t \cos 45° = .707X \sin \omega t =$ the light vector entering the #1 Q.W.P. axis.

$x_{2e} = .707X \sin \omega t =$ the light vector entering the #2 Q.W.P. axis.

In the second quarter-wave plate:

$x_{3e} = x_{1l} = .707X \sin \omega t =$ the light vector leaving the #1 Q.W.P. and entering the #3 axis of the second Q.W.P.

$$x_{4e} = .707X \sin\left(\omega t + \frac{\pi}{2}\right),$$

or $x_{4e} = .707X \cos \omega t =$ the light vector leaving the first Q.W.P. and entering the #4 axis of the second Q.W.P. (*Note:* One-fourth of a wavelength ($\pi/2$) out of phase with x_{1l}.)

In the analyzer:

$x_{3l} = .707X \sin\left(\omega t + \frac{\pi}{2}\right) = .707X \cos \omega t =$ The light vector leaving the #3 axis of the second Q.W.P. and falling on the analyzer axis.

$x_{4l} = x_{4e} = .707X \cos \omega t =$ the light vector leaving the #4 axis of the second Q.W.P. and falling on the analyzer axis.

Concluding Remarks: The light transmitted through the analyzer is $x_t = \frac{X}{2} \cos \omega t - \frac{X}{2} \cos \omega t = 0$; i.e., this polariscope arrangement gives a dark field.

Fig. 6-5. Circular polariscope (crossed-polarizers, crossed quarter-wave plates).

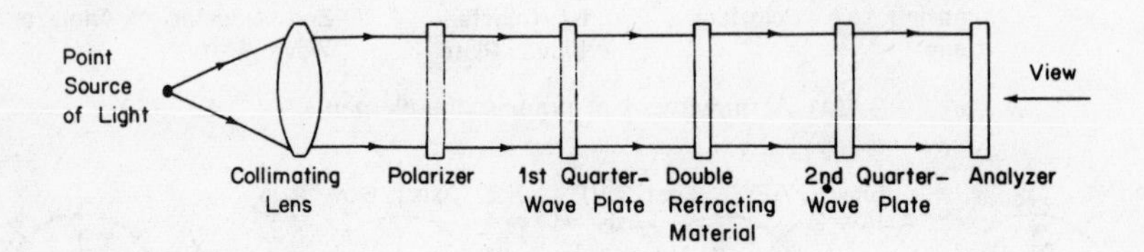

(a) Arrangement of polariscope elements

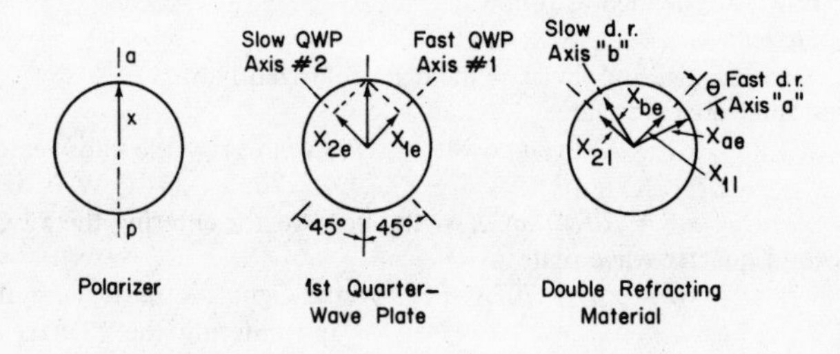

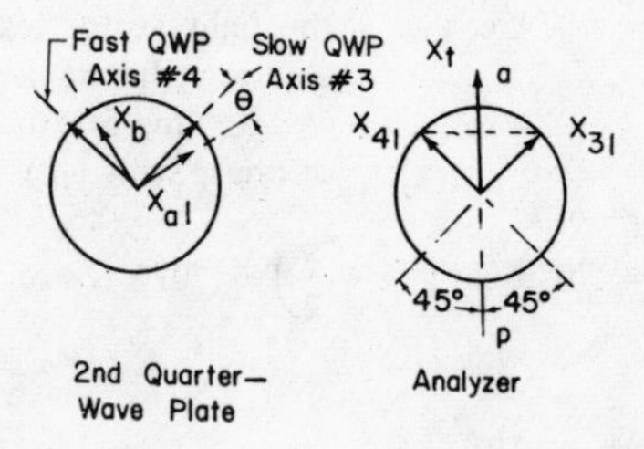

(b) Orientation of light vectors passing through polariscope elements

Fig. 6-6. Circular polariscope with model in place (parallel polarizers and crossed quarter-wave plates).

Vectors shown in Fig. 6-6 are defined as follows:

In the polarizer:

$x = X \sin \omega t.$

In the first quarter-wave plate:

$x_{1e} = 0.707X \sin \omega t.$

$x_{2e} = 0.707X \sin \omega t.$

In the double refracting material:

θ = the angle between the Q.W.P. axis and the double refracting axis.

$x_{1l} = x_{1e} = 0.707X \sin \omega t$ = the light vector leaving the #1 axis of the first Q.W.P. and falling on double refracting material.

$x_{2l} = .707X \sin\left(\omega t + \frac{\pi}{2}\right) = 0.707 \cos \omega t$ = the light vector leaving the #2 axis of the first Q.W.P. and falling on double refracting material. (*Note:* one-fourth wavelength $\left(\frac{\pi}{2}\right)$ out of phase with x_{2e}.)

The component of the light vector entering "a" axis is $x_{ae} = 0.707X \sin \omega t \cos \theta - 0.707X \cos \omega t \sin \theta$, and entering "b" axis is: $x_{be} = 0.707X \sin \omega t \sin \theta + 0.707X \cos \omega t \cos \theta$.

In the second quarter-wave plate:

$x_{al} = x_{ae} = 0.707X \sin \omega t \cos \theta - 0.707X \cos \omega t \sin \theta = 0.707X \sin (\omega t - \theta)$ = the light vector leaving the "a" axis of the d.r. material and falling on second Q.W.P.

$x_{bl} = 0.707X \cos \omega(t + dt) \cos \theta + 0.707X \sin \omega(t + dt) \sin \theta.$

$x_{bl} = 0.707X \cos (\omega t + \omega\, dt - \theta)$ = the light vector leaving the "b" axis of the d.r. material and falling on second Q.W.P.

Note: x_{bl} delayed relative to x_{al} by dt time. The component of the light vectoı entering the #3 axis is

$x_{3e} = 0.707X \sin (\omega t - \theta) \cos \theta + 0.707X \cos (\omega t + \omega\, dt - \theta) \sin \theta$, and entering the #4 axis is

$x_{4e} = 0.707X \cos (\omega t + \omega\, dt - \theta) \cos \theta - 0.707X \sin (\omega t - \theta) \sin \theta.$

In the analyzer:

$$x_{3l} = 0.707X \sin\left(\omega t + \frac{\pi}{2} - \theta\right) \cos \theta + 0.707X \cos\left(\omega t + \omega\, dt + \frac{\pi}{2} - \theta\right) \sin \theta.$$

$x_{3l} = 0.707X \cos (\omega t - \theta) \cos \theta - 0.707X \sin (\omega t + \omega\, dt - \theta) \sin \theta$ = the light vector leaving the #3 axis of the second Q.W.P. and falling on the analyzer. (*Note:* delayed relative to x_{al} by $\frac{1}{4}$ wavelength.

$x_{4l} = x_{4e} = 0.707X \cos (\omega t + \omega\, dt - \theta) \cos \theta - 0.707X \sin (\omega t - \theta) \sin \theta$. The light transmitted through the analyzer is

$x_t = x_{3l} \sin 45° + x_{4l} \sin 45°.$

$$x_t = \frac{X}{2} [\cos \omega t + \cos (\omega t + \omega\, dt)].$$

the retardation of one component relative to the other is equal to $2\pi n$ divided by the frequency of that color (ω). If the light is monochromatic of frequency (ω_1), then no light will be transmitted when $dt = 2\pi n/\omega_1$. If the light is a mixture of frequencies (ω_1, ω_2, ω_3, etc.), then each color will be selectively removed from the mixture when $dt = 2\pi n/\omega_m$.

By making certain additions to the polariscope shown in Fig. 6-4, we obtain the system shown in Fig. 6-5. This system, which is called a circular polariscope, is the second basic instrument used in the photoelastic method. The items which have been added are two identical disks of doubly refracting material with doubly refracting axes 90 deg apart. The thickness of these disks has been adjusted so that, in each disk, one component of the transmitted light is retarded relative to the other component by one-fourth of a wavelength; i.e., $dt = \pi/2$. When the elements just described are inserted in a field of polarized light with their doubly refracting axes making angles of 45 deg with the axis of the polarizer, they are referred to as quarter-wave plates. Notice that the thickness of such a plate must be adjusted to retard a specific frequency (color) of light by one-fourth of its wavelength—and hence a given plate is only a true quarter-wave plate for one specific frequency. The light transmitted through the first quarter-wave plate in Fig. 6-5 is called circularly polarized. In Fig. 6-5 the polarizing axis of the polarizer and the analyzer are perpendicular—hence the term "crossed polarizers." In the same figure the fast transmission axis of the first quarter-wave plate is aligned with the slow transmission axis of the second quarter-wave plate; consequently, the quarter-wave plates are said to be "crossed." The equations developed show that this arrangement of elements, called a crossed-crossed polariscope, gives zero light transmission when there is no doubly refracting material inserted between the quarter-wave plates; i.e., the crossed-crossed polariscope gives a dark field.

Other possible arrangements are (1) crossed-parallel; i.e., polarizing axis of polarizer and analyzer perpendicular, fast axis of quarter-wave plates aligned. An analysis of this arrangement will show that it gives total light transmission—light field. (2) parallel-parallel; i.e., polarizing axis of polarizer and analyzer parallel, fast axes of the quarter-wave plates aligned—dark field. (3) parallel-crossed, i.e., polarizing axes of polarizer and analyzer parallel, fast axis of the first quarter-wave plate aligned with the slow axis of the second quarter-wave plate—light field.

Figure 6-6 shows a doubly refracting material inserted between the quarter-wave plates in a parallel-crossed polariscope. Again, the equation developed for the light transmitted (x_t) is of great importance.

$$x_t = \frac{X}{2}[\cos \omega t + \cos (\omega t + \omega\, dt)]. \tag{6-3}$$

Study of Eq. (6-3) first reveals that the light transmitted (x_t) is independent of θ, and hence the observed pattern is not affected by the orientation of the optical axis of the doubly refracting material. This result (x_t independent of θ) is obtained for any of the four* possible configu-

* Crossed-crossed, crossed-parallel, and parallel-parallel, in addition to the parallel-crossed system used in Fig. 6-6.

rations of the circular polariscope; indeed, this is the reason for using the circular polariscope.

Again inspecting Eq. (6-3), we find that the amount of transmitted light (x_t) is maximum when $\cos \omega t = \cos (\omega t + \omega\, dt)$ or when $\omega\, dt = 2\pi n$, since the cosines of angles separated by 360 deg are equal. Hence, for this system, which has been shown to be a light-field arrangement, x_t is a maximum when $dt = 2\pi n/\omega$, in which n is any integer 0, 1, 2, 3, etc. If monochromatic light of $\omega = \omega_1$ is used, then the total light is transmitted when $dt = 2\pi n/\omega_1$; if the light consists of a mixture of frequencies, then the transmission of the component of frequency of ω_n is maximum when $dt = 2\pi n/\omega_n$. If we analyze either of the two dark-field arrangements (crossed-crossed or parallel-parallel), we will find that x_t is zero when $dt = 2\pi n/\omega$. From this we draw the following conclusion: when a circular polariscope and monochromatic light are used, the light transmitted through a doubly refracting material at a point where $dt = 2\pi n/\omega$ is equal to the light transmitted with no doubly refracting material in the field; i.e., the light transmitted is equal to the background light.

6-3 Stress-optical relationships

As has already been pointed out, certain transparent materials are doubly refracting in their natural state. Materials in this category include certain crystals such as quartz and mica.

Most materials which are not doubly refracting in their natural state become doubly refracting when they are stressed. It has been found that the refracting axes coincide with the principal stress axes and that the difference in the change of velocity of transmission of light through these two axes is proportional to the difference in magnitude of the principal stresses.* This is the basis of the photoelastic method of stress analysis.

The relationship between magnitude of stress difference and velocity difference is

$$S_1 - S_2 = C\left(\frac{v}{v_1} - \frac{v}{v_2}\right) = Cv\left(\frac{v_2 - v_1}{v_1 v_2}\right), \tag{6-4}$$

in which S_1 and S_2 are normal stresses along the principal (1 and 2) axes.

* If the material is assumed to be stressed in its elastic region. M. M. Frocht [16] has investigated the alignment of the refracting axes and the principal stress axes when certain materials are strained plastically, and B. Fried [17] has investigated the functional relationship between velocity change and stress difference when certain materials are strained plastically.

C is a constant of proportionality whose value depends on the material, temperature, magnitude of strain, etc.

v is the velocity of light transmission outside the doubly refracting medium.

v_1 and v_2 are the velocities of light transmission through the doubly refracting medium on the principal planes.

The time for light transmission through the 1 and 2 axes can be written as

$$t_1 = \frac{d}{v_1} \quad \text{and} \quad t_2 = \frac{d}{v_2},$$

in which d is the thickness of the material made doubly refracting by stressing. The retardation of one component relative to the other as they emerge from the stressed material is

$$dt = \frac{d}{v_1} - \frac{d}{v_2} = d\left(\frac{1}{v_1} - \frac{1}{v_2}\right) = d\frac{(v_2 - v_1)}{v_1 v_2},$$

and substituting the relationship between velocity and stress [Eq. (6-4)], we have

$$dt = \frac{d}{Cv}(S_1 - S_2). \tag{6-5}$$

Equation (6-5) states that the relative retardation at any point in the stressed material is proportional to the difference of the principal stresses at that point.

From our previous discussion we remember that, when

$$dt = \frac{2\pi n}{\omega}, \tag{6-6}$$

the light transmitted through a doubly refracting material is just equal to the background light for a monochromatic light source. Equating Eqs. (6-5) and (6-6), we obtain

$$(S_1 - S_2) = \frac{Cv}{d}\frac{2\pi n}{\omega} = \frac{Kn}{d} \tag{6-7}$$

Equation (6-7) indicates that whenever the principal stress difference at a point is equal to an integer times K/d, the relative retardation of the transmitted components will be such that the total light transmitted (x_t) through that point will be equal to the background light. The constant K depends not only on the material of which the stressed solid is made, but upon the frequency of the light as well.

Several examples will illustrate how Eq. (6-7) serves to relate optical patterns to stresses and how the constant K can be determined.

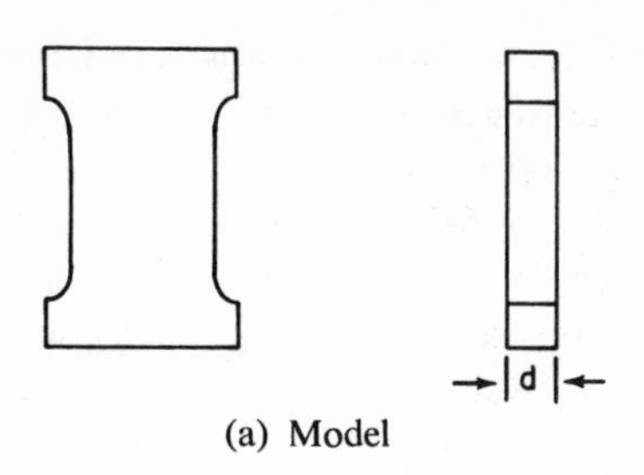

(a) Model

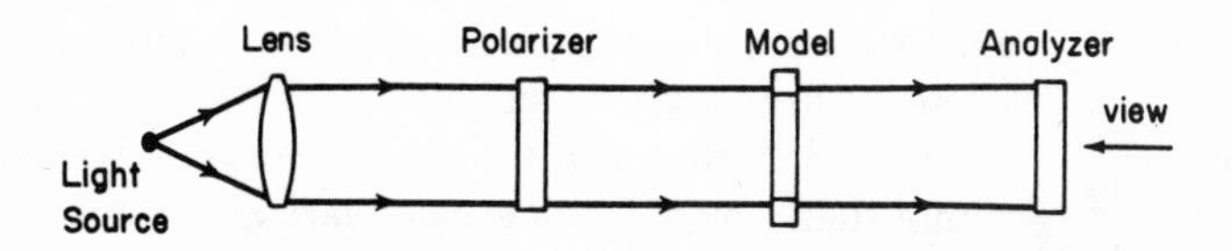

(b) Arrangement of elements in plane polariscope

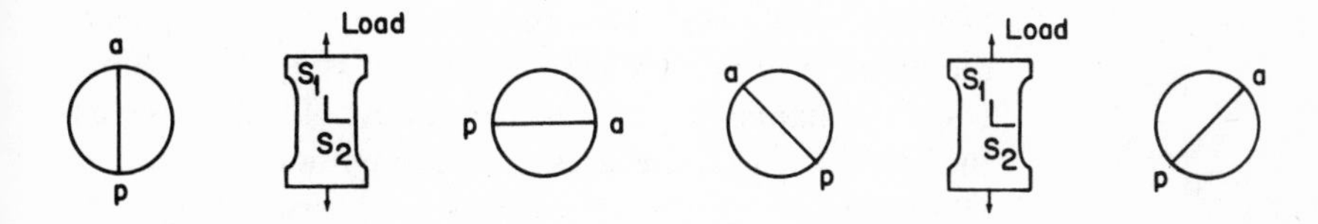

(c) Axis of polarization aligned with principal stress axis

(d) Axis of polarization at 45° to the principal stress axes

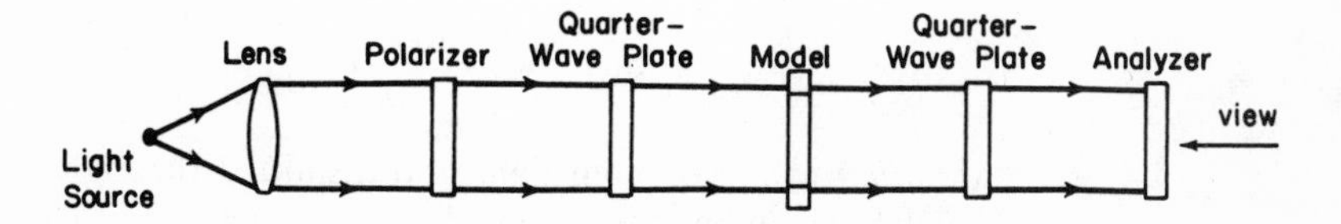

(e) Arrangement of elements in a circular polariscope

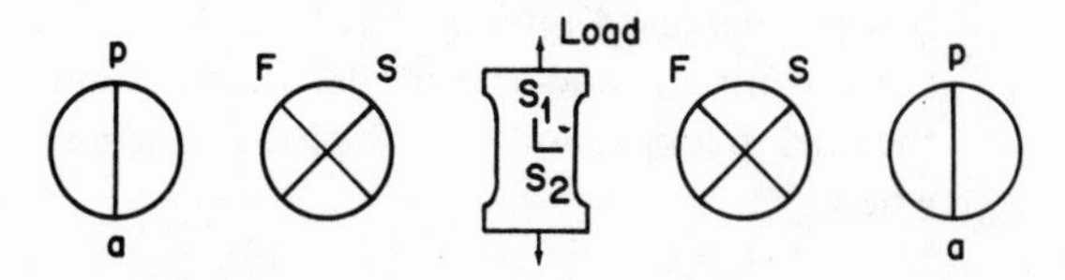

(f) Orientation of axes in the elements of a circular polariscope

Fig. 6-7. Plane and circular polariscope, model in tension.

Example 6-1. Consider a suitable transparent plastic cut in the form of a tensile specimen as shown in Fig. 6-7a. This specimen is placed in the field of a plane polariscope as shown in 6-7c. Assume that a monochromatic light source is used. Before the load is applied the entire field is dark. What happens as the load increases? The answer is that the field remains dark. This is the case since the direction of principal stress is aligned with the axis of polarization, i.e., $\theta = 0$ [Eq. (6-2)]. This is the *isoclinic* effect—zero light transmission due to the alignment of principal stress axis and axis of polarization.

If we are to study the effect of magnitude of stress, we must first eliminate the isoclinic effect. We may accomplish this by realigning the polarizer and the analyzer as in Fig. 6-7d—the elements remain crossed, but $\theta = 45$ deg, and hence $\sin 2\theta = 1$. Or we may eliminate the isoclinic effect by using a circular polariscope as in Fig. 6-7e and 6-7f. With this parallel-parallel arrangement, the entire field is dark before the load is applied. Now what will happen as the load increases? In this case, as the load increases, the stress in the longitudinal direction (S_1) increases, and the stress in the transverse direction (S_2) remains zero. Hence ($S_1 - S_2$) increases with load, and the relative retardation in the principal directions (longitudinal and transverse) varies in accordance with Eq. (6-5). When

$$S_1 - S_2 = \frac{K(1/2)}{d}$$

(i.e., $n = \frac{1}{2}$), maximum light is transmitted through the model, which has been made doubly refracting by stressing, and the central section of the model (constant-stress section) appears light on a dark field. As the load is further increased until $n = 1$, $S_1 - S_2 = K(1)/d$, no light is transmitted, and the model is indistinguishable from the dark background. As the load continues to increase: when

$$(S_1 - S_2) = \frac{K(3/2)}{d},$$

maximum light is transmitted; when $(S_1 - S_2) = K(2)/d$, zero light is transmitted, etc.

Points of light intensity on the image of the model due to the fact that at that point $S_1 - S_2 = Kn/d$ ($n = 1, 2, 3$, etc.) are called *fringes*. When $n = 1$, we see the first fringe; when $n = 2$, the second fringe, etc. In this example, the fringes are associated with recurring darkness, since the system is dark field. If the polariscope were set up with light field (crossed-parallel or parallel-crossed), then the whole-order fringes ($S_1 - S_2 = K(1)/d$, or $S_1 - S_2 = K(2)/d$, etc.) would be associated with recurring light, and half-order fringes ($S_1 - S_2 = K(1/2)/d$, or $S_1 - S_2 = K(3/2)/d$, etc.) would be associated with recurring darkness.

In this example, if the photoelastic coefficient K is known, the value of the applied load could be determined by counting the fringe order n produced by that load and substituting into Eq. (6-7). Alternately, by measuring the applied load and counting the fringe order n developed by that load, the photoelastic coefficient K can be determined. It is interesting to consider the effect of using a light source of mixed frequencies in this example. For the system shown in Fig. 6-7d, the entire field is dark for load = 0. As the load increases, the model will appear in constantly varying colors. This can be explained as follows: when $S_1 - S_2 = K_1 1/d$, in which $K_1 = Cv2\pi/\omega_1$, the component of color associated with frequency ω_1 is removed, and the result is light of the color with the component of frequency ω_1 absent. Then when $S_1 - S_2 = K_2 1/d$, in which $K_2 = Cv2\pi/\omega_2$, the result is the color associated with the component of frequency ω_2 absent, etc. When white light or light of mixed frequencies is used, the distinctive colors associated with $S_1 - S_2 = K_x n/d$ are referred to as *isochromatics* rather than fringes. The use of white, or mixed frequencies of light, will be discussed again in Sects. 6-4 and 7-1, but, for the present, we will return to examples in which monochromatic light is used.

The tensile test just considered is much too simple to require an experimental solution and is not a very satisfactory method for establishing the photoelastic constant K.

Example 6-2. Consider a suitable transparent plastic loaded as a simply supported beam with a constant-moment section. The beam is mounted in the field of a crossed-parallel circular polariscope as shown in Fig. 6-8a. The background is

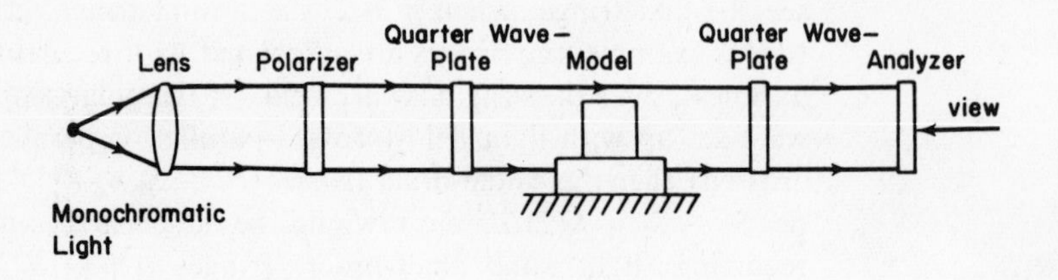

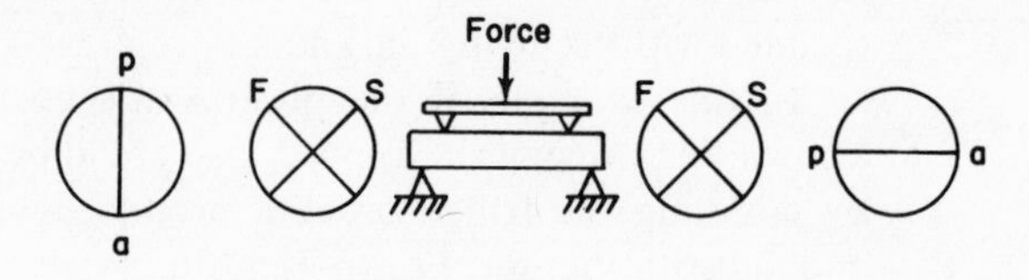

(a) Arrangement of elements and orientation of axes

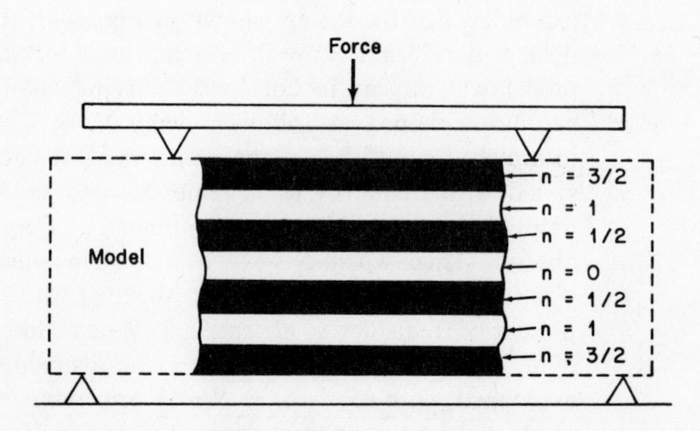

(b) Fringe pattern developed

Fig. 6-8. Circular polariscope; constant-moment-section model.

light, and, when monochromatic light is used, the whole-order fringes will appear as points of light and the half-order fringes will appear as points of darkness. For a given applied load, the fringe pattern within the constant-moment section of the beam will consist of a series of equally spaced light and dark lines; see Fig. 6-8b. Since the stress situation in this section is uniaxial ($S_{vertical} = 0$), and since the stress is easily computed as Mc/I, in which M is the moment, I is the second moment of area of the cross section, and c is the distance from the neutral plane, the value of K can be computed from a photograph or sketch, such as Fig. 6-8b. Since K can be computed from the observed position of a number of fringes, it can be determined over what range of fringe order the value of K remains constant.

Notice that in the examples just considered the thickness of the model (d) is constant over the area of interest, the directions of the principal stresses at a given point are constant across the thickness, and the stress in the direction of optical axis (parallel to the direction of light propagation) is zero. Also note that the fringe pattern could only be interpreted in terms of the magnitude of $(S_1 - S_2)$ and that neither S_1 nor S_2 could be individually evaluated from the observed fringe pattern, except at a free edge where one stress is known to be zero.

6-4 Equipment and models

As we have already pointed out, the basic instrument used in photoelastic stress analysis is the polariscope. Many different forms are available and in use, but the differences generally involve location of lens, kind of light source, and arrangement used for viewing or photographing the fringes and isoclinic patterns in the loaded model. Polariscopes utilizing a point light source contain the elements shown in Fig. 6-9.

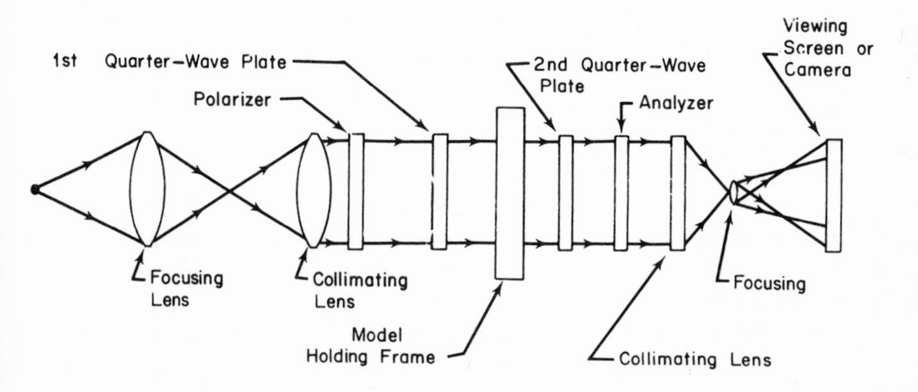

Fig. 6-9. Polariscope arrangement.

With very large field instruments, diffused light sources are generally substituted for the point source. In this case, the focusing lens and collimating lens are eliminated. The diffused light source often consists of a staggered bank of fluorescent tubes; see Ref. [18]. The light-source stand is generally made so that several sources may be readily interchanged. This is convenient, since white light is often used in a plane polariscope to study isoclinics. When white light is used, the isoclinics appear as black lines, whereas the fringes appear as colored bands. An ordinary incandescent electric bulb of sufficient wattage will serve as an adequate white light source. For determination of stress magnitudes, the fringes need to be studied and, for this purpose, a circular polariscope using monochromatic light is most often used. Mercury vapor lamps are commonly used as monochromatic light sources, but for this use it is necessary to filter out all of the emission except the predominant mercury green line. For this purpose, glass filters are generally inserted between the light source and the first lens.

The polarizer and analyzer are most often made of Polaroid plastic. They are generally housed in frames so that they can be rotated about the optical axis of the polariscope. This feature enables the operator to study the direction of principal stress in the model (isoclinic lines) without rotating the model in the polarized light field.

The quarter-wave plates are most often made of permanently strained plastic. As has already been pointed out, such a plate can only function as a true quarter-wave plate for the particular frequency of light for which it was designed. Hence, the monochromatic light source should be the one for which the quarter-wave plates were designed. The quarter-wave plates are generally housed in pivoted frames so that they can be swung completely out of the field. This permits the polariscope to function as a plane polariscope for the study of isoclinics or as a circular polariscope for the study of fringe lines. In addition, both quarter-wave plates can generally be rotated about the optical axis, permitting the operator to select any desired polariscope arrangement: crossed-crossed, crossed-parallel, parallel-parallel, or parallel-crossed.

The model holding frame can take an infinite variety of forms. In some cases the stress pattern is frozen* into the model and, hence, the model need not be loaded when it is being observed—in this case, the holding frame is any fixture that will conveniently position the model in the light field.

Existing testing machines are often used to apply tensile, compressive, or flexural loads to models during observation. In many cases, elements

* See Sect. 6-5b for a discussion of the frozen stress techniques.

to the left of the model holding frame (see Fig. 6-9) are aligned on one bench, and all of the elements to the right of the model holding frame are aligned on a second bench. Then the polariscope can be "built around" any existing loading device.

In the study of thermally induced stress* the model holding frame may take the form of a combination loading frame and controlled-temperature chamber.

Some additional items of equipment used in photoelastic work for special purposes will be discussed, together with the function they serve, in the following pages.

Since almost all materials which are optically isotropic when unstressed become doubly refracting when stressed, the problem of the selection of model material becomes one of making the best choice for a particu ar problem.

The most obvious desired properties are (1) transparency, (2) suitable value of stress-optical coefficient (K), (3) suitable elastic properties, and (4) ease of model-making. A brief discussion of several materials which have been, and are being, used will serve to indicate the importance of these properties and the desirability of several others.

In some of the very early photoelastic studies, various glasses were used. In general, glass is not satisfactory for two reasons: first, the stress-optical coefficient (K) is high compared to the ultimate strength; hence, before many fringe orders are developed the model will fail. Rearranging Eq. (6-7), we have

$$K = \frac{(S_1 - S_2)\,d}{n}.$$

That is, the stress-optical coefficient (K) is a measure of the stress difference required per fringe order formed for a given thickness (d) of model. The usual units for K are

$$\frac{(\text{lb/in.}^2) \times \text{in.}}{\text{fringe}} \quad \text{or} \quad \frac{\text{lb}}{\text{fringe} - \text{in.}}.$$

Second, glass is difficult to form and to machine.

Celluloid was widely used in early studies. Although celluloid has a suitable stress-optical coefficient and is reasonably easy to machine, it has several shortcomings. First, it is linearly elastic over a very limited stress range, hence, it is not suitable as a model for a part or structure in which stress is proportional to strain under the applied load. Second, the value of K is very dependent upon temperature, so celluloid could only be used in a carefully controlled temperature environment.

* See Sect. 6-7 for a discussion of photothermoelasticity.

A type of Bakelite* has been used for many two-dimensional studies and for some three-dimensional studies (see Ref. [19]); it is seldom used at the present time, however. This material is available in unpolished sheet form, and, in general, it must be annealed to remove residual stresses, and hence residual fringes, before being machined into the desired form. This material can be machined by using standard tools and methods. After a model is shaped, it must be polished to obtain the necessary transparency. Catalin 61-893 has good optical sensitivity, i.e., low stress-optical coefficient (K), the value of K being in the neighborhood of

$$100 \frac{\frac{\text{lb}}{\text{in.}^2} \times \text{in.}}{\text{fringe}}.$$

Catalin 61-893 also has favorable elastic properties; the proportional limit stress ($S_{\text{p.l.}}$) being about 6000 psi and the modulus of elasticity (E) being about 600,000 psi. These elastic properties are almost as important as is the K value.

The larger the ratio $S_{\text{p.l.}}/K$, the more fringes can be formed before the proportional limit is exceeded. The larger the ratio of E/K, the more fringes formed per unit of strain or deformation; this ratio of modulus to stress-optical coefficient (E/K) is called the "figure of merit." A high figure of merit is required to limit deformations to the model to the same order as the deformations that will occur in the actual prototype material of interest.

Catalin 61-893, along with several other plastics of this type, develops residual stresses and fringes near the free edges over a period of time. This is referred to as the time-edge effect, and photoelastic models subject to this effect must be analyzed soon after the annealing and finishing operation.

More recently, various other types of plastics have been used. Another plastic, CR-39, developed by the Pittsburgh Plate Glass Company, is very similar to the Bakelite just described. CR-39 is available in polished-sheet form.†

Various polyester resins have also been used in photoelastic work. A particular plastic of this type, marketed as Castolite,‡ is available as an uncatalyzed liquid. The solid material is prepared by mixing a liquid catalyst (such as cumene hydroperoxide) to the resin. The use of Castolite as a photoelastic model material has been thoroughly studied by

* Marketed as "Catalin Cast Resin 61-893" by Catalin Corporation of America.

† Homalite Company, Wilmington, Del.

‡ Castolite Company, Woodstock, Ill.

R. E. Matzdorff [20] and M. M. Frocht and H. Pih [21]. They report fair values of

$$K\left(\frac{175\,\dfrac{\text{lb}}{\text{in.}^2}\times\text{in.}}{\text{fringe}}\right)$$

and E (600,000 psi) at room temperature and a good value for figure of merit (E/K) even at elevated temperatures.* Castolite can be formed into rather complicated models by casting or by bonding Castolite parts together, using additional unset Castolite as the cement. In general, the finished model must be annealed to remove residual stresses, and fringes; but, once residuals are removed, the model will remain free of time-edge stress for a considerable period.

Various epoxy resins† have also been used to make photoelastic models. These plastics are available as uncatalyzed resins, and the models are prepared by catalyzing and casting. In general, the epoxies are easier to cast than are the polyesters (Castolite), and they exhibit comparable optical and elastic properties. M. M. Levin and A. M. Wahl [22] report that the figures of merit (E/K) at elevated temperatures for certain epoxies are greater than that of either Bakelite or Castolite. Most epoxies develop time-edge stresses soon after casting.

More recently, various urethane rubbers have been used as photoelastic model materials. This material is available in sheet form from which two-dimensional models may be shaped, or as an uncatalyzed liquid resin which can be used to cast models.‡ J. W. Dally [23] used a urethane rubber of very low K and very low E in order to study transient stress waves photoelastically.§ The low value of E was desirable in this case, since a low velocity of stress-wave propagation was necessary for photographing the moving fringe order.**

---

* The importance of high figure of merit at elevated temperatures for three-dimensional and thermal-stress studies will be further discussed in Sects. 6-5b and 6-7.

† Maraglas, The Marblette Corporation, Long Island City, N.Y. Armstrong C-9, Armstrong Products Company, Warsaw, Ind. Hysol 8531, Houghton Laboratories, Incorporated, Olean, N.Y.

‡ Hysol 8530, Houghton Laboratories, Incorporated, Olean, N.Y.

§ See Sect. 6-6 for additional discussion of dynamic photoelasticity.

** The velocity of strain-wave propagation is

$$c = \sqrt{\frac{E}{\rho}},$$

in which c is propagation velocity, E is modulus of elasticity, and ρ is density.

6-5 Static-stress analysis

6-5a Two-dimensional model techniques

In the preceding paragraphs we have developed the necessary optical theory and the relationships between optical pattern and stresses. The results of these efforts are best summarized by Eqs. (6-2) and (6-7). Thus:

$$x_t = \frac{X}{2} \sin 2\theta \, [\sin \omega(t + dt) - \sin \omega t], \tag{6-2}$$

and

$$S_1 - S_2 = \frac{Kn}{d}. \tag{6-7}$$

Equation (6-2) indicates that when a plane model, made doubly refracting by stressing, is placed in the field of plane polarized light, then points of zero transmission may be associated with points at which one of the principal stresses is parallel to the axis of polarization of the polarizer; i.e., $\sin 2\theta = 0$. To eliminate points of zero transmission associated with the magnitude of principal stresses, it is necessary only to use white light, since in this case fringe orders are colored.

The dark lines formed by a series of points of zero transmission due to the alignment of a principal stress axis and the polarizing axis are called *isoclinic lines*. At all points along a given isoclinic line the principal stress directions are the same. Figure 6-10 is a photograph showing isoclinic lines in a disk loaded across the diameter. These photographs were obtained by rotating the polarizer and analyzer 20 deg between exposures, the polarizer and analyzer remaining crossed at all times.

If all isoclinic lines are superimposed on one picture, as in Fig. 6-11a, a set of stress trajectories, as shown in Fig. 6-11b, may be constructed. Stress trajectories are lines which are tangent or perpendicular to the principal stress at every point along the line. The construction of the stress trajectories from the isoclines is accomplished graphically. The procedure is tedious and requires skill and practice. Methods for developing stress trajectories from isoclinic lines are treated in detail in Ref. [24].

Equation (6-7) indicates that, when a plane model in the field of polarized monochromatic light is made doubly refracting by stressing, the points at which the transmitted light is equal to the background light may be associated with points at which the difference of principal stress magnitudes has a specific value. The lines formed by a series of such points are called fringe lines. At all points on the fringe line of order 1 (first-order fringe), the magnitude of principal stress difference $(S_1 - S_2)$ is one times K/d; at all points on the fringe line of order 2 (second-order

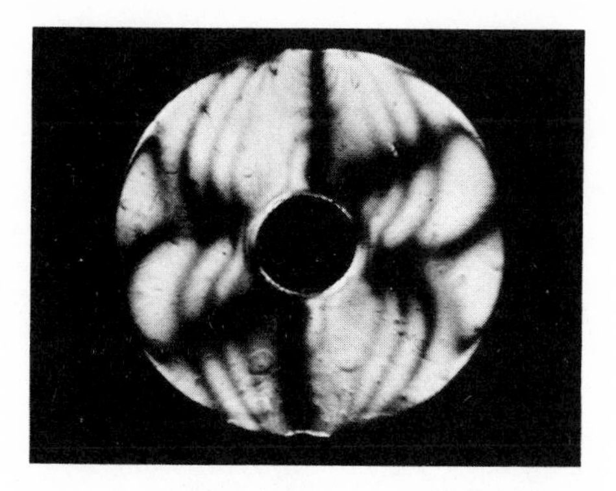

(a) 10-degree isoclinic

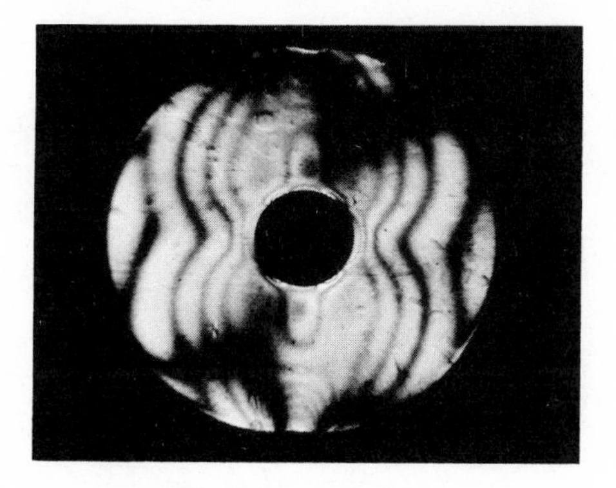

(b) 30-degree isoclinic

Fig. 6-10. Isoclinic lines in a disk containing a central hole.

fringe) $(S_1 - S_2)$ is two times K/d, etc. Fringe lines are often called iso-shear lines, since they connect points of equal shear stress.* Figure 6-12a is a photograph of the fringe pattern formed on a disk loaded across a diameter. Notice that, since the fringes of various orders have the same appearance, it is imperative that the observer be able to determine the correct order of each line. If the location of a point at which $S_1 - S_2 = 0$ is known, the fringe orders can be counted from this point. Such a point is known as an isotropic point. If such a point is not available, it is generally necessary to observe the growth of the fringe pattern as the load is applied in order to count the change in fringe order at a point as it occurs. Figure 6-12b indicates the fringe-order numbers associated with the pattern in Fig. 6-12a.

* Maximum shearing stress (S_{12}) is equal to $(S_1 - S_2)/2$.

OD = 5.0 in.
ID = 1.25 in.
d = 0.562 in.
Mat'l = Urethane rubber

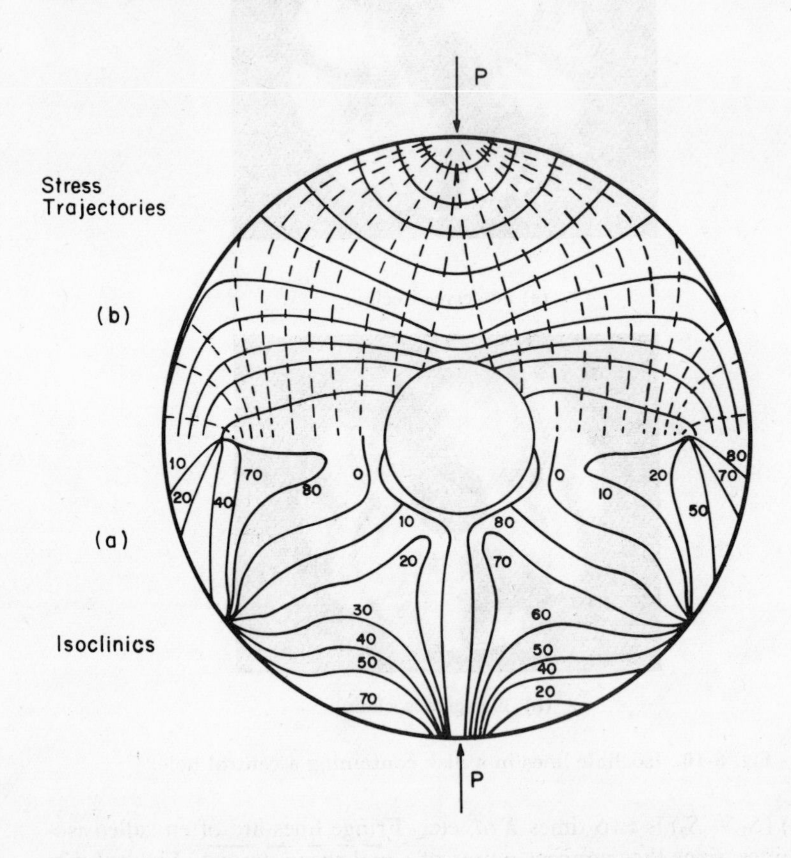

Fig. 6-11. Isoclinic pattern and stress trajectories.

Using the equipment, equations, and methods discussed to this point, we can determine directions of principal stresses and magnitude of principal stress difference (or maximum shearing stress) over a large field on a plane model. In certain problems this may be all that is required. For example, when it is known that the maximum stress occurs at a free boundary where one principal stress is zero, we obtain the magnitude of the maximum principal stress directly; i.e., $S_1 - 0 = Kn/d$. This is the situation that exists for many cases of discontinuities, such as holes and notches in plates. Hence, the value of stress concentration factor for

Fig. 6-12a. Fringe pattern in disk containing a central hole.

Fig. 6-12b. Fringe pattern in disk containing a central hole.

many types of discontinuities in plane stressed members have been determined by photoelasticity. See Refs. [2], [3], [4], and [5]. Figure 6-13 shows the fringe pattern on two beams. One is notched and one is not; both are of the same material of the same dimensions and are subjected to the same load. In each case, the maximum stress occurs at a free boundary. Hence, we may compute the maximum stress in each as

$$S_{max} = \frac{Kn_{max}}{d}.$$

For the notched beam

$$S'_{max} = \frac{Kn'_{max}}{d}.$$

For the unnotched beam

$$S_{max} = \frac{Kn_{max}}{d}.$$

Therefore, the stress-concentration factor associated with this discontinuity for this loading situation is

$$F = \frac{S'_{max}}{S_{max}} = \frac{n'_{max}}{n_{max}}.$$

In the solution of two-dimensional stress problems, the accuracy of the results obtained by photoelastic analysis often depends upon how precisely the fringe order can be determined at a given point.

One approach to this problem is to use a model material of low K and a large load, thus producing a large number of fringes. If, for example, ten fringes are produced at the point of interest, then estimating the fringe value to the nearest half order will give no more than five per cent error in the magnitude of $(S_1 - S_2)$ at that point. Unfortunately, with all available model materials, loads that will produce high fringe orders at all points of interest will, in general, produce deflections so large as to change the stress distribution from what it would be in the loaded metal prototype.

Some investigators prefer to use white light when studying a fringe pattern in which only a few fringes are produced. When white light is used, the black and white lines are replaced by bands of continuously varying color and, by studying the repetition of the color pattern, fractional fringe orders can be determined. This use of white light is discussed further in Sect. 7-1.

For the greatest resolution of fringe order, a technique known as compensation is used. In compensation, a full or half fringe of known

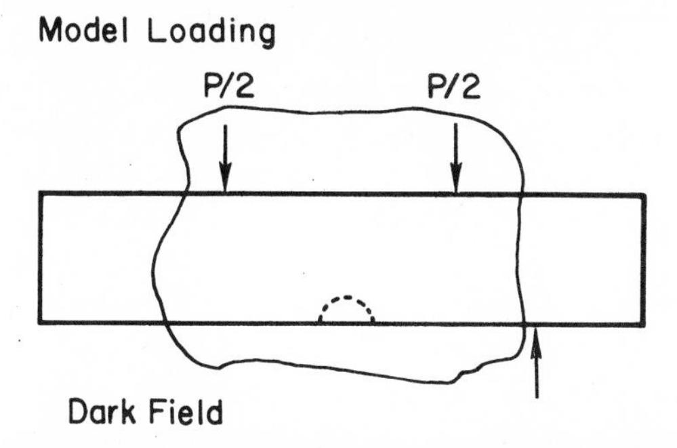

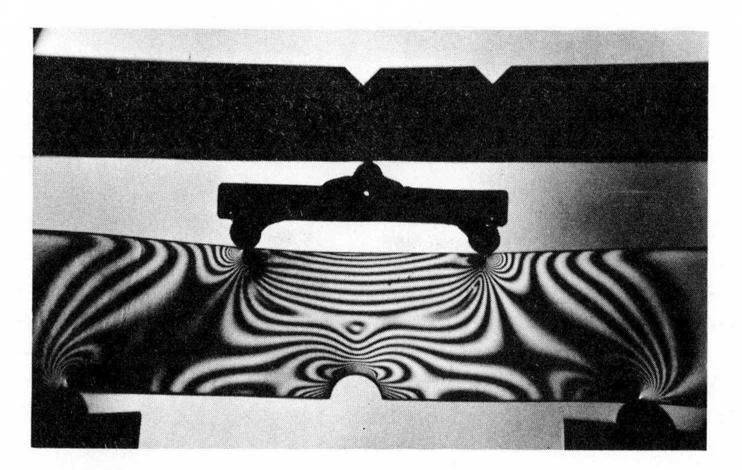

Fig. 6-13. Stress-concentration factor determined by photo-elasticity.

order is "moved" to the point of interest. The fringe order at that point is then evaluated as the known fringe order plus a fraction which can be computed from the correction necessary to move the known fringe to the point. Several physical arrangements can be used to accomplish compensation, but in any case one of two basic principles is involved. See Ref. [24], pp. 861–5, for a description of several specific types of compensators. In the first method a second doubly refracting material (the compensator) is inserted into the optical field in "series" with the model under test; that is, the refracting axes of the compensator are aligned with the refracting axes of the model *at the point of interest.* The total retardation is now the sum of the retardation occurring in the compensator and the model; this sum can be adjusted to produce a whole-order fringe if the retardation of the compensator can be varied. Retardation in the compensator can be adjusted in several ways. If a naturally doubly refracting material (such as quartz) is used, the retardation is directly proportional to thickness of the material through which the light must pass; hence, wedge-shaped pieces may be used by calibrating them to relate insertion in the optical field to thickness in the field and, hence, to retardation and fractional fringe order produced. (Babinet and Soleil-Babinet compensators are of this type.) The compensator can also be made of a material that becomes doubly refracting when stressed. In this case the retardation (and, hence, the fractional fringe order) produced in the compensator can be varied and computed from the stress applied to the compensator. (The Coker compensator is of this type.)

In the second method of compensation (Tardy method), the analyzer is used to "move" a whole fringe order to the point of interest. From our discussion of possible polariscope arrangements (crossed-crossed, crossed-parallel, etc.), we realize that a rotation of the analyzer of 90 deg will change the fringe order by a value of $\frac{1}{2}$. It can be shown* that, if polarizer and analyzer are aligned with the principal stress axes at the point of interest, and the analyzer is then rotated n degrees, the fringe order at the point of interest is changed by $n/180$ of a full fringe order. For example: a polariscope is set up to give dark field (whole-order fringes dark), and the pattern shown in Fig. 6-14 is observed. The principal stress directions (1 and 2) at the point of interest (X) were previously determined by finding the isoclinic line which passed through the point X. The entire optical system of the polariscope (polarizer, analyzer, and both quarter-wave plates) is now rotated (the polariscope elements remaining in the same position relative to each other), so that the polarizer axis is aligned with a principal stress axis at point X. This does not change the

* See Ref. [25] for the details of the optical equations involved.

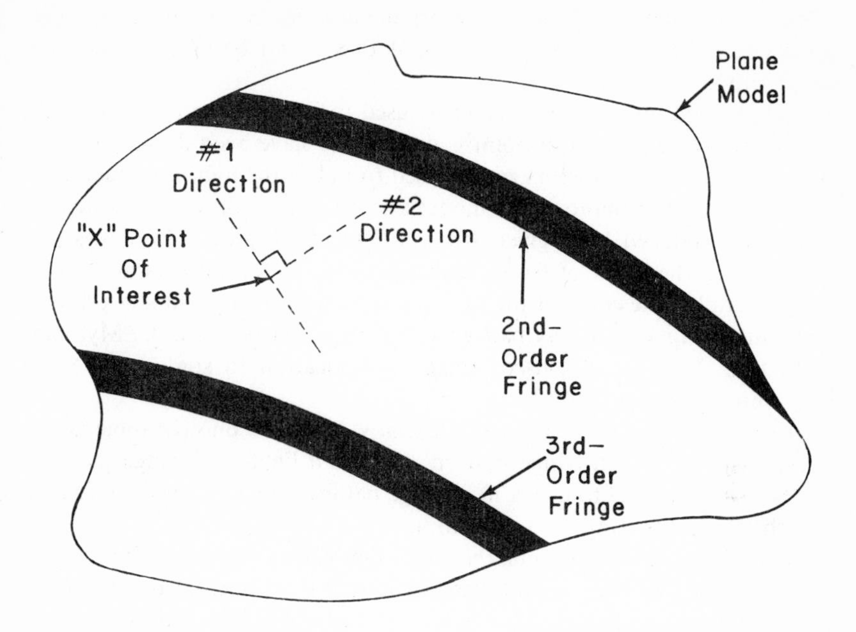

Fig. 6-14. Tardy method for determining fractional fringe orders.

observed pattern. If the analyzer is now rotated n deg to move the second-order fringe to point X, the fringe order at point X is

$$N_x = 2 + \frac{n}{180}.$$

This value can be checked by rotating the analyzer m deg in the opposite direction to move the third-order fringe to point X. The fringe value at point X is

$$N_x = 3 - \frac{m}{180}.$$

As a check,

$$2 + \frac{n}{180} = 3 - \frac{m}{180}.$$

Although these compensation techniques establish the fringe order at a point with precision, they all have two serious drawbacks. (1) To use a compensation technique, it is necessary first to establish the principal stress directions at all points of interest (an isoclinic study). (2) These techniques reduce the photoelastic method to a point-by-point analysis method—and one of the strongest arguments that can be made for the photoelastic method of stress analysis is that it can be used as a whole-field method.

Whole-field methods which can be used to increase the precision with which the fringe order at a point is determined have been developed. D. Post [26] shows how mirrors can be used to reflect the light rays back and forth through the photoelastic model and thereby to increase the fringe order (n) produced by a given stress difference. Figure 6-15 shows the method and the effect of fringe multiplication. If the mirrors are maintained parallel, the effect of the multiple reflections is to yield sharp black and white fringes on a gray background (fringe sharpening). C. Mylonas and D. C. Drucker [27] used fringe multiplication to study stresses in very thin tapes ($d = 0.0112$ in.).

J. W. Dally and F. J. Ahimaz (28) show how two photographic negatives, one a dark-field fringe pattern and one a light-field fringe pattern, can be superimposed to give a new fringe pattern which locates one-fourth and three-fourths fringe-order positions.

If it is desired to determine the individual values of S_1 and S_2 at points removed from the free boundaries, additional experimental or analytical work is required. Specifically, since the study of fringe orders gives us but one equation involving S_1 and S_2 ($S_1 - S_2 = Kn/d$), we need to develop an additional independent equation involving S_1 and S_2. This can be accomplished in a number of ways, but we shall discuss only those which are primarily experimental methods.*

At first glance, the simplest method of solution appears to be the determination of $(S_1 + S_2)$ by means of strain measurement. This can be accomplished by measuring strain across the thickness of the model. See Fig. 6-16.

$$\epsilon_3 = \frac{S_3}{E} - \frac{\mu}{E}(S_1 + S_2).$$

But, since $S_3 = 0$,

$$\epsilon_3 = -\frac{\mu}{E}(S_1 + S_2),$$

or

$$S_1 + S_2 = -\frac{E}{\mu}\epsilon_3 = -\frac{E}{\mu}\frac{\Delta d}{d}, \tag{6-8}$$

in which $\Delta d/d$ is the change in thickness divided by the original thickness. Solving Eqs. (6-8) and (6-7) simultaneously yields values of S_1 and

---

* For a discussion of analytical methods that can be used in conjunction with photoelastic methods to obtain values for S_1 and S_2, see Ref. [24], pp. 885–92; Ref. [29], pp. 202–8 and pp. 212–23; and Ref. [30].

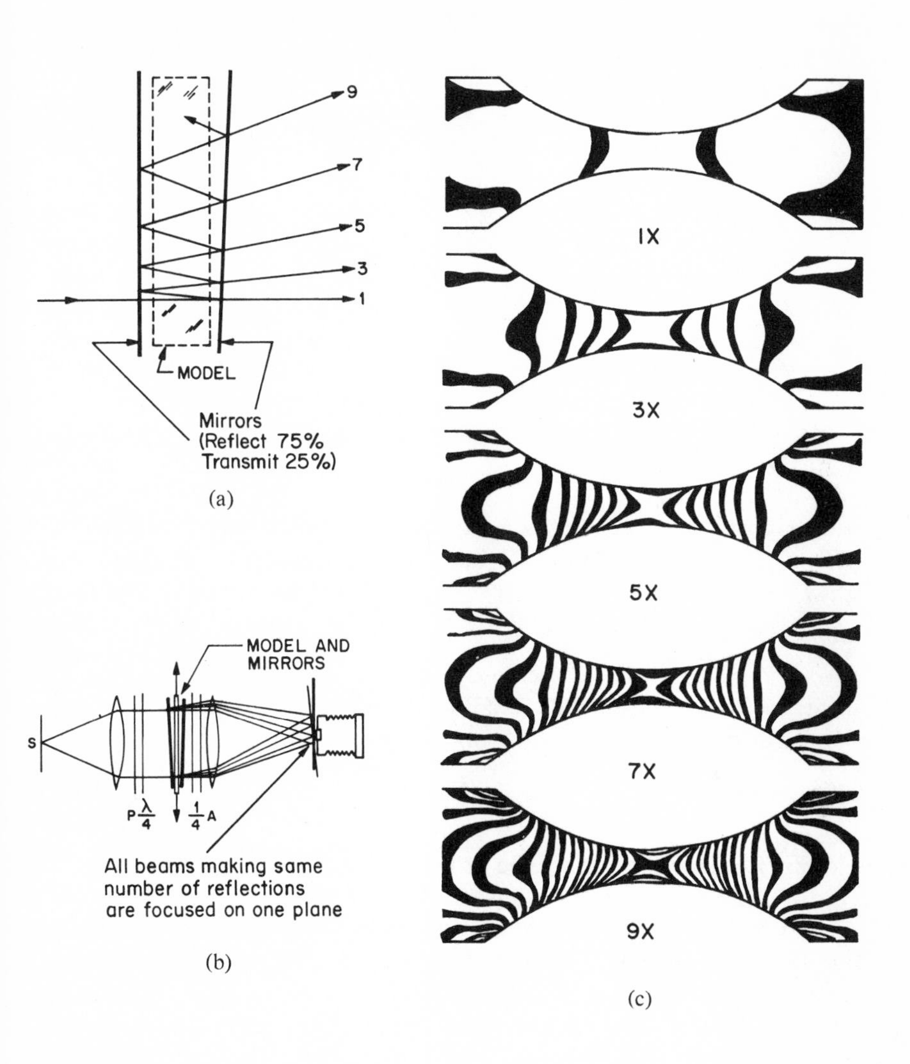

Fig. 6-15. Fringe multiplication. (*Courtesy Polarizing Instrument Company, Inc.*)

S_2. The first difficulty with this method is the fact that the model thickness must be measured before and after loading at every point at which principal stresses are to be determined, i.e., a point-by-point method. The second difficulty is the fact that these measurements must be made

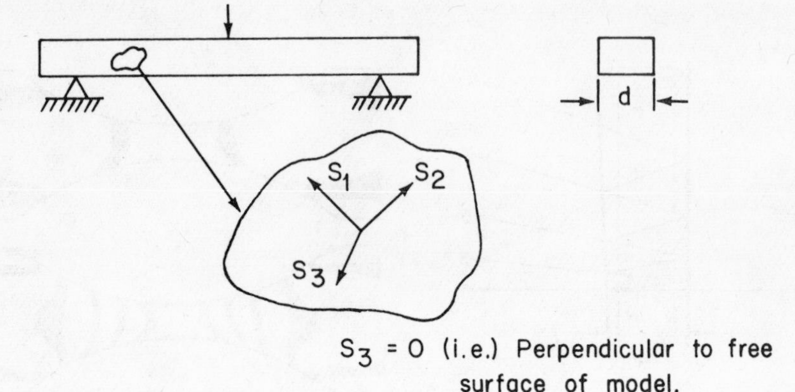

Fig. 6-16. Determination of $S_1 + S_2$.

with a high degree of precision. Assuming a model material modulus (E) of 1×10^6 psi and a Poisson's ratio (μ) of $\frac{1}{3}$, we see that $\frac{\Delta d}{d} = \frac{1/3}{1 \times 10^6} = \frac{1}{3}\mu$ in. per psi of stress sum per inch of model thickness. Several investigators have developed special gages for making this measurement; see Refs. [31] and [32]. Another possibility which suggests itself is the use of special semiconductor gages which measure $S_1 + S_2$. See Ref. [33].

An additional equation involving S_1 and S_2 can also be established by making use of the directions of S_1 and S_2 (which can be determined by plotting isoclinic lines) and some of the basic equations of elastic theory. Again, using a beam as an example, we shall assume that the directions of principal stresses have been determined by plotting the isoclinic lines and that the fringes have been plotted. Refer to Fig. 6-17. To determine the value of S_1 and S_2 at some point X, we proceed as follows: choosing an origin at 0, we divide the section of interest into small squares of Δx by Δy, where for convenience we let $\Delta x = \Delta y$. Referring to the free-body diagram (Fig. 6-17b) of a general square (Δx by Δy) and writing $\Sigma F_y = 0$, we have

$$S_{y_n} = S_{y_{n-1}} - \Delta S_{xy}. \tag{6-9}$$

The value of shear stress on any surface can be computed from the equation*

$$S_{xy} = \frac{S_1 - S_2}{2} \sin 2\theta, \tag{6-10}$$

* Developed in most texts concerning mechanics of materials.

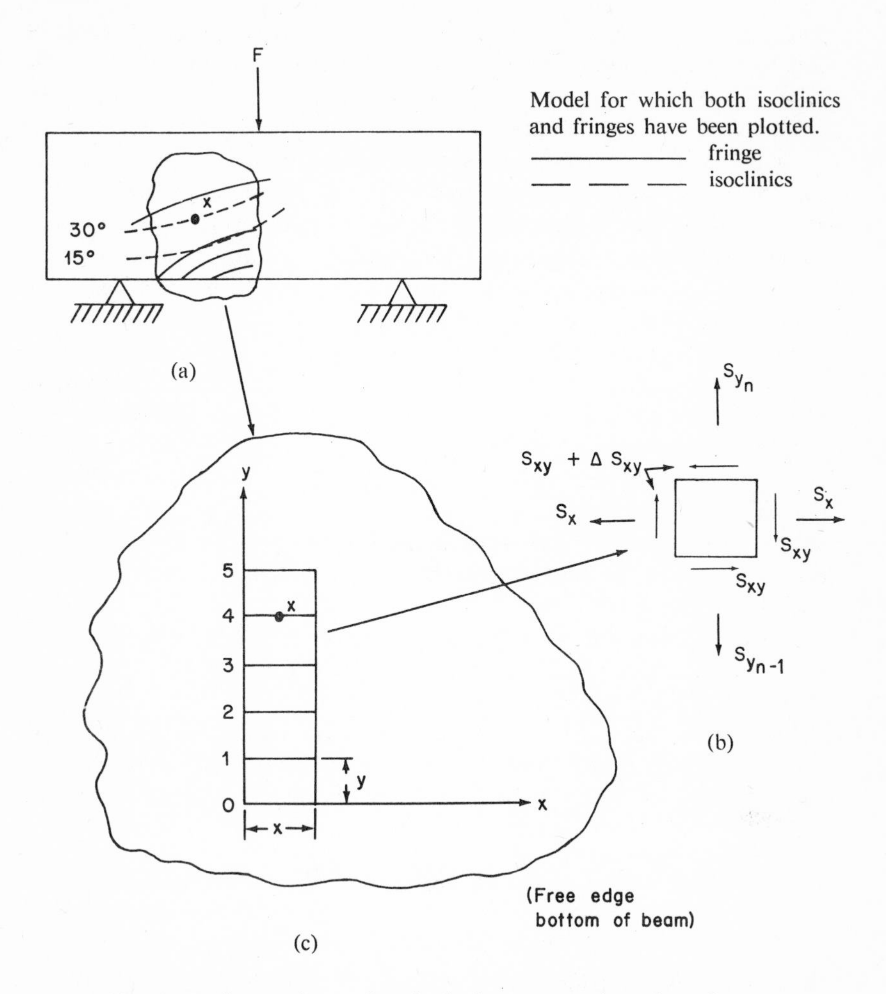

Fig. 6-17. Separation of principal stresses by the shear-difference method.

where $(S_1 - S_2)$ is known from the fringe order at the point of interest and θ, which is the angle between the principal stress (S_1) direction and the x axis, is known from the isoclinic value at that same point.

With the value of S_{xy} on each surface (0 through n) determined, ΔS_{xy} across each Δy can be computed, and Eq. (6-9) can be solved for values of S_y on every surface. The value of S_x can be computed by using the equation

$$S_x - S_y = (S_1 - S_2) \cos 2\theta,$$

or

$$S_x = S_y + (S_1 - S_2) \cos 2\theta. \tag{6-11}$$

Since $S_x + S_y = S_1 + S_2$, we now have a second equation involving S_1 and S_2, and by combining with Eq. (6-7) we can determine both S_1 and S_2.

This method for determining S_1 and S_2 requires that the complete isoclinic pattern be determined. Notice that the squares (Δx by Δy) must be small if the equation of equilibrium is to be approximated as Eq. (6-9), but, when small squares are used, the variation in $(S_1 - S_2)$ and θ must be known with great accuracy if Eq. (6-10) is to give accurate enough values for determining ΔS_{xy} across Δy. In any case, the method is tedious and time-consuming if many points are to be investigated or if points of interest are far from a free boundary. Again, this type of analysis reduces photoelastic analysis to a point-by-point method.

The next method for separating S_1 and S_2 to be discussed here is the method of oblique incidence, which was proposed by D. C. Drucker and R. D. Mindlin [10].

As has already been shown, when a plane model is placed perpendicular to the incident polarized light, the relationship between principal stress difference and fringe order is given by Eq. (6-7). This method of observation is called normal incidence, since the light vector is normal to model; see Fig. 6-18a.

Now, if the model is rotated about one of the principal stress vectors (say S_1) at some point of interest (say P in Fig. 6-18) so that the angle of incidence between the light vector and the model is ϕ, then the principal stresses in the plane perpendicular to the light vector will be S_1 and $S_2 \cos^2 \phi$. See Fig. 6-18b. Since the relative retardation (dt) depends upon the difference of the principal stresses in the plane normal to the light vector, in this case the governing equation will be

$$S_1 - S_2 \cos^2 \phi = \frac{Kn_o}{\dfrac{d}{\cos \phi}}, \tag{6-12}$$

in which n_o is the fringe order at point P as determined with oblique incidence; ϕ is the angle of incidence between light vector and the plane of the model, and $d/\cos \phi$ is the thickness of model traversed by the light in the oblique-incident condition. Combining Eqs. (6-7) and (6-12), we can obtain both S_1 and S_2 at point P.

$$S_2 = \frac{K}{d}\left(\frac{n - n_o \cos \phi}{\cos^2 \phi - 1}\right), \tag{6-13}$$

and

$$S_1 = \frac{K}{d}\left(\frac{n \cos^2 \phi - n_o \cos \phi}{\cos^2 \phi - 1}\right). \tag{6-13}$$

Notice that, since the model must be rotated about a principal stress axis, it is necessary to establish principal stress directions at points of

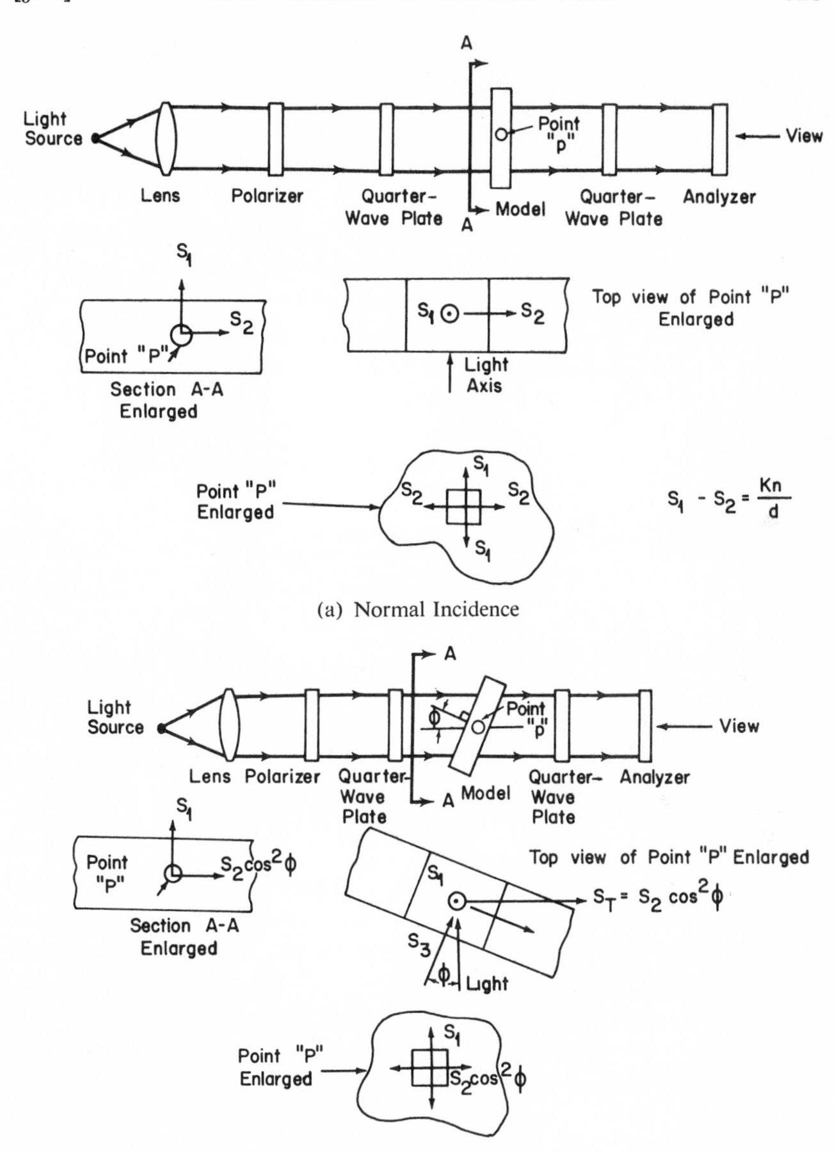

(a) Normal Incidence

(b) Oblique Incidence

Note: $S_T = S_2 \cos^2 \phi + S_3 \sin^2 \phi - S_{23} \sin 2\phi$, but $S_{23} = 0$, since S_2 and S_3 are principal stresses; i.e., no shear on principal planes and $S_3 = 0$, so $S_T = S_2 \cos^2 \phi$.

Fig. 6-18. Normal- and oblique-incidence methods.

interest before the oblique-incidence method can be used to establish S_1 and S_2. Notice also that, if ϕ is made large in order to give a large difference between n and n_o at point P, then in regions of high stress gradient the fringes will be blurred because of the variation in stress as the light traverses the model in the oblique position. In the oblique position the effective gage length is increased.

The values of the individual principal stresses have also been determined by using a special polariscope which measures the retardation (dt) of the light as it passes through each principal axis—rather than the difference of the retardation in one plane as compared to the other. This method, called the Favre method, not only requires very specialized optical apparatus, but again it reduces photoelasticity to a point-by-point method. See Ref. [34].

6-5b Three-dimensional techniques

The photoelastic method has been extended to study stresses in three-dimensional shapes, and two procedures are in use. In one method a sheet of photoelastic plastic is bonded to the surface of the three-dimensional shape, and a reflective-type polariscope is used. In this type of polariscope, the polarized light passes through the photoelastic coating, is reflected from the interface between photoelastic coating and the surface of the test piece, and passes back through the coating to the analyzer. This surface-coating technique, which can give only surface-strain information, is discussed in detail in Sect. 7-1.

In the second method used to study three-dimensional shapes, the shape of interest is made of a suitable photoelastic plastic—i.e., a model-study technique. The theory governing the strain-optical effects when polarized light is passed through a varying stress field in a three-dimensional shape is similar to, but more complicated than, the theory developed for the plane-stress case (Sect. 6-3).*

Although two methods have been proposed to analyze three-dimensional photoelastic models, only one, the stress-freezing technique, has been applied with any degree of success.† In the stress-freezing technique, the model is loaded at an elevated temperature, and the temperature is then lowered while the load is maintained. When the model reaches room temperature, the strain and, hence, the fringe pattern produced by the applied load are "frozen in" the model and will remain after the load is removed. (Or, as an alternative, a suitable material may be held at load

* See Ref. [10] for a discussion of three-dimensional stress-optical theory.

† The other technique which uses light scattered from interior points in the model is discussed in Refs. [35] and [36].

and allowed to creep at ordinary temperatures. Then when the load is removed, the strain pattern is retained long enough for analysis. See Ref. [37].) The model is then sliced, and the individual slices are placed in a polariscope and analyzed—hence, a small-field method even when only maximum shear stress at a surface is to be determined. To determine the magnitude of the individual principal stresses at a free surface, a point-by-point analysis is required, and the determination of the stress state (three principal stress magnitudes and directions) at an interior point becomes almost hopelessly complicated.

Several investigators have constructed and analyzed three-dimensional models (Refs. [9], [38], [39], [40], [41], [42], [43]). The analysis made by Levin [43] of nuclear-reactor components is an excellent example of a three-dimensional photoelastic study of a complex shape.

6-6 Dynamic-stress analysis

Attempts to utilize the photoelastic method in the study of dynamic stresses in plane models were made as early as 1932. Indeed, M. M. Frocht [44] indicated that he undertook the study of dynamic stresses because he felt that too much emphasis was being placed on the photoelastic determination of stress-concentration factors. Over the years this application of photoelasticity to dynamic-stress analysis has received less total attention than have certain other areas. However, the interest in dynamic photoelasticity has been steadily increasing. One reason for this interest is the fact that, whereas dynamic studies using strain gages give the variation of strain (and hence stress) with time at only a few preselected points, a photoelastic study may show the stress pattern in an entire area of interest at any instant as well as how the pattern varies with time.

The photoelastic equipment used for the study of dynamic stress is the standard circular polariscope with modifications in the light source and in the scheme used to observe and record the fringe patterns. Three different approaches have been used to "stop" the traveling fringe lines for observation and recording.

One approach to recording the moving fringes produced by impact or other dynamic loading has been to use a continuous light source* and a high-speed framing camera. In the work previously referred to (Ref. [44]), Frocht used a camera that took only 64 frames per second. However, since 1932, camera framing speeds have been increased to several

* Such as a mercury vapor bulb with filters, as is used in static work.

million frames per second, and over the years cameras with higher framing speeds have been used in photoelasticity.

In 1949, Ludwig Foeppl [45] reported on his photoelastic study of simply supported beams impacted at midspan. Foeppl used a camera which took 3020 frames per second with an exposure time of about five microseconds. Foeppl's results agreed well with the results predicted by the classical theory of St. Venant.

In 1956, A. J. Durelli and W. F. Riley [46] reported on the use of a standard eight mm Fastax camera in a dynamic photoelastic study. This camera will record 14,000 frames per second with an exposure time of approximately 14 microseconds. Durelli and Riley were particularly interested in developing and testing a photoelastic material having such a low value of stress-wave propagation velocity that cameras with modest framing speeds would be adequate for dynamic photoelastic studies.

In 1957, G. W. Sutton [47] reported on a dynamic photoelastic study in which he used an ultra-high-speed camera developed by A. T. Ellis [48]. He reports,

> This camera has a repetition rate up to one million frames per second for about a millisec with a frame exposure of about 0.08 microsec. The camera is a revolving mirror type; the mirror distributes a series of images onto the inner periphery of a stationary drum in which a $7\frac{1}{2}$ ft length of 35 mm Tri-X film has been placed. The exposure for each frame is achieved by a Kerr cell. The Kerr cell consists of a glass container, on the front and back of which are crossed polaroids so that normally no light is transmitted through the cell. On either side of the cell are two flat electrodes spaced 0.25 in. apart; when a voltage difference of 13,000 volts exists across the electrodes, the nitrobenzene in the container becomes sufficiently optically active to rotate the plane of the light that had been polarized by the front polaroid so that it passes through the rear polaroid.
>
> The Kerr cell is electrically pulsed for about 0.08 microsec to achieve each frame, and is pulsed continuously only during one revolution of the mirror. During this revolution, a General Electric FT524 flash tube is illuminated by discharging through it the energy stored in a bank of capacitors. Suitable inductances cause the light intensity to be almost constant for about a millisec.

Unfortunately, as framing speed increases and exposure time decreases, it becomes increasingly difficult to provide sufficient light for proper exposure of the film. The advantage of using a framing camera is that it gives a picture of how stress* varies in the entire field as a function of time.

---

* $(S_1 - S_2)$ or S_{12}.

A second approach for recording the moving fringes produced by dynamic photoelasticity is to use streak photography. Z. Tuzi and M. Nisida [49] used this method as early as 1935, and Frocht and others have used it since in dynamic photoelasticity. In this method the model is masked off except for a small slit (see Fig. 6-19). The light source is

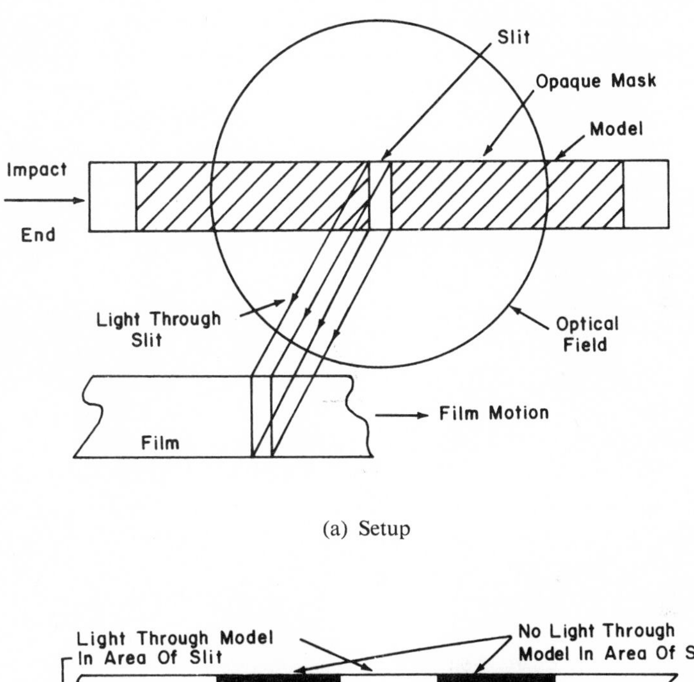

(a) Setup

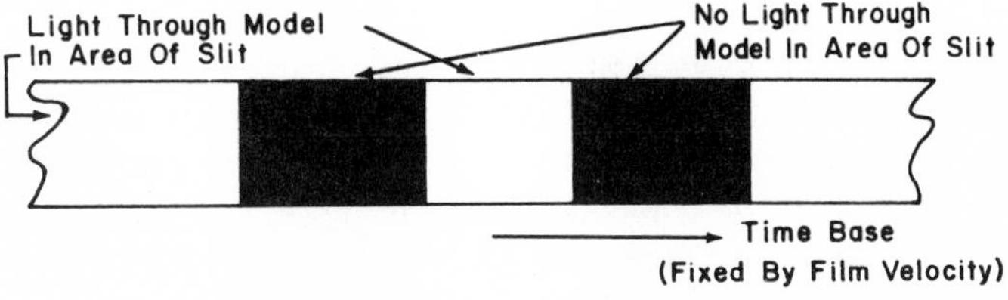

(b) Record

Fig. 6-19. Setup for streak photography.

continuous, and the light transmitted through the slit is recorded on a moving film in an open-shutter camera. As the transmitted light varies due to fringes passing the slit, a record of varying exposed and unexposed lengths is made on the moving film strip. The time base is established by the film speed. Frocht and P. D. Flynn [50] studied the longitudinal propagation of stress waves in rods, using streak photography. The rods were made of Castolite and were fixed at one end and impacted on the opposite end by means of a pendulum hammer. The model was masked off except for a transverse slit 0.0043 in. wide and a longitudinal slit 0.0020 in. wide. Using the streak-photography method, Frocht and Flynn obtained records equivalent in resolution to 1,500,000 frames per second. A. B. J. Clark [51] used much the same technique as Frocht and Flynn on a similar problem. But, instead of projecting the light passed by the model through the slit onto a film strip, Clark recorded the variation in transmitted light by using a photomultiplier tube. By displaying the output of the photomultiplier on a cathode ray oscilloscope the variation in fringe order at the slit is recorded as a function of time.

The principal disadvantage of the streak-photography method is that the variation of stress with time is measured only across a narrow slit—the whole-field advantage has been lost.

The third approach to the problem of recording moving fringes makes use of an intermittent light source. For problems in which the dynamic stresses are cyclic in nature, the use of a stroboscope as a light source enables the fringe pattern to be "stopped" and hence, recorded as in static photoelastic analysis. W. M. Murray [52] has used this technique to study the stress pattern in a vibrating beam. H. Becker [53] shows how to synchronize a light source and an impacting tool to study fringes produced by impact by using stil photography.

When the stresses are not cyclic, a high-intensity, short-duration light source may be used to, in effect, "stop" the moving fringes so that they may be recorded on stationary film. This method, which has been used by several investigators (Refs. [54], [55], and [56]), shows the fringe distribution over the entire field but at a single instant. If the loading can be repeated and the instant of illumination can be varied in a controlled manner for each loading, then a series of pictures can be taken which show the variation in fringe pattern with time. The high-intensity, short-duration light flash required in this method is commonly obtained by discharging the energy stored in a bank of capacitors across a gas-filled tube.

Even after the recording system and/or the light source have been modified to allow the polariscope to be used for dynamic studies, certain problems still remain.

Most of the light sources used to obtain very high intensity are far from monochromatic, and the filters required to make the source sufficiently monochromatic must be determined by trial and error. Probably the best method for determining whether or not a given light source and filter system is adequate is as follows: a model should be loaded statically to produce slightly higher-order fringes than will be formed in the dynamic study. A "reference" picture is then taken, a known monochromatic source being used. A second picture (same model, same load) is then taken, and the light source which is proposed for dynamic work is used. If all of the fringes visible in the first picture are not visible in the second picture, then the second source is not adequate and should be modified.

Since the accuracy of stresses determined photoelastically can be no greater than the accuracy of the value of stress-optical coefficient (K) used in their determination, it is imperative that the value of K used be the value that applies under the actual test conditions. It is well-known that the values of the elastic properties (particularly the modulus of elasticity E) of many plastics are affected by the rate of loading. In addition, several investigators have shown that the value of the stress-optical coefficient (K) is also affected by the rate of loading. It follows that in dynamic photoelasticity the values of K and E used in all computations must be the values that apply for the actual test conditions. In general, this means that dynamic-property evaluation tests must precede the dynamic photoelastic analysis.

The importance of this effect may be illustrated by reference to the variation in K and E with rate of loading for several commonly used photoelastic materials. Clark [51] reports that when the loading time on CR-39 is 1000 sec the value of K is

$$79 \frac{\text{lb}}{\text{lb}^2} \times \frac{\text{in.}}{\text{fringe}},$$

but with a loading time of 10^{-4} sec the value of K is

$$113 \frac{\text{lb}}{\text{lb}^2} \times \frac{\text{in.}}{\text{fringe}}.$$

For the same values of loading time E varies from 275,000 psi to 435,000 psi.

A new term, *strain-optical coefficient* K_ϵ, may be defined as $K_\epsilon = (\epsilon_1 - \epsilon_2)d/n$, in which ϵ_1 and ϵ_2 are principal strains. The relationship between K and K_ϵ depends upon the appropriate stress-strain relationship* for the calibration and use conditions. Clark [51] reports that in his uniaxial stress calibration of CR-39 the simultaneous variations in K and E with rate of loading were such as to make K_ϵ almost independent of rate of loading. Durelli and Riley [46] report similar findings for a photoelastic material of the epoxy-resin family. That is, they find a

---

* Uniaxial stress: $S_2 = 0,\ \epsilon_1 = S_1/E,\ \epsilon_2 = -\mu\epsilon_1.$

Biaxial stress: $\epsilon_1 = \frac{S_1}{E} - \mu\frac{S_2}{E},\ \epsilon_2 = \frac{S_2}{E} - \mu\frac{S_1}{E}.$

variation in both K and E with loading rate, but in a uniaxial-stress situation K_ϵ is essentially constant.

O. Jones and A. Ellis [57] point out that analysis of results obtained from dynamic photoelastic studies depends on the existence of a state of generalized plane stress, and in some cases this may not be satisfied.

6-7 Thermal-stress analysis

The photoelastic method has recently been extended to the study of thermal-stress problems, and this use of photoelasticity has been called photothermoelasticity. In 1956, G. Gerard and A. C. Gilbert [14] reported photoelastic studies of several plane thermal-stress problems, and in 1960 H. Tramposch and Gerard [15] reported a photoelastic study of a three-dimensional thermal-stress problem.

The polariscope used in the study of thermal stress is identical to the polariscope used in the study of static-load-induced stresses. When equilibrium thermal stresses are to be investigated, the stress (and hence, fringe) pattern is static. Even when transient thermal stresses are to be investigated, the standard polariscope, light source, and recording scheme can be used. This is possible because of the relatively low thermal diffusivity of most materials used for photoelastic models. Low diffusivity limits significant changes in stress (and fringe) patterns to the order of seconds, and the change in fringe pattern can be recorded by taking photographs at intervals spaced by several seconds or even minutes.

In photothermoelastic studies the loading frame is replaced by whatever is necessary to subject the model to the desired thermal environment as it is held in the field of the polariscope.

The model will, in general, be studied at a temperature different from ordinary room temperature, and the temperature may vary during the test period and from one point in the model to another. Hence, it is imperative that the stress-optical coefficient (K), the elastic properties (E and μ), and the thermal properties be known over the range of temperatures to be encountered. Indeed, to simplify the analysis of the data, it is desirable to work over a temperature range in which all of these pertinent properties remain essentially constant. Gerard, et. al. have conducted their studies in the temperature range of from 80°F downward to −40°F, since the properties of the useful plastics remain more nearly constant as temperatures vary below 80°F than they do as temperatures vary above 80°F. In any case, before a photothermoelastic study is undertaken, the properties of the model material must be thoroughly investigated. Figure 6-20, which is taken from Ref. [15], shows the equilibrium

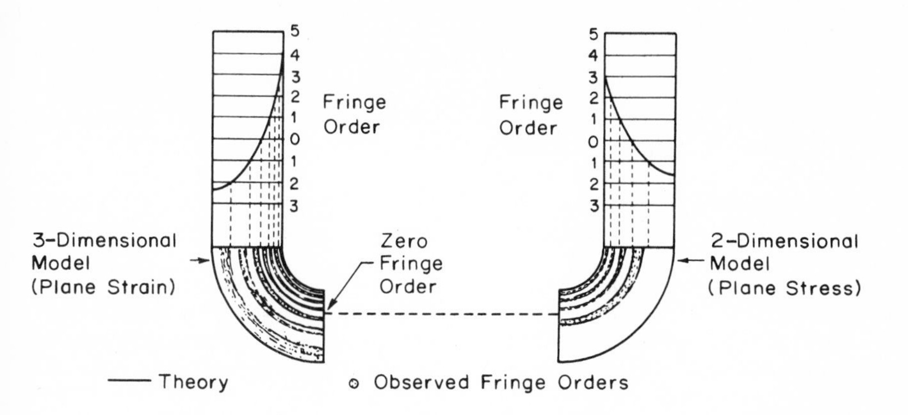

Fig. 6-20. **Correlation of experimental and theoretical results of a cylinder and a disk, both exposed to same steady-state temperature distribution (ΔT max 49 deg F).** (*Courtesy of Journal of Applied Mechanics.*)

fringe pattern developed in a cylinder and in a disk subject to the same radial temperature gradient. I. M. Daniel and A. J. Durelli [58] have used the photothermoelastic technique to study the thermal-stress distribution in a solid-fuel rocket motor.

The developments in the field of photothermoelasticity during the years 1957–1962 are summarized in Ref. [59].

6-8 References listed in Chapter 6

1. Coker, E. G. and L. N. G. Filon, *A Treatise on Photoelasticity*. London: Cambridge University Press, 1931.
2. Durelli, A. J. and W. M. Murray, "Stress Distribution Around an Elliptical Discontinuity in Any Two-Dimensional, Uniform and Axial, System of Combined Stress," *Proceedings of the Society for Experimental Stress Analysis*, Vol. 1, No. 1, p. 19.
3. Frocht, M. M., "Factors of Stress Concentration Photoelastically Determined," *Journal of Applied Mechanics*, Trans. ASME, Vol. 2, No. 2 (June 1935), p. A-67.
4. Wahl, A. M. and R. Beeuwkes, "Stress Concentration Produced by Holes and Notches," *Trans. ASME*, Vol. **56** (1934), pp. 617–25.
5. Weibel, E. E., "Studies in Photoelastic Stress Determination," *Trans. ASME*, Vol. **56** (1934), pp. 637–58.
6. Oppel, G., "Photoelastic Investigation of Three-Dimensional Stress and Strain Conditions," *National Advisory Committee Aeronautics Technical Memorandum 824*, 1937.

7. Hetényi, M., "Photoelastic Stress Analysis Made in Three Dimensions," *Machine Design*, Vol. 10 (1938), pp. 40–41.
8. Hetényi, M., "The Application of Hardening Resins in Three-Dimensional Photoelastic Studies," *Journal of Applied Physics*, Vol. 10 (1939), pp. 295–300.
9. Hetényi, M., "A Photoelastic Study of Bolt and Nut Fastenings," *Journal of Applied Mechanics*, Trans. ASME, Vol. 65 (1943), pp. A-93–100.
10. Drucker, D. C. and R. D. Mindlin, "Stress Analysis by Three-Dimensional Photoelastic Methods," *Journal of Applied Physics*, Vol. 11 (1940), pp. 724–32.
11. Frocht, M. M., *Photoelasticity*, Vols. 1 and 2. New York: John Wiley and Sons, 1941, 1948.
12. Zandman, F. and M. R. Wood, "Photostress, A New Technique for Photoelastic Stress Analysis for Observing and Measuring Surface Strains on Actual Structures and Parts," *Product Engineering*, New York (Sept. 1956).
13. D'Agostino, J., D. C. Drucker, C. K. Liu, and C. Mylonas, "An Analysis of Plastic Behavior of Metals with Bonded Birefringent Plastic," *Proceedings of the Society for Experimental Stress Analysis*, Vol. 12, No. 2, pp. 115–22.
14. Gerard, G. and A. C. Gilbert, "Photothermoelasticity: An Exploratory Study," *Journal of Applied Mechanics*, Vol. 24 (Sept. 1957), pp. 355–60.
15. Tramposch, H. and G. Gerard, "An Exploratory Study of Three-Dimensional Photothermoelasticity," *Journal of Applied Mechanics*, Vol. 28 (Mar. 1961), pp. 35–40.
16. Frocht, M. M. and R. A. Thomson, "Experiments in Mechanical and Optical Coincidence in Photoelasticity," *Proceedings of the Society for Experimental Stress Analysis*, Vol. 18, No. 1, pp. 43–47.
17. Fried, B., "Some Observations on Photoelastic Materials Stressed Beyond the Elastic Limit," *Proceedings of the Society for Experimental Stress Analysis*, Vol. 8, No. 2, pp. 143–8.
18. Durelli, A. J., "Discussion of The Paper Entitled Photoelasticity Laboratory at the Newport News Shipbuilding and Dry Dock Company," *Proceedings of the Society for Experimental Stress Analysis*, Vol. 6, No. 1, pp. 106–10.
19. Hetényi, M., "The Distribution of Stress in Threaded Connections," *Proceedings of the Society for Experimental Stress Analysis*, Vol. 1, No. 2, pp. 147–56.
20. Matzdorff, R. E., "Castable Plastics in Photoelastic Stress Analysis," Ph.D. thesis, California Institute of Technology, 1950.
21. Frocht, M. M. and Hui Pih, "A New Cementable Material for Two and Three-Dimensional Photoelastic Research," *Preceedings of the Society for Experimental Stress Analysis*, Vol. 12, No. 1, pp. 55–64.
22. Levin, M. M. and A. M. Wahl, "Three-Dimensional Photoelasticity," *Machine Design* (Mar. 6, 1958), pp. 150–4.
23. Dally, J. W., "Experimental Means for Determining Transient Stress and Strain," Ph.D. thesis, Illinois Institute of Technology, June 1958.
24. Dolan, T. J. and W. M. Murray, "Photoelasticity," *Handbook of Experimental Stress Analysis*, M. Hetényi (ed.). New York: John Wiley and Sons, Inc. (1950).
25. Goranson, R. W. and L. H. Adams, "A Method for the Precise Measurement of Optical Path-Difference, Especially in Stressed Glass," *J. Franklin Inst.*, Vol. 216, No. 4 (Oct. 1933), pp. 475–504.
26. Post, D., "Isochromatic Fringe Sharpening and Fringe Multiplication in Photoelasticity," *Proceedings of the Society for Experimental Stress Analysis*, Vol. 12, No. 2, pp. 143–56.

27. Mylonas, C. and D. C. Drucker, "Twisting Stresses in Tape," *Proceedings of the Society for Experimental Stress Analysis*, Vol. 18, No. 2, pp. 23–32.
28. Dally, J. W. and F. J. Ahimaz, "Photographic Method to Sharpen and Double Isochromatic Fringes," *Experimental Mechanics*, Vol. 2, No. 6 (June 1962), pp. 170–5.
29. Lee, G. H., *An Introduction to Experimental Stress Analysis.* New York: John Wiley and Sons, Inc., 1950.
30. Frocht, M. M., "Isopachic Patterns and Principal Stresses in Bars with Deep Notches in Tension," *Proceedings of the Society for Experimental Stress Analysis*, Vol. 8, No. 2, pp. 171–86.
31. DeForest, A. V. and A. R. Anderson, "A New Lateral Extensometer," *Proceedings 10th Eastern Photoelasticity Conference* (1939), p. 31. See also *Journal of Applied Mechanics*, Vol. 3, No. 4 (Dec. 1941), p. A-152.
32. Peterson, R. E. and A. M. Wahl, "Fatigue of Shafts at Fitted Members with a Related Photoelastic Analysis," *Journal of Applied Mechanics*, Trans. ASME, Vol. 2, No. 1 (Mar. 1935), p. A-1.
33. Pfann, W. G. and R. N. Thurston, "Semiconducting Stress Transducers Utilizing the Transverse and Shear Piezoresistance Effects," *Journal of Applied Physics*. Vol. 32 (Oct. 1961), pp. 2008–19.
34. Brahtz, J. H. A. and J. E. Soehrens, "Direct Optical Measurement of Individual Principal Stresses," *Journal of Applied Physics*, Vol. 10, No. 4 (Apr. 1939), p. 242.
35. Weller, R., "Three-Dimensional Photoelasticity Using Scattered Light," *Journal of Applied Physics*, Vol. 12 (1941), pp. 610–16.
36. Leven, M. M., "Stresses in Keyways by Photoelastic Methods and Comparison with Numerical Solutions," *Proceedings of the Society for Experimental Stress Analysis*, Vol. 7, No. 2, pp. 141–54.
37. Durelli, A. J. and R. L. Lake, "Some Unorthodox Procedures in Photoelasticity," *Proceedings of the Society for Experimental Stress Analysis*, Vol. 9, No. 1, pp. 97–122.
38. Leven, M. M., "Quantitative Three-Dimensional Photoelasticity," *Proceedings of the Society for Experimental Stress Analysis*, Vol. 12, No. 2, pp. 157–71.
39. Franz, W. F., "A Three-Dimensional Photoelastic Stress Analysis of a Threaded Drill Pipe Joint," *Proceedings of the Society for Experimental Stress Analysis*, Vol. 9, No. 2, pp. 185–94.
40. Lee, L. H. N. and C. I. Ades, "Stress Concentration Factors for Circular Fillets in Stepped Wall Cylinders Subject to Axial Tension," *Proceedings of the Society for Experimental Stress Analysis*, Vol. 14, No. 1, pp. 99–108.
41. Taylor, C. E. and J. W. Schweiker, "A Three-Dimensional Photoelastic Investigation of the Stresses Near a Reinforced Opening in a Reactor Pressure Vessel," *Proceedings of the Society for Experimental Stress Analysis*, Vol. 17, No. 1, pp. 25–36.
42. Riley, W. F. and A. J. Durelli, "Boundary Stresses at the Ends of Pressurized Cylindrical Holes Axially Located in a Large Cylinder," *Proceedings of the Society for Experimental Stress Analysis*, Vol. 17, No. 1, pp. 115–26.
43. Leven, M. M. and R. C. Sampson, "Photoelastic Stress and Deformation Analysis of Nuclear Reactor Components," *Proceedings of the Society for Experimental Stress Analysis*, Vol. 17, No. 1, pp. 161–80.
44. Frocht, M. M., "Kinematography in Photoelasticity," *Trans. ASME*, APM-54-9 (1932), p. 83.

45. Foeppl, L., "Slow Motion Pictures of Impact Tests by Means of Photoelasticity," *Journal of Applied Mechanics*, Vol. 16 (1949), p. 173.
46. Durelli, A. J. and W. F. Riley, "Experiments for the Determination of Transient Stress and Strain Distributions in Two-Dimensional Problems," *Journal of Applied Mechanics*, Vol. 24 (Mar. 1957), pp. 69–76.
47. Sutton, G. W., "A Photoelastic Study of Strain Waves Caused by Cavitation," *Journal of Applied Mechanics*, Vol. 24 (Sept. 1957), pp. 340–8.
48. Ellis, A. T., "Observations on Cavitation Bubble Collapse," C. I. T. Hydrodynamics Laboratory, Report No. 21-12, Dec. 1952.
49. Tuzi, Z. and M. Nisida, "Photoelastic Study of Stresses Due to Impact," *Philosophical Magazine*, Series 7, Vol. 21 (1936), pp. 448–73.
50. Frocht, M. M. and P. D. Flynn, "Studies in Dynamic Photoelasticity," *Journal of Applied Mechanics*, Vol. 23, No. 1 (Mar. 1956), p. 116. Discussed in *Journal of Applied Mechanics*, Vol. 23, No. 3 (Sept. 1956) p. 482.
51. Clark, A. B. J., "Static and Dynamic Calibration of a Photoelastic Model Material, CR-39." NRL Report 4779, Naval Research Laboratory, Washington, D.C., 1956.
52. Murray, W. M., "A Photoelastic Study in Vibrations," *Journal of Applied Physics*, Vol. 12 (1941), p. 617.
53. Becker, H., "Simplified Equipment for Photoelastic Studies of Propagating Stress Waves," *Proceedings of the Society for Experimental Stress Analysis*, Vol. 18, No. 2, pp. 214–16.
54. Senior, D. A. and A. A. Wells, "A Photo-elastic Study of Stress Waves," *Philosophical Magazine*, Vol. 37, No. 270 (July 1946), pp. 463–9.
55. Wells, A. A. and D. Post, "The Dynamic Stress Distribution Surrounding a Running Crack—A Photoelastic Analysis," NRL Report No. 4935, 1957.
56. Christie, D. G., "An Investigation of Cracks and Stress Waves in Glass and Plastic by High-Speed Photography," *Journal of the Society of Glass Technology*, Vol. 36 (1952), pp. 74–89.
57. Jones, O. and A. Ellis, "An Experimental Study of Longitudinal Strain Pulse Propagation in Wide Rectangular Bars," Hyde Laboratory, C. I. T. Report No. E-108.15, 1961.
58. Daniel, I. M. and A. J. Durelli, "Photothermoelastic Analysis of Bonded Propellant Grains," *Proceedings of the Society for Experimental Stress Analysis*, Vol. 18, No. 1, pp. 97–104.
59. Gerard, G., "Progress in Photothermoelasticity," *Proceedings of the International Symposium on Photoelasticity*. New York: Pergamon Press.

6-9 Problems

6-1 Prove that a crossed-parallel polariscope gives a light field.

6-2 Develop an equation comparable to Eq. (6-3) for a crossed-crossed polariscope.

6-3 A single quarter-wave plate is placed between a polarizer and analyzer with its axes at 45 deg with respect to the axis of polarization. Show that the amount of light passed by the analyzer is independent of the alignment of the analyzer's polarizing axis.

6-4 In Fig. 6-21, (a) shows a photoelastic model loaded as a beam with constant-moment section. If dark field is used, the fringe pattern in the constant-moment section appears as shown in (b). The moment in this section is 42 in.-lb. What is the stress-optical coefficient (K) of this material?

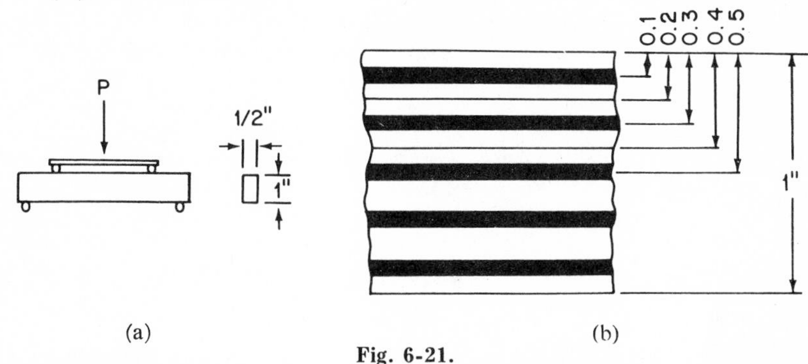

Fig. 6-21.

6-5 The photoelastic material in Prob. 6-4 has a modulus of 500,000 psi. What is the figure of merit of this material?

6-6 The tensile specimen shown in Fig. 6-22 was analyzed in a light-field photoelastic polariscope. Under no load the specimen was all light. The load was increased slowly until it was 500 lb. During the loading the following observations were made: the area far from the two grooves went *from* light at $P = 0$, to dark, to light, to dark, and back to light at $P = 500$ lb. This area is numbered 2, indicating that it returned from dark to light twice. (a) What is the photoelastic constant (K) for this material? (b) What is the stress-concentration factor for this discontinuity based on the stress in the gross section (i.e., area far removed from the grooves)? (c) What is the stress-concentration factor for this discontinuity based on the average stress in the *net* section (i.e., area between the base of the grooves)?

$d = 0.50$ in., $t = 0.25$ in., $D = 1.00$ in.

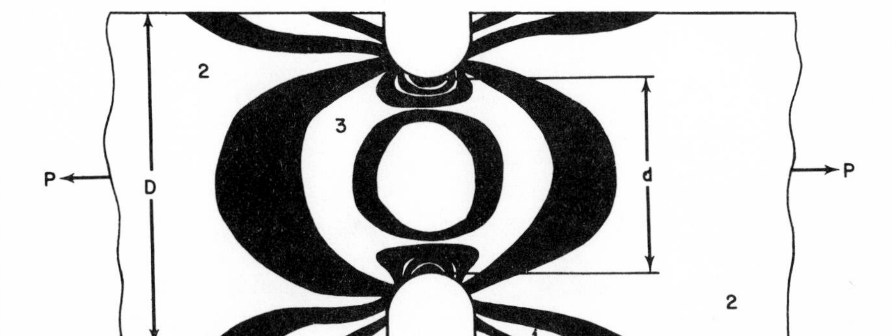

Fig. 6-22.

6-7 What is the value of the stress-concentration factor associated with the notched beam shown in Fig. 6-13?

6-8 Using polar co-ordinate paper, make a plot showing stress variation around the inside surface of the hole in the disk shown in Fig. 6-12.

6-9 The sketch of equipment setup, data sheet, and tracings of isoclinic and fringe patterns taken during the performance of Laboratory Experiment 6-3 are given below. Write the report asked for.

Equipment Setup:

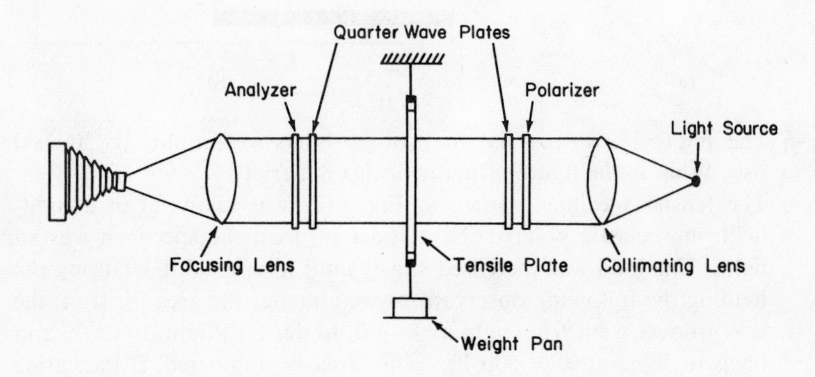

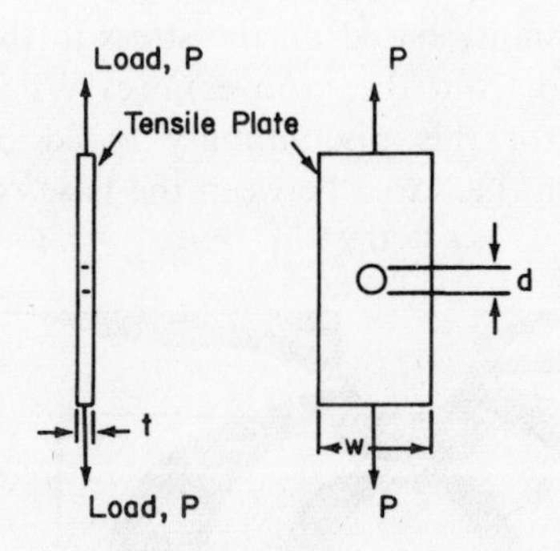

Fig. 6-23.

Data Sheet:

$d = 0.97$ in.
$W = 5.0$ in.
$t = 0.5$ in
$p = 11.81$ lb

$$K = \frac{t(S_1 - S_2)}{n}$$

$$K = 1.0$$

Isoclinics and Fringe Pattern:

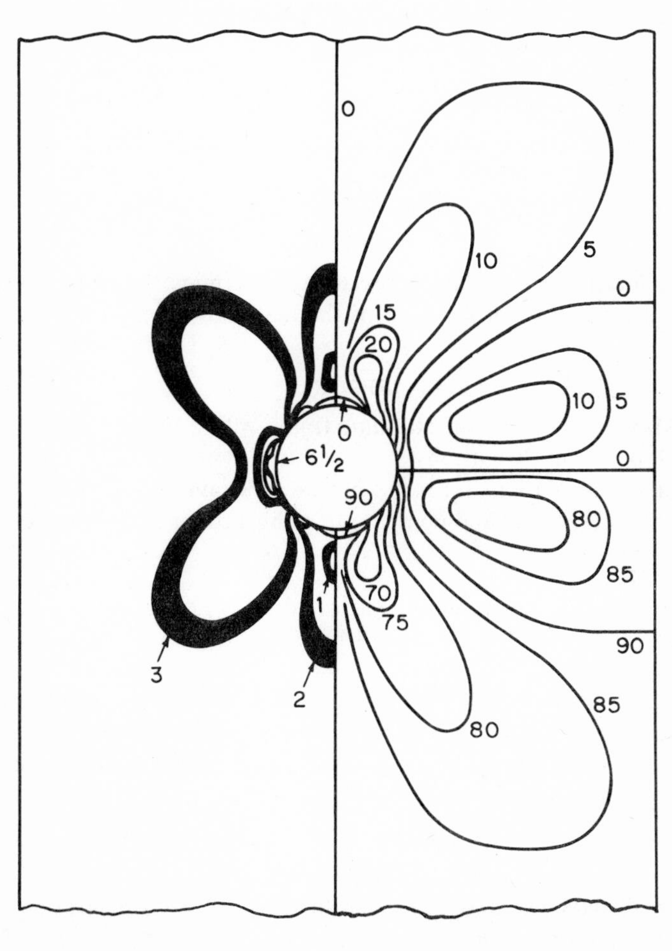

Fig. 6-24.

6-10 Suggested laboratory experiments

Experiment 6-1 Determination of stress-optical coefficient

EQUIPMENT NECESSARY

1. Photoelastic polariscope with viewing screen.
2. Provision for tracing and/or photographing fringe patterns.
3. Straining frame in which applied force, moment, or strain can be measured.
4. Beams of several photoelastic materials.

If a reflective polariscope is available, the plastic may be bonded as a surface coating to a metal beam.

PROCEDURE

Take and record all data necessary to determine the stress-optical or strain-optical coefficient for each of the materials furnished.

REPORT

1. Make a sketch of the straining frame with a model in place. Give all pertinent dimensions.
2. Show calculations for stress-optical or strain-optical coefficient.
3. Tabulate results and compare to published values where possible.

Experiment 6-2 Photoelastic determination of stress-concentration factor

EQUIPMENT NECESSARY

1. Items 1, 2, and 3 from Laboratory Experiment 6-1.
2. A photoelastic model, or a metal model with a photoelastic coating, containing a discontinuity.

PROCEDURE

Take all data necessary to determine the stress-concentration factor associated with the given discontinuity.

REPORT

1. Show all computations.
2. Compare the result obtained to that available from theory or other experimental studies.

Experiment 6-3 Determination of principal stress directions and maximum shear-stress magnitudes

EQUIPMENT NECESSARY

1. Items 1, 2, and 3 from Laboratory Experiment 6-1.
2. A suitable photoelastic model.*

PROCEDURE

1. Using white light, take all data necessary for plotting isoclinic lines on the model furnished.
2. Using a monochromatic light source, take all data necessary for plotting the isoshear lines on the model furnished.
3. Determine the stress-optical coefficient of the model material if this has not already been done in Laboratory Experiment 6-1.

REPORT

1. Furnish the following plots.
   a. Isoclinics (give values in degrees from horizontal).
   b. Stress trajectories.
   c. Isoshear lines (give values in psi).
   d. Maximum principal stress around the inside surface of the hole.
2. Discussion. Compare results to those available in references, to those obtained by other experimental methods, and to those predicted from theory.

---

* Any interesting shape can be used; however, the authors use a urethane rubber model in the form of a flat-plate tensile specimen containing a centrally located hole. This is the same model used in Laboratory Experiment 1-2: the line pattern applied for the moiré fringe method does not interfere with the photoelastic pattern.

CHAPTER 7

Stress Analysis by Photoelastic Coatings

7-1 Surface-coating techniques

The idea of using photoelasticity to study the surface stresses on actual parts of any shape is not new. In 1930, Mesnager, working in France, proposed and investigated the use of photoelastic material bonded to the polished surface of a metal prototype. Other experimentalists working in Germany and France attempted to use the same method during the 1930's. These early attempts did not succeed for two reasons: first, the stress optical coefficient (K) of the plastics used was high. For this reason, insufficient fringes were developed. Second, it was difficult to bond the photoelastic plastic to the metal in such a way that the plastic was subjected to the same surface strains as existed in the metal prototype.

With the development of more sensitive photoelastic plastics and better adhesives, Mesnager's idea appeared more promising and was used by several investigators in the 1950's; see Refs. [12] and [13] at the end of

Chap. 6. Zandman (see Ref. [12] at the end of Chap. 6) has continued to develop specialized equipment and techniques to be used with this method of photoelasticity. Specialized equipment and plastics are now commercially available.*

The polariscope used in this work consists of the same basic elements as are used in other photoelastic studies, but they are arranged in a slightly different form. Figure 7-1 is a diagram of one possible polariscope

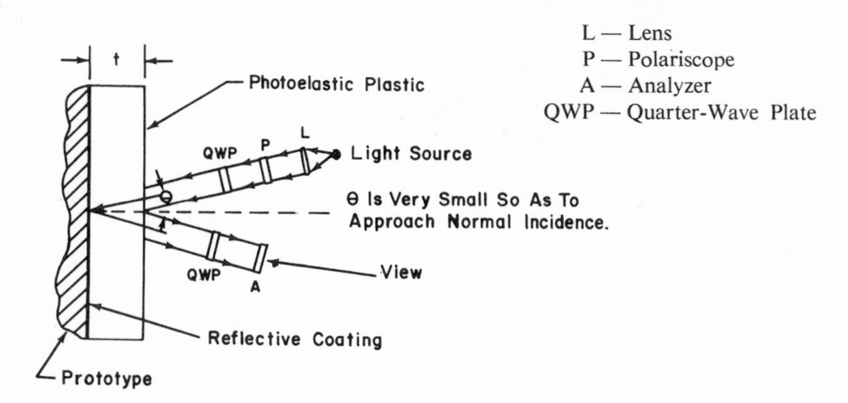

Fig. 7-1. Reflective polariscope.

arrangement for use in surface-coating studies. Figure 7-2 is a photograph of such an instrument. T. Slot [1] describes a reflective polariscope which is particularly suited for photographing patterns.

The prototype to be analyzed is first polished or painted to make the surface of interest reflective. The photoelastic plastic may be applied by bonding sheet plastic to the surface or by brushing on a liquid, which is then hardened by heating.

The basic equations, previously developed, which relate relative retardation to light transmission and relative retardation to stress difference still apply. That is, first, light transmitted through the plastic equals the background light when the relative retardation (dt) is

$$dt = \frac{2\pi n}{\omega}, \tag{6-6}$$

and second, relative retardation (dt) is related to principal stress difference by the equation

$$dt = \frac{d}{Cv}(S_1 - S_2). \tag{6-5}$$

* The Instruments Division, The Budd Company; and Photoelastic, Incorporated.

L — Lens
P — Polariscope
A — Analyzer
QWP — Quarter-Wave Plate

Fig. 7-2. Reflective polariscope (quarter-wave plate out of field for isoclinic study). (*Courtesy of Instruments Division, The Budd Company.*)

However, in surface-coating work the light transmitted by the photoelastic plastic passes through the plastic twice (see Fig. 7-1). Hence, the length of the effective light path is twice the thickness of the plastic coating ($2t$). Replacing (d) by ($2t$) in Eq. (6-5), and combining these two equations, we obtain

$$(S_1 - S_2) = \frac{Cv\, 2\pi n}{2t\omega},$$

or (7-1)

$$(S_1 - S_2)_p = \frac{Kn}{2t},$$

in which the principal stress difference $(S_1 - S_2)$ has been subscripted p to emphasize that this is the magnitude of principal stress difference *in the plastic coating*. In photoelastic coating studies we are interested in the magnitude of stress in the prototype to which the photoelastic coating is bonded. Hence, we first rewrite Eq. (7-1) in terms of strains. The plastic coating will be in a state of plane stress only when there is no strain gradient tangent to the interface (between plastic and test piece) on the test-piece surface, when the plastic and base have the same μ, and when no curvature of this surface is produced during the straining. Hence, when a strain gradient exists or when surface curvature is produced by straining, the analysis that follows is not correct. Errors associated with those effects and methods of correcting such errors are discussed later in this section. For the plane stress situation (a free surface) and with the plastic coating stressed within its linear elastic region,

$$\epsilon_{1p} = \frac{S_{1p}}{E_p} - \mu_p \frac{S_{2p}}{E_p}$$

and (7-2)

$$\epsilon_{2p} = \frac{S_{2p}}{E_p} - \mu \frac{S_{1p}}{E_p},$$

in which E_p and μ_p are the elastic modulus and "Poisson's ratio" of the plastic coating. Substituting these two equations into Eq. (7-1), we obtain

$$(\epsilon_1 - \epsilon_2)_p = \frac{Kn}{2t} \frac{(1 + \mu_p)}{E_p}. \tag{7-3}$$

Now, since the plastic is bonded to the prototype surface, we can write

$$(\epsilon_1 - \epsilon_2)_B = (\epsilon_1 - \epsilon_2)_p, \tag{7-4}$$

in which the subscript B is used to indicate the base or prototype to which the plastic is bonded. Substituting Eq. (7-4) into Eq. (7-3), we obtain

$$(\epsilon_1 - \epsilon_2)_B = \frac{Kn}{2t} \times \frac{(1 + \mu_p)}{E_p}. \tag{7-5}$$

Equation (7-5) enables us to determine the principal strain difference at the surface of the prototype in terms of the observed fringe pattern, the thickness of the plastic coating, the stress-optical coefficient of the plastic coating, and the elastic properties of the plastic coating. Since K, μ_p, and E_p are all associated with the plastic coating, a single constant (Q) equal to $K(1 + \mu_p)/E_p$ can be given for each plastic. Then

$$(\epsilon_1 - \epsilon_2)_B = \frac{Qn}{2t}. \tag{7-6}$$

Now, if the surface strains are in the *elastic region*, we may rewrite Eqs. (7-5) and (7-6) in terms of principal stress difference. Thus:

$$\epsilon_{1_B} = \frac{S_{1_B}}{E_B} - \mu_B \frac{S_{2_B}}{E_B},$$

and

$$\epsilon_{2_B} = \frac{S_{2_B}}{E_B} - \mu_B \frac{S_{1_B}}{E_B}.$$

Substituting these into Eqs. (7-5) and (7-6), we obtain

$$(S_1 - S_2)_B = \frac{Kn}{2t} \times \frac{1 + \mu_p}{1 + \mu_B} \times \frac{E_B}{E_p} = \frac{Qn}{2t} \frac{E_B}{(1 + \mu_B)}. \tag{7-7}$$

As before, we may use either monochromatic or white light. As in other applications of the photoelastic method, the directions of the principal stresses are usually determined by studying the isoclinics using a plane polariscope with a white light source. Fringe lines are usually observed using a circular polariscope. If monochromatic light is used, the fringes appear as dark and light lines. If white light is used, the fringes appear as monochromatic lines, i.e., lines of constant color.

In photoelastic surface-coating work the strains in the photoelastic pattern are equal to the surface strains in the loaded prototype. This eliminates one of the objections raised against testing photoelastic models —that strains and deflections are often much larger in the model than in the prototype. However, as a result, the number of fringes formed is generally less in surface-coating work than in other applications of the photoelastic method. For this reason, white light is often used for fringe determination in this method. By preparing a calibration piece (such as a cantilever beam on which a sheet of the photoelastic plastic has been bonded) the color fringes associated with a particular value of principal strain difference can be determined. Then by comparison of the colored fringes on the test piece to those on the calibration specimen, the values of principal strain difference at points on the test piece can be established. At low fringe orders this permits greater resolution of fringe orders than can be obtained by the use of monochromatic light. However, beyond three fringe orders the recurring colors fade together, and the pattern can not be interpreted.

Of course, compensation* can be, and is, used with either monochromatic or white light to aid in accurate determination of fringe order.

In the photoelastic coating method the determination of the individual values of the principal stresses (S_1 and S_2) is most often accomplished by

---

* See p. 314.

using the oblique-incident method.* If the light vector is rotated about a principal stress axis, the equation relating fringe order and principal stress difference is

$$S_{1_p} - S_{2_p} \cos^2 \phi = \frac{Kn_o}{2t/\cos \phi} \tag{7-8}$$

(plastic assumed to be rotated relative to the light vector about the #1 axis; see Fig. 7-3), in which n_o is the fringe order obtained under oblique

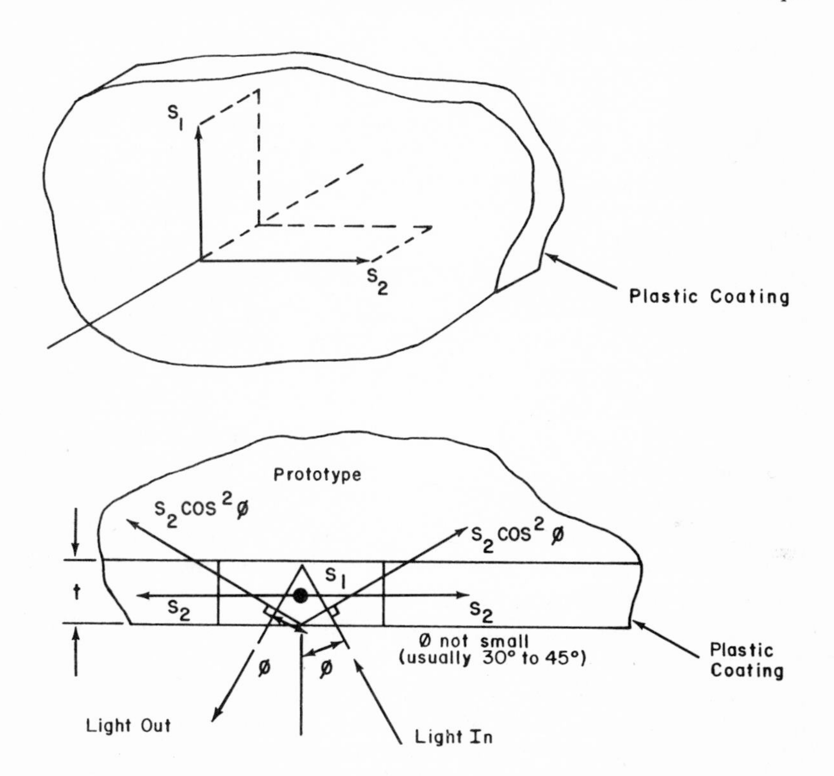

Fig. 7-3. Reflective polariscope—oblique incidence.

incidence. Combining Eqs. (7-1) and (7-8), we obtain

$$S_{2_p} = \frac{K}{2t} \frac{(n - n_o \cos \phi)}{(\cos^2 \phi - 1)},$$

and (7-9)

$$S_{1_p} = \frac{K}{2t} \frac{(n \cos^2 \phi - n_o \cos \phi)}{(\cos^2 \phi - 1)}.$$

* See p. 320.

As before, these expressions may be written in terms of principal strains and then in terms of principal stresses in the prototype.

$$S_{1_B} = \frac{K}{2t(1 - \cos^2\phi)} \times \frac{E_B}{(1 - \mu_B)^2 E_p} [n_o \cos\phi(1 - \mu_p)(1 + \mu_B) - n\cos^2\phi(1 + \mu_B\mu_p) + n(\mu_p - \mu_B)],$$

and (7-10)

$$S_{2_B} = \frac{K}{2t(1 - \cos^2\phi)} \times \frac{E_B}{(1 - \mu_B)^2 E_p} [n_o \cos\phi(1 - \mu_p)(1 + \mu_B) + n\cos^2\phi(\mu_p - \mu_B) - n(1 - \mu_p\mu_B)].$$

In surface-coating studies separation of principal stresses by oblique incidence are subject to the same difficulties and limitations discussed in connection with a photoelastic model study.* In addition, oblique-incidence measurements may be very difficult or impossible in regions having considerable variation in surface contour, and since reflection with large angles of incidence produces some relative retardation, it will be necessary to take oblique-incidence measurements during loaded and unloaded conditions so that fringe patterns may be corrected for this effect. Figure 7-4 is a photograph of a refective polariscope with an oblique-incidence attachment.

Since the thickness (t) of the plastic coating is involved in all of these equations for stress magnitudes, it is apparent that (t) must be known with accuracy. If the plastic coating is applied by bonding on a sheet of plastic, the thickness may be measured before the sheet is applied. If the plastic coating is applied by brushing on a liquid, the thickness must be determined by using a coating-thickness gage.

Since the number of fringes formed (n) per unit of stress difference ($S_1 - S_2$) is directly proportional to the thickness of plastic coating applied, the temptation is to use whatever thickness of coating is necessary to yield the desired number of fringes and hence the desired resolution. Unfortunately, use of too great a thickness of coating will yield only an incorrect result with high resolution. There are two reasons for this: first, the plastic coating reinforces the surface to which it is bonded and, hence, changes the strain field to be measured.† Obviously, the importance of this effect depends upon the size and modulus of the item to be coated, the thickness and modulus of the coating material, and whether the coating is in tension, flexure, etc. In many cases this effect will be

---

* See p. 320.

† This instrument effect on the quantity it is to measure is a basic problem which must be considered when any measuring device is used; for example, see discussion of strain-gage reinforcing effect on p. 217.

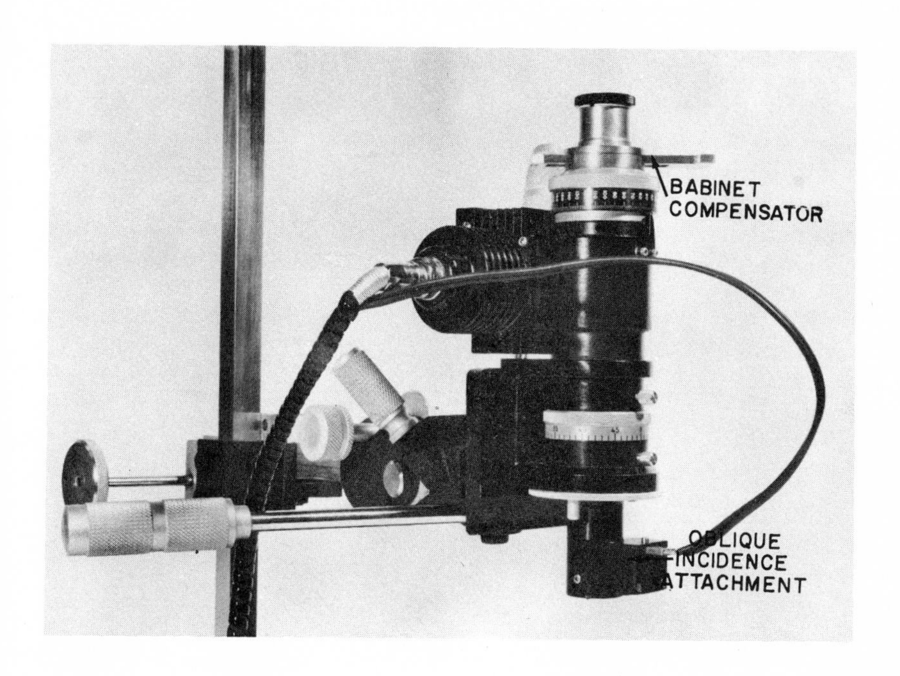

Fig. 7-4. Reflective polariscope with oblique-incidence attachment. (*Courtesy of Instruments Division, The Budd Company.*)

negligible; in other cases, it may be possible to calculate the effect and apply appropriate corrections to the results, but in other cases involving complicated loading and shape this factor may limit accuracy of the method. F. Zandman, S. S. Redner, and E. I. Riegner [2] discuss this reinforcing effect for several loading cases with various materials. Correction factors are presented in graphical form.

The second effect of coating thickness is related to the assumption made on p. 341 and used in deriving the relationships between fringe patterns and surface strain—namely, that the plastic coating is in a state of plane stress. Under certain conditions, a state of plane stress will not exist in a surface coating of finite thickness, and, in general, the departure from the plane-stress condition (and hence the error in our previous analysis) will be directly dependent upon coating thickness. Specifically, if surface curvature is produced by the loading, there will be a stress gradient in the plastic coating, perpendicular to the surface, and the fringe pattern observed will be related to the average stress in the plastic and not to the strain values at the interface between the plastic and the base to which it is bonded. Also, wherever there is a strain gradient tangent to the interface surface, there will be a strain gradient through the plastic coating, and in this case the fringe pattern will be dependent upon the strain gradient along the interface as well as upon the strain at the interface. This last case is illustrated in Fig. 7-5. A large strain gradient

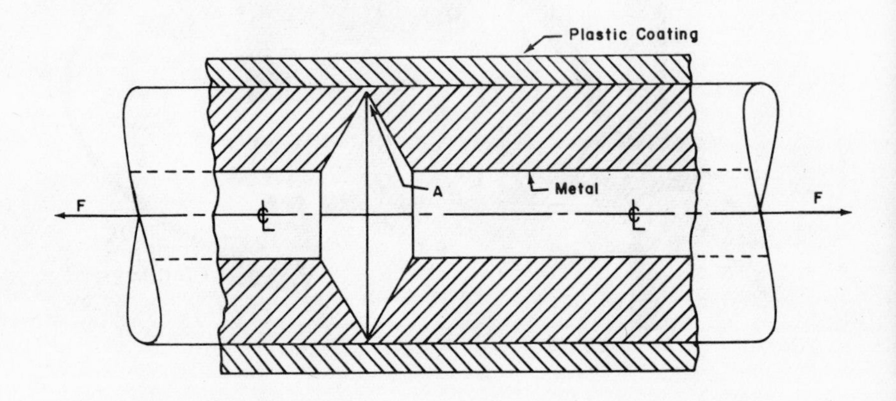

Fig. 7-5. Effect of surface-strain gradient on the stress field in a photoelastic coating.

exists along the interface (test item to plastic coating) in the neighborhood of point *A*. Because of shear traction at the interface, the strain pattern on the metal surface is transferred to the plastic at the interface, but this pattern varies progressively from interface to outside surface, and the fringe pattern is dependent upon the average pattern through the thickness of the plastic coating.

Unfortunately, in many problems of interest, surfaces do undergo curvature with loading, and very often points of greatest interest are points of high stress gradient. J. Duffy, T. C. Lee, and C. Mylonas ([3] and [4]) have made an extensive analysis of the errors introduced by both surface curvature and tangential strain gradient, and they demonstrate that the errors can be large. They have developed factors for the correction of observed fringe patterns; however, the required corrections depend upon the amount of surface curvature and strain gradient—both unknown quantities in the general case. This means that additional analytical and/or experimental work will be required. D. Post and F. Zandman [5] have investigated the error produced by strain gradient experimentally, and Zandman [6] suggests that any error due to surface-coating-thickness effects can be isolated and eliminated in the following way. After a fringe pattern has been plotted, the photoelastic coating thickness can be decreased by machining, or increased by bonding on a second coating on top of the first and the fringe pattern replotted. If the change in fringe order is such as to show that fringe order is linearly proportional to thickness, no measurable error is introduced by coating-thickness effects. If this is not the case, then the test must be repeated with a thinner coating, and presumably the effect of this coating will need to be checked in the same way.

Clearly, this procedure greatly increases the amount of experimental effort. In the limit, the thickness of coating necessary to reduce thickness-effect errors to a tolerable level may result in such low maximum fringe order that the accuracy of results may be limited by the resolution of fringe order. E. E. Day [7] considered this very problem (use of a thin plastic coating) and used fringe multiplication (see p. 316 for a discussion of this technique) to increase the resolution of the method. The photoelastic surface-coating method has been applied to a number of structures for static-stress analysis; see Refs. [8], [9], and [10]. This method has also been applied to dynamic problems (see Ref. [11]); to thermal-stress problems (see Ref. [12]); and for the construction of strain and stress gages (see the following section).

7-2 Photoelastic strain gages

It is possible to make strain gages using the photoelastic principal, and several gages of this type are commercially available.*

Imagine a strip of photoelastic plastic laid along the length of a cantilever beam and bonded to it, as shown in Fig. 7-6a. If the beam were then loaded as shown in Fig. 7-6b, the strain in the plastic would vary linearly as shown in Fig. 7-6c. If this loading is done at an elevated temperature and the temperature is then lowered while the load remains constant, this linear strain pattern will be "frozen" in the plastic strip. If such a strip, containing frozen residual strains, were viewed in a polariscope, a series of equally spaced fringe lines would be visible, as shown in Fig. 7-6d. (An alternate method of freezing in the desired linear strain

---

* Baldwin-Lima-Hamilton Corporation, Electronics & Instruments Division, Waltham 54, Mass. The Budd Company, P. O. Box 245, Phoenixville, Pa.

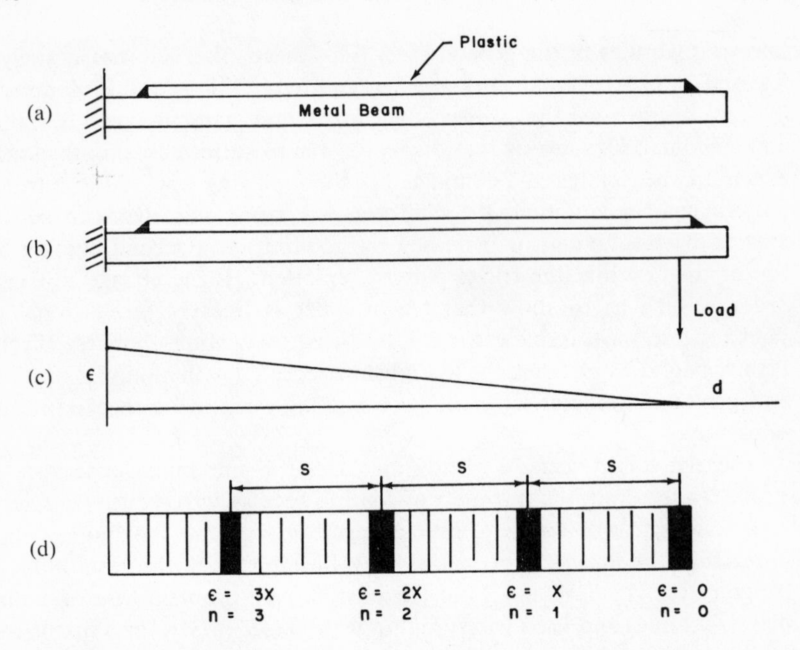

Fig. 7-6. Frozen strain pattern in a uniaxial photoelastic strain gage.

pattern, and the one actually used to produce a large number of such strips simultaneously, is outlined by G. U. Oppel [13].)

Photoelastic plastic strips containing a frozen residual strain pattern in which the strains vary linearly along the length are silvered on one surface and covered with a polarizing film on the other for use as strain gages. See Fig. 7-7. The gage may be used to measure uniaxial surface strains by bonding, silvered side down, the gage to the surface of interest. When lighted from above, the light is polarized, passed through the photoelastic plastic, reflected, returned through the plastic, passed through the polarizer, and viewed. Straining will cause the residual fringes (colored bands when viewed in white light) to move, and the magnitude of strain can be related to the amount of fringe movement. Figure 7-8a shows a plan view of such a gage mounted on the surface of a test piece; the applied strain is zero, and the fringes shown are the residual pattern. Figure 7-8b shows the effect of an applied tensile strain. The strain at every point in the plastic is ($\epsilon_{\text{residual}} + \epsilon_{\text{applied}}$), and hence the fringes move as shown. The strain per fringe-order (X μin./in./fringe) is easily computed from the calibration conditions, Fig. 7-6. When this value is known, the applied strain can be computed as $(\Delta/S) \times X$ μin./in. Figure

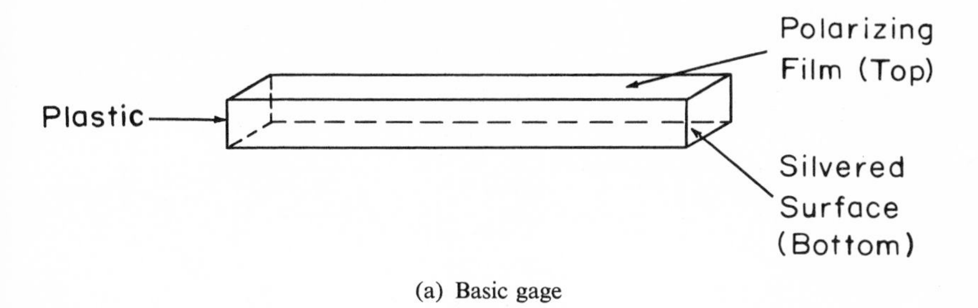

(a) Basic gage

(b) Commercially available type

Fig. 7-7. Uniaxial photoelastic strain gage.

7-8c shows the fringe motion associated with an applied compressive strain.

Photoelastic strain gages which indicate directions and magnitudes of principal strains are also available. These gages are made of a suitable photoelastic plastic, formed in a thin disk with a central hole. The plastic is silvered on one surface, covered with a polarizing film on the opposite surface, and bonded around the periphery, silvered side down, to the test surface. See Fig. 7-9.

Since the distribution of maximum shearing stress in a ring loaded around the circumference can be determined analytically (the Kirsch solution for stress distribution around a hole in an infinite plate is used as an approximation. See Refs. [13] and [14].) for any combination of applied principal stress, the fringe pattern associated with any combination of applied principal stresses can be developed. That is,

$$(S_1 - S_2)_p = \frac{Kn}{2t},$$

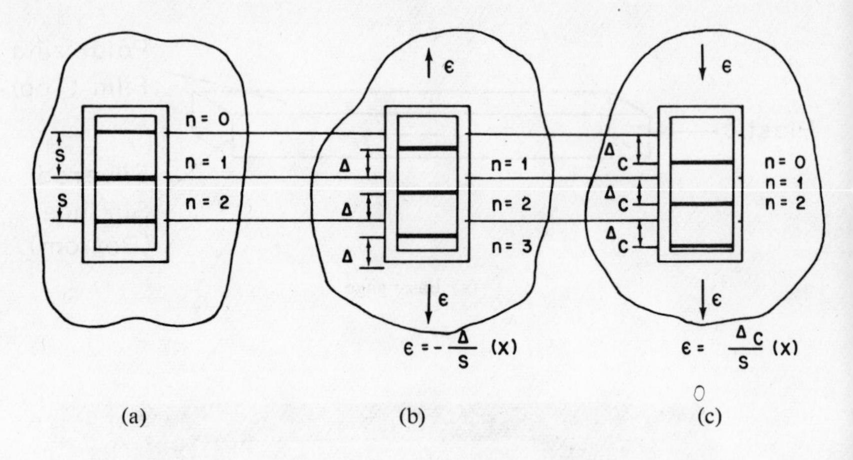

Fig. 7-8. Reading strains.

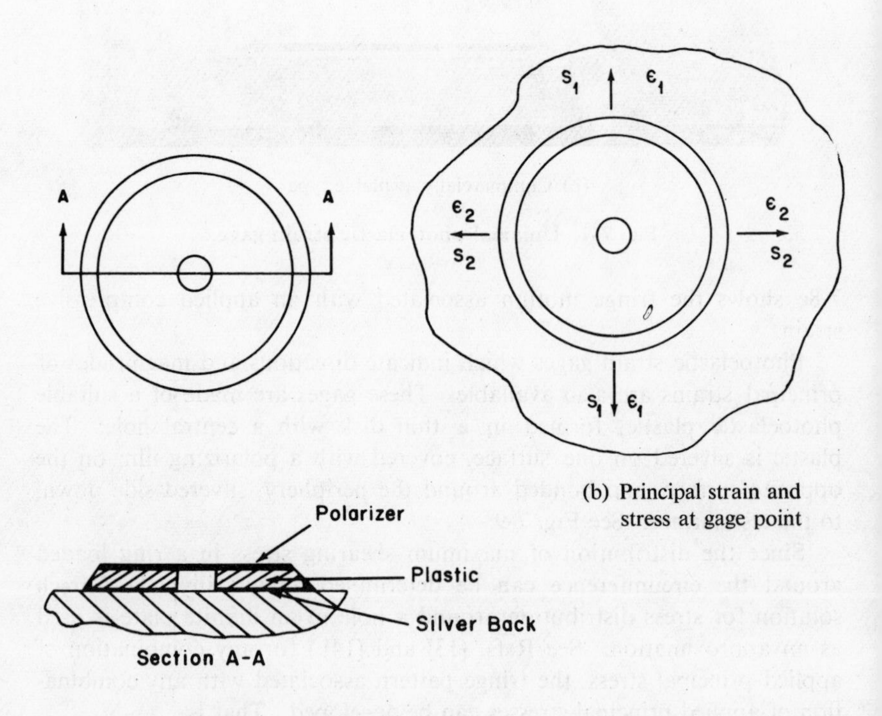

(a) Gage construction

(b) Principal strain and stress at gage point

Fig. 7-9. Biaxial photoelastic strain gage.

and the maximum shearing stress

$$S_{12_p} = \left(\frac{S_1 - S_2}{2}\right)_p,$$

so

$$S_{12_p} = \frac{Kn}{4t}. \tag{7-11}$$

Values of S_{12} can be computed at all points in the ring for a given combination of applied principal stresses (S_1 and S_2). Then by using Eq. (7-11) the fringe value can be computed at all points, and the fringe pattern developed by the applied principal stresses is thus established.

If such a gage is mounted on the surface of a test piece and the test piece is then stressed, the magnitude and directions of the principal stresses in the test piece at the gage location can be determined by comparing the fringe pattern developed to fringe patterns developed for known combinations of applied principal stresses. It can be shown that the axes of symmetry of the fringe pattern always coincide with the applied principal stress axes; hence, the directions of principal stress are readily established. Figure 7-10 shows the fringe patterns associated with a few selected principal stress combinations.

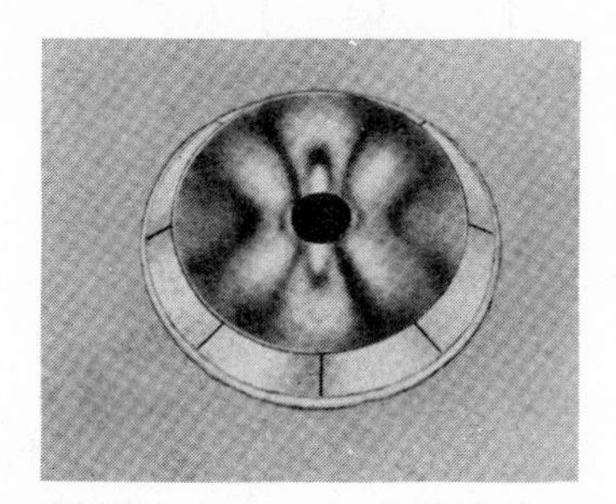

(a) Photograph of actual fringe pattern

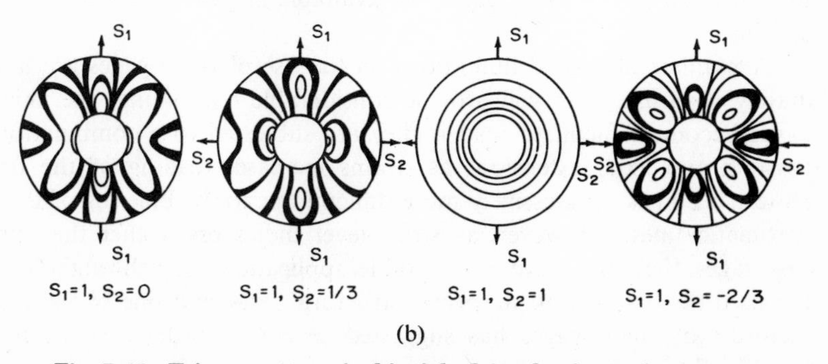

(b)

Fig. 7-10. Fringe pattern in biaxial photoelastic strain gages.

In gages of this type it is possible to "freeze" in a residual fringe pattern consisting of a series of concentric circles. This is accomplished by loading the gage in a uniform biaxial stress field at an elevated temperature and cooling under load. When a gage having these residual ring fringes is bonded to a test surface and stressed, the magnitude of the applied principal stresses can be related to the extent of the distortion of these ring fringes. See Fig. 7-11. As before, the principal stress axes coincide with the axes of symmetry of the resultant fringe pattern.

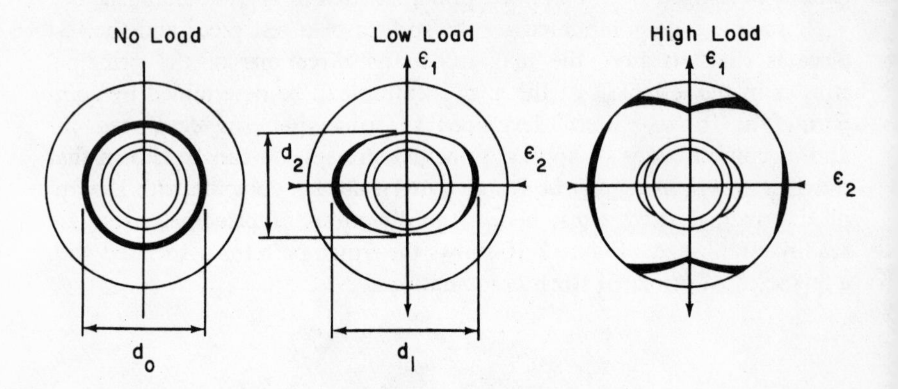

Fig. 7-11. Biaxial photoelastic strain gage with a residual fringe pattern.

Uniaxial photoelastic gages are available in gage lengths of from $\frac{3}{4}$ to 3 in., and under favorable conditions (good lighting, strain limited so that the colored fringes remain reasonably distinct; use of monochromatic light would improve readability) have a resolution of less than 100 μin./in. Biaxial photoelastic strain gages are available in gage diameters as small as $\frac{3}{8}$ in.

A number of special limitations on the use of these gages are immediately obvious. They will provide considerable reinforcing; the uniaxial gages become difficult to read if they are subjected to a combination of twisting and axial extension; as strains increase, reading of the fringe pattern becomes progressively more difficult due to the blurring of the isochromatic lines. However, as strain-level indicators, rather than precision gages, they may have considerable application. J. Schwaighofer [15] has used the biaxial type in several structural tests, and one of the manufacturers of these gages has suggested several transducer applications. See Fig. 7-12.

AS A SAFETY DEVICE

As shown here, two gages have been applied to the columns of a hydraulic press. The gages indicate the magnitude of strain on each column and show and measure any unequal load on the columns. They also indicate any overload. In the case of yielding, the fringes do not come back to zero. Since zero and sensitivity are independent of time, periodical checks will indicate the safety of the structure (PhotoStress plastic, applied to the concrete block in the press, shows the stress pattern in the block under a 5,000-lb compression load).

AS A PRESSURE GAGE

The gage shown is bonded to a pressure diaphragm. It indicates pressure values in psi.

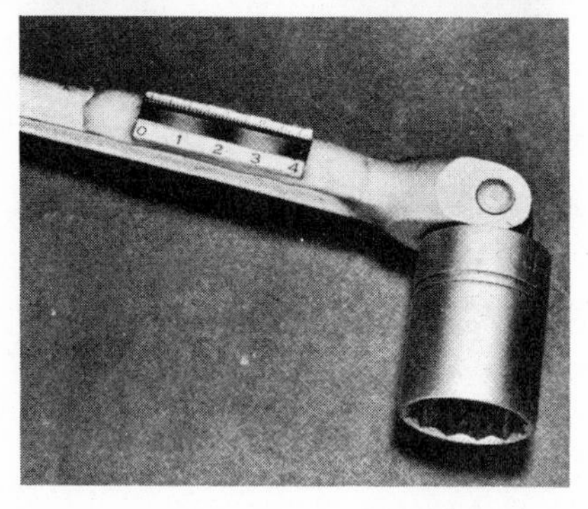

AS A TORQUE WRENCH

As shown here, an ordinary wrench was converted to a torque measuring wrench by bonding the PHOTOSTRESS GAGE to its handle. The wrench is calibrated in inch-lbs. torque. Other tools can be instrumented in a similar way.

Fig. 7-12. Transducer applications of photoelastic strain gages. (*Courtesy of Instruments Division, The Budd Company.*)

Zandman [16] has suggested the use of the photoelastic method for the construction of a "stress" gage. A "stress" gage is defined as a gage which produces a signal or reading which is related to the stress along a prescribed axis.* The basic feature of this gage is that the light passes through the photoelastic gage on a path which is parallel to the surface on which the gage is bonded. See Fig. 7-13. Since the fringe pattern developed depends upon the difference of the principal stresses in a plane perpendicular to the transmitted light, the observed fringes are related to $(S_z - S_y)_p$ by the basic photoelastic equation.

$$(S_z - S_y)_p = \frac{Kn}{d}.$$

But since $S_{y_p} = 0$, this reduces to

$$S_{z_p} = \frac{Kn}{d}.$$

Zandman [16] shows how the stress in the plastic (S_{z_p}) can be related to stress on the surface of test piece (S_{z_B}) by using the stress-strain relationships and the elastic properties of both the plastic and the test piece (E_p, μ_p, E_B, μ_B), and investigates several other forms in addition to the disk shape shown in Fig. 7-13.

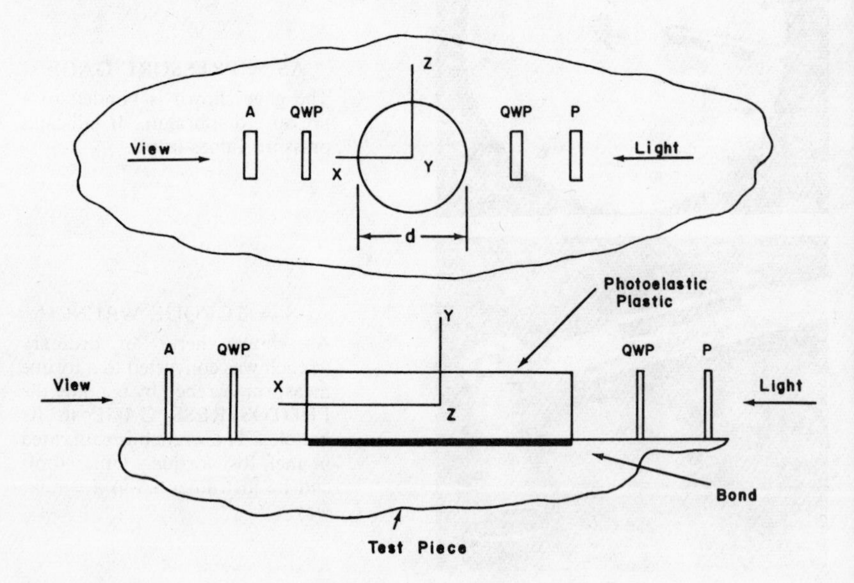

Fig. 7-13. Photoelastic stress gage.

* See Sect. 5-3e for a discussion of a variable-resistance-type stress gage.

7-3 References listed in Chapter 7

1. Slot, T., "Reflection Polariscope for Photography of Photoelastic Coatings," *Experimental Mechanics*, Vol. 2, No. 2 (Feb. 1962), pp. 41–47.
2. Zandman, F., S. S. Redner, and E. I. Riegner, "Reinforcing Effect of Birefringent Coatings," *Experimental Mechanics*, Vol. 2, No. 2 (Feb. 1962), pp. 55–64.
3. Duffy, J., "Effects of the Thickness of Birefringent Coatings," *Proceedings of the Society for Experimental Stress Analysis*, Vol. 18, No. 1, pp. 74–82.
4. Lee, T. C., C. Mylonas, and J. Duffy, "Thickness Effects in Birefringent Coatings with Radial Symmetry," *Proceedings of the Society for Experimental Stress Analysis*, Vol. 18, No. 2, pp. 134–42.
5. Post, D. and F. Zandman, "Accuracy of Birefringent-Coating Method for Coatings of Arbitrary Thickness," *Proceedings of the Society for Experimental Stress Analysis*, Vol. 18, No. 1, pp. 21–32.
6. Zandman, F., "Discussion of Thickness Effects in Birefringent Coatings with Radial Symmetry," Ref. [4], above, *Proceedings of the Society for Experimental Stress Analysis*, Vol. 18, No. 2, pp. 141–2.
7. Day, E. E., A. S. Kobayaski, and C. N. Larson, "Fringe Multiplication and Thickness Effects in Birefringent Coating," *Experimental Mechanics*, Vol. 2, No. 4 (Apr. 1962), pp. 115–21.
8. Smith, C. R. and F. Zandman, "PhotoStress Plastic for Measuring Stress Distribution Around Rivets," *Proceedings of the Society for Experimental Stress Analysis*, Vol. 17, No. 1, pp. 23–24.
9. Zandman, F., "Stress Analysis of a Guided Missile Tail Section with Photoelastic Coating," *Proceedings of the Society for Experimental Stress Analysis*, Vol. 17, No. 2, pp. 135–50.
10. Zandman, F., M. Watter, S. S. Redner, "Stress Analysis of Rocket-Motor Case by Birefringent-Coating Method," *Experimental Mechanics*, Vol. 2, No. 7 (July 1962), pp. 215–21.
11. Duffy, J. and T. C. Lee, "Measurement of Surface Strain by Means of Bonded Birefringent Strips," *Proceedings of the Society for Experimental Stress Analysis*, Vol. 12, No. 2, pp. 109–12.
12. Zandman, F., S. S. Redner, and D. Post, "Photoelastic-Coating Analysis in Thermal Fields," *Proceedings of the International Symposium on Photoelasticity*, Pergamon Press, New York.
13. Oppel, G. U., "Photoelastic Strain Gages," *Proceedings of the Society for Experimental Stress Analysis*, Vol. 18, No. 1, pp. 65–73.
14. Timoshinko, S. and J. N. Goodier, *Theory of Elasticity*. New York: (1951) McGraw-Hill.
15. Schwaighofer, J., "Application of Photoelastic Strain Gages," *Proceedings of the Society for Experimental Stress Analysis*, Vol. 18, No. 2, pp. 198–202.
16. Zandman, F., "Concepts of the Photoelastic Stress Gage," *Experimental Mechanics*, Vol. 2, No. 8 (Aug. 1962), pp. 225–33.

7-4 Problems

7-1 Figure 7-14 shows the isoclinic and fringe pattern obtained on a part coated with photostress plastic. Find the magnitude of the maximum shearing stress in the base at point X. Show the orientation of the plane on which the shearing stress is a maximum.

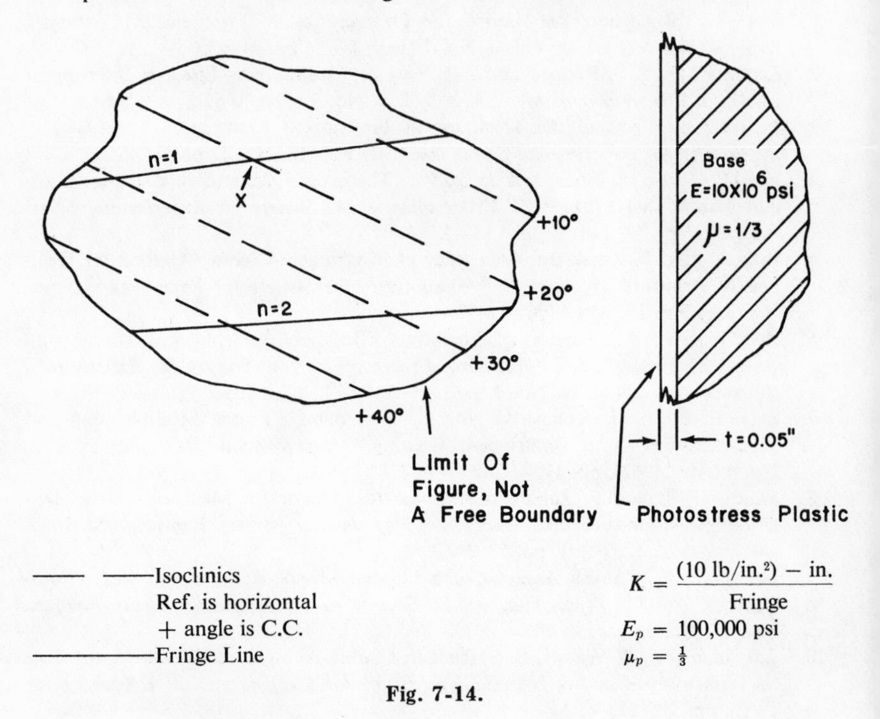

Fig. 7-14.

7-2 The sketch of equipment setup, data sheet, and tracings of isoclinic and fringe patterns taken during the performance of Laboratory Experiment 7-1 are given. Write the report asked for.

Equipment Setup:

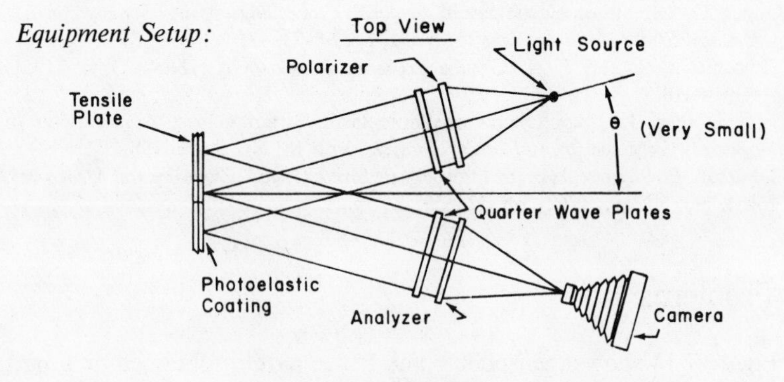

Fig. 7-15.

Data Sheet:

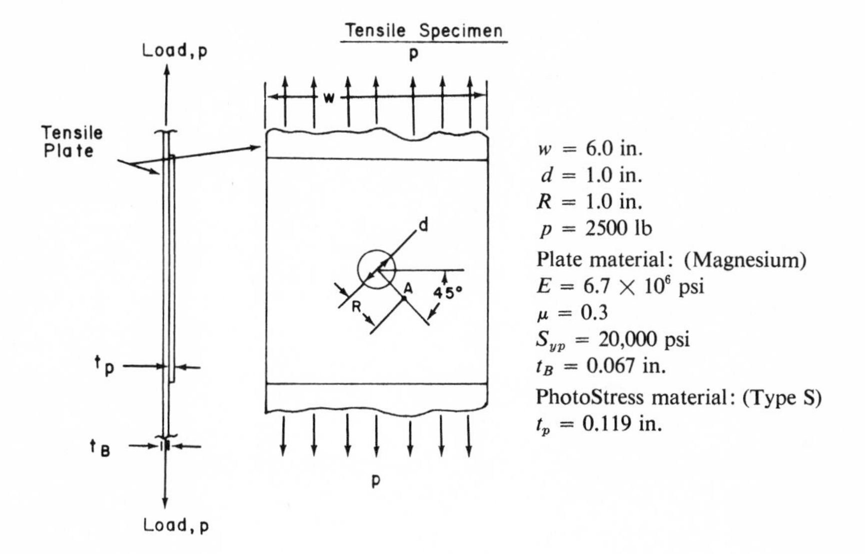

$w = 6.0$ in.
$d = 1.0$ in.
$R = 1.0$ in.
$p = 2500$ lb
Plate material: (Magnesium)
$E = 6.7 \times 10^6$ psi
$\mu = 0.3$
$S_{yp} = 20{,}000$ psi
$t_B = 0.067$ in.
PhotoStress material: (Type S)
$t_p = 0.119$ in.

Fig. 7-16.

Calibration Data:

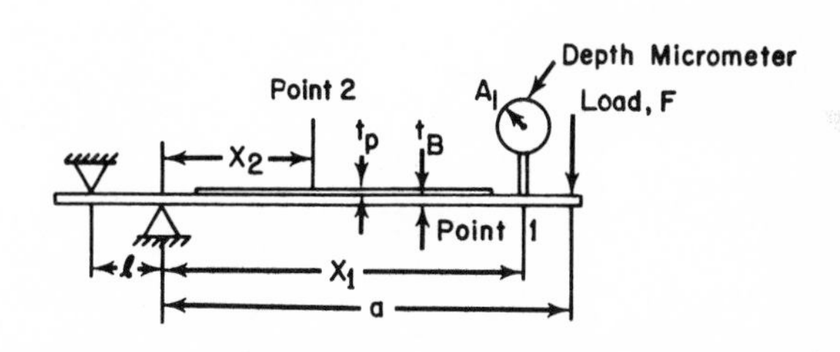

$a = 10$ in.
$x_1 = 8.75$ in.
$x_2 = 3$ in.
$l = 1$ in.
$t_p = 0.119$ in.
$t_B = 0.5$ in.
$\Delta_1 = 0.229$ in.
at point 2, $n = 2$
$C_3 = 1.2$

Note: $$(\epsilon_1 - \epsilon_2)_0 = \frac{1}{C_3}(\bar{\epsilon}_1 - \bar{\epsilon}_2),$$

where $(\epsilon_1 - \epsilon_2)_0$ = strain at point 2 found from beam deflection theory.

$(\bar{\epsilon}_1 - \bar{\epsilon}_2)$ = average strain seen in photoelastic coating due to bending.

C_3 = correction factor for beam in bending for imposed deflection (see *Experimental Mechanics*, Vol. 2, No. 2, (p. 57).

Then, $$Q = \frac{2t_p(\bar{\epsilon}_1 - \bar{\epsilon}_2)}{n}$$

Fig. 7-17.

Fringe Pattern:

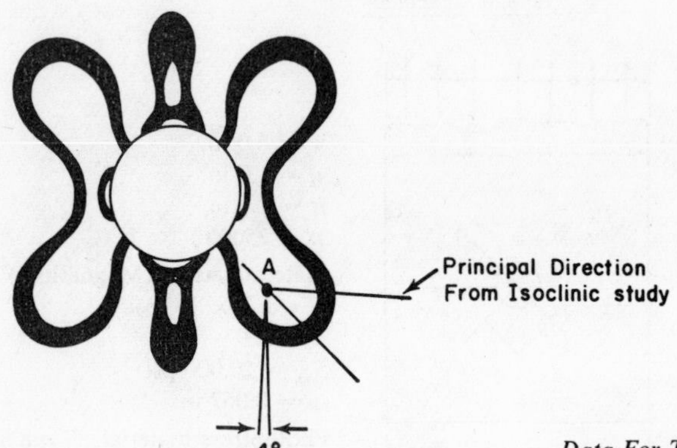

Data For Tardy Method
Analyzer rotated 22 deg to move $1\frac{1}{2}$ fringe to point *A*.

Note: $(\epsilon_1 - \epsilon_2)_0 = \frac{1}{C_1}(\epsilon_1 - \epsilon_2)$

where $(\epsilon_1 - \epsilon_2)_0$ = strain in plate with no coating.
$(\epsilon_1 - \epsilon_2)$ = strain in plate with coating.
C_1 = reinforcement correction factor (see *Experimental Mechanics*, Vol. 2, No. 2, p. 57).
$C_1 = 0.9$.

Fig. 7-18.

7-5 Suggested laboratory experiments

Experiment 7-1 Study of the photoelastic coating method

EQUIPMENT NECESSARY

1. Reflective polariscope.
2. Provisions for tracing and/or photographing fringe patterns.
3. Flat-plate tensile specimen containing a centrally located hole on which a sheet of photoelastic plastic has been bonded.*
4. A beam on which the photoelastic plastic is bonded, for calibration of the plastic coating.

* The authors use the same plate as was used in Exp. 5-1. The electric strain gages are mounted on one side of the plate, the photoelastic coating on the other.

PROCEDURE

1. Using the beam, take data necessary to determine the *strain-optical* coefficient of the photoelastic coating in this experiment.
2. Load the flat plate in tension.
   a. Take data necessary to establish the directions of principal stresses at the points specified by the instructor.
   b. Take data necessary to determine the magnitude of the maximum shearing stress at the points specified by the instructor. Use the Tardy method to determine the fringe order at the specified points.
3. If oblique-incidence equipment is available, take data necessary to determine the individual magnitudes of the principal stresses at the points specified.

REPORT

1. Compare the experimentally determined strain-optical coefficient to the one furnished by the manufacturer of the photoelastic coating.
2. Compare the experimentally determined values of principal stress directions, maximum shear stress magnitudes, and principal stress magnitudes with values determined by other experimental techniques, and with values predicted by theory.

Part II

Motion Measurement

CHAPTER 8

Measurement of Displacement, Velocity, and Acceleration

8-1 Introduction

Motion measurement is used here to indicate measurement of displacement, velocities, and accelerations. Motion may be, and is, measured by using mechanical (dial indicators), optical (high-speed framing cameras), and electrical devices, but we shall confine our discussion here to most frequently used electrical transducers.* The electrical transducers require a considerable amount of auxiliary equipment (circuit elements and recorders), but they have the advantages of small size and mass and versatility in recording data.

---

* For a discussion of mechanical displacement gages, see Chap. 3 of Ref. [1]. For a discussion of a large number of special-purpose displacement, velocity, and acceleration gages, see Chap. 14 of Ref. [2].

It is convenient to consider three distinct conditions. First, we shall consider the measurement of motion when we have a reference point available, i.e., when one element of the transducer can be located at each of the two points between which the motion is to be measured. Second, we shall consider the measurement of motion when it is possible to measure forces and relate forces to motion by using Newton's laws. And third, we shall consider the measurement of motion when no reference is available or when the use of a reference point is not convenient. As an example of a case where no reference is available, consider the measurement of ground swell during an earthquake. As an example of a case where the use of a fixed reference is not convenient, consider the measurement of velocity and acceleration of an artificial earth satellite.

The definitions of velocity ($v = ds/dt$) and acceleration ($a = dv/dt$) suggests that any desired motion quantity (displacement s, velocity v, or acceleration a) can be obtained by measuring any convenient quantity and then differentiating or integrating the signal as is indicated. This is indeed a useful approach, and it is discussed in Sect. 11-8.

8-2 Motion measurement using a reference

8-2a Measurement of displacement

When a reference point is available, displacements may be measured with many types of electric transducers. Of the various types available, those most used employ variable resistance, variable inductance, or photoelectric principles.

VARIABLE-RESISTANCE DISPLACEMENT GAGES

One of the most common type of variable-resistance displacement transducer is shown in Fig. 8-1a. In this rectilinear potentiometer, the pickup is a slide-wire potentiometer, i.e., a helical coil of insulated (varnished) wire upon which a wiper or contact point moves along a path from which the insulation has been removed. The simple DC potentiometer (or half-bridge) circuit into which this type of displacement gage is often connected is shown in Fig. 8-1b. Since this is a constant-current half bridge, it is apparent that if the resistance per unit length between points a and b is a constant, then the resistance between c and b will be a linear function of the position of c. Hence, the open circuit potential (E_{bc}) will be a linear function of the position of c; i.e.,

$$E_{bc} = \frac{R_{cb}}{R_{ab}} E_s.$$

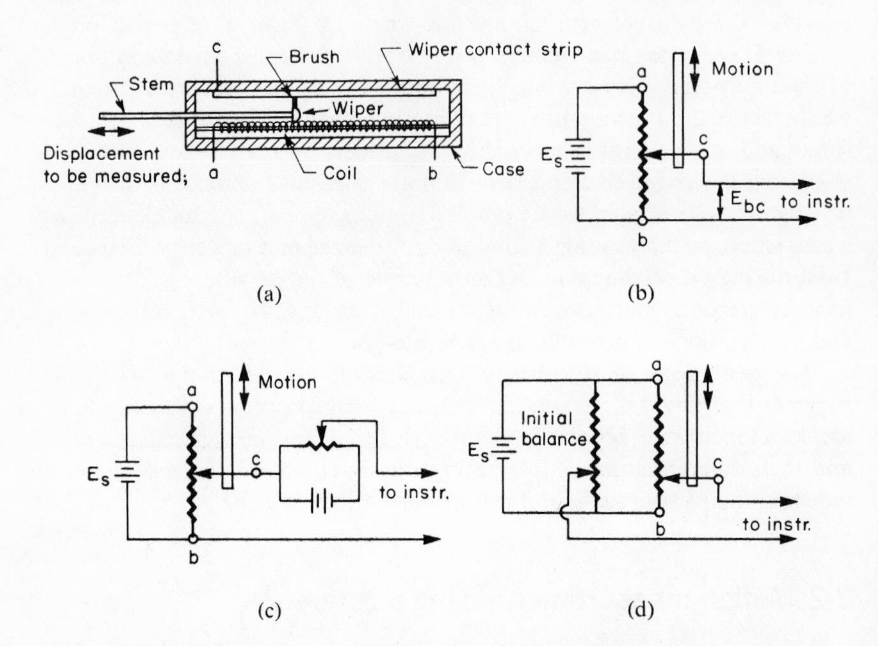

Fig. 8-1. Variable-resistance displacement gage and circuitry.

The value of the potential between points c and b at the starting position may be large compared to the change in that value that will accompany motion; hence, it is generally necessary to eliminate or reduce the value of E_{bc} corresponding to the zero or starting position. This can be accomplished either by using the zeroing circuit shown in Fig. 8-1c or by using the constant-current full bridge shown in Fig. 8-1d. The output may be displayed on almost any type of indicating or recording device (deflection-type voltmeter, digital voltmeter, recording galvanometer, or cathode ray oscilloscope), but the load imposed by the recorder (R_L) may cause the output voltage to be a nonlinear function of displacement. The effect of loading the circuit can readily be investigated by using Thevenin's theorem.* The loaded-circuit output voltage is

$$E = \frac{R_{cb}}{R_{ab}} E_s \times \left(\frac{R_L}{R_L + \dfrac{R_{ac} \times R_{cb}}{R_{ab}}} \right),$$

* This type of analysis was made in connection with strain-gage circuitry and will not be repeated here. See Sect. 2-2.

which can be rewritten as

$$\frac{E}{E_s} = \frac{R_{cb}}{R_{ab}} \times \left[\frac{\dfrac{R_L}{R_{ab}}}{\dfrac{R_L}{R_{ab}} + \dfrac{R_{cb}}{R_{ab}}\left(1 - \dfrac{R_{cb}}{R_{ab}}\right)} \right].$$

A plot of E/E_s versus R_{cb}/R_{ab} for various values of the ratio of load resistance to potentiometer resistance (R_L/R_{ab}) shows that R_L/R_{ab} must be large if E is to be linear over a wide range of displacement, i.e., if there are large changes in R_{cb}. See Fig. 8-2.

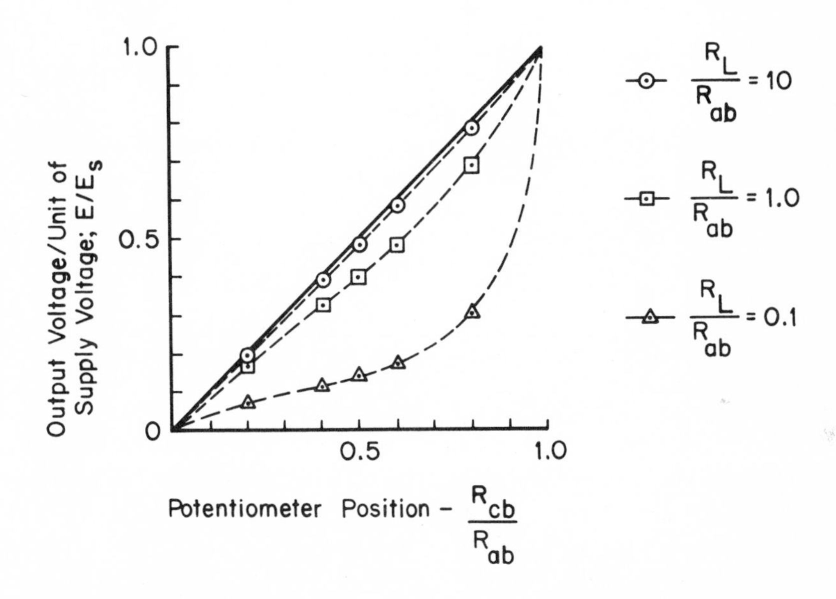

Fig. 8-2. Effect of load resistance on output voltage.

Since the output signal of a given transducer depends upon the supply voltage and the recording-instrument sensitivity (two variables), it is almost essential to have a convenient calibration system. The system shown in Fig. 8-3 effectively accomplishes calibration. Two identical displacement transducers are used. The one is located at the test area, and the other is part of the permanent circuit board. The transducer to be used is positioned, and its output (E_{cb}) is adjusted to zero position. The transducer to be used is then replaced by the calibration transducer, and it is adjusted (point c' set) to give zero output with the same zeroing

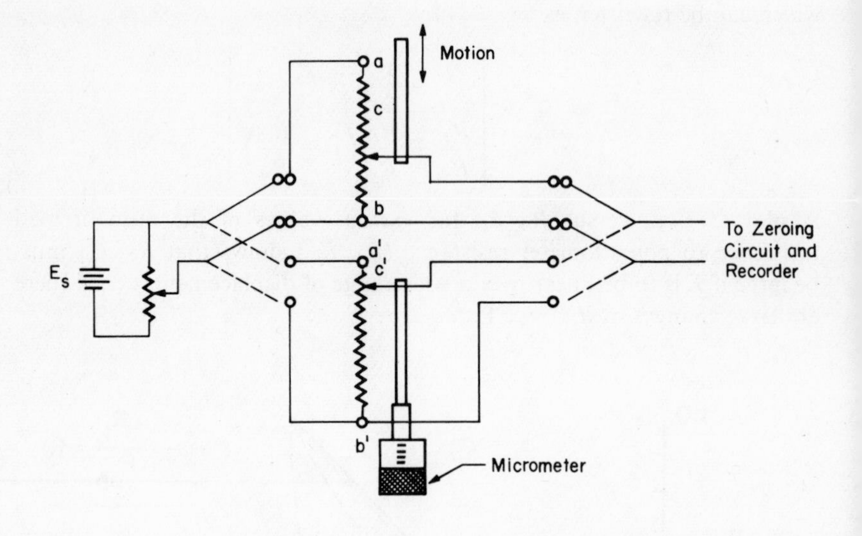

Fig. 8-3. Calibration of a linear potentiometer displacement gage.

circuit setting. The supply voltage and/or recorder gain are then adjusted to give the desired record deflection per unit of motion set on the calibration transducer.

The variable-resistance displacement transducers of this type are only slightly longer than the displacement range for which they are designed. The range available runs from less than one-half in. to 11 in. and greater on special order. A typical weight would be one ounce per inch of allowable travel. The resistance offered to motion can be expected to be between one and five oz. These devices are generally not suitable for use in cases where they may be subjected to high acceleration, since the wiper and coil may break contact. (They are, of course, more sensitive to acceleration perpendicular to the coil than along the coil. Accelerations of from 50 to 100 g's along the coil will cause erratic signals with most models.) In general, the motion must be uniaxial, since motion perpendicular to the transducer coil will damage the unit. Some models are equipped with universal joints on the displacement stem which will permit considerable misalignment, however.

The resolution of this type of transducer is limited by the spacing of the coils on which the wiper rides, since the wiper actually makes contact first on one turn and then on the next. For example, if the coil is made of three mil (0.003 in. diameter) wire, the motion can only be resolved into steps of 0.003 in. This is a common value for commercially available transducers of this type, although they are available with a resolution of 0.001 in.

If we try to improve the resolution by making the coil with wire having a smaller diameter, the life expectancy of the transducer is decreased, because the wiper will wear away the finer coil wire more rapidly. If we try to improve the resolution by replacing the coil by a single straight length of conductor, we generally have such low resistance per unit of length that changes in resistance accompanying motion may be of the same order as the variation in the contact resistance between wiper and resistance element.

The output signal from this type of transducer can be made very linear over the entire range of stem displacement. Linearity of ±0.5 per cent over the full range of travel is typical. The available values of element-resistance and power-dissipation capacity vary rather widely, but 2000 ohms per inch of coil and 0.5 w per inch of coil are typical values. Using these values, we can compute a typical sensitivity.

Since $$W = \frac{E^2}{R},$$

in which W = power in watts,

E = potential in volts,

and R = resistance in ohms,

we find that a permissible potential is

$$E = \sqrt{WR} = \sqrt{\frac{2000}{2}} \simeq 30 \text{ v/in. of coil.}$$

Therefore, the open-circuit potential signal produced by wiper motion is

$$\frac{\Delta E}{\Delta d} = 30 \text{ v/in.,} \qquad \text{or} \qquad 30 \text{ mv/0.001 in.}$$

Obviously, a rotary potentiometer can be used in the manner just described to measure angular displacement.

Figure 8-4 is a photograph of, and specifications for, a typical linear potentiometer displacement gage.

Variable-resistance displacement gages are also constructed by using unbonded resistance-strain-sensitive wire. The arrangement of elements and the principle of operation are shown in Fig. 8-5.

> The transducer consists of a frame *E*, supporting a movable armature *F*, by two thin cantilever plates. Four sets of strain sensitive filaments *A*, *B*, *C*, *D* are strung under initial tension between the

TRAVEL (INCHES)	0.5	1.0 1.31	2.0 2.25	4.0	6.0
RESISTANCES (K OHMS)	1,2 5,10	1,2 5,10	2,5 10,20	2,5 10,20	2,5 10,20
LINEARITY, MAX. INDEPEND'T-%	±.75	±.5	±.5	±.5	±.5
POWER RATING	2.5 WATTS/INCH OF COIL AT 40° C. (104° F.)				
SHAFT FRICTION	4 OZS. NOMINAL				
OPERATIVE TEMP. RANGE	-55 TO +175° C. (-67 TO +347° F.)				
WEIGHT	8 TO 16 OZS. PACKED FOR SHIP'G				

Fig. 8-4. Linear potentiometer displacement gage. (*Courtesy of Bourns Laboratories.*)

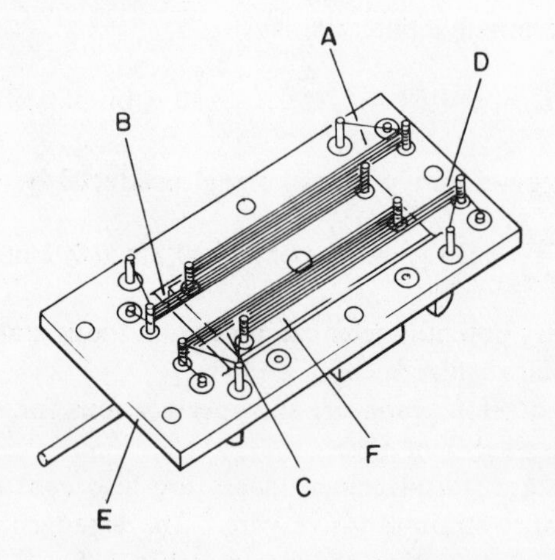

Fig. 8-5.* Unbonded wire, variable-resistance displacement gage.

* Figure 8-5 and the quoted material is from product bulletins published by Statham Laboratories, Inc.

frame and armature in the manner shown. When the armature is displaced longitudinally, two of the sets of filaments will be elongated, while the other two sets will shorten. The elongated filaments will increase in electrical resistance, while the resistance of the shortened filaments will decrease. The change in electrical resistance of the filaments will be proportional to their change in length. The transducer is so wired that the filaments are connected in a Wheatstone bridge circuit.

For the measurement of displacement (or force), a linkage pin is attached directly to the armature. The armature travel is limited mechanically to protect the wires from overload. The size, force, and displacement ranges available, circuit parameters, and sensitivities of units of this type are shown in Fig. 8-6.

Selection Table

Model	Range	Excitation Voltage	Nominal Bridge Resistance	Approximate Output
G1-1.5-300	±1.5 oz	9 v	300 ohms	±20 mv
G1-4-250	±4 oz	9 v	250 ohms	±20 mv
G1-8-350	±8 oz	12 v	350 ohms	±30 mv
G1-16-350	±16 oz	12 v	350 ohms	±30 mv
G1-24-350	±24 oz	14 v	350 ohms	±35 mv
G1-32-350	±32 oz	14 v	350 ohms	±38 mv
G1-48-675	±48 oz	20 v	675 ohms	±53 mv
G1-80-350	±80 oz	15 v	350 ohms	±38 mv

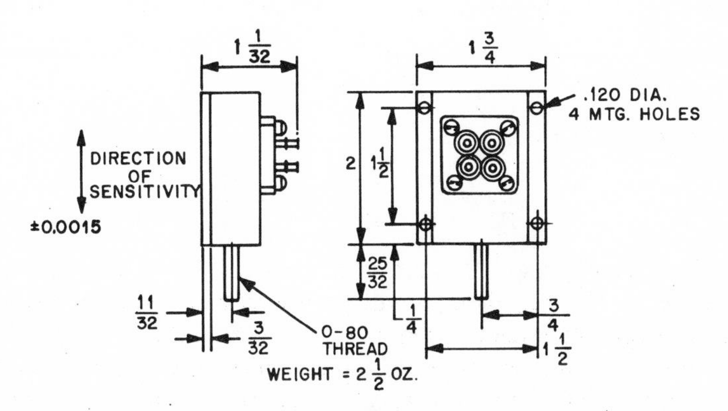

Fig. 8-6. Unbonded wire displacement gage. (*Courtesy Statham Laboratories.*)

Since the transducer element in these instruments is a four-arm bridge, all of the circuitry and recording equipment discussed in connection with bonded resistance strain gages can be used with these displacement gages.*

Another useful form of a variable-resistance displacement gage uses multiple contact points. As an example of this approach, consider the system shown in Fig. 8-7.

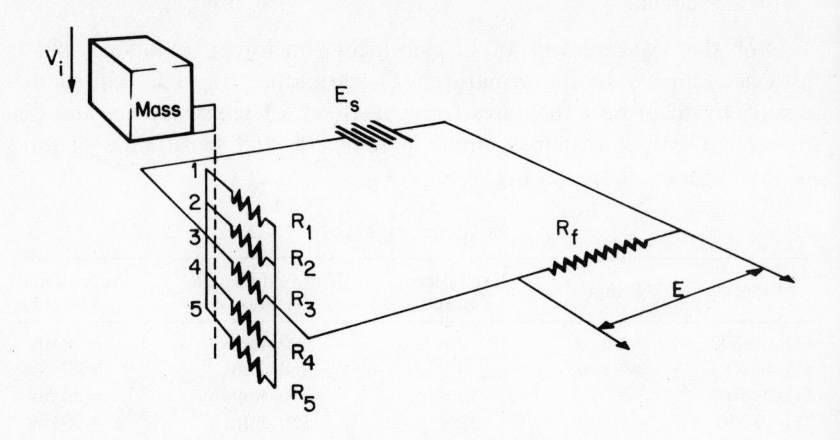

Fig. 8-7. Measurement of displacement by using multiple contact points to detect position of moving object.

For a fixed supply voltage (E_s) the voltage drops across R_f will be

$$\frac{R_f}{R_f + R_p} E_s,$$

in which R_p is defined as

$$\frac{1}{R_p} = \frac{1}{R_1} + \frac{1}{R_2} + \cdots + \frac{1}{R_n}.$$

Now if the moving mass M successively cuts out R_1, R_2, etc., as it moves a distance Δ_1, Δ_2, etc., then E_f will change as each of these resistors is removed from the circuit. Hence, if the signal (E_f) is displayed as a function of time, the results are an indication of mass position as a function of time. See Fig. 8-8. It is apparent that the resolution of this system depends upon the spacing of the contact points and that the system must be rewired after every test.

* See Sect. 2-2 and Chap. 3.

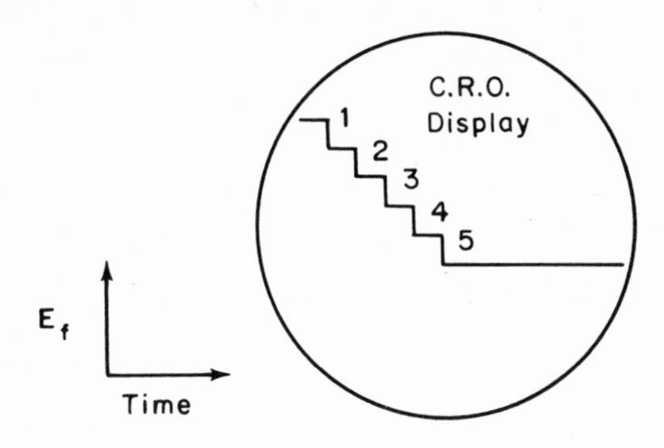

Fig. 8-8. CRO display obtained by using a multiple-contact-point technique.

VARIABLE-INDUCTANCE DISPLACEMENT GAGES

One of the most common types of variable-inductance displacement transducers is shown schematically in Fig. 8-9.* In this instrument,

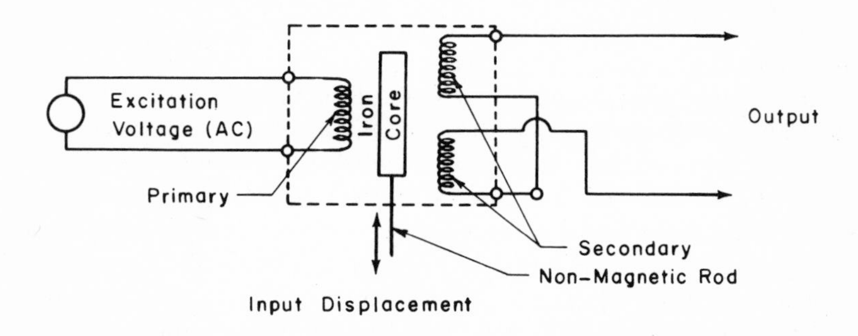

Fig. 8-9. Differential transformer displacement gage.

commonly called a differential transformer, the primary winding must be supplied with AC. The AC excitation voltage induced in the secondary winding depends upon the coupling between primary and secondary, and this, in turn, depends upon the position of the iron core which is driven by the displacement being measured.

When the core is centered, the voltages induced in the two secondary coils will be equal, due to symmetry of the magnetic coupling to the

* For a discussion of other types of variable-inductance displacement gages, see Chap. 6 of Ref. [1], or Chap. 15 of Ref. [2].

primary. When the secondary coils are connected in series opposition, as shown in Fig. 8-9, these two equal voltages will cancel and the output will be zero. Now when the core is moved away from center, the voltage in one secondary will increase, whereas the voltage in the other will decrease. The amplitude of the net AC output will be proportioned to the displacement from the center, and the direction of the motion can be determined from the phase polarity of the signal.

Commercially available displacement transducers of this type are generally in the form of hollow cylinders with the primary and secondary windings potted (cast in plastic) in the cylinder wall, and the core is positioned inside the cylinder by the displacement to be measured. The frequency of the excitation voltage is generally preselected for a given design to give the primary and secondary windings the desired impedance; however, a wide range of frequencies (60 cps to 40,000 cps) has been used. Since the output of this type of transducer is an AC voltage, the amplitude of which varies with the magnitude of the displacement being measured, i.e., an amplitude-modulated carrier wave, all of the circuitry and equipment used in connection with AC-powered (carrier) strain-gage bridges can be used with this type of displacement transducer.* Specifically, the primary is connected across the AC power supply (one diagonal of the bridge in the strain-gage circuit), and the secondary is connected to the indicating system (the other diagonal of the bridge).

For a discussion of several types of circuits that are used with variable differential transformers, see Ref. [3]. Figure 8-10 is a photograph of, and specifications for, typical variable-differential-transformer displacement gages. As was the case with the variable-resistance displacement gage, some method for direct calibration of this entire system (transducer, circuit, and indicator) is very desirable. The same kind of system described in Fig. 8-3 can be used, provided, of course, that the supply is the proper AC frequency and that the recording system will handle the AC output.

Recently, a differential transformer has become available which contains a built-in oscillator, phase-sensitive demodulator, and filter, thus eliminating entirely the need for a carrier supply and carrier amplifier system.†

The resolution of variable-inductance displacement transducers is infinite, the final value depends on the resolution of the recorder. The output is high (a typical value is three mv open circuit/0.001 in. displacement/v of excitation voltage, with an excitation voltage of six v possible).

---

* See Sect. 2-2.

† Sanborn Company, D.C. Differential Transformer, Model 7DCDT.

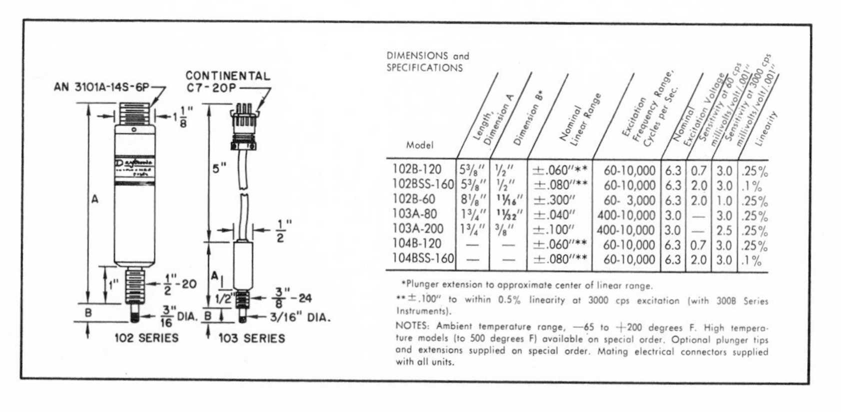

DIMENSIONS and SPECIFICATIONS

Model	Length, Dimension A	Dimension B*	Nominal Linear Range	Excitation Frequency Range, Cycles per Sec.	Nominal Excitation Voltage	Sensitivity at 60 cps millivolts/volt/.001"	Sensitivity at 3000 cps millivolts/volt/.001"	Linearity
102B-120	5 3/8"	1/2"	±.060"**	60-10,000	6.3	0.7	3.0	.25%
102BSS-160	5 3/8"	1/2"	±.080"**	60-10,000	6.3	2.0	3.0	.1%
102B-60	8 1/8"	1 1/16"	±.300"	60- 3,000	6.3	2.0	1.0	.25%
103A-80	1 3/4"	1 1/32"	±.040"	400-10,000	3.0	—	3.0	.25%
103A-200	1 3/4"	3/8"	±.100"	400-10,000	3.0	—	2.5	.25%
104B-120	—	—	±.060"**	60-10,000	6.3	0.7	3.0	.25%
104BSS-160	—	—	±.080"**	60-10,000	6.3	2.0	3.0	.1%

*Plunger extension to approximate center of linear range.

**±.100" to within 0.5% linearity at 3000 cps excitation (with 300B Series Instruments).

NOTES: Ambient temperature range, —65 to +200 degrees F. High temperature models (to 500 degrees F) available on special order. Optional plunger tips and extensions supplied on special order. Mating electrical connectors supplied with all units.

Fig. 8-10. Variable-differential-transformer displacement gage. (*Courtesy of Daytronic Corporation.*)

Since there is no mechanical frictional resistance to motion (no physical contact between moving core and fixed coils), the resistance offered to displacement by this type of transducer is much less than with the variable-resistance type.

Unfortunately, the output from a differential transformer is linear only over a very small range of motion on either side of core center position. Therefore, these units tend to be considerably longer than the range over which they function as linear displacement transducers. A transducer two in. in length with a linear range of ± 0.10 in. is typical. Although they can be used in the nonlinear range, this complicates data reduction, and the output signal tends to decrease very rapidly beyond the linear region.

As in the case of the variable-resistance gage, the displacement must be rectilinear and of known direction, as the gage will accommodate only relatively small amounts of cross motion. Mounting of variable-inductance gages must be done carefully and preferably without the use of magnetic materials; otherwise, excessive nonlinearities in output may result.

PHOTOELECTRIC DISPLACEMENT GAGES

Another useful displacement-measuring device may be constructed by using a light source and a photoelectric cell. A photocell is essentially a current-generating device for which the amount of current generated is proportional to the amount of the light falling on the cell—hence, if the light falling on the cell can be made proportional to displacement, the photocell becomes a displacement transducer. A schematic of a photoelectric system for measuring displacement is shown in Fig. 8-11.

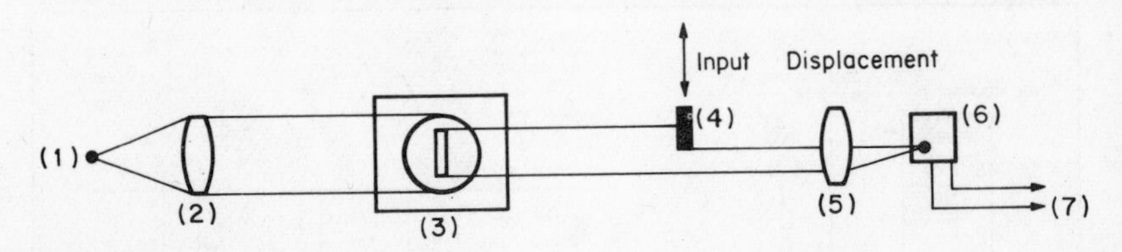

(1) Light source
(2) Collimating lens
(3) Reticle
(4) Opaque flag driven by displacement
(5) Focusing lens
(6) Photo tube or photomultiplier tube
(7) Electrical output to recording system

Fig. 8-11. Schematic of a photoelectric system for measuring displacement.

The phototube consists of a cathode coated with a material (such as lithium) which emits electrons when struck by light. If this electron emmitter is connected in a circuit as shown in Fig. 8-12, the emitted electrons flow to the anode and through the load resistance (R_L).

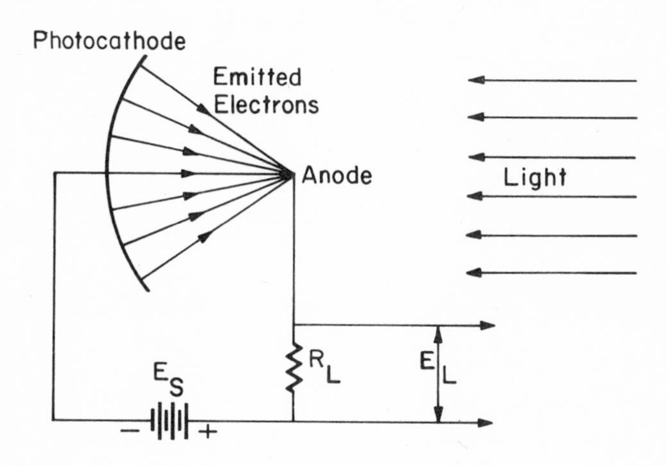

Fig. 8-12. Photoelectric cell.

The potential across the load (E_L) is proportional to the current (or electron) flow ($E_L = IR_L$) and hence to the light falling on the photocathode. Since the current from a photocell is very small, a photomultiplier tube is usually used. With reference to Fig. 8-13, the photomultiplier tube can be explained as follows: each electron emitted from the photocathode is accelerated as it flows to the first multiplier stage (S_1) because of the potential difference between the photocathode and S_1.

When this high-velocity electron strikes the first stage, several electrons are dislodged. These electrons are accelerated as they flow to S_2, and at S_2 each of these high-velocity electrons dislodges several more, etc. Multiplication of electrons (hence current and E_L) of 10^6 can be accomplished in this manner.

The frequency response of the photomultiplier tube itself (related to the time required for electron flow from cathode to anode) is very much higher than the frequencies involved in mechanical studies; hence, the limitations on this type of displacement transducer are imposed by the optical system and the associated recording system.

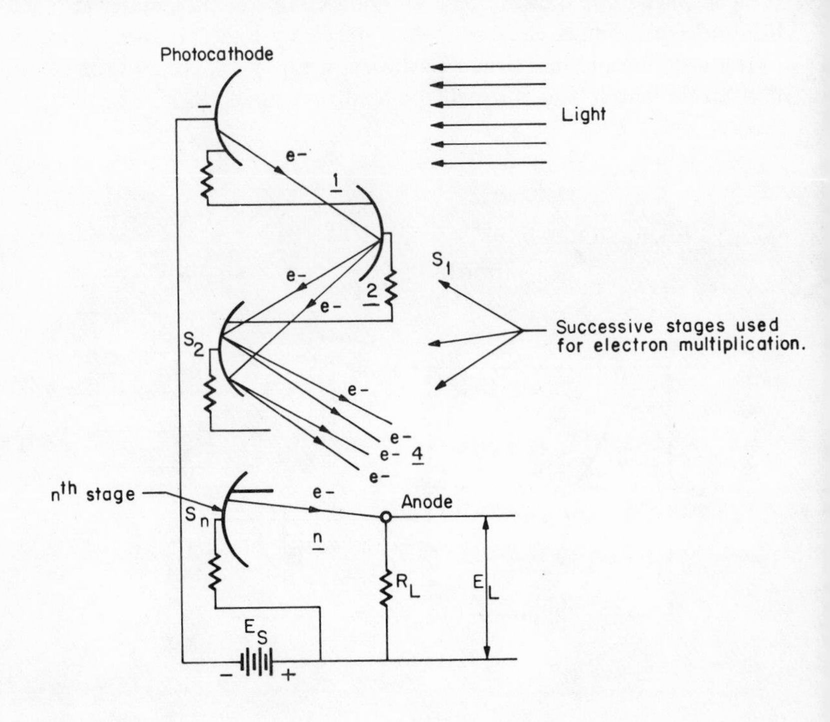

Fig. 8-13. Photomultiplier tube.

With reference to Fig. 8-11, the following points concerning the optical system should be noted: the light source, item 1 in Fig. 8-11, should be a "point" source, since the collimating lens, item 2, can collimate only light originating from its focal point. A true point source is clearly impossible, and a compromise must be made between the smallest source possible (for best collimation) and a source large enough to give the required quantity of light. It is apparent that any variation in the strength of the light source will give an output signal which is indistinguishable from the output signal produced by displacement of the opaque flag, item 4; hence, the light must be operated with a highly stabilized DC potential. The available size of collimating lens, item 2, will determine the size of the collimated light field and hence the maximum displacement that can be measured. Any optical imperfections in the collimating lens will cause unequal distribution of light in the field, and hence the system will be nonlinear. The light field is usually masked by a reticle, item 3, to give a ribbon of light which can be cut by the displacement flag 4. The focusing, or condensing, lens, item 5, must be as optically perfect as possible to insure linearity of the system.

The recording system which is driven by the photomultiplier output (connected across R_L, Fig. 8-13) must be designed so that record deflection will be linearly proportional to E_L and so that the deflection per unit of light falling on the tube is constant over the entire frequency range in which the transducer is used. To accomplish these ends, the load resistance (R_L) is made as small as possible while still giving the measurable E_L. This makes the external load, associated with the recording circuit, relatively large, and hence we approach open-circuit-output conditions.

An example of how the photoelectric displacement transducer just discussed has been used in impact studies will illustrate calibration techniques and other considerations. Refer to Fig. 8-14. A large mass M is

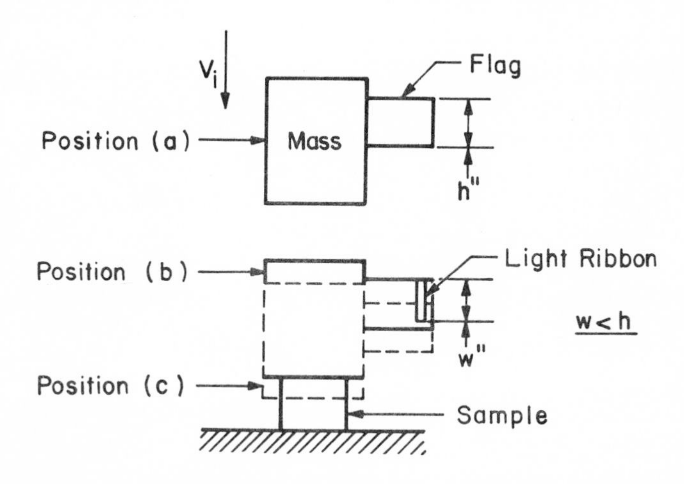

Fig. 8-14. Scheme for using photoelectric displacement transducers in impact studies.

shot vertically downward to compress the plastic sample. The photoelectric displacement transducer is used to record compression as a function of time. This is accomplished in the following manner. When the mass is in position (a), the ribbon of collimated light is completely uninterrupted by the flag on the mass, and hence the output from the photomultiplier tube is at its maximum value. See Fig. 8-15.

As the flag enters the light field, E_L decreases until the light ribbon is completely cut off. Notice that the distance between maximum and minimum E_L is the trace deflection corresponding to a flag motion of W in. and hence calibrates the system. Also notice that the slope of the

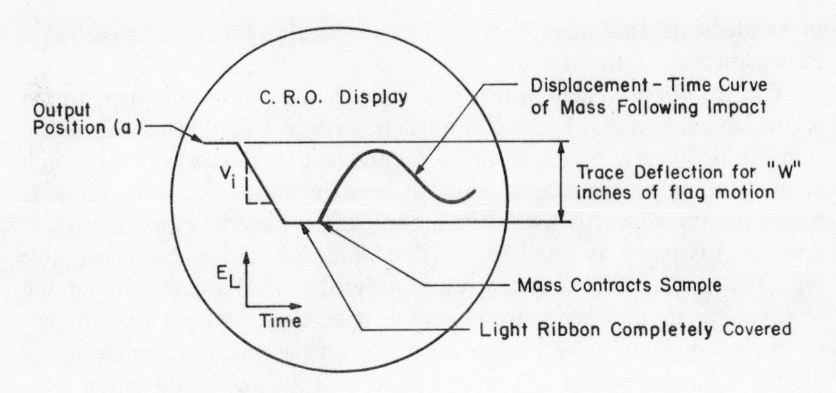

Fig. 8-15. CRO display obtained by using scheme shown in Fig. 8-14.

trace between the two flats is a measure of the mass velocity v_i. If the light ribbon has been positioned so that the trailing edge of the flag just clears the ribbon as the mass contacts the sample, then the upturn of the CRO trace as light is readmitted to the photomultiplier marks the time of contact between mass and sample. The trace that follows is a record of the mass displacement as a function of time following impact. In the sample record shown, rebound is indicated.

A displacement-measuring system which makes use of an interesting combination of optics and electronics is shown in Fig. 8-16.

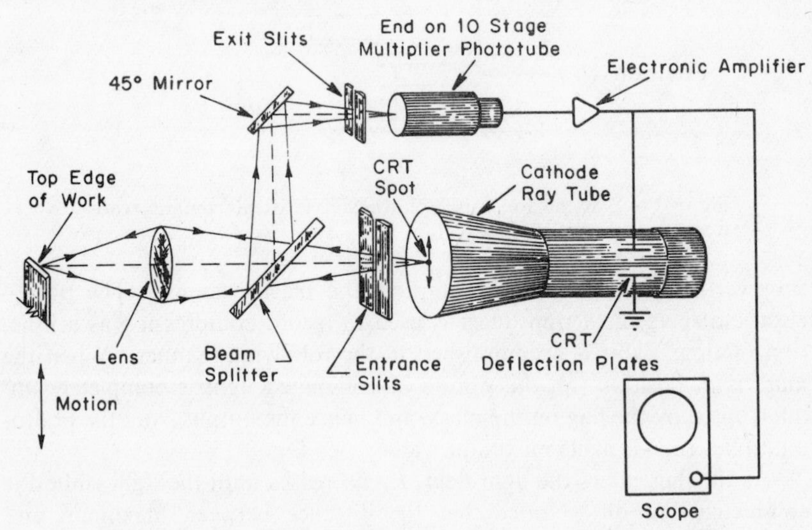

Fig. 8-16. Photoelectric displacement gage. (*Courtesy of Optron Corp.*)

Light from the cathode ray tube spot is focused on the edge of a surface whose motion is to be recorded. Fifty per cent of the spot diameter is above the edge, and fifty per cent is below. As the edge moves, the photomultiplier tube detects the change in light reflected from the edge and drives the CRT spot through a servo system to keep the spot centered on the edge. Hence, the spot "rides" the edge, and the servo output voltage, which can be recorded, is a duplicate of the edge's motion. The manufacturer of this device gives its resolution as 0.000,012 in., its frequency response as DC to 7000 cps, and its full-scale displacement as two in.

With proper design a photoelectric displacement-measuring device can tolerate considerable displacement in a direction perpendicular to the intended motion axis. However, most photoelectric displacement-measuring systems tend to be "laboratory" rather than "field test" setups.

In many field-test situations, where the motion to be measured is not rectilinear and may not even be predictable, photographic techniques are indispensible. High-speed framing cameras are used for this purpose, but a "film-plane, image-motion synchronization camera" is especially suited for high-speed motion studies; see Ref. [4].

8-2b Measurement of velocity

Even with a reference point, the measurement of velocity is considerably more difficult than is the measurement of displacement.

Figure 8-17 is a schematic of one of the few transducers for the direct measurement of linear velocity. The coil is housed in a hollow circular

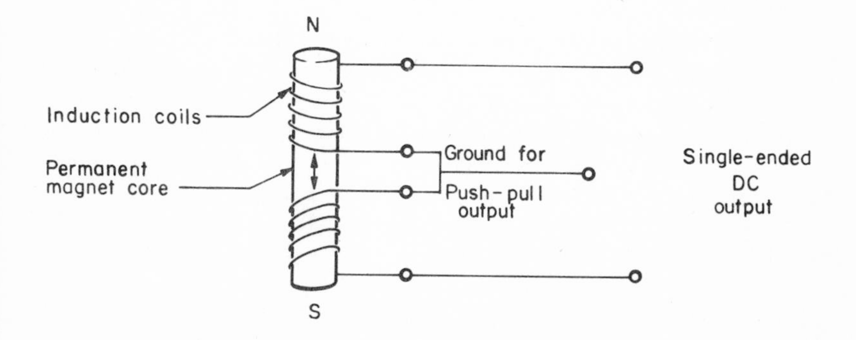

Fig. 8-17. A transducer used for the direct measurement of linear velocity. (*Courtesy of Sanborn Co.*)

cylinder through which a permanent magnet core can pass. The magnitude of DC voltage generated in the coil is proportional to the velocity of the core. This transducer has good resolution and high output (several hundred mv/in./sec of velocity), but its usefulness is limited to those cases in which the object, the velocity of which is to be measured, can be effectively attached to the core. The velocity must be parallel to the coil center line, and it can only be measured over a displacement of something less than the coil length.

For the measurement of angular velocity the transducer just discussed becomes a standard DC generator.

Average linear velocity over a prescribed displacement is often determined by measuring the time required for an object to pass two selected stations. The system shown in Fig. 8-7 is an example of this. This particular scheme has been used to check the velocity of rocket-powered test sleds (see Fig. 8-18).

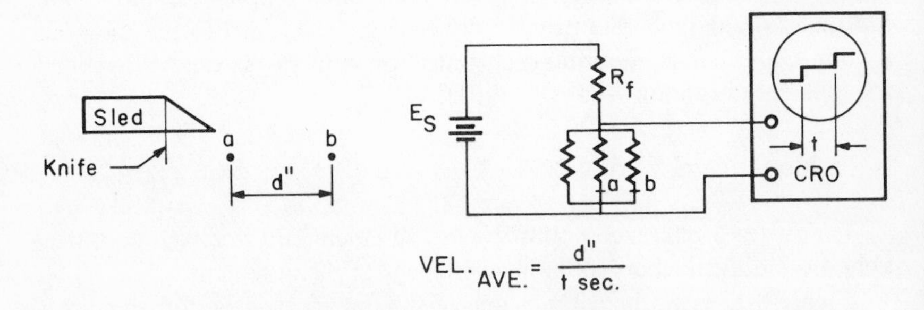

Fig. 8-18. Velocity measurement by using a multiple contact point.

The contact rods a and b which are broken by the sled are glass coated with a conductive paint. It is obvious that the signal from the selected stations could just as well be developed by photoelectric or variable-inductance devices. Of course, this scheme can be extended by the use of series of contact points, but in any case the values obtained are average velocities over the selected interval.

8-3 Motion measurement using force transducers

8-3a Measurement of angular velocity and acceleration

Angular velocity may readily be measured by using a force transducer. The normal acceleration of a point on a rotating body may be written as

$$a_n = r\omega^2,$$

in which a_n = normal acceleration of a point.
r = the radius of curvature of the path traversed by the point.
ω = the angular velocity of the rotating body on which the point is located.

Normal acceleration is related to normal force by Newton's second law.

$$F_n = Ma_n,$$

in which F_n = the force applied to the mass M in the normal direction to produce the acceleration a_n.

Hence,

$$\omega^2 = \frac{a_n}{r} = \frac{F_n}{Mr}.$$

Figure 8-19 illustrates how two spherical masses can be attached to a rotating shaft and instrumented with bonded strain gages to measure the angular velocity of the shaft. Two masses are used in order not to unbalance the shaft. The gages are mounted back to back on the connection links so that strain due to tangential forces, which will cause bending of these links, will be cancelled.

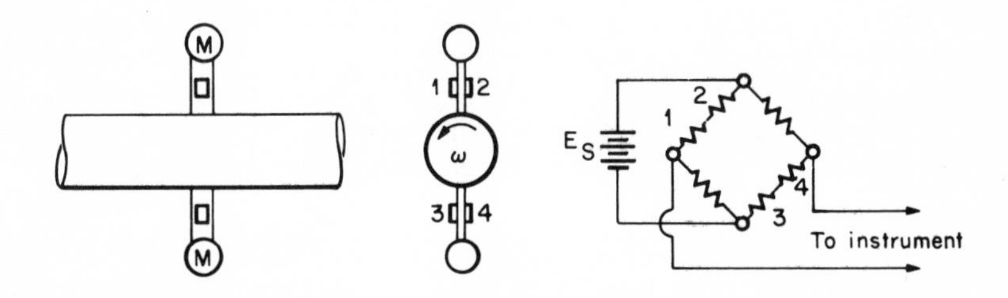

Fig. 8-19. Scheme for using bonded strain gages to measure angular velocity.

Our discussion of angular velocity can be extended to illustrate how angular acceleration can also be measured by using force transducers. Angular acceleration α is related to the tangential acceleration of a point on a rotating body (a_t) by the equation

$$a_t = r\alpha,$$

in which r is the radius of curvature of the path of the point of interest. Tangential acceleration is related to tangential force by Newton's second law.

$$F_t = Ma_t.$$

Hence, a measurement of tangential force may serve to measure angular acceleration α.

$$\alpha = \frac{a_t}{r} = \frac{F_t}{Mr}.$$

Figure 8-20 shows two masses mounted on a rotating shaft and instrumented with bonded strain gages to evaluate angular acceleration. Notice that strains due to normal forces produce signals that cancel, whereas strains due to tangential forces, which bend the connecting links, produce signals which are additive.

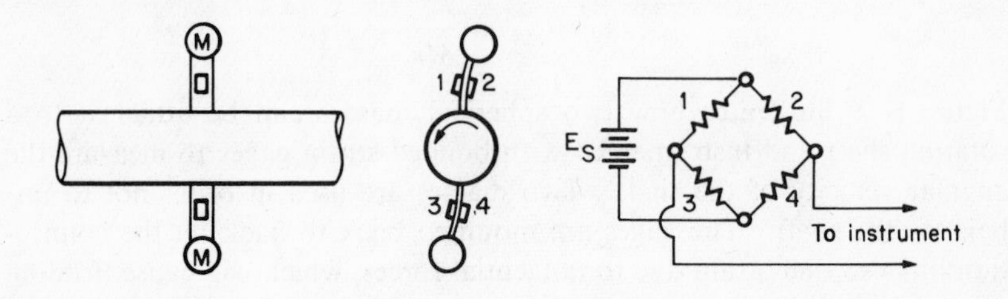

Fig. 8-20. Use of bonded strain gages to measure angular acceleration.

The transducing element used in the devices just discussed was the bonded strain gage. It is obvious that unbonded wire variable-resistance transducers, potentiometer transducers, or variable-inductance transducers could be adapted for the same purpose. In fact, angular accelerometers utilizing all three of these transducer types are commercially available.

8-3b Measurement of linear acceleration

When the total force acting to accelerate a mass can be measured by one or more force links, then the acceleration of the mass can be determined by using force transducers and Newton's second law. Figure 8-21 illustrates a falling mass which is brought to rest by impacting on the surface shown. If a force link is inserted between the mass M and the impact surface as shown in Fig. 8-21, the force applied to the mass can be measured and the acceleration of the mass computed.

Such a force link can be made in the form of a hollow circular cylinder, and it may be instrumented by using a bonded resistance strain gage, as shown in the figure. The complete analysis necessary to relate strain-gage signal to acceleration may be helpful.

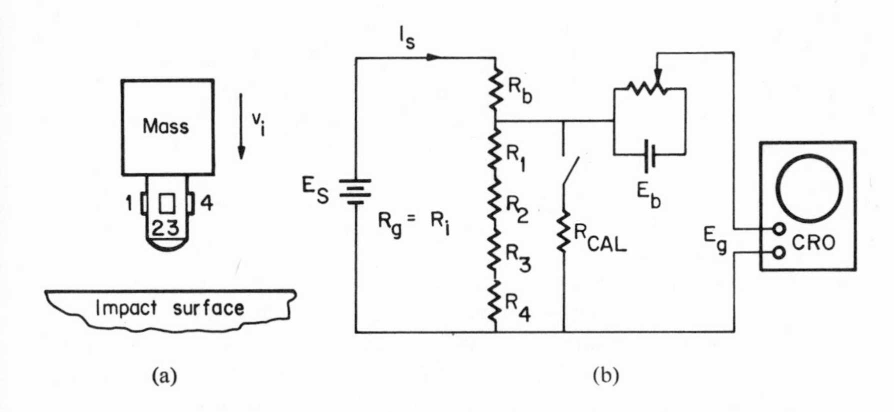

Fig. 8-21. Use of a bonded-strain-gage force link to measure acceleration.

Writing Newton's second law and substituting known relationships, we have

$$a = \frac{F}{M} = \frac{\sigma A}{M} = \frac{E\epsilon A}{M},$$

in which
a = acceleration of the mass in in./sec².
F = force applied to the mass through the force link in lb.
M = magnitude of the mass in lb-sec²/in.
σ = stress in the force link in lb/in.²
A = stressed cross-sectional area of the force link in in.²
E = modulus of elasticity of the force link in lb/in.²
ϵ = strain in the force link in in./in.

With the relationship between acceleration and strain established, it is necessary only to establish the relationship between strain and recorder deflection; i.e.,

$$\frac{E_g}{\epsilon} = \frac{R_b R_g F I_g}{(R_b + R_g)},$$

in which
$\frac{E_g}{\epsilon}$ = the output signal (in volts) per unit of strain for the potentiometer circuit shown in Fig. 8-21b.
R_b = ballast resistance in ohms.
R_g = total effective gage resistance $(R_1 + R_2 + R_3 + R_4)$ in ohms.
F = gage factor.
I_g = current flowing through the gage.

Substituting the second equation into the first gives

$$\frac{E_g}{a} = \frac{R_b R_g F I_g}{(R_b + R_g)} \frac{M}{EA},$$

for the sensitivity in volts per in./sec² of acceleration. Substitution of $M = W/g$ gives

$$\frac{E_g}{a_{g's}} = \frac{R_b R_g F I_g}{(R_b + R_g)} \frac{W}{EA},$$

in which $a_{g's}$ is the acceleration in "g" units (one g of acceleration = 386 in./sec²). This last equation serves to point up what quantities must be known in order to relate force-link output to acceleration. In addition to the usual circuit and gage parameters (R_b, R_g, I_g, and F), the force-link modulus (E) and strained area (A) must be known. Since doubt may exist concerning the exact value for either or both of these quantities, the best procedure is to establish the relationship between force-link signal (E_g) and applied force by force calibration. This force calibration is usually accomplished under static conditions—it must be remembered that this does not qualify as a direct calibration, since it is necessary to assume that transducer behavior under dynamic conditions (the condition of use) is the same as under static (calibration) conditions. Fortunately, if the link is properly designed this type of calibration is adequate, but several examples of poor design will illustrate the pitfalls: (1) if the force link is made of a material which has a different value of modulus (E) under static loading from that which it has under impact loading, then static calibration is not adequate. (2) If the strain distribution during static loading is different from what it is under impact conditions, then static calibration is not adequate.

Before we leave this discussion of the use of force links to measure acceleration, the limitations of this technique should be emphasized. First, the method is of use only when the total force acting on the mass can be measured. A force link mounted between the rocket motor and the rocket body may serve to determine acceleration during take-off, when the thrust force is very much larger than any other forces present; however, when the rocket has obtained considerable velocity, the measurement of thrust force will not serve to determine acceleration, since the total force now consists of the thrust force plus the friction drag force, the magnitude of which is unknown. Second, the presence of the force link must not change the point of application or distribution of the applied force. Third, the use of a force link to measure acceleration is useful only when all parts of the mass have essentially the same acceleration at any instant. If a force link were mounted at the end of a long rod and subjected to a hammer blow, then the force as measured by the force link could not be related to the acceleration of the rod by using the equation

$$a = \frac{F}{M},$$

in which M is taken as the total mass of the rod. This would not be correct because each particle of mass in the rod is not subjected to the same acceleration. Indeed, there is no such thing as "the rod" acceleration in this case, since, at any given instant, points along the rod have different values of acceleration. Fourth, the introduction of the force link must not change the nature of the force pulse, and hence the acceleration, applied to the system. This is a difficult problem and involves a complete understanding of the response of the system to applied transients. As a guide, let us state that a force link must be very rigid (compared to the other parts of the system) so that it does not act to cushion the system.*

8-4 References listed in Chapter 8

1. Hetényi, M., ed., *Handbook of Experimental Stress Analysis.* New York: John Wiley and Sons, 1950.
2. Harris, C. M. and C. E. Crede, eds., *Shock and Vibration Handbook*, Vol. 1, "Basic Theory and Measurements." New York: McGraw-Hill, 1961.
3. Schaevitz, H., "The Linear Variable Differential Transformer," *Proceedings of the Society for Experimental Stress Analysis*, Vol. 4, No. 2, pp. 79–88.
4. Fastle, D. L., "A Film-Plane, Image-Motion Synchronization (FIS) Camera," *SCTM 116-61(72)*, Sandia Corporation, Albuquerque, N.Mex., Nov. 1961.
5. Baker, W. E., "Transient Calibration of Piezoelectric Accelerometers," unpublished M.S. thesis, University of New Mexico, Albuquerque, N.Mex., pp. 40–42, pp. 72–81.

8-5 Suggested laboratory experiments

Experiment 8-1 Characteristics of several motion transducers, associated circuitry, and recording equipment

EQUIPMENT NECESSARY

1. Various types of motion transducers, such as
   a. Variable-resistance-type linear potentiometer.

---

* For a discussion of the design, calibration, and use of force links, see Ref. [5].

b. Variable-resistance-type bonded or unbonded resistance-strain-gage type.
c. Variable-inductance-type differential transformer.
d. Variable-capacitance type.
e. Photoelectric type.

2. Suitable power supplies and readout equipment.*
3. A calibration stand to apply motion to the transducer over a specified range (this can easily be made by using a depth micrometer).

PROCEDURE

With each type of transducer

1. Mount in the calibration stand; connect to a suitable circuit and recording device.
2. Determine output signal as a function of input motion over the transducer's entire range.
3. Determine the resolution of the transducer.
4. Work out a system-calibration technique for each transducer (comparable to the use of parallel resistors for calibration of strain-gage circuits).
5. Investigate the response of each transducer to various extraneous phenomena, such as magnetic fields, magnetic materials, electrical fields, light sources, etc.

REPORT

1. For each transducer
   a. Draw a circuit diagram, including the calibration circuit.
   b. Plot output signal versus input motion. Discuss range and linearity.
   c. Determine the sensitivity of each transducer (output signal/unit input/unit motion).
   d. Determine the resolution of each transducer.
   e. Discuss extraneous effects.
2. Design equipment necessary to measure the resistive force that a transducer offers to motion.

---

* Specialized equipment is not necessary. A $22\frac{1}{2}$ v battery will serve as the supply for the variable-resistance transducers, and 60 cycle AC for a properly selected differential transformer. Either a vacuum-tube voltmeter or a cathode ray oscilloscope can be used for readout.

Experiment 8-2 Characteristics of several force and pressure transducers, associated circuitry, and recording equipment

EQUIPMENT NECESSARY

1. Force and pressure transducers of various types, such as*
   a. Bonded strain-gage load cell, tensile link, proving ring, or torsion bar.
   b. Variable-resistance-type pressure gage.
   c. Variable-inductance-type force and/or pressure gages.
2 Circuitry and recording equipment
3. Loading devices for applying known forces and pressures.

PROCEDURE

With each type of transducer

1. Calibrate the transducer so that range, linearity, resolution, and sensitivity can be established.
2. Determine the motion per unit force (or torque) for the force transducers.
3. Determine the natural frequency of the transducer.
4. Construct a *system calibration* circuit for use with the transducer.

REPORT

For each transducer

1. Plot signal output versus input.
2. Determine range, sensitivity, and resolution.
3. Compare measured values of sensitivity, motion per unit of force, and natural frequency with the values computed by using design parameters.

* At least one "homemade" transducer should be included so that all design parameters are available for the computation of sensitivity, etc.

CHAPTER 9

Motion Measurement With No Reference—Seismic Systems

9-1 Basic seismic theory

Before we discuss specific transducers and circuits for the measuring of motion when no reference point is used, it will be necessary to develop the basic theory on which their operation depends. Motion transducers of this type are called seismic instruments, and the theory of their behavior is discussed in detail in most textbooks devoted to the study of vibration; see Ref. [1]. We may establish the necessary basic theory by considering the system shown in Fig. 9-1a.

The mass shown is attached to the base by means of a linear spring of modulus K (lb/in.) and a viscous damping element of viscous coefficient c (lb/in./sec). Assume that both the mass and the base are dis-

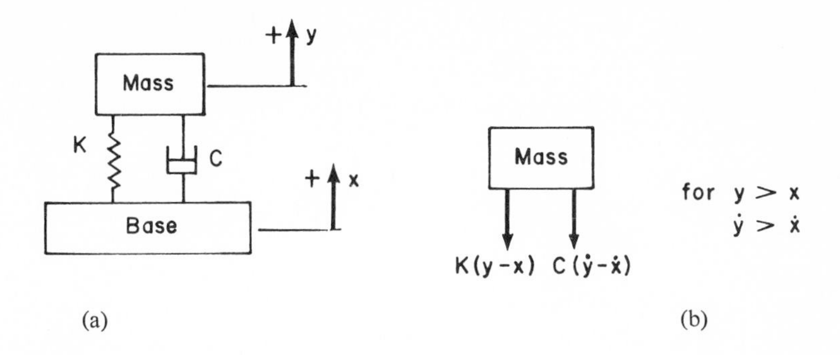

Fig. 9-1. Basic system used for the analysis of seismic instruments.

placed in the positive direction and that y is greater than x and $\dot{y}$ is greater than $\dot{x}$. For this assumed displacement, a free-body diagram of the mass is shown in Fig. 9-1b. Summing the forces acting on the mass and equating to the product of the mass times its acceleration, we have

$$-K(y - x) - c(\dot{y} - \dot{x}) = Ma_m = M\ddot{y}. \tag{9-1}$$

By defining the displacement of the mass relative to the base as z we may write

$$\begin{aligned} z &= y - x, \\ \dot{z} &= \dot{y} - \dot{x}, \\ \ddot{z} &= \ddot{y} - \ddot{x}, \end{aligned} \tag{9-2}$$

and substituting these definitions into Eq. (9-1) gives

$$M\ddot{z} + c\dot{z} + Kz = -M\ddot{x}, \tag{9-3}$$

which is the differential equation of relative motion for this system.

9-1a Steady-state response

We shall begin by considering the solution of Eq. (9-3) when the input motion to the base is periodic. Since any periodic input can be represented as the sum of a series of harmonic motions (by the use of a Fourier series) it will be adequate to investigate the solution to Eq. (9-3) when x is harmonic; i.e.,

$$x = X \sin \omega t, \tag{9-4}$$

in which X is the maximum amplitude of base displacement and ω is the circular frequency (rad/sec) of the base motion. Substitution of Eq. (9-4) into Eq. (9-3) gives

$$M\ddot{z} + c\dot{z} + Kz = M\omega^2 X \sin \omega t. \tag{9-3a}$$

The solution to this equation consists of two parts. The first part is the complementary solution obtained by setting the right-hand side of the equation equal to zero. Since this reduces the equation to the equation of motion for a damped free vibration, this part of the general solution is of interest only until the free vibration resulting from initial displacement and velocity is damped out.

The second part of the general solution is the particular solution; this is the part of the solution of interest in analyzing the response of the system when it is subjected to steady-state harmonic input after steady-state response conditions have been established. The particular solution for Eq. (9-3a) is

$$z = Z \sin (\omega t - \phi), \tag{9-5}$$

in which Z is the maximum amplitude of the relative motion between mass and base, and ϕ is the phase angle between the input motion (x) and the relative motion (z). Substitution of Eq. (9-5) into Eq. (9-3a) gives

$$Z = \frac{\omega^2 X}{\sqrt{\left(\frac{K}{M} - \omega^2\right)^2 + \left(\frac{\omega c}{M}\right)^2}}$$

and

$$\phi = \tan^{-1} \frac{\frac{\omega c}{M}}{\frac{K}{M} - \omega^2}.$$

These can be rewritten as

$$Z = \frac{\omega^2 X}{\omega_n^2 \sqrt{\left[1 - \left(\frac{\omega}{\omega_n}\right)^2\right]^2 + \left[2h\frac{\omega}{\omega_n}\right]^2}} \tag{9-6}$$

and

$$\phi = \tan^{-1} \frac{2h\frac{\omega}{\omega_n}}{1 - \left(\frac{\omega}{\omega_n}\right)^2}, \tag{9-7}$$

in which $\omega_n = \sqrt{\frac{K}{M}}$, the natural frequency of undamped free vibration.

$h = \frac{c}{2M\omega_n} = \frac{c}{c_c}$, the ratio of the damping present to the amount of damping required to critically* damp the system (c_c).

* A system is critically damped if, when displaced from equilibrium and released, it returns to equilibrium in the minimum time but without overshooting the equilibrium position. $c_c = 2\omega_n M$.

Equation (9-6) is of interest because it shows how the amplitude of the relative motion (Z) is related to the motion of the base, and Eq. (9-7) shows how the relative motion is delayed as compared to the motion of the base.

We first observe that when the frequency of the base motion (ω) is much greater than the natural frequency of the system (ω_n), Eq. (9-6) reduces to

$$Z \simeq \frac{\omega^2 X}{\omega_n^2 \sqrt{\left[\left(\dfrac{\omega}{\omega_n}\right)^2\right]^2}} \simeq X. \tag{9-6a}$$

That is, when the ratio of (ω/ω_n) is very large, the relative displacement between the mass and the base is almost identical to the displacement of the base. This is the basis for seismic instruments used for displacement and velocity measurement. When a displacement transducer is mounted between the mass and the base, so as to produce a signal proportional to Z, the signal is also proportional to X—if ω/ω_n is large. When a velocity transducer is mounted between the mass and base, so as to produce a signal proportional to $\dot{Z}$, the signal is also proportional to $\dot{X}$—if ω/ω_n is large. If large displacements are to be measured, instruments of this type are necessarily large, because they must provide for relative motion (Z) as large as the input motion (X). Although theory shows that $Z = X$ (or $\dot{Z} = \dot{X}$) for large values of ω/ω_n, there is a practical upper frequency limit for seismic displacement or velocity gages. First, with very high frequency motions the displacements are generally small; hence, for a given seismic displacement transducer the upper frequency limit may be determined by the limiting resolution of the transducer used to measure the relative motion (Z). Second, at very high frequencies, higher-order resonances, involving spring elements not considered in our single-degree-of-freedom analysis, may invalidate the conclusions reached in this single-degree-of-freedom analysis. Since Eq. (9-6) was written for $\omega/\omega_n >> 1$, Fig. 9-2 is included to show how the ratio Z/X (or $\dot{Z}/\dot{X}$) varies with frequency ratio for several values of h. Notice that if $h = 0.7$, $Z \simeq X$ for values of ω/ω_n as low as 2.0.

We next observe that if (ω/ω_n) is very small Eq. (9-6) reduces to

$$Z \simeq \frac{\omega^2 X}{\omega_n^2 \sqrt{1}}. \tag{9-6b}$$

This is of particular interest when we remember that for $x = X \sin \omega t$, the acceleration of the base ($\ddot{x}$) is

$$a_{\text{Base}} = \ddot{x} = -\omega^2 X \sin \omega t,$$

or

$$a_{\text{Base}_{\text{Max}}} = -\omega^2 X.$$

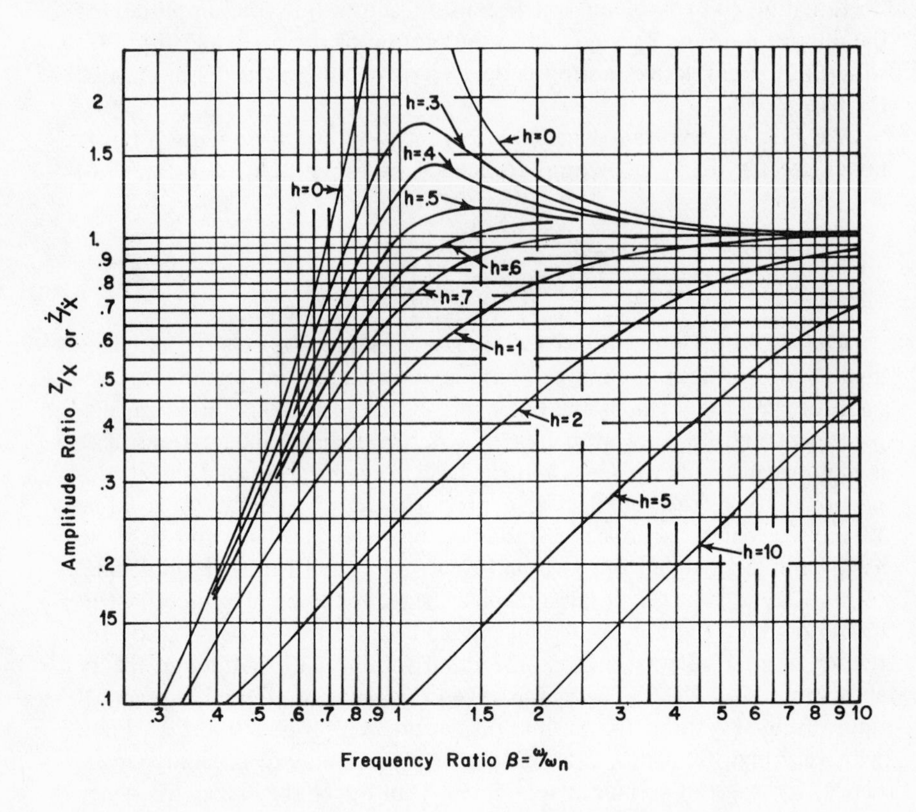

Fig. 9-2. Steady-state response of a seismic system to harmonic base displacement.

Hence,

$$Z \simeq -\frac{a_{\text{Base}_{\text{Max}}}}{\omega_n^2}. \tag{9-6c}$$

Therefore, Eq. (9-6c) indicates that the relative displacement Z is proportional to the acceleration of the base. It is interesting to note that Eq. (9-6c) can be reduced to the equation on p. 383 for relating force-link strain to mass acceleration. This is the basis for seismic-type accelerometers—a displacement transducer is mounted between the mass and the base to produce a signal proportional to Z, but if ω/ω_n is very small the signal is also proportional to the acceleration of the base. The constant of proportionality is $1/\omega_n^2$.

Since Eq. (9-6c) was written for $\omega/\omega_n << 1$, Fig. 9-3 is included to show how the ratio of output signal (proportional to $\omega_n^2 Z$) to input acceleration ($\ddot{X}$) varies with frequency ratio for several values of h. Notice that for $h = 0$ (no damping) this ratio is nearly one for values of ω/ω_n as large as 0.2, and for $h = 0.7$ this ratio is nearly one for values of ω/ω_n as large as 0.4.

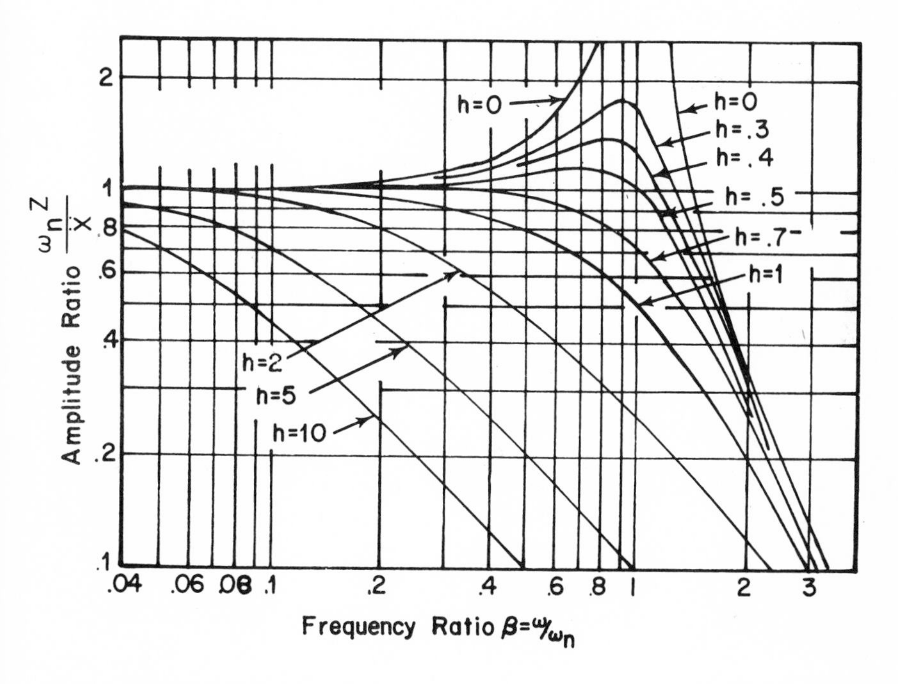

Fig. 9-3. Steady-state response of a seismic system to harmonic base acceleration.

For either of these seismic-type instruments,* the way in which the output signal (Z) is phased with respect to the input (x) can be found with the aid of Eq. (9-7). Equation (9-7) has been plotted as Fig. 9-4.

We see that, for seismic displacement transducers, as $\omega/\omega_n \to \infty$ $\phi \to 180$ deg, regardless of the value of h, and for $h = 0$, $\phi = 180$ deg for all values of $\omega/\omega_n > 1.0$. To see how this will affect the shape of a complex wave form, consider an input motion composed of two sine waves, each of which has a frequency much greater than ω_n (see Fig. 9-5). The output will consist of the same two sine waves, each shifted by 180 deg. Referring to Fig. 9-5, we note that the output wave is inverted but not distorted.

---

* Really only one instrument, but the use conditions differ, i.e., for $\omega/\omega_n >> 1$ a displacement gage, for $\omega/\omega_n << 1$ an accelerometer.

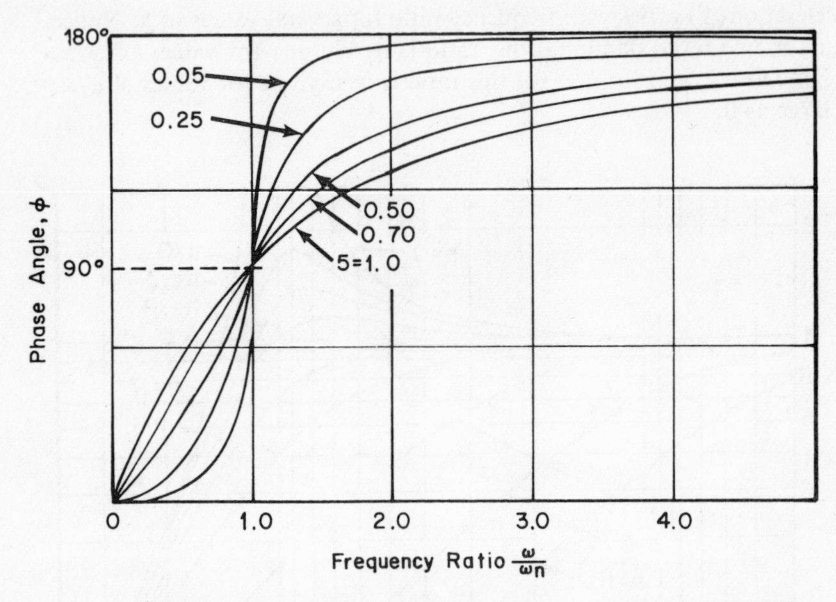

Fig. 9-4. Phase shift of a seismic instrument as a function of the frequency ratio and damping factor.

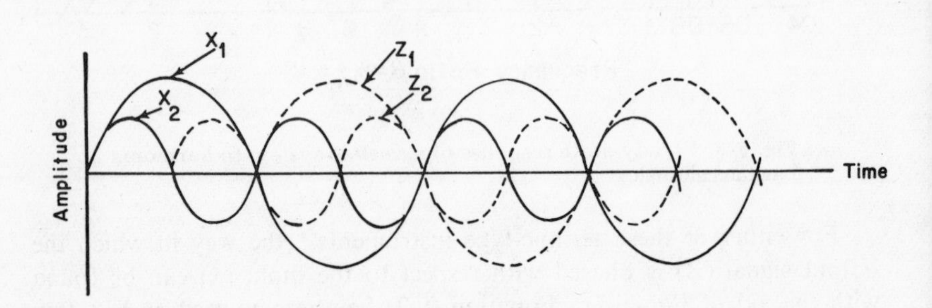

Fig. 9-5. Inversion of output when the phase angle = 180 deg.

It is important to note that the presence of a suitable amount of damping ($h = 0.7$) allows a seismic displacement (or velocity) transducer to function with a one-to-one amplitude ratio to lower values of frequency ratio than is possible with no damping ($h = 0$) (see Fig. 9-2); however, the presence of this damping causes nonlinear phase shift of the components of a multifrequency signal and hence limits usage to higher frequency ratios. See Fig. 9-4.

Figure 9-4 indicates that for values of ω/ω_n less than unity the angle ϕ varies linearly with ω/ω_n if the damping factor (h) is 0.7. This indicates that if h is made equal to 0.7 in seismic accelerometers, for which ω/ω_n is small, phase shifting of the various frequency components will not result in distortion of a complex wave. This is illustrated in Fig. 9-6.

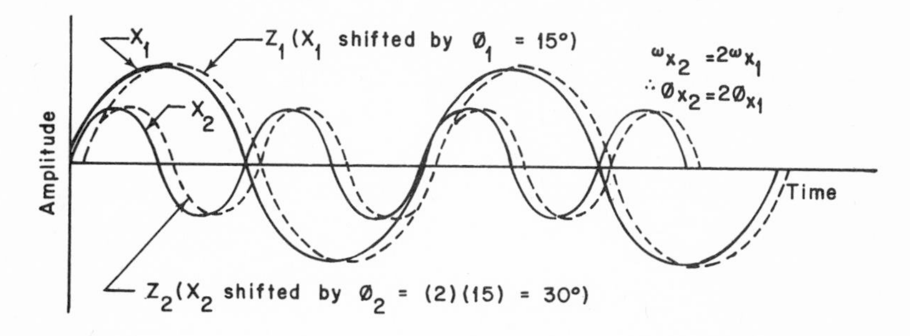

Fig. 9-6. Effect of linear phase shift.

If the damping factor of a seismic-type accelerometer is equal to zero, (no damping), then for all values of $\omega/\omega_n < 1$, the phase angle (ϕ) is equal to zero and, again, no phase distortion will occur.

9-1b Transient response

When seismic instruments are excited by transient inputs or when the response is desired at times before steady state is reached, it is not appropriate to neglect the complementary (transient) solution to the equation of motion. Hence, the investigation just completed is not adequate for an understanding of how seismic instruments respond to transients.

Any one of several analytical approaches may be made, but in any case the starting point is the equation of motion of the seismic system.

$$M\ddot{z} + c\dot{z} + Kz = -M\ddot{x} \tag{9-3}$$

Given the shape of the input pulse applied to the base, x, $\dot{x}$, or $\ddot{x}$ as a function of time, it is possible to solve, by any one of several methods, for the response z as a function of time. This equation has been solved for various functions of $\ddot{x}$ by means of numerical integration [2], by means of analog computers [3], by means of Laplace transformations [4] and by means of a phase-plane technique [5].

Motions to be measured may have an infinite number of forms, but we may investigate the relationship between relative motion (z) and base motion (x, $\dot{x}$, or $\ddot{x}$) by assuming a variety of forms for base motion and obtaining the complete solution for Eq. (9-3). From such an approach

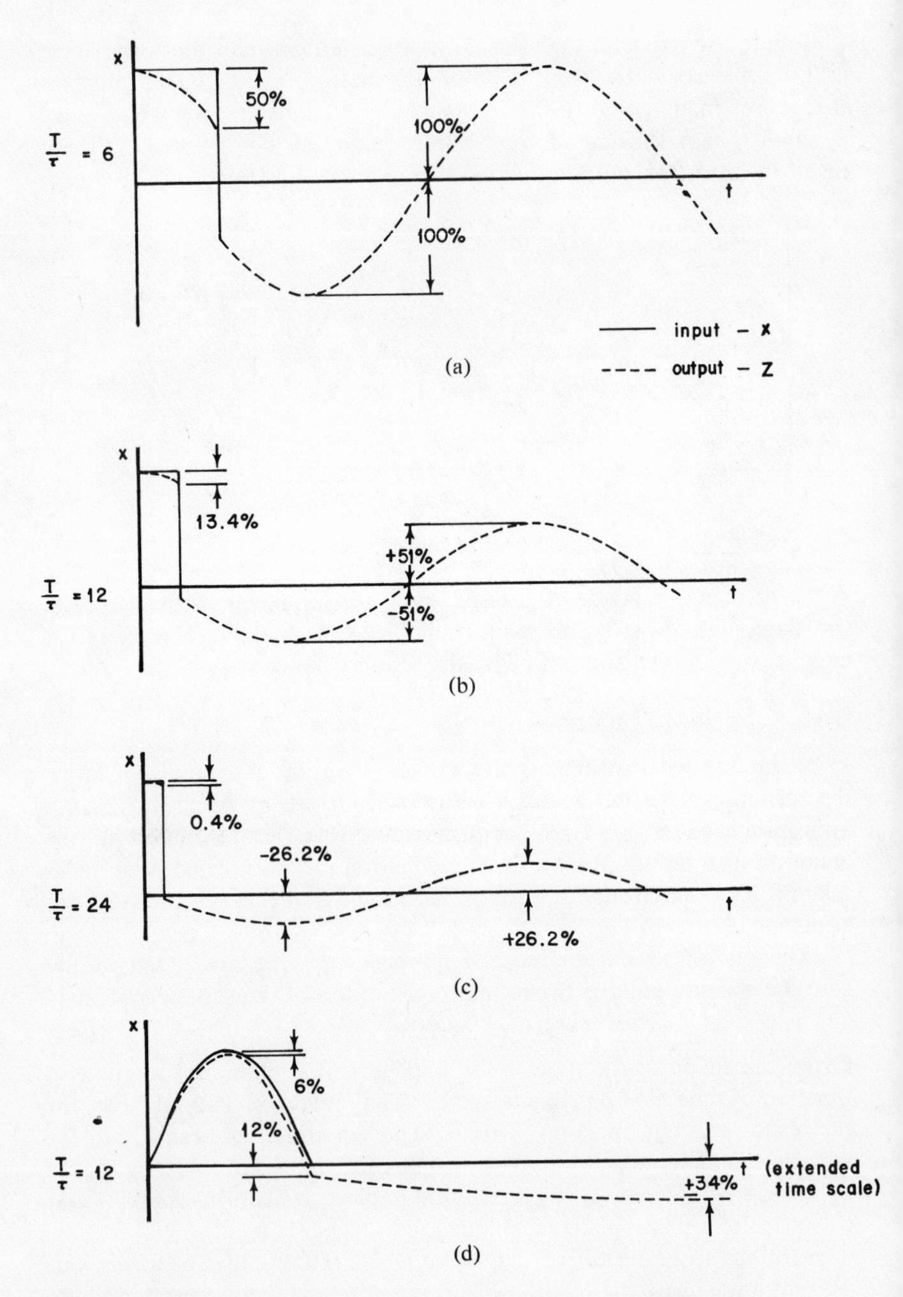

Fig. 9-7. Response to displacement transients.

we can draw some conclusions concerning the response of seismic systems to almost any form of transient.

In the study of response to transients, there appears to have been far less interest in seismic displacement transducers than in seismic accelerometers, possibly because in most transients problems the displacements desired are relative displacements between two items and a seismic transducer is not necessary. The time-relative displacement response curves shown in Fig. 9-7 indicate how an undamped seismic displacement transducer responds to several forms of transient input. For an instrument natural period (T) equal to six times the duration of the base motion (τ), the relative motion output (Z) falls considerably short of duplicating the base motion (x). See Fig. 9-7a. The situation improves, however, as the ratio T/τ becomes larger (Figs. 9-7b and 9-7c). For the half-sine-wave base motion with $T/\tau = 12$, Fig. 9-7d, the shape of the input motion is reasonably well duplicated by the relative motion even though the peak amplitude is in error. Continuation of the study of response to selected pulse shapes will verify that the shape of the relative motion curve continues to approach the shape of the base motion as the duration of the base motion becomes shorter compared to the natural period of the instrument. This will be true regardless of the shape of the pulse.

If the instrument is damped, the relative motion generally follows the base motion less well during the duration of the input phase; however, the residual motion is reduced to zero by the presence of damping.

Seismic accelerometers are more frequently than not used to measure transient accelerations; hence, the study of accelerometer response to transients has received a great deal of attention. S. Levy and W. D. Kroll [2] and R. W. Kearns [3] investigated seismic accelerometer response to three pulse shapes (half-sine-wave, triangular, and square) of different durations and with different amounts of damping.

The information presented in Figs. 9-8 through 9-13 was taken from the paper by Kearns. For all three pulse shapes, the transducer output (proportional to z) is greatly different from the acceleration input when the ratio of the natural period of the instrument (T) to the pulse duration (τ) is 1.0 (or larger). This is true regardless of the amount of damping (h). See Figs. 9-8, 9-9, and 9-10. For the half-sine-wave and the triangular pulse, the output signal approaches the acceleration input as the T/τ ratio becomes smaller. See Figs. 9-11 and 9-12. Damping functions to reduce the oscillation at the instrument's natural frequency of the output signal during both the forcing period and the residual era. With a square input acceleration the output signal from an undamped accelerometer overshoots by 100 per cent regardless of the T/τ ratio. In this case only damping is effective. See Fig. 9-13.

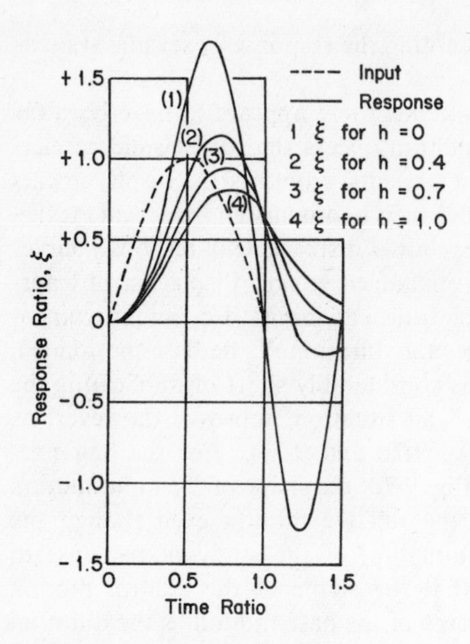

Fig. 9-8. Response to half-sine pulse, $\frac{T}{\tau} = 1$.

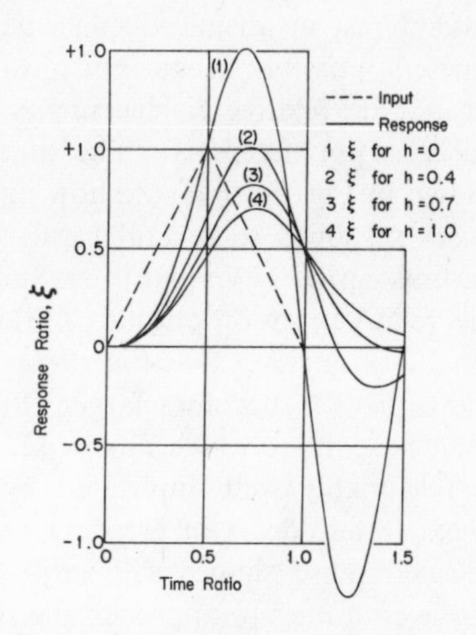

Fig. 9-9. Response to triangular pulse, $\frac{T}{\tau} = 1$.

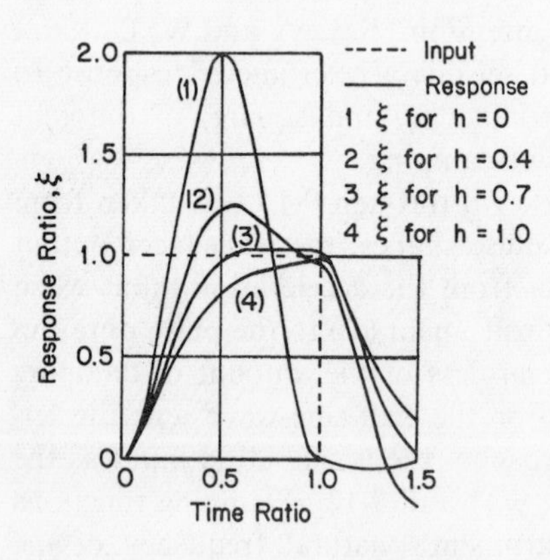

Fig. 9-10. Response to square pulse, $\frac{T}{\tau} = 1$.

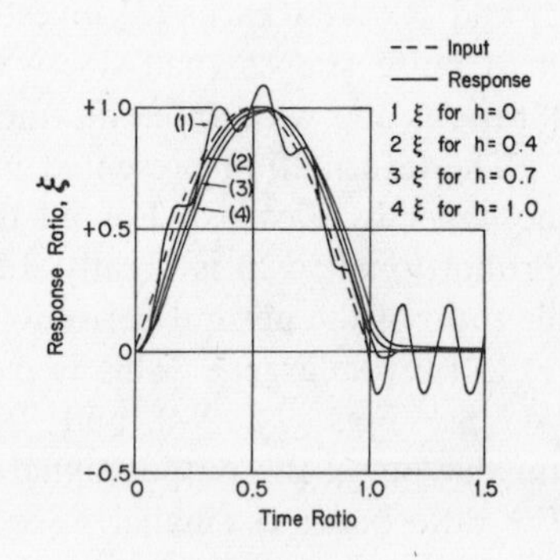

Fig. 9-11. Response to half-sine pulse, $\frac{T}{\tau} = \frac{1}{5}$.

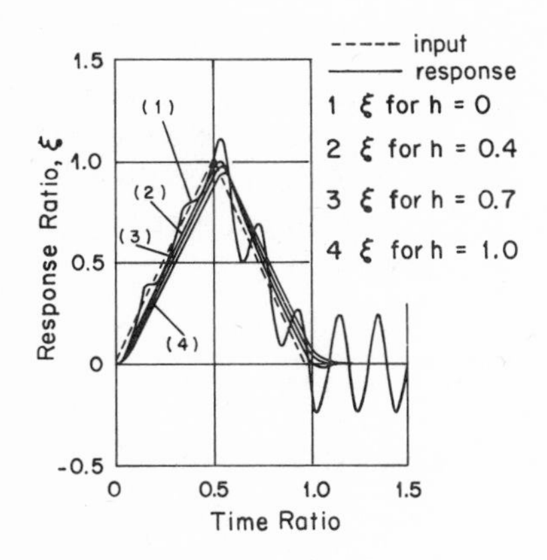

Fig. 9-12. Response to triangular pulse, $\frac{T}{\tau} = \frac{1}{5}$.

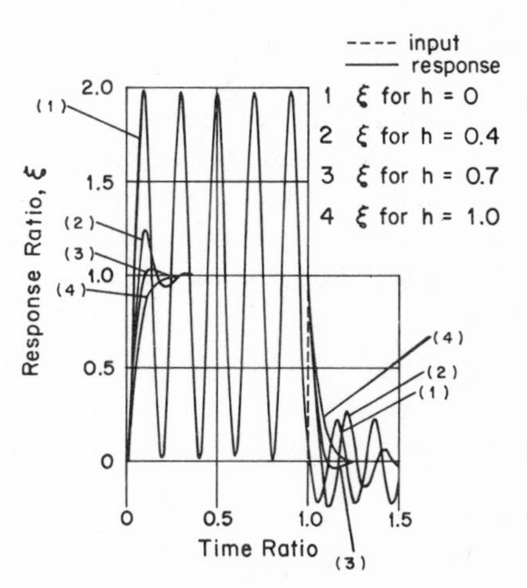

Fig. 9-13. Response to square pulse, $\frac{T}{\tau} = \frac{1}{5}$.

Fortunately, input accelerations with zero rise times do not occur in practice, and the presence of a finite rise time improves the response characteristic over those shown for a square wave. For a ramp-type input acceleration, see Fig. 9-14; the ratio of natural period to rise time

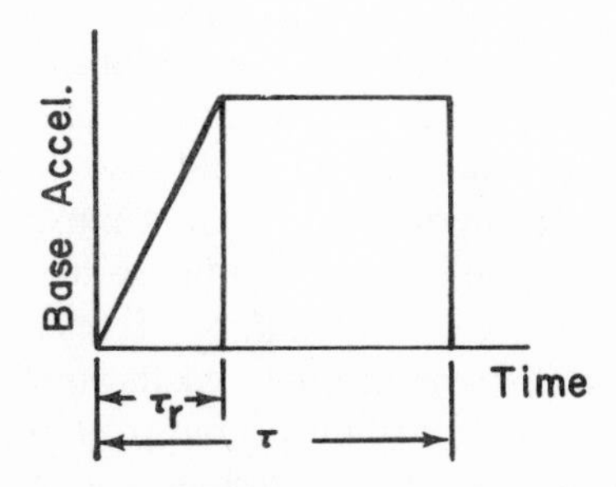

Fig. 9-14. Ramp-type acceleration input.

(T/τ_r) is more important than the total time duration of the input pulse (τ). A good approximation of the response to a ramp input with rise time (τ_r) can be made by investigating the response of the system to the first half of a triangular pulse for which

$$\frac{T}{\tau/2} = \frac{T}{\tau_r}.$$

From a study of response curves of the type just presented certain additional conclusions can be reached. (1) For a given peak amplitude and duration of acceleration input, the response of a given accelerometer will become progressively better as the rise time of input acceleration increases. Thus, for the three input pulses shown in Fig. 9-15; the response of a given accelerometer will be better for pulse (b) than for pulse (a), and better for pulse (c) than for pulse (b). (2) With undamped accelerometers, random-shaped input pulses which contain segments of rapidly changing input acceleration will excite an output component which oscillates with accelerometer natural frequency about the input signal. See Figs. 9-11 and 9-12. In this case a more nearly correct result can be obtained by fairing the output signal. If an oscillatory signal exists with a frequency less than the accelerometer's natural frequency (mounted natural frequency will be lower than unmounted natural frequency), fairing does not give the true acceleration signal at the accelerometer location; however, fairing may still be used. In this case, fairing may be justified if the high-frequency components are known to be beyond the range of frequencies that produce damage to the test item and/or if only data on velocity change is desired. With damped accelerometers ($h = 0.7$ is most common) these oscillations are reduced in amplitude. But as the effective T/τ ratio approaches 1.0, the output from the damped accelerometer becomes progressively distorted without giving any marked indication of error. See Figs. 9-8, 9-9, and 9-10.

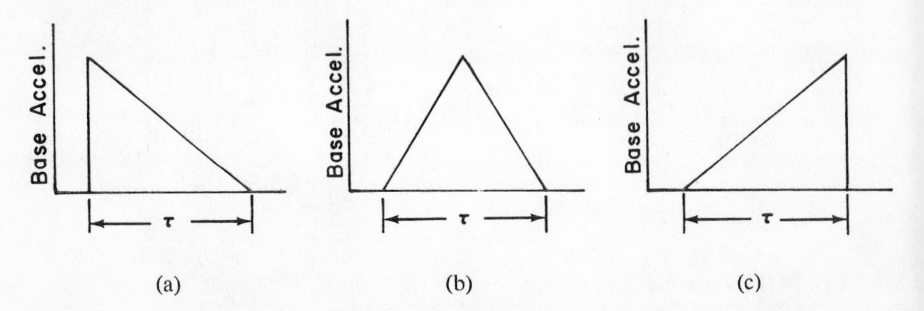

Fig. 9-15. Various acceleration-input forms.

9-2 Seismic instruments

As we pointed out in the preceding section, a seismic instrument is a single-degree-of-freedom system, i.e., a mass attached to a rigid base by an elastic element, with or without damping. Since the motion of interest (base displacement, velocity, or acceleration) is inferred from the relative displacement or velocity between the mass and the base, the item of interest is this relative motion. Any of the displacement or velocity transducers can be used in this application, but we shall again confine our attention to the most frequently used electrical types. For an excellent discussion of a large number of shock and vibration instruments, see Chaps. 8, 13, 14, 15, and 16 in Ref. [2] given in Sect. 8-4 of this book.

Potentiometer-type variable-resistance displacement gages, discussed in Sect. 8-2a, have been used in seismic accelerometers. Figure 9-16 is a diagram showing one possible arrangement of a variable-resistance displacement gage in a seismic instrument.

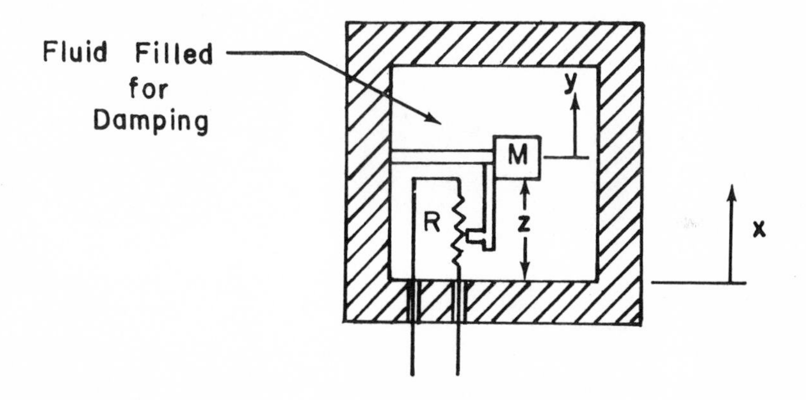

Fig. 9-16. A simple accelerometer using a slide-wire potentiometer as the sensing element.

The electrical circuitry required is the same as when the transducer is used as an ordinary displacement transducer. Because of the rather large masses and dimensions involved in this type of transducer, the natural frequency of seismic instruments using it tends to be low (usually less than 100 cps). Therefore, as an accelerometer its upper frequency limit tends to be low (say, 0.4 of its natural frequency if it is damped with $h = 0.7$). As an accelerometer it has a lower frequency limit of zero, however.

This type of variable-resistance transducer is not often used in a seismic displacement instrument because of its rather poor resolution.

Accelerometers utilizing this type of displacement transducer generally are of considerable size and weight (2 × 2 × 2 in. and 16 oz are typical). How the mass and stiffening effect of an accelerometer affect the measurement to be made is considered in Sect. 11-7.

The unbonded wire variable-resistance displacement transducer, discussed in Sect. 8-2a, has also been used as the displacement transducer in seismic accelerometers. Figure 9-17 is a photograph of one such accelerometer.

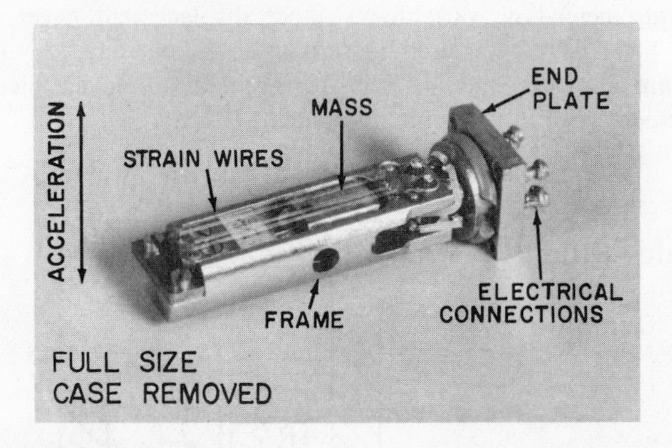

Fig. 9-17. Unbonded wire accelerometer. (*Courtesy of Statham Laboratories, Inc.*)

In this design (shown with case removed) the pretensioned, strain-sensitive wires connect one end (left end in Fig. 9-17) of the seismic mass to the frame. The seismic mass is mounted to the frame through a cantilever flexure plate so that when acceleration is applied, as shown, the seismic mass moves in the plane containing the acceleration vector. As explained on p. 367, this transducer contains all four arms of an equal bridge circuit, and all arms are active. In Fig. 9-17, two of the elements are below the seismic mass and not visible. The circuitry and recording instruments used with bonded resistance strain gages* can be used with accelerometers of this type. Table 9-1 gives the important specifications

* See Sect. 2-2 and Chap. 3 for a discussion of strain-gage circuits and recording equipment.

of some standard accelerometers of this type. A miniature accelerometer of the same type is shown in Fig. 9-18.

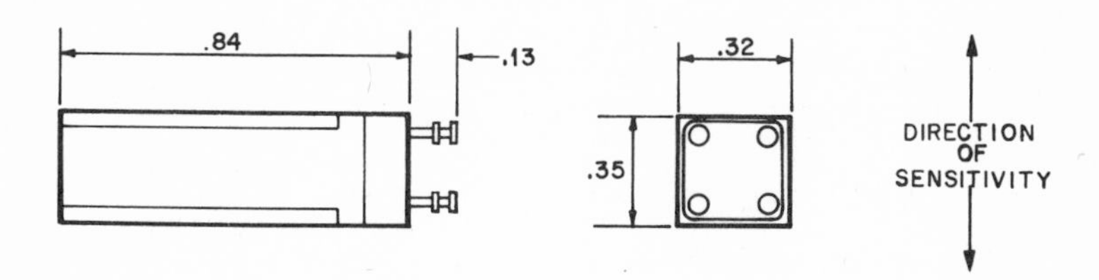

Model Designation	Range	Excitation DC or AC (rms)	Approx. Output Open Circuit	Non-linearity and Hysteresis	Approximate Weight
A52	±5 to ±100g	8 volts	±32 millivolts	< ±1.0% FS	3/10 oz.

Fig. 9-18. Miniature unbonded wire accelerometer. (*Courtesy of Statham Laboratories, Inc.*)

Accelerometers of this type are generally damped to about 0.7 of critical ($h = 0.7$) to provide the largest frequency region with uniform response. Silicone fluids are often used for damping because of their relatively good viscosity constancy with temperature; even so, under variable temperature conditions the damping variation is usually sufficient to cause variation in high-frequency response. One practical solution to this problem is to design for the desired damping at some elevated temperature and then to maintain this elevated temperature at all times by means of an electric heater and thermostat.*

Accelerometers of this type have also been gas-damped. Gas damping is advantageous because of the fact that temperature changes that will change the viscosity of a silicone oil by a factor of two change the viscosity of a gas by only a few per cent. It is difficult to produce large, linear damping forces by using a gas, however. C. K. Stedman [6] describes one type of gas damper and discusses its characteristics.

Variable-inductance displacement gages of several types have also been used in seismic instruments.† Of the various types, the differential

* Statham Laboratories, Inc., uses this method. Damping is designed for +135°F, and the heater maintains this temperature with operating temperatures as low as −65°F.

† For a complete discussion of variable-inductance pickups, see Chap. 14 of Ref. [2] listed in Sect. 8-4 of this book.

Table 9-1

(Courtesy of Statham Laboratories, Inc.)

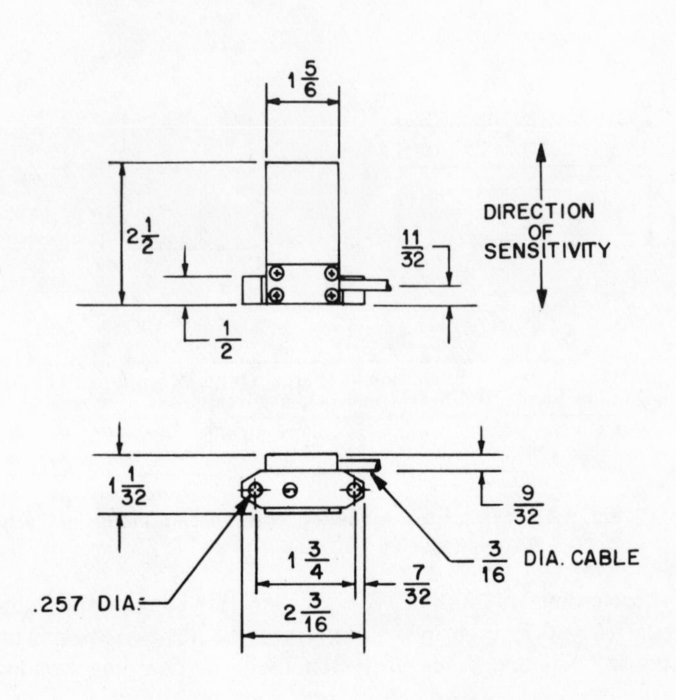

MODEL A5A ACCELEROMETER

Weight: 4 oz., approximately.

Selection Table 1

Ranges	Natural Frequency	Transducer Input Voltage DC or AC	Approx. Full Scale Open Circuit Output	Model Designation
±2g	120 cps	10 v	30 mv	A5A-2-350
±5g	160 cps	10 v	37 mv	A5A-5-350
±10g	250 cps	11 v	44 mv	A5A-10-350
±15g	300 cps	10 v	43 mv	A5A-15-350
±20g	350 cps	11 v	44 mv	A5A-20-350
±25g	375 cps	10 v	40 mv	A5A-25-350
±50g	500 cps	12 v	47 mv	A5A-50-350
±100g	600 cps	11 v	44 mv	A5A-100-350
±200g	800 cps	11 v	44 mv	A5A-200-350

As indicated by the foregoing model designations, a nominal bridge resistance of 350 ohms is furnished unless an order or a request stipulates a preferred resistance.

Table 9-1 (cont.)

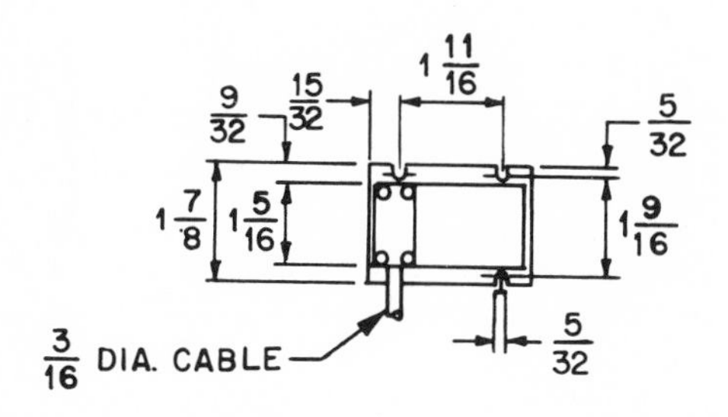

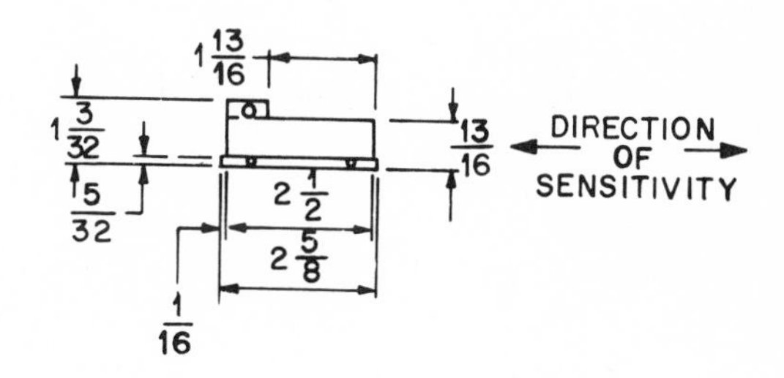

MODEL A45 ACCELEROMETER
Weight: 5 oz., approximately.

Selection Table 2

Ranges	Natural Frequency	Transducer Input Voltage DC or AC	Approx. Full Scale Open Circuit Output	Model Designation
±2g	120 cps	10 v	30 mv	A45-2-350
±5g	160 cps	10 v	37 mv	A45-5-350
±10g	250 cps	11 v	44 mv	A45-10-350
±15g	300 cps	10 v	43 mv	A45-15-350

As indicated by the foregoing model designations, a nominal bridge resistance of 350 ohms is furnished unless an order or a request stipulates a preferred resistance.

Table 9-1 (cont.)

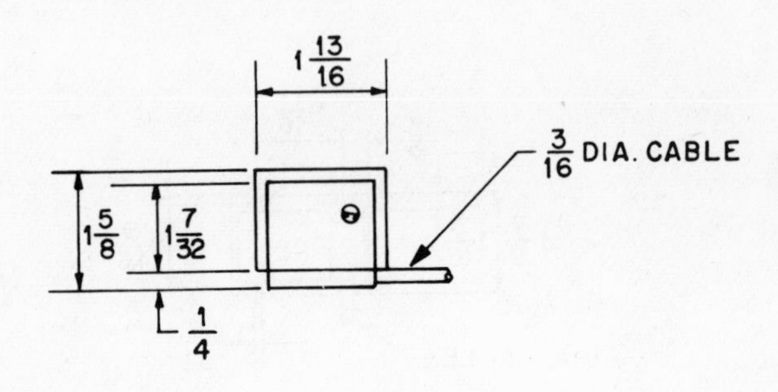

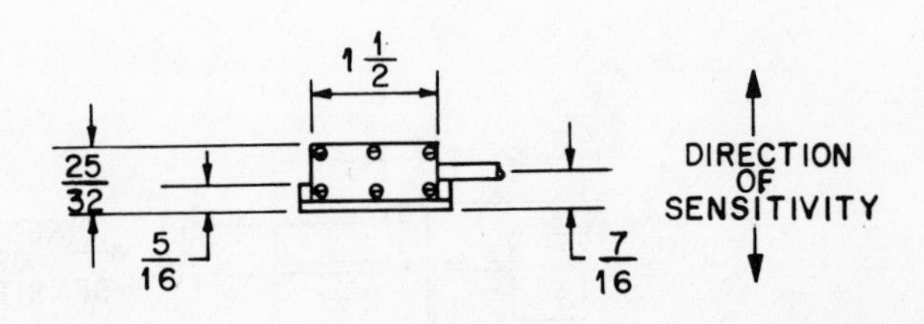

MODEL C ACCELEROMETER

Weight: 2.5 oz., approximately.

Selection Table 3

Ranges	Natural Frequency	Transducer Input Voltage DC or AC	Approx. Full Scale Open Circuit Output	Model Designation
±1g	40 cps	9 v	12 mv	C-1-350
±2g	50 cps	11 v	20 mv	C-2-350
±3g	60 cps	12 v	25 mv	C-3-350
±4g	70 cps	12 v	25 mv	C-4-350
±5g	75 cps	11 v	23 mv	C-5-350
±6g	85 cps	11 v	24 mv	C-6-350
±10g	110 cps	11 v	24 mv	C-10-350
±15g	160 cps	11 v	25 mv	C-15-350
±25g	200 cps	11 v	24 mv	C-25-350
±50g	300 cps	12 v	26 mv	C-50-350

As indicated by the foregoing model designations, a nominal bridge resistance of 350 ohms is furnished unless an order or a request stipulates a preferred resistance.

transformer, discussed in Sect. 8-2a, has been most used in seismic displacement gages and seismic accelerometers. Figure 9-19 is a diagram

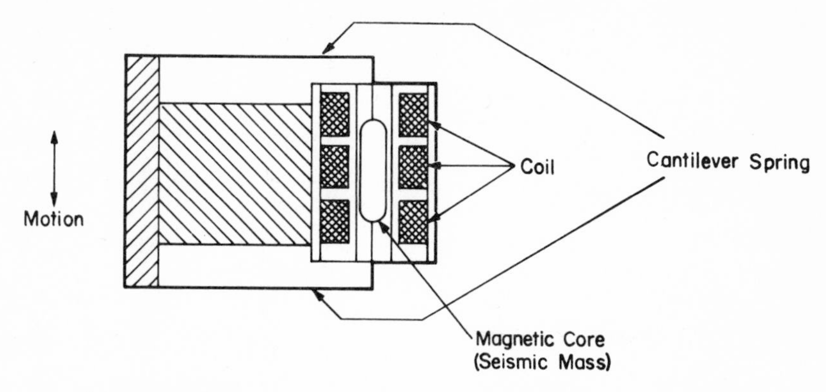

Fig. 9-19. Differential transformer accelerometer. (*Courtesy of SESA, Ref.* [3], *listed in Sect. 8-4 of this book.*)

showing one possible arrangement of a differential transformer displacement gage in a seismic instrument. The electrical circuitry required is the same as when the transducer is used as an ordinary displacement gage (see p. 371). Seismic accelerometers of this type are capable of zero frequency response.

Because of relatively large mass and dimensions, the natural frequency of seismic instruments of this type is generally low (several hundred cycles per second at most), and hence their usable upper frequency limit as accelerometers is low, essentially 0.4 of ω_n for $h = 0.7$. However, as was pointed out in our discussion of displacement gages, the differential transformer offers less resistance to motion, better resolution, and higher output than the variable-resistance gage. Seismic instruments utilizing differential transformers as transducers have typical sensitivities of 2000 mv output/v of excitation/in. of motion (displacement gage) and 10 mv output/v of excitation/g of acceleration input (accelerometer). Seismic instruments of this type may weigh from several ounces to a pound or more.

In seismic-type velocity gages the electro-dynamic velocity transducer discussed in Sect. 8-2b is most often used. Figure 9-20 shows one possible design.

Since these instruments operate as velocity pickups when used above the instrument natural frequency, low natural frequency is an advantage. Typical pickups of this type weigh from several ounces to several pounds, are usable at frequencies from several cycles per second to several thousand

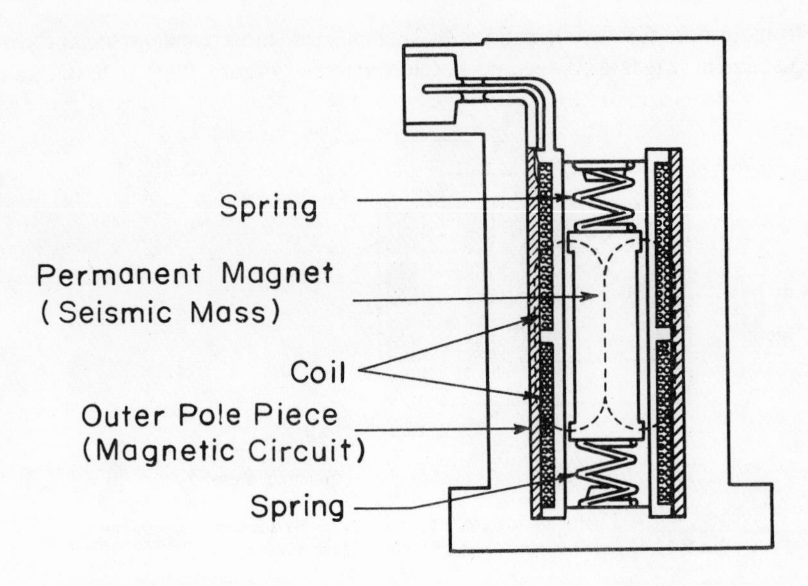

Fig. 9-20. Seismic velocity gage. *(Courtesy of Consolidated Electrodynamics.)*

cycles per second, and have sensitivities of several hundred mv output/in./sec of velocity input.

Variable-resistance strain gages of the bonded type can also be used as the transducer element in seismic instruments.* Figure 9-21 shows one

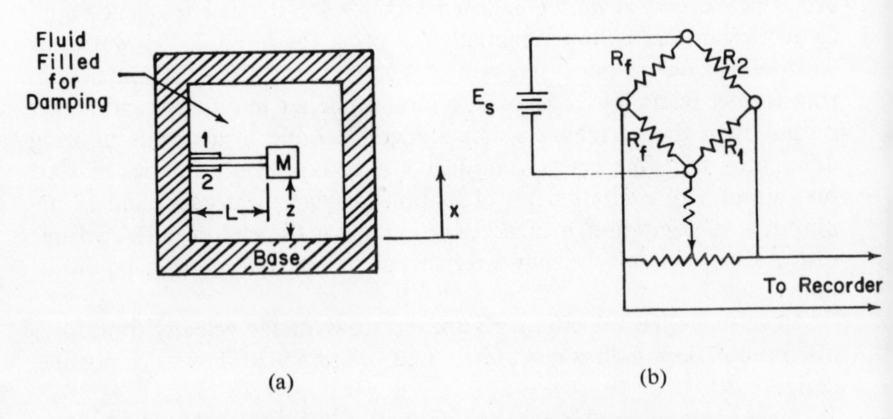

Fig. 9-21. A simple accelerometer using bonded strain gages in a flexural element.

* For a discussion of variable-resistance strain gages, see Chap. 2.

possible design which utilizes bonded resistance strain gages to measure the displacement of the mass M relative to the case.

Development of the relationship between strain produced by relative motion (Z) and base acceleration may prove instructive.

The spring constant K of the system is, by definition,

$$K = \frac{\text{Force } (F)}{\text{Unit deflection } (Z)},$$

and since the deflection (Z) of a cantilever beam is

$$Z = \frac{1}{3}\frac{FL^3}{EI},$$

in which E = elastic modulus of the beam material,

and I = moment of inertia of area of the beam cross section,

we may write

$$K = \frac{3EI}{L^3}.$$

Now, as this instrument is to be used as an accelerometer, the design condition is

$$\omega \leq 0.4\omega_n,$$

or

$$\omega \leq 0.4\sqrt{\frac{K}{M}} = 0.4\sqrt{\frac{3EI}{L^3M}}, \tag{9-8}$$

in which M = effective mass at the free end of the beam. The strain produced by bending is

$$\epsilon = \frac{\sigma}{E} = \frac{M'c'}{EI} = \frac{FLc'}{EI},$$

in which M' is moment and c' is the distance from the neutral surface to the surface on which the strain is to be measured.

The force applied to the beam can be related to the relative displacement (Z) produced by base acceleration, since

$$Z = \frac{\omega^2 X}{\omega_n^2},$$

and hence

$$\frac{\omega^2 X}{\omega_n^2} = \frac{1}{3}\frac{FL^3}{EI} = \frac{1}{3}\frac{\epsilon L^2}{c'}.$$

We may write

$$\epsilon = \frac{3(\omega^2 X)c'}{\omega_n^2 L^2} = \frac{3(\omega^2 X)c'M}{KL^2} = \frac{Mc'L}{EI} \text{ (Acc. base)}$$

or

$$\frac{\epsilon}{\text{Acc. base}} = \frac{Mc'L}{EI}, \tag{9-9}$$

in which ϵ/Acc. base is the strain per unit of base acceleration, usually expressed as μin./in./in./sec^2.

With this particular design it is difficult to obtain a high natural frequency (above several hundred cps) because of physical limitations on the size of the beam on which the gages must be mounted. In any case, as the natural frequency is increased, the output z (proportional to ϵ in this case) must decrease; i.e.,

$$Z = \frac{\omega^2 X}{\omega_n^2 \sqrt{\left[1 - \left(\frac{\omega}{\omega_n}\right)^2\right]^2 + \left[2h\frac{\omega}{\omega_n}\right]^2}} \, . \tag{9-6}$$

Another possible design for a seismic instrument in which the high-sensitivity semiconductor gages could be used is shown in Fig. 9-22.*

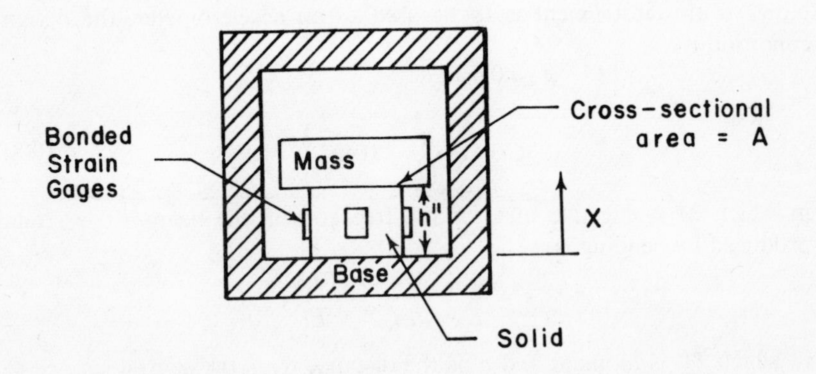

Fig. 9-22. A simple accelerometer using bonded strain gages on a compression element.

In this case the seismic mass is supported by a solid material which functions as the spring support and on (or in) which the strain gages are mounted. In general, seismic instruments of this type would have no damping other than the internal damping of the solid spring.

Again, development of certain design conditions and sensitivity relationships may prove to be helpful.

---

* For a discussion of semiconductor gages, see Chap. 2.

The spring constant K of the solid material is

$$K = \frac{F}{Z} = \frac{F}{\epsilon h} = \frac{F}{\frac{\sigma}{E}h} = \frac{F}{\frac{F}{AE}h} = \frac{AE}{h},$$

so

$$\omega_n = \sqrt{\frac{K}{M}} = \sqrt{\frac{AE}{Mh}}.$$

If the device is to function as an accelerometer,

$$\omega \leq 0.2\omega_n,$$

or

$$\omega_n \geq 5\omega, \qquad \text{since} \qquad h \simeq 0.0.$$

Hence, the design condition is

$$\sqrt{\frac{AE}{hM}} \geq 5\omega.$$

The strain produced is

$$\epsilon = \frac{\sigma}{E} = \frac{F}{AE} = \frac{M(\text{Acc.})}{AE},$$

and henc:

$$\frac{\epsilon}{(\text{Acc.})} = \frac{M}{AE}.$$

With this design, natural frequencies of several thousand cycles per second can be realized, and the signal from the semiconductor gages will be large enough to permit use for accelerations as low as 100 g's.

Seismic accelerometers utilizing bonded strain gages have a lower frequency limit of zero (DC), and the circuitry is the same as is used with the gages in strain-measurement applications.*

In accelerometers similar to the type just analyzed (Fig. 9-22) the solid material is most often a piezoelectric crystal. Piezoelectric materials generate a charge when strained; hence, when they are connected to a recording instrument through suitable circuitry, they can function to measure the relative motion between mass M and case, i.e., Z. Many materials are piezoelectric. Some common ones are quartz, ADP (ammonium dihydrogen phosphate), tourmaline, Rochelle salts, and barium titanate. All of these materials contain oriented crystal domains, and when stress is applied the relative displacement of these domains generates a charge.

* For a discussion of circuitry and recording equipment used with variable-resistance strain gages, see Sect. 2-2 and Chap. 3.

In some (quartz and Rochelle salts) these domains are naturally occurring, and the sensitive axis is determined by the crystal orientation. In others, these domains are established during the manufacturing process by the application of a polarizing voltage at a suitable temperature. Barium titanate is most used in accelerometers for two reasons: (1) it is a polycrystalline material, and its sensitive axis can be established in any desired direction during manufacture. (2) Many of its characteristics, such as charge-generating capacity (sensitivity), internal resistance and capacitance, and stability with temperature, can be controlled by the inclusions of minute amounts of "impurities" which are purposely added during the manufacturing process.*

One possible physical arrangement of a piezoelectric accelerometer is shown in Fig. 9-23. Other arrangements are used. In some cases, two

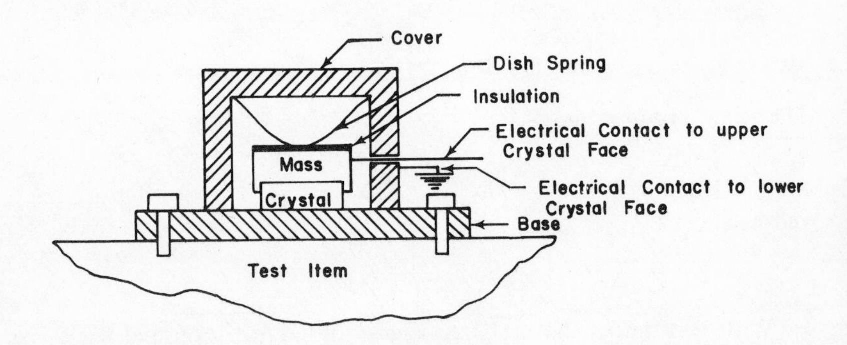

Fig. 9-23. Cross-sectional view of a piezoelectric accelerometer.

crystals are stacked below the seismic mass, and an electrical contact is inserted between the crystal faces. The crystals are polarized so that their output is additive (charge generators connected in series), but doubling the effective spring length (the crystal stack) lowers the natural frequency. In other designs, the piezoelectric crystals support the seismic mass in such a way that the crystals are strained in flexure or shear. These designs also result in lower natural frequencies than those obtained when a single crystal is used in direct compression, but they have other attendant advantages.

Piezoelectric accelerometers are characterized by small size, large output, high natural frequency, inability to measure very low frequency acceleration signals (down to zero frequency, DC), and need of rather specialized circuitry.

---

* For an extensive discussion of barium titanate accelerometers, see Ref. [7].

Figure 9-24 shows several commercially available accelerometers and indicates the acceleration range, range of size and shape, natural frequency, and signal level obtainable. Figure 9-24a shows a somewhat standard

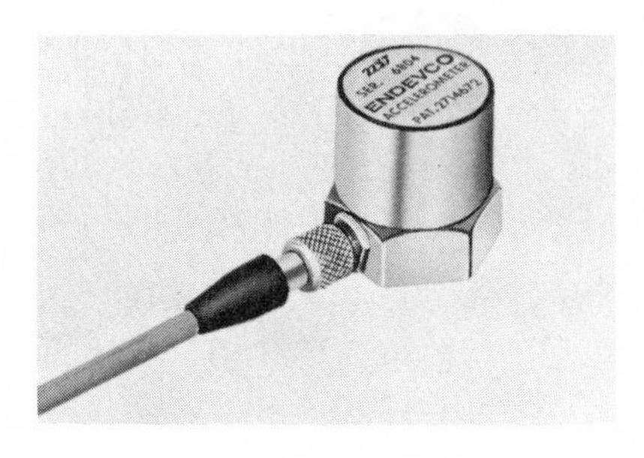

(*a*)
High output
This accelerometer provides a high sensitivity of 72 pk mv/pk g and a wide frequency range (resonance frequency is 35 kc). The weight is only 1.1 ounce.

(*b*)
Shock accelerometer
This accelerometer has a high resonance frequency of 80 kc. Dynamic range of this transducer is a maximum sinusoidal 10,000 g and a maximum shock of 20,000 g with a 75 μsec half-sine pulse. Nominal sensitivity is 0.6 pk mv/pk g.

(*c*)
Microminiature accelerometers
These accelerometers have an output of 5.0 pk mv/pk g with six ft cables, with weight of only 2.95 gr. Size: $\frac{3}{8}$ in. hexagon by $\frac{3}{16}$ in. high.

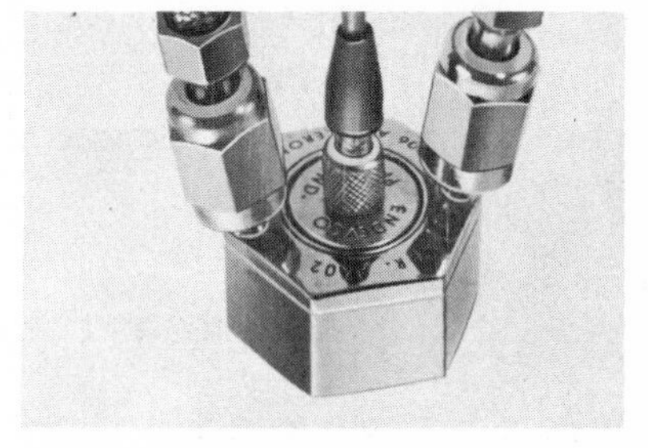

(*d*)
2200°F accelerometer
This accelerometer measures vibrations at high temperature (2200°F at base). This liquid-cooled transducer will measure accelerations up to 1000 g's and provides large output of 12 pk mv/pk g with high resonance frequency of 20 kc.

Fig. 9-24. Piezoelectric accelerometer types. (*Courtesy of Endevco Corp.*)

form. The particular model shown has been designed for high output, 72 pk mv/pk g over an acceleration range of several thousand g's. Other models, of this same form and weight, are available with sensitivities ranging from less than ten pk mv/pk g to more than 200 pk mv/pk g. It must be remembered, however, that, in general, increase in sensitivity is obtained at the expense of natural frequency. (This rule cannot be rigorously applied, since all manufacturers use crystals which have different properties in their various models of accelerometers.) Figure 9-24b shows a typical shock or "high g accelerometer." Units of this type are characterized by high natural frequency, ability to produce an output linearly proportional to acceleration input to a very high acceleration level, small size and mass.

Figure 9-24c shows several miniature accelerometers. The single unit in the form of a $\frac{3}{8}$ in. hexagon by $\frac{3}{16}$ in. high weighs 2.75 gr. These single units may be assembled in a block as shown to form a triaxial accelerometer.

Piezoelectric crystals have been produced that show less than ± 5 per cent change in sensitivity over the temperature range $-320°F$ to $+500°F$, but for use at even higher temperatures forced cooling of the accelerometer is used. Figure 9-24d shows a liquid-cooled model designed to function at temperatures as high as 2200°F.

Since the circuitry used with piezoelectric accelerometers is different from that used for strain gages and other transducers already discussed, this subject will be discussed in detail in the next section.

Since the low-frequency response of piezoelectric accelerometers is primarily dependent on the external circuitry, this item will be discussed in connection with circuitry.

9-3 Circuitry for piezoelectric accelerometers

9-3a Sensitivity considerations

For purposes of circuit analysis a piezoelectric crystal can be represented as a charge generator of capacitance, C_p. See Fig. 9-25. The open-circuit voltage output (E_o) of the crystal is

$$E_o = q/C_p, \tag{9-12}$$

in which q = the charge generated by straining the crystal. When the crystal is connected to a recording circuit, additional capacitance is shunted across the crystal as shown in Fig. 9-26. This additional capacitance (C_E for external capacitance) is the sum of the capacitance of the connecting cables, connectors, and the input capacitance of the instrument to which the accelerometer may be connected. The voltage E is now

$$E = \frac{q}{C_p + C_E}, \tag{9-13}$$

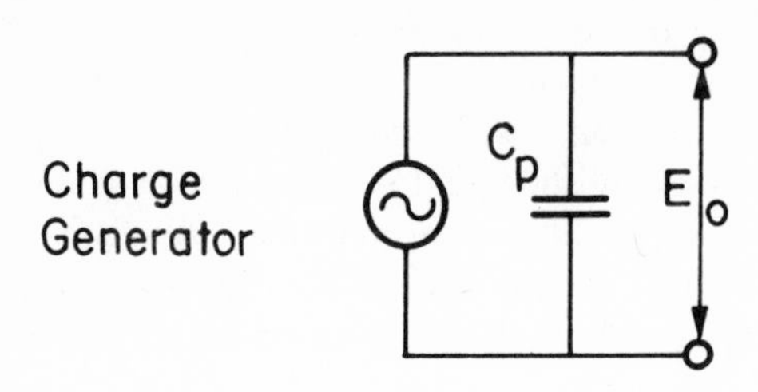

Fig. 9-25. Equivalent-circuit piezoelectric crystal.

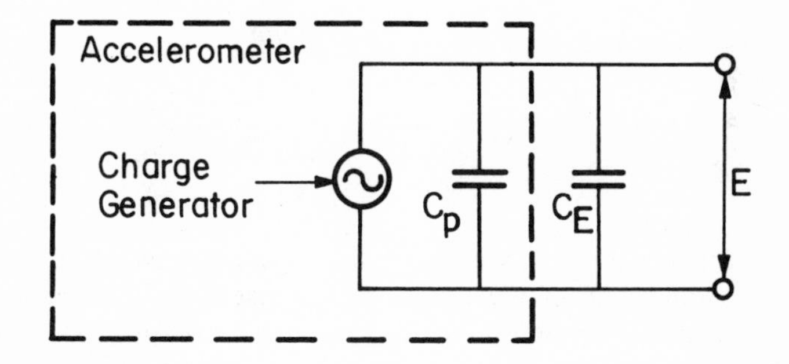

Fig. 9-26. External capacitance shunted with piezoelectric crystal.

which indicates that the voltage output of a given piezoelectric crystal varies inversely with the total capacitance associated with the crystal and circuitry.

Most piezoelectric accelerometers are calibrated* by using a system of known standard external capacitance (C_{Std}), and the voltage sensitivity is then given as $E_{\text{Cal}} = N$ mv/g, with $C_{\text{Ext}} = C_{\text{Std}}$.†

The voltage sensitivity for use with any given circuit is then computed as

$$E = E_{\text{Cal}} \times \frac{C_p + C_{\text{Std}}}{C_p + C_E}, \tag{9-14}$$

in which C_E is the total external capacitance of the circuit used. An example will illustrate the procedure.

* Calibration is discussed in Chap. 10.

† Voltage sensitivities may be established, given, and used in terms of: (1) pk mv/pk g; or (2) rms mv/pk g. The first (pk mv/pk g) is used in transient acceleration studies; either may be used in harmonic acceleration studies. (*Note:* Sensitivity in rms mv/pk g = 0.707 × sensitivity in pk mv/pk g.)

Example 9-1. A piezoelectric accelerometer having an internal capacitance (C_p) of 500 micromicrofarads (500 $\mu\mu$f)* was calibrated; a system having an external capacitance (C_{Std}) of 100 $\mu\mu$f was used. The voltage sensitivity (E_{Cal}) was established as 15.00 pk mv/pk g. What is the sensitivity of this accelerometer when it is connected to an amplifier having a residual input capacitance of 50 $\mu\mu$f by a cable having a capacitance of 100 $\mu\mu$f?

Solution: The total external capacitance of the recording system is

$$C_E = C_{\text{Cable}} + C_{\text{Ampl.}}$$
$$= 100 + 50$$
$$= 150\ \mu\mu\text{f}.$$

Hence,

$$E = 15 + \frac{500 + 100}{500 + 150}$$
$$= 13.83 \text{ pk mv/pk g}.$$

It is apparent that the voltage sensitivity (E) may be set to any desired value by adjustment of the circuit capacitance (C_E). This is sometimes done to standardize the output from several accelerometers. More frequently, however, this method of signal attenuation is used to prevent the large signal produced by high accelerations from overdriving the first stages of the recording system.

If the piezoelectric crystal is connected to an instrument which senses charge (q) rather than voltage (E), we can establish and use a charge sensitivity (Q = picocoulombs/g) which is independent of circuit capacitance. Such instruments, known as "charge amplifiers," are available. These instruments consist of a voltage amplifier and a feedback loop. The output voltage which results from the charge input is returned to the input side to reduce the input voltage to zero; thus no charge is stored in the accelerometer crystal or in the cables. The transfer from input charge to output voltage (gain = mv/picocoulomb) depends on the size of the feedback capacitor ($E = q/C_{\text{feedback}}$) rather than on the capacitance of the crystal and external circuit. Hence, the sensitivity of the accelerometer *in its circuit* is unaffected by variations in shunt capacitance in the circuit. However, there are limitations on the total shunt capacitance that can precede the charge amplifier without affecting its operation. When very long cables are used between the accelerometer and the charge

* One micromicro unit ($\mu\mu$) = 1 pico unit (p) = 1×10^{-12} unit. Thus, 500 p f = 500×10^{-12} f.

amplifier, the instrument's gain and noise level* or high-frequency response† may be affected.

The charge sensitivity is given for many accelerometers (picocoulombs/g). If only the voltage sensitivity and calibration conditions are given, the charge sensitivity can easily be computed as

$$Q = \frac{E_{\text{Cal}}(C_p + C_{\text{Std}})}{1000}, \tag{9-15}$$

in which Q = picocoulombs/g.
E_{Cal} = mv/g.
C_p = crystal capacitance in picofarads.
C_{Std} = external capacitance in picofarads used when E_{Cal} was established.

9-3b Low-frequency response considerations

The lower limit of frequency response of a given piezoelectric accelerometer is primarily dependent upon the external circuitry. Figure 9-27 shows a load impedance (R_L) added to the circuit previously discussed.

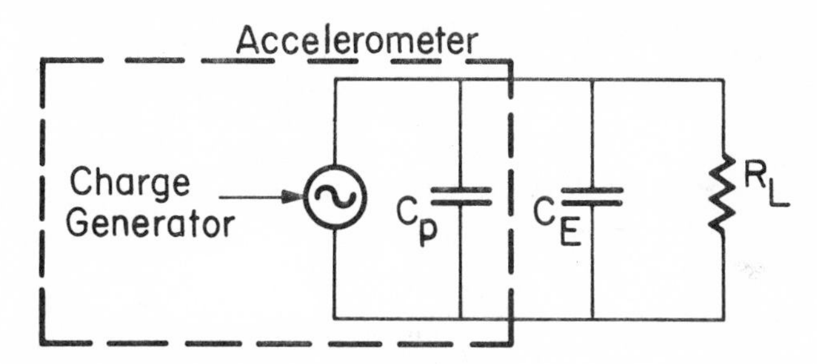

Fig. 9-27. Piezoelectric accelerometer, external capacitance, and load impedance.

If a constant acceleration produces a constant strain on the crystal, a charge of q is developed. The output voltage signal (E) will not remain constant, however, since the charge will be dissipated as current flows through the circuit. The rate at which this charge decays depends upon the size of the charged capacitance ($C_p + C_E$) and the size of the load impedance (R_L) through which the charge is dissipated. Hence, the low-frequency response is determined by the value of the product R_LC_T (circuit time constant), in which R_L is total load impedance and C_T is total

* See the manual for Kistler Instrument Corporation Model 568, Universal Electrostatic Charge Amplifier.

† See the manual for Endevco Corporation, Model 2620 Amplifier.

capacitance of the system ($C_p + C_E$). The larger the value of the product R_LC_T, the lower is the cutoff frequency.

If a charge amplifier is used, the circuit time constant is determined by the impedance and capacitance of the charge amplifier feedback loop R_FC_F. See Fig. 9-28. For harmonic signals the relative response equation applies.*

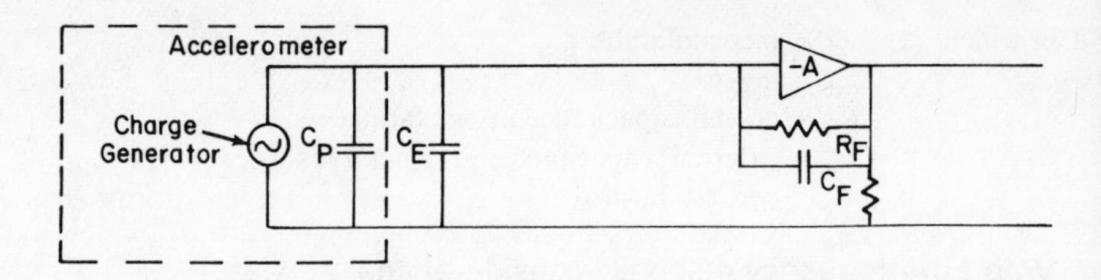

Fig. 9-28. Piezoelectric accelerometer, external capacitance, and charge amplifier circuit.

$$\text{Relative response} = \frac{1}{\sqrt{\left(\frac{1}{2\pi fRC}\right)^2 + 1}}, \tag{9-16}$$

in which f is the frequency in cps.
R is the load impedance in ohms, R_L or R_F.
C is the total capacitance in farads, ($C_p + C_E$) or C_F.

This equation is plotted as Fig. 9-29. An example will serve to illustrate how it can be used to compute the low-frequency response, to a harmonic input, of a given accelerometer in a given circuit.

Example 9-2. It is desired to measure an acceleration having a component of five cps. A voltage amplifier is used. The total capacitance (accelerometer, cable, and recording system input) is $500 + 85 - 15 = 600$ $\mu\mu$f. The input impedance of the recording system is 100 megohms.

$$fR_LC_T = 5 \times 100 \times 10^6 \times 600 \times 10^{-12} = 0.30.$$

Entering Fig. 9-29 with this value, we read

$$p = 0.89;$$

i.e., the signal is down 11 per cent, as compared to its value if R_LC_T were equal to infinity.

* See Ref. [8] for the derivation of this expression.

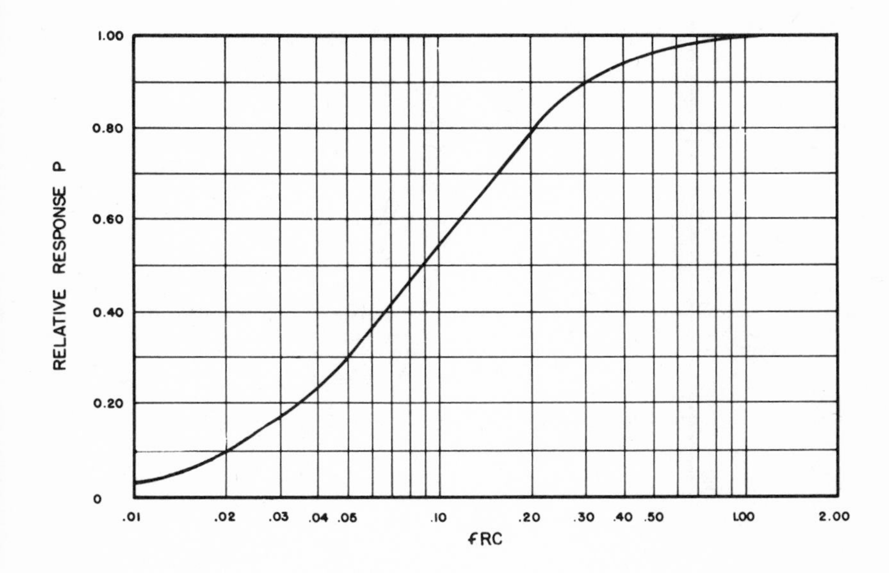

Fig. 9-29. Low-frequency response versus loading.

Since C_p is fixed for a given accelerometer and C_E is usually fixed by sensitivity considerations [see Eq. (9-13)], we conclude that in order to obtain good low-frequency response with a voltage-type amplifier, the load impedance should be very high. Some accelerometers are made with high crystal capacitance (Cp) so that they can be connected directly to a cathode ray oscilloscope ($R_L \simeq 2 \times 10^6$ ohms) and still respond to frequencies below 100 cps.* More frequently, piezoelectric accelerometers are connected to a cathode follower—a device which has a high input impedance and signal gain of approximately unity.†

Cathode followers having an input impedance of 5000×10^6 ohms are commercially available.

Use of a cathode follower will extend the low-frequency response to below ten cps. For the lowest possible frequency response, piezoelectric

* Endevco Model 2215 is of this type; $C_p = 7000\ \mu\mu f$.

† Cathode follower circuits are discussed on pp. 173-223 of Ref. [7].

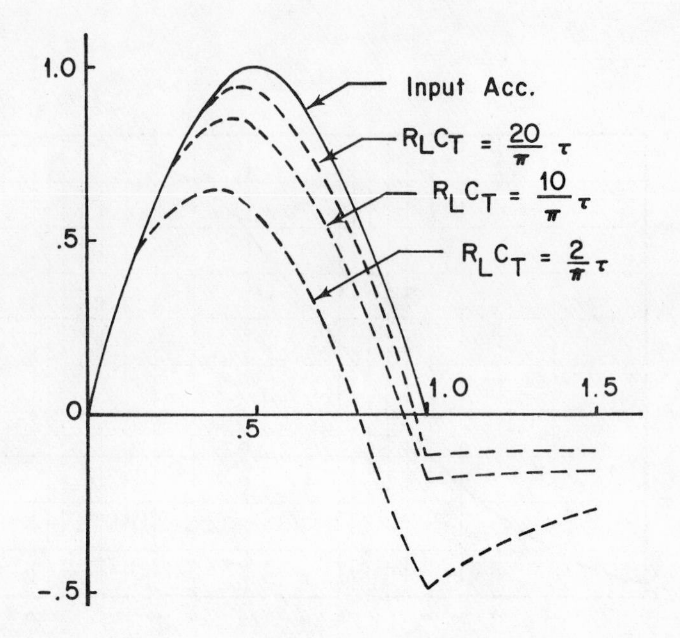

Fig. 9-30. Response to half-sine wave.

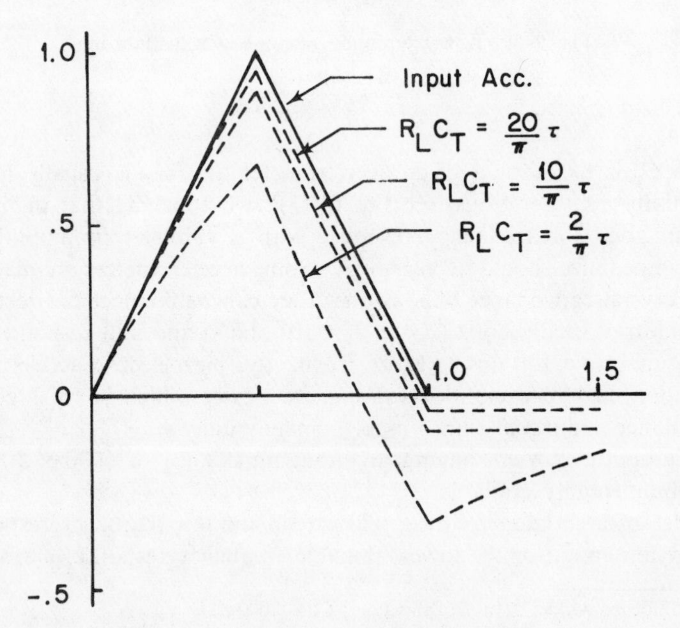

Fig. 9-31. Response to triangular wave.

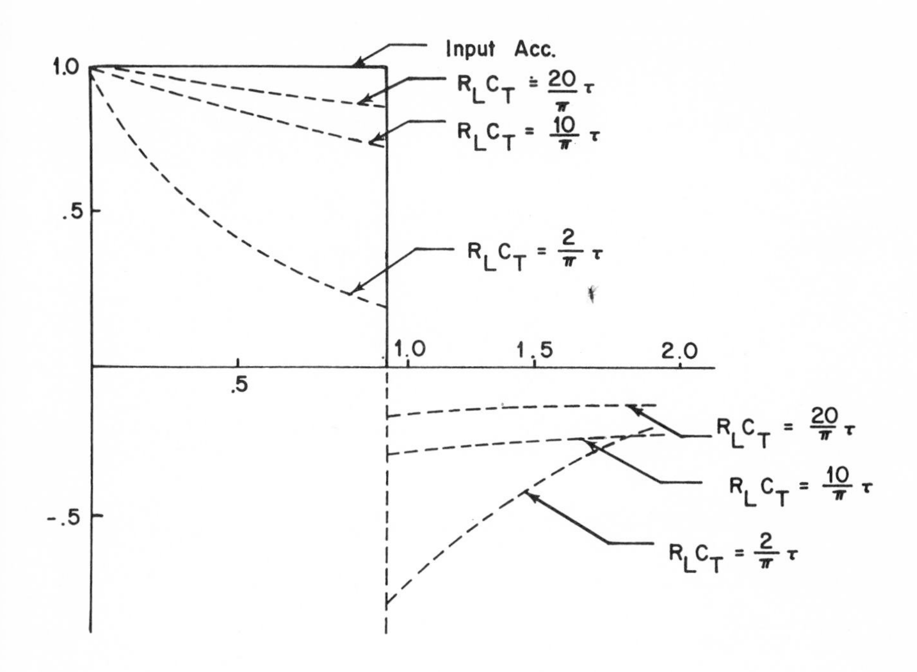

Fig. 9-32. Response to square wave.

accelerometers are connected to an electrometer tube circuit. Electrometer tube circuits are available which have 10^{11} to 10^{14} ohms input impedance.*

With charge amplifiers, both R_F and C_F can be made large. In one model† R_F is 10^{10} to 10^{14} ohms. It must be remembered that increasing C_F lowers sensitivity; $E = q/C_F$.

This discussion of low-frequency response has all been in terms of harmonic input acceleration. When transients are to be measured, it must be remembered that a transient contains components of all frequencies down to DC. M. E. Gurtin [10] has made a study of the low-frequency response of a typical piezoelectric accelerometer circuit (Fig. 9-27) to three transient pulse shapes: half-sine-wave, triangular, and square. Some of Gurtin's results are presented in Figs. 9-30, 9-31, and 9-32. In these figures the duration of the input acceleration is τ, and the circuit time constant is R_LC_T. It is readily apparent that if any of these

* The use of electrometer tube circuits is discussed in Ref. [9].

† Kistler Instrument Corporation, Model 568.

transients are to be measured with a reasonable degree of fidelity, the circuit time constant ($R_L C_T$) should be at least $20/\pi$ times the duration of the pulse (τ). Notice that the square pulse is the most difficult shape to handle and that the effect of having too small a circuit time constant (inadequate low-frequency response) is reduced peak reading followed by a signal undershoot.

Based on this type of transient analysis, J. E. Rhodes [11] makes the recommendations shown in Table 9-2. An example will illustrate the use of this table.

Table 9-2. Effect of circuit time constant ($R_L C_T$) on amplitude of transients

Pulse Shape	Approximate Minimum Time Constant ($R_L C_T$) for Amplitude Accuracy Shown	
	2%	5%
Half-Sine	16τ	7τ
Sawtooth	16τ	7τ
Square	50τ	20τ

Example 9-3. A sawtooth pulse with an expected duration of three millisec is to be measured. The total external capacitance (cable and cathode follower input) is 200 picofarads, and the crystal capacitance is 350 picofarads. Find the minimum cathode-follower input impedance that will assure five per cent accuracy of the peak value.

Solution:

$$C_T = 200 + 350 = 550 \text{ picofarads } (550 \times 10^{-12}\text{ f}),$$

$$\tau = 3 \times 10^{-3} \text{ sec},$$

$$(C_T R_L)_{\min} = 7\tau,$$

$$R_{L_{\min}} = \frac{(7)(3 \times 10^{-3})}{550 \times 10^{-12}} = 3.82 \times 10^7$$

$$= 38.2 \text{ megohms}.$$

Since too small a time constant ($R_L C_T$) causes the signal from a transient to undershoot, this undershoot can be used to indicate when the system is inadequate. For simple transients of known shape the amount of indicated undershoot can be used to correct the indicated peak to obtain the true peak value. A. F. Lawrence [9] gives such a correction for use with half-sine-wave transients. See Fig. 9-33. Unfortunately, in practice, transients shapes are often not simple in form.

With the effect of circuitry on piezoelectric accelerometer sensitivity and low-frequency response established, it will now be possible to discuss, in order, the items that make up a complete piezoelectric accelerometer circuit.

9-3c System components

ACCELEROMETER

The accelerometer itself should be chosen with several considerations in mind: size, acceleration range, sensitivity, and high-frequency response. All of these items are covered in Sect. 9-2.

CABLES

Since the amount of shunt capacitance connected with the accelerometer varies almost directly with the length of the connecting cable, it must be realized that the accelerometer voltage output will vary inversely with cable length, and with variation in cable capacitance. (This is not the case if a charge amplifier is used, however.) Typical accelerometer cables have capacitances of from 20 to 30 picofarads per foot.*

It must also be remembered that one end of the cable and its connector are subjected to the same shock as the accelerometer. This may produce an electrical signal which appears superimposed on the accelerometer as noise. Irwin Vigness [12] offers the following explanation as to the source of this noise.

> The cable noise is generated principally between a cable conductor and its dielectric. The cable noise is caused by a friction-generated bound charge on the dielectric. A separation of the dielectric and the conductor under shock results in an effective change of capacity between the conductor and dielectric surface. As there is a fixed charge on the dielectric, this will cause a momentary change of potential of the system. Low-noise cables may be obtained by having the conductors bonded to the dielectric, by a conducting coating for the surfaces of the dielectric that are normally in contact with a conductor, by having no unbonded interfaces of several dielectrics, and by selecting dielectric materials for which the triboelectric effect is small.

* Such as Microdot #50-3804.

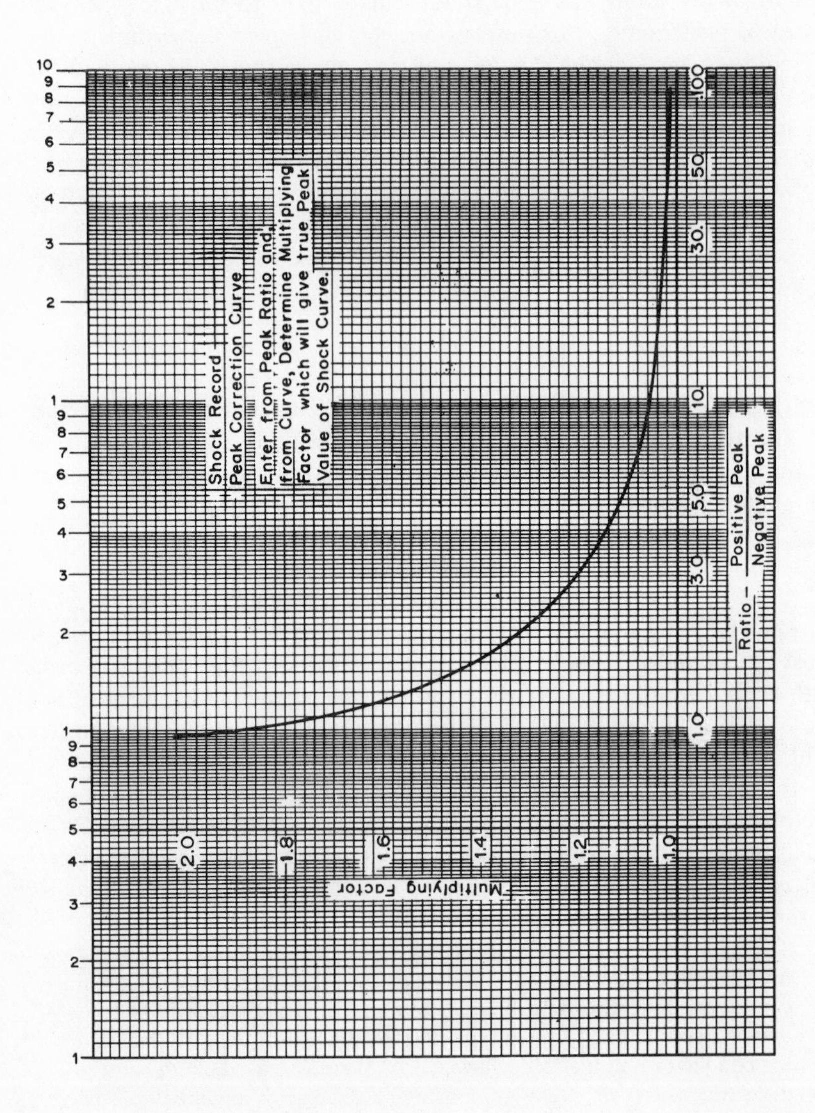

Fig. 9-33. Correction factors for use with half-sine-wave transients that undershoot because of inadequate low-frequency response.

Low-noise cables are commercially available.* Accelerometer cables should be secured in such a way as to reduce cable whipping, flexing, and longitudinal straining to a minimum.

SIGNAL CONDITIONERS

The term is used here in a very broad sense as any item inserted between the accelerometer and the final recording device.

Because the potential signal produced may be very large, the first conditioning necessary may be attenuation. This is accomplished by adding shunt capacitance. A variable shunt capacitance which permits output voltage adjustments in 0.1 per cent steps is shown in Fig. 9-34.

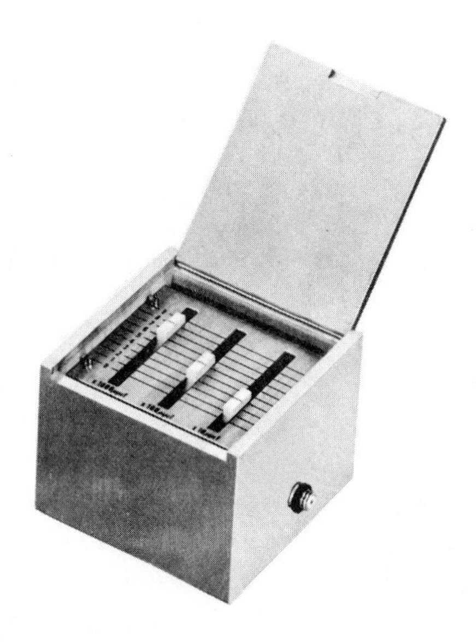

Fig. 9-34. Piezoelectric accelerometer attenuator. (*Courtesy of Endevco Corporation.*)

If low-frequency response is important, the accelerometer is connected to a cathode-follower or electrometer-type preamplifier or to a charge preamplifier. These serve to couple the accelerometer to the lower impedance recorder. These preamplifiers must be able to handle

* Microdot #50-3804, and others.

the accelerometer output without being overloaded. If the final signal is recorded after filtering, one must realize that the peak voltage at the preamplifier may be orders of magnitude larger than those recorded. The signal distortion that results from overloading preamplifiers is sometimes difficult to recognize in the final record, and hence this is a particularly dangerous source of error.

Both cathode-follower and charge-type preamplifiers have been miniaturized and protected so that they can be mounted on the test item very near the accelerometer, thus keeping the cable length between accelerometer and preamplifier to a minimum.

In some cases the output of the cathode follower or electrometer is connected directly to recording device, but more frequently some type of preamplifier is needed. If the recording device has a relatively high input impedance (say, above 10,000 ohms) and the cables between the cathode follower and recorder are short (say, up to 25 ft of low-capacitance cable), a voltage-type preamplifier is used. A typical application of this type is the amplification of cathode-follower output into the voltage range to drive a telemetering oscillator or tape recorder. If the recording device has a low impedance (such as an oscillographic galvanometer), a current preamplifier is needed. That is, the amplifier must be capable of supplying the required current to the low-impedance load at the maximum rated voltage without distortion.

Cathode-follower-preamplifier combinations are available for both of these purposes. An example of the first type (voltage amplification) offers an impedance of 1000×10^6 ohms to the accelerometer and will supply seven v output into a load of 10,000 (or more) ohms.*

An example of the second type (current amplification) offers an impedance of 1000×10^6 ohms to the accelerometer and will supply seven v output into a load of 1000 ohms.† With very low impedance recorders (less than 1000 ohms) it will generally be necessary to limit the amplifier voltage gain to keep the current flow within the rated value, to insert a step-down transformer between amplifier and recorder, or to add resistance in series with the recorder.

When the cable between cathode-follower-preamplifier combination and the recorder is long, its effect on the circuit load must not be overlooked. The part of the load impedance (Z_L) that is due to cable capacitance (C_C) will decrease as signal frequency (f cps) increases. Thus

$$Z_L = \frac{1}{2\pi f C_C}. \tag{9-17}$$

* Endevco #2607.

† Endevco #2609.

Therefore, an amplifier which drives long lines may be overloaded for high-frequency applications. J. E. Rhodes [13] discussed the problem of long cables between preamplifier and recorder in some detail.

A low-pass filter is sometimes inserted in an accelerometer circuit ahead of the recorder. A low-pass filter is a circuit which progressively attenuates signal components having frequencies above some preselected value (cutoff frequency). Low-pass filters are used to eliminate from the record high-frequency components which are invariably excited when the accelerometer is shock-excited. Their use is often justified on the basis that high-frequency signals make the record difficult to read and tend to obscure low-amplitude, low-frequency signals; however, the use of low-pass filters is full of pitfalls. It is easy to overfilter a signal and hence to eliminate acceleration amplitude that should be of interest. Filters may distort the signal due to the fact that the filter circuit does not show a linear phase-shift frequency relationship (see Fig. 9-6, p. 395). In general, for each new test condition it is very desirable to record both filtered and unfiltered signals until the effect of the filter in that particular environment is well understood.

RECORDERS

All types of recorders are used to record from piezoelectric accelerometers.* The choice is more influenced by the frequency response required than by any other consideration. In general, oscillographic galvanometers are not suitable for recording frequencies above 5000 cps. (R. Tengwell [14] discusses the use of galvanometers with piezoelectric accelerometers.)

All of the common damped galvanometers ($h = 0.7$) provide high-frequency filtering, since, for a given amplitude of input, they show progressively less response as the signal frequency increases above about 0.4 of the galvanometer natural frequency. [The response of a damped galvanometer (indicator deflection/current input) versus frequency ratio (ω/ω_n galvanometer) is the same as the response curve shown in Fig. 9-3.] For higher frequencies, cathode ray oscilloscopes and tape recorders are used.

9-3d System frequency response

To obtain the desired low-frequency response all parts of the system (cathode follower, preamplifiers, filters, and recorders) must have at least as good low-frequency response as has been established by proper selection of the accelerometer circuit, $R_L C_T$ time constant. For transient

* See Chap. 3 for a discussion of various recording systems.

studies Rhodes [11] suggests that, for five per cent whole-system accuracy (no more than five per cent reduction in signal), each part of the system must be capable of handling frequencies of

$$f = \frac{1}{2R_L C_T},$$

where f is in cps.

$R_L C_T$ is the circuit time constant selected to give two per cent accuracy for the expected transient (see Table 9-2, p. 422).

To obtain the desired high-frequency response, the accelerometer must have a sufficiently high natural frequency.

As shown in Sect. 9-1a for a piezoelectric accelerometer ($h \simeq 0$), the ratio of output signal to input acceleration is essentially constant for harmonic input acceleration frequencies equal to, or less than, 0.2 of the accelerometer's natural frequency ($\omega/\omega_n \leq 0.2$). Hence, for periodic motion, the piezoelectric accelerometer should have a natural frequency at least five times as great as the frequency of the highest frequency component of significance in the input.

As shown in Sect. 9-1b, when a piezoelectric accelerometer is used to measure transients, the rise time of the transient must be long compared to the natural period of the accelerometer. Based on the type of analysis presented in Sect. 9-1b, Rhodes [11] makes the following recommendations: (1) for measuring transients that are approximated by either half-sine-wave or triangular pulses, the minimum required natural frequency for the acceleration is as shown in Table 9-3. (2) Even if the pulse dur-

Table 9-3. Required resonant frequency for undamped transducers measuring half-sine or triangular transients

Pulse Width (τ) (microsec)	Required Natural Period (T) (microsec) $T = \tau/5$	Required Minimum Resonant Frequency (f) (kc/sec) $f = 1/T$
200 μsec	40 μsec	25 kc
150 μsec	30 μsec	33 kc
100 μsec	20 μsec	50 kc
75 μsec	15 μsec	67 kc
50 μsec	10 μsec	100 kc

ation is greater than 200 μsec, the accelerometer's natural frequency should be at least as high as 25 kc. This is necessary since in practice the transients will not be true half-sine or triangular, but will contain higher frequency components superimposed on the main pulse. (3) For measuring unsymmetrical transients the natural period of the accelerometer (T) should be equal to, or less than, one-third of the transient rise time (τ_r); i.e., $T \leq \tau_r/3$.

After the accelerometer has been selected to obtain the desired high-frequency response, it becomes imperative to insure that the remainder of the system will have adequate high-frequency response. The high-frequency response characteristics of many items of equipment (cathode followers, preamplifiers, filters, recorders) are given in terms of response versus frequency (or rise time). (As an example, a cathode ray oscilloscope with a given preamplifier may show essentially flat response from DC to 300 kc.) These specifications should be consulted in choosing the system to give a desired high-frequency response. However, exact analysis for the frequency response of the system as a whole is difficult (particularly as regarding response to transients), and final check is probably best done by test.

System frequency response can be checked by inserting some desired signal of known wave form into the system at the accelerometer output and observing the final form of the recorded signal. The method used by the author may be outlined as follows:*

> The complete instrumentation system shall be checked for fidelity in the following manner before initial use and each time the instrumentation is changed. (a) The accelerometer shall be replaced with a square wave generator and a series capacitor. The capacitance of the capacitor shall be equal to the accelerometer capacitance. The square wave generator shall have the same output as the expected output of the accelerometer (peak g $\times$ sensitivity) and the same half period as the expected shock pulse duration (frequency = $0.5/D$). (b) The recorded output wave form shall closely resemble the input wave form. Figure 9-35 presents typical output wave forms that can be used as a guide in establishing acceptable wave forms. Wave form (a) in the figure shows an ideal output as it exactly reproduces the input wave form, whereas Fig. 9-35b illustrates an output which is unacceptable. Since ideal output wave forms are difficult to establish in actual practice, formulas for acceptance limits for typical output wave forms are presented in Figs. 9-35c, e, and g. Points (1) and (2) in Figs. 9-35c and d are arbitrarily established on any straight portion of the curve. Points (1) and (2) are not necessarily equidistant from the horizontal axis.

* Quoted from "Engineering Development-Sandia Corporation Standard Test Methods," Organization 7300, SC-4452A (M) Sect. 3.2.4, pp. 22-23.

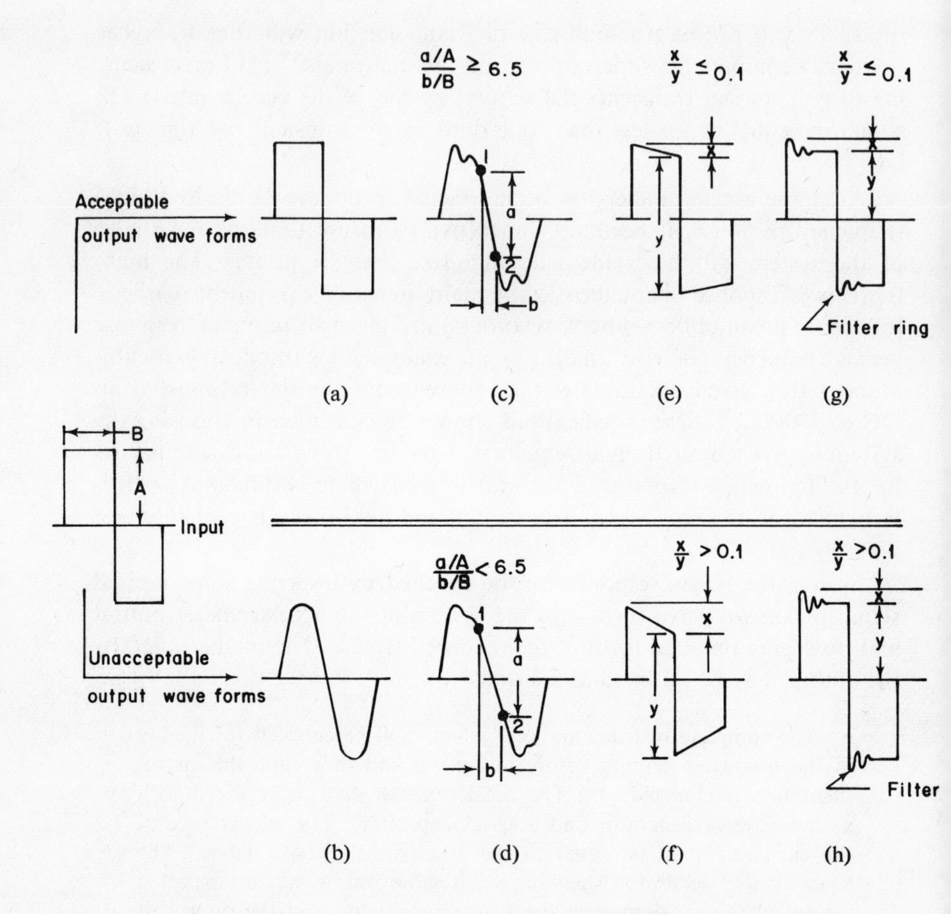

Fig. 9-35. Wave forms used to check accelerometer systems.

9-4 References listed in Chapter 9

1. Thomson, W. T., *Mechanical Vibrations*, 2nd ed. New York: Prentice-Hall, Inc., 1953, pp. 96–99.
2. Levy, S. and W. D. Kroll, "Response of Accelerometers to Transient Accelerations," *Journal of Research of the National Bureau of Standards*, Vol. 45, No. 4 (Oct. 1950), Research Paper 2138.
3. Kearns, R. W., "Velocities and Displacements Associated with the Transient Response of Accelerometers," Paper No. 534, SESA (May 1961).
4. MacDuff, J. N. and J. R. Curreri, *Vibration Control.* New York: McGraw-Hill, 1958, Chap. 7.
5. Jacobsen, L. S. and R. S. Ayre, *Engineering Vibrations.* New York: McGraw-Hill, 1958, Chaps. 3, 4, 5.

6. Stedman, C. K., "Some Characteristics of Gas Damped Accelerometers," *Statham Instrument Notes Number 33*, Statham Instruments, Incorporated (Oct. 1958).
7. *Proceedings of Symposium on Barium Titanate Accelerometers*, National Bureau of Standards Report No. 2654, U. S. Department of Commerce National Bureau of Standards (Aug. 1953).
8. *Reference Data for Radio Engineers* (equations for RLC circuits), 4th ed. International Telephone and Telegraph Corporation, 320 Park Ave., New York, N.Y. Chap. 5, p. 148, "Fundamentals of Networks."
9. Lawrence, A. F., "Crystal Accelerometer Response to Mechanical Shock Impulses," *SCTM 168-56-16*, Sandia Corporation, Albuquerque, N.Mex., 1956.
10. Gurtin, M. E., "The Effect of Accelerometer Low-Frequency Response on Transient Measurements," *Proceedings of the Society for Experimental Stress Analysis*, Vol. 18, No. 1, pp. 206–8.
11. Rhodes, J. E., "Transducer System Frequency Requirements for Transient Measurements," Endevco Corporation Tech-Data Report (Sept. 22, 1960).
12. Vigness, Irwin, "Measurement of Shock," *Shock and Structural Response*, ASME (1960), pp. 18–34.
13. Rhodes, J. E., "Driving Long Lines," Endevco Corporation Tech-Data Report (Jan. 3, 1961).
14. Tengwell, R., "Driving Galvanometers," Endevco Corporation Tech-Data Report (May 25, 1961).

9-5 Problems

9-1 The accelerometer pulse shown in Fig. 9-36 is to be measured. What is the lowest value of accelerometer natural frequency that you would use if the accelerometer is damped to 0.7 of critical?

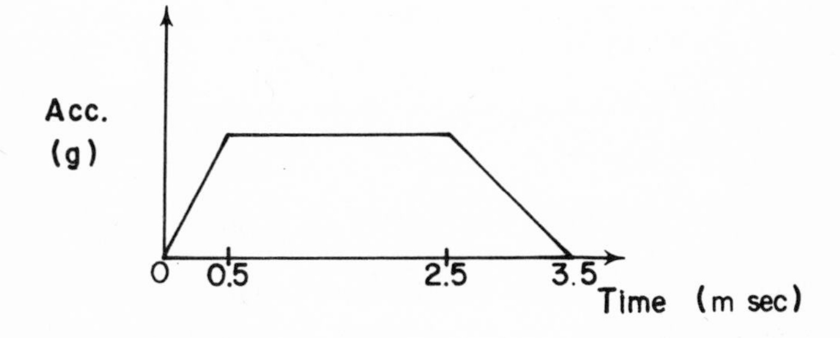

Fig. 9-36.

9-2 A graduate student has built an accelerometer by embedding a single strain gage in plastic. See Fig. 9-37. (a) Compute the sensitivity of this accelerometer in μin./in./g (vertical). (b) What is the natural frequency of this accelerometer (cps)? (c) What is its useful frequency range? (d) What change could be made to double the output of this accelerometer without changing the natural frequency?

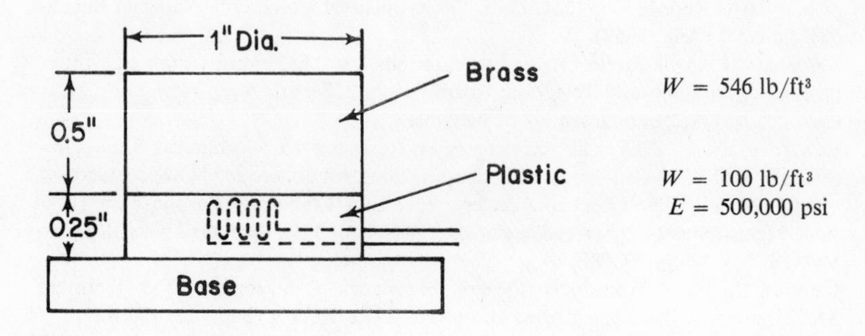

Fig. 9-37.

9-3 Figure 9-38 shows an accelerometer design which uses bonded resistance strain gages. Find the maximum frequency of base motion allowable if this instrument is to function as accelerometer.

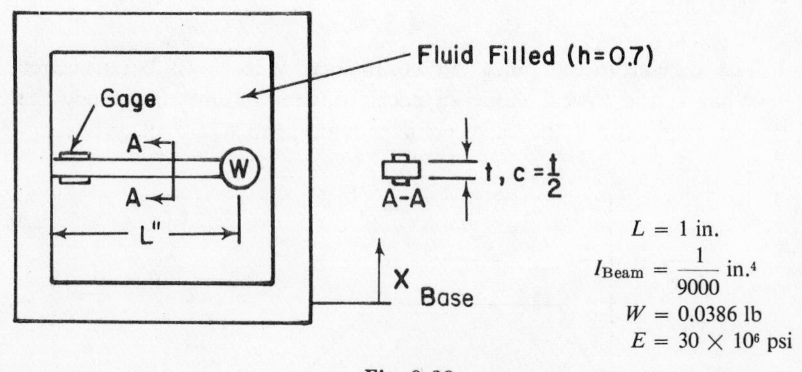

Fig. 9-38.

9-4 A piezoelectric accelerometer has an internal capacitance of 500 pfd. When connected in a circuit having a capacitance of 500 pfd its voltage sensitivity was found to be 17.5 pk mv/pk g. What is the charge sensitivity of this accelerometer (picocoulombs/g)? What is the voltage sensitivity of this accelerometer when it is connected in a circuit having a capacitance of 100 pfd?

9-5 A piezoelectric accelerometer has an internal capacitance of 500 pfd and a charge sensitivity of 50 picocoulombs per peak g. It is connected in a circuit for which $C_E = 1000$ pfd and $R_L = 1 \times 10^6$

ohms. (a) What will be the relative response of this accelerometer system to an acceleration signal of ten cps? (b) If a relative response of unity is desired, what value of R_L must be used if C_E remains 1000 pfd? (c) If R_L is left at 1×10^6 ohms and a relative response of unity is obtained by varying C_E, how much will the signal be reduced, as compared to the signal obtained for case (b)?

9-6 A piezoelectric accelerometer has an internal capacitance of 300 pfd. It is to be used to measure acceleration pulses of the shape shown in the figure. If C_E is set at 200 pfd, what value of R_L would you use to obtain five per cent accuracy?

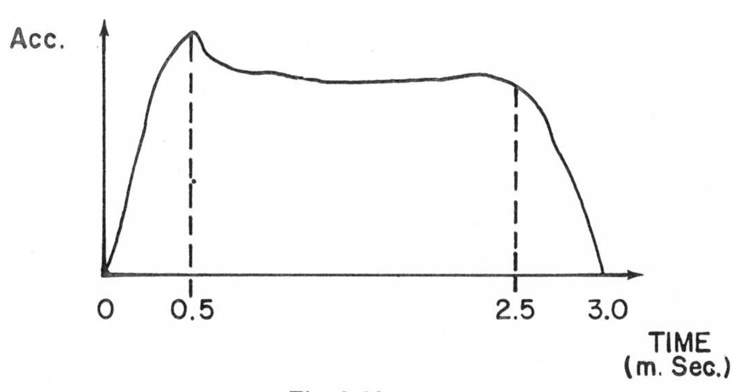

Fig. 9-39.

9-6 Suggested laboratory experiments

Experiment 9-1 Frequency response of accelerometer systems

EQUIPMENT NECESSARY

1. One or more types of accelerometers—at least one piezoelectric.
2. Cathode followers and/or charge amplifiers having different input impedances.
3. An electrodynamic shaker to provide a known harmonic acceleration value over a range of frequencies and/or a method for producing transient accelerations of various periods.*
4. One or more low-pass filters.

* A mass dropped on different kinds and thickness of cushions will serve this purpose. A wide-range system can be used to monitor the pulse and other values compared to this standard.

PROCEDURE

With each available accelerometer connected in the various circuits available, record accelerometer signal over a range of frequencies and/or transient periods.

REPORT

1. Evaluate the response of each accelerometer system over the range of frequencies and periods investigated.
2. Discuss the results. Wherever possible, compare measured results to the result that is predicted by theory.

CHAPTER 10

Accelerometer Calibration

10-1 Introduction

Since all of the accelerometers which have been discussed are designed to produce a voltage signal which can be related to an applied acceleration, we might define accelerometer calibration as the determination of the ratio of signal voltage (E) to applied acceleration (A). Thus

$$S = \frac{E}{A}.$$

This ratio (S) is indeed important, and is generally referred to as amplitude sensitivity.

However, from our study of seismic theory we realize that a given instrument can act as an accelerometer only in a given frequency range, and that if nonharmonic accelerations are to be measured, signal components of all frequencies must either undergo no phase shift, or phase shift must be linearly proportional to frequency. It is for these reasons that the measurement of the effect of frequency on amplitude sensitivity

(S) and phase shift (ϕ) is also a very important part of accelerometer calibration.

As is true with all kinds of transducers, complete calibration involves the determination of environmental effects on sensitivity and behavior. In the case of accelerometers, a complete calibration will involve, in addition to amplitude sensitivity and frequency response, such things as (1) determination of usable acceleration range and extent of variation in sensitivity within that range; (2) effect of temperature, humidity, nuclear radiation, etc., on sensitivity and basic instrument parameters such as capacitance and/or resistance; (3) sensitivity to acceleration components perpendicular to the intended use axis (transverse sensitivity).

The methods most used for determining amplitude sensitivity (S) can be divided into three groups. These are (1) constant-acceleration methods, (2) sinusoidal-motion methods, and (3) transient-motion methods. All of these, as well as some additional proposed methods, are described and discussed in the American Standard S2.2-1959, Ref. [1].

In this section we will attempt only to outline the most-used methods for determining amplitude sensitivity (S), with emphasis on principles involved and range of use. For more detailed information the reader should consult the references cited.

10-2 Constant-acceleration methods

Calibration of an accelerometer in a constant acceleration field is possible only when the accelerometer and its associated circuitry are capable of DC response. Hence, the variable-resistance accelerometers can be calibrated under constant acceleration, whereas the piezoelectric accelerometers cannot.

There are two constant-acceleration methods in use. In the tilting-support method the accelerometer to be calibrated is mounted on a support which can be very accurately aligned in the earth's gravitational field. Starting with the accelerometer's sensitive axis aligned parallel to the gravitational field, where it is subjected to $+1$ g acceleration, it is progressively tilted to vary the component of the applied acceleration along its sensitive axis. See Fig. 10-1. This method is probably the most accurate of all calibration methods, but it is useful only over the range from $+1$ g to -1 g.

The second constant-acceleration calibration method involves subjecting the accelerometer to a normal acceleration produced by rotation about a fixed center. The accelerometer is mounted, with its sensitive axis aligned radially, on a centrifuge at a known distance (r) from the

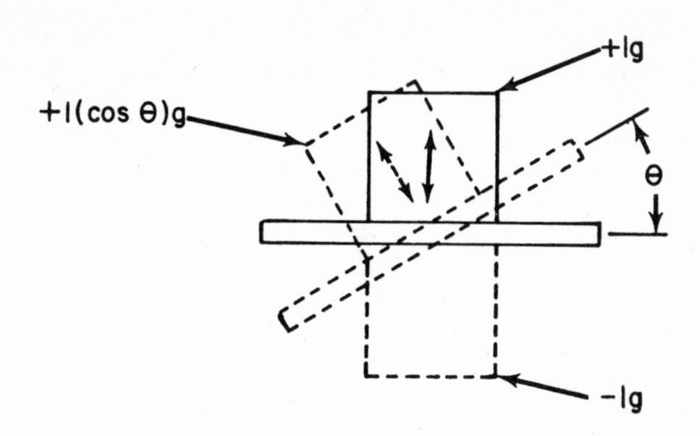

Fig. 10-1. Tilting-support calibration.

center of rotation and rotated at a given angular velocity (ω rad/sec). The normal acceleration to which the accelerometer is subjected is

$$a_n = r\omega^2.$$

Since both r and ω can be measured with a high degree of accuracy, this is an accurate calibration method and can be used to cover the range from 0 g to several thousand g's. R. R. Bouche [2] states that error in acceleration input can be held to +1 per cent, and calibration of 60,000 g's has been achieved.

With accelerometers using a variable-resistance transducer in the form of a four-arm bridge, the following technique is particularly useful. The accelerometer is wired into a typical bridge circuit; see Fig. 10-2. With the accelerometer subjected to zero acceleration, a series of calibrate resistors (R_c) is connected as shown, and the corresponding indicator readings are taken. The centrifuge is then started, and the speed is progressively increased to obtain indicator readings equal to those produced by the calibration resistors. The calibration data is then reported by giving the acceleration value that produces the same signal as is produced by a given calibration resistor, i.e.,

R_{cal} (ohms)	Acceleration (g's)
500,000	3.10
200,000	7.75

etc.

This data makes it very easy to calibrate the entire accelerometer system when this accelerometer is used later in a test.

It is important to remember that no frequency-response information is made available from constant-acceleration calibrations.

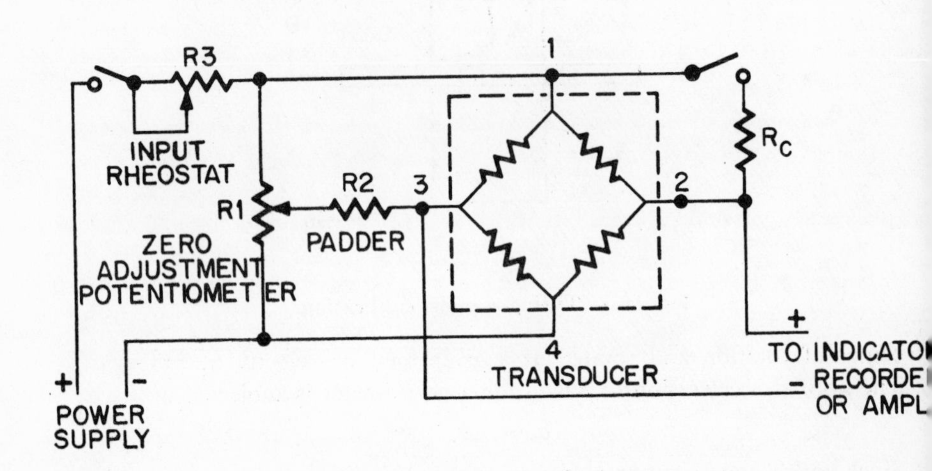

TYPICAL TRANSDUCER CIRCUIT SCHEMATIC

Transducer terminals 1 and 4 = power input. Transducer terminals 2 and 3 = output to receiving instrument

E = energizing voltage (AC or DC), as rated for transducer

R_c = calibrating resistor

R = transducer bridge resistance in ohms measured between terminals 2 and 3

R_{IN} = transducer bridge resistance in ohms measured between terminals 1 and 4

R_1 = wire-wound potentiometer with a value between 20,000 and 30,000 ohms

R_2 = wire-wound resistor with a value of about 100R for full scale zero adjustment range

R_3 = Wire-wound rheostat for transducer input voltage adjustment (sensitivity)

Fig. 10-2. Four-arm bridge-type accelerometer.

10-3 Sinusoidal-motion methods

Piezoelectric accelerometers are most often calibrated by using sinusoidal-motion methods, and even those accelerometers capable of DC response are often calibrated by these methods to determine their frequency response Sinusoidal-motion methods differ in the way the sinusoidal motion is produced and in the way the resulting input motion is measured.

For this purpose, sinusoidal motion has been produced by using a beam driven by an electromagnet, Ref. [3], by means of an electromagnetic shaker (Refs. [4], [5], [6], and [7]), and by means of piezoelectric crystals excited by an AC voltage (Refs. [6] and [8]).

The input acceleration is normally determined by measuring the frequency (ω = rad/sec) and the maximum displacement (r) or the maximum velocity (v), and computing the peak acceleration as $r\omega^2$ or $v\omega$. It is the accuracy of motion measurement that places the limits on the useful range of this calibration method. Since acceleration is proportional to frequency (ω) squared, the displacement (r) becomes very small at high frequency—even for large values of acceleration.

With vibrating-beam-type motion generators, electric resistance strain gages have been used to measure displacement, Ref. [3]. W. A. Yates and M. Davidson [9] designed an electric displacement gage for a range from 0.01 in. to 100 microin. for a frequency band of 10 to 20,000 cps; and for 10 microin. from 60 to 10,000 cps. These values cover an acceleration range from 2×10^{-4} to 40,000 g's.

A microscope can be used to observe a point of light on the vibrating member. The double amplitude of motion is measured on the microscope-calibrated reticle. F. G. Tyzzer and H. C. Hardy [3] used this method and reported an amplitude-measurement error of $\pm 0.2 \times 10^{-3}$ cm, which corresponds to an eight per cent error at 2000 cps for 200 g's. A stroboscope-microscope combination has also been used in this application. P. G. Sulzer, E. R. Smith, and S. Edleman [10] describe such a device and report that it is usable at frequencies to 10,000 cps. Edleman, E. Jones, and Smith [6] used this device and report measuring displacements from 0.2 to 6×10^{-4} cm by direct viewing. "Interferometer techniques" have also been used for motion measurement in this application. Edleman, Jones, and Smith [6] used a Fizeau interferometer in the frequency range from 50 to 11,000 cps. Smith et al. [8] describe a stroboscopic interferometer method usable from 1.3×10^{-3} g's at 108 cps to 105 g's at 20,000 cps.

It is possible to calibrate by using sinusoidal motion without making a displacement measurement. This technique is known as the reciprocity method. To perform this calibration, two linear transducers are required, and one of these must be bilateral. A bilateral transducer is one which functions conveniently (transduces) in either direction. In the case of an accelerometer, an acceleration at the mechanical side produces voltage at the electrical side, or a voltage at the electrical side produces an acceleration at the mechanical side. Since piezoelectric accelerometers are bilateral, this method may be used for their calibration.

The first experiment which is performed is to use a vibration generator to subject the two transducers to the same motion. The voltage output of each accelerometer is measured, and the ratio of the sensitivities is determined.

The second experiment consists of rigidly connecting together the mechanical sides of the transducers. In the case of piezoelectric accelerometers, the bases are clamped together. The bilateral transducer is excited with an alternating current, and the resulting voltage from the other transducer is measured.

For the third experiment, the mechanical side of each transducer is rigidly connected to opposite ends of a known mass. The bilateral transducer is again excited with an alternating current, and the resulting voltage from the other transducer is measured.

Using these electrical measurements, H. M. Trent [11] has shown how the sensitivity of a transducer, on which the voltage output was measured in experiments two and three, may be determined.

S. Levy and R. R. Bouche [12] also used the reciprocity method for calibration of a variable-resistance-type accelerometer and a piezoelectric type. The frequency range covered for the piezoelectric transducer was 30 to 5000 cps. This calibration was conducted at a nominal acceleration level of two g's.

Within limits, sinusoidal-motion methods can be used to check variations of amplitude sensitivity S at a constant frequency with variable acceleration level—i.e., to test for amplitude distortion. This is accomplished by holding (ω) constant while the acceleration level is varied by varying the amplitude of motion (r). Also within limits, sinusoidal-motion methods can be used to check variation of S at a constant acceleration with variable frequency—i.e., to test for frequency distortion. This is accomplished by varying (ω) while the acceleration is held constant by simultaneously varying amplitude of motion (r).

10-4 Transient-motion methods

As was pointed out in our discussion of seismic theory, Sect. 9-1, prediction of the system's response to transients from a study of its response to sinusoidal motions is somewhat complicated. Therefore, accelerometers that are used to measure transients should be calibrated under transient conditions. In this method the transient is produced by impacting two masses. The accelerometer to be calibrated is mounted on one of the two masses. (In a few cases the accelerometer is unmounted and is one of the impacting masses.) Both masses may be free to move, as in the ballistic-pendulum technique (see Fig. 10-3). Or the mass on

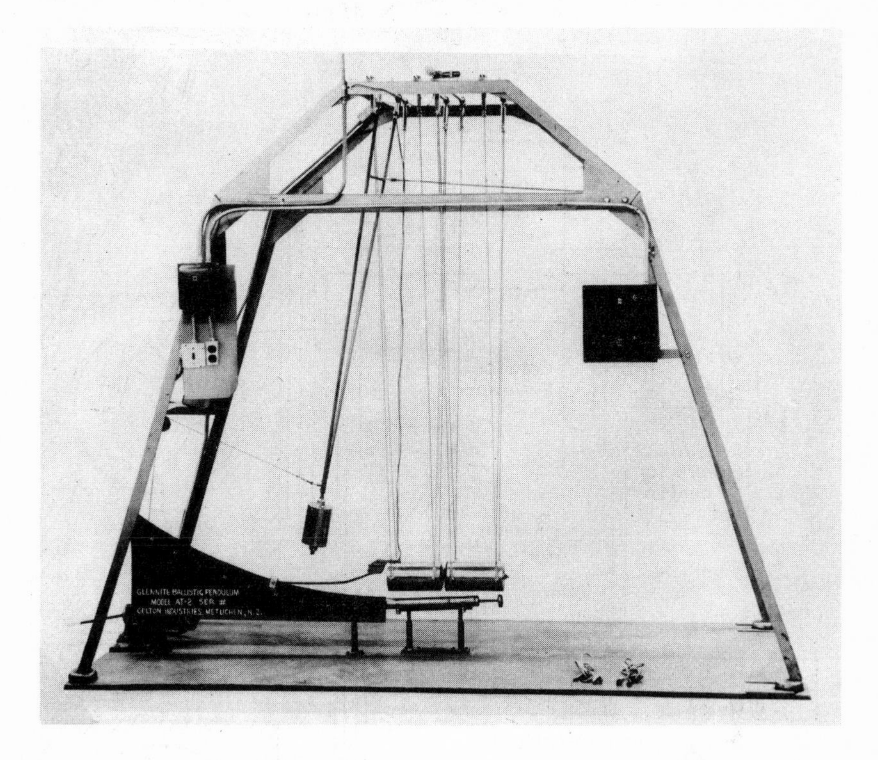

Fig. 10-3. Ballistic pendulum used for accelerometer calibration. (*Courtesy of Gulton Mfg. Corp.*)

which the accelerometer is mounted may be impacted on a fixed anvil (see Fig. 10-4). Calibration is achieved by either of two procedures. In the first, the accelerometer output is assumed to be linear with acceleration. The accelerometer output is displayed as a function of time t so that

$$\int_{t_1}^{t_2} a\,dt$$

can be evaluated. The change in velocity Δv of the mass on which the accelerometer is mounted is measured so that calibration can be accomplished by writing

$$\Delta v_{1-2} = \int_{t_1}^{t_2} a\,dt,$$

in which a is expressed as the desired constant of proportionality K times the output signal in millivolts, M.

$$a = K \frac{\text{in./sec}^2}{\text{mv}} \times M \text{ mv}.$$

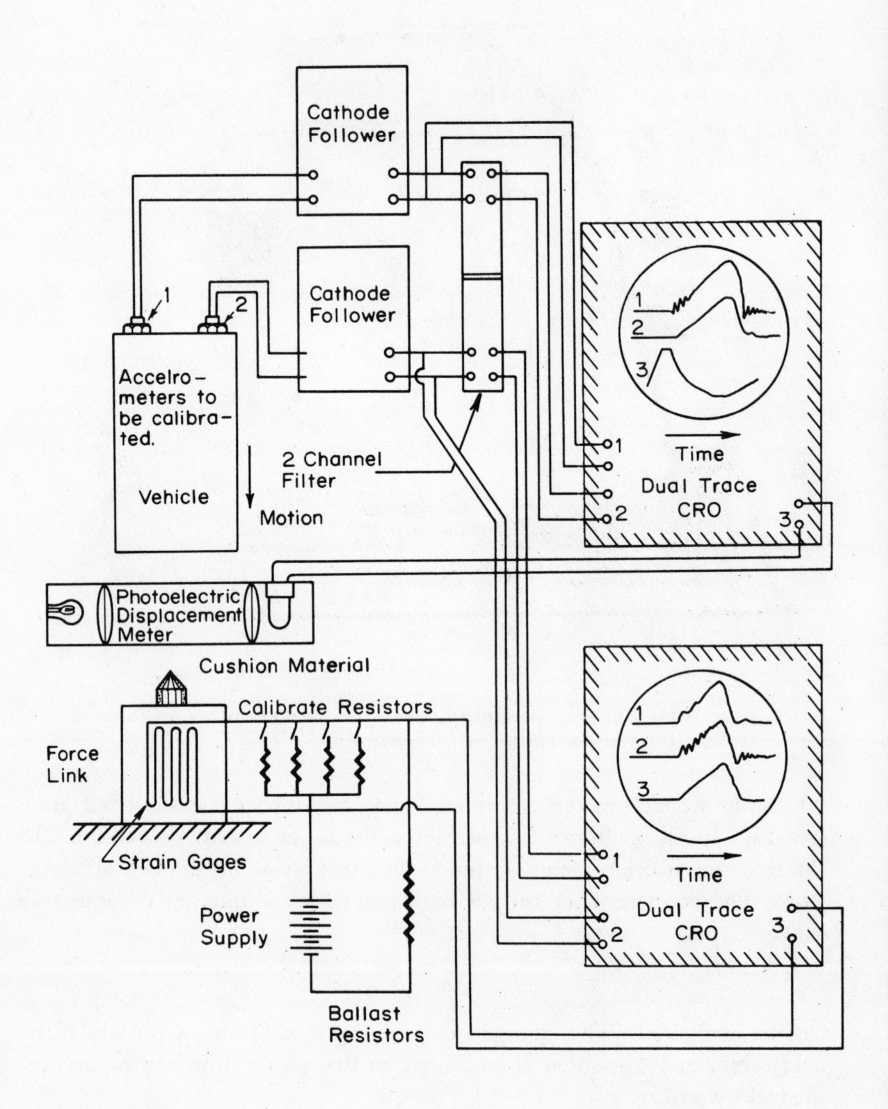

Fig. 10-4. Drop tower used for accelerometer calibration.

R. W. Conrad and I. Vigness [13] used both a ballistic pendulum and a drop tester to calibrate piezoelectric accelerometers. With the pendulum, the change in the velocity of the impacted mass on which the accelerometer was mounted could be computed from the height of pendulum swing produced by impact. As a check, the change in velocity was measured by using a photoelectric cell, i.e., the mass cut light beams at two stations which were separated by a known distance. With the drop tester the change in velocity during impact was determined as the sum of impact and rebound velocity. These were measured electrically. Conrad and Vigness studied pulses ranging from 0.35 ms to 2 ms and with peaks as high as 7000 g's.

T. A. Perls [14] used an impact method to determine accelerometer sensitivities up to 12,000 g's. To obtain these high accelerations, the unmounted accelerometer was allowed to swing through an arc and to make contact with an anvil. The method of computing sensitivities was essentially the same as that used by Conrad and Vigness. The differences were that the change in velocity was computed from the measured arc during fall and the measured arc during rebound, and that the area under the acceleration-time diagram was determined by electrical integration. The rebound arc was determined from observation at point of zero velocity.

Perls plotted accelerometer sensitivity versus peak acceleration. There was considerable scatter. However, the best average sensitivity was the same as that determined by sinusoidal excitation at ± 1 g, 20 cps. Pulse duration encountered during this test was from 40 to 200 microseconds.

Perls and C. W. Kissinger [15] continued the work of calibration at high g levels. Several methods were used to obtain the high g levels. The ballistic pendulum was useful in the range of pulses having accelerations from 150 to 8000 g's, and durations from 40 microsec to one millisec. The pulses were also obtained by using an air gun to fire a projectile into a small target on which the accelerometer was mounted. Durations from 25 to 800 microsec were obtained, and the accelerations obtained were low.

Pulses were also obtained by rolling a ball down an inclined trough into an accelerometer, or an object on which an accelerometer was mounted. This method gave pulse durations from 18 microsec to 2.5 millisec, and accelerations to 4000 g's.

Data from tests conducted in the above ways were reduced by using the equation

$$\Delta V_{1-2} = \int_{t_1}^{t_2} a\, dt,$$

and the integration was performed electrically.

Bouche [16] describes a drop-ball shock machine which produces half-sine-wave acceleration pulses as high as 15,000 g's, with 50 microsec duration, and as low as 460 g, with 1.5 millisec duration. Again, calibration is obtained by setting

$$\Delta V_{1-2} = \int_{t_1}^{t_2} a\,dt,$$

and ΔV is measured photoelectrically.

In the second method of transient calibration the force transient applied to produce the acceleration transient is measured. Then acceleration is computed by solving the equation

$$F = Ma,$$

in which M is the mass accelerated. If both force and acceleration are recorded as functions of time, the sensitivity can be checked at various acceleration values, and hence it is not necessary to assume that accelerometer output is linear with acceleration. In this method the force transient is usually measured with a bonded-wire strain-gage force link. W. E. Baker [17], who used this method, calibrated accelerometers using three pulse shapes (half-sine-wave, sawtooth, rectangular) over a range of one millisec to 35 millisec and for accelerations as high as 2200 g's. D. F. Palmer [18] used a commercially available strain-gage load cell for the same purpose.

The fundamental deficiency associated with this method is that the force transducer must be calibrated under static conditions, and then its behavior is assumed to be the same under transient conditions.

10-5 Calibration by comparison to a standard

After an accelerometer has been calibrated by one of the methods previously described, it can be used as a secondary standard for the calibration of other accelerometers. The National Bureau of Standards has established a service for calibrating secondary vibration standards, and a great many laboratories now calibrate their accelerometers by comparison to a National Bureau of Standards calibrated secondary standard. Most frequently the National Bureau of Standards calibrated secondary standard is used only to calibrate a working standard at periodic intervals; this working standard is, in turn, used to calibrate other accelerometers that are used in the laboratories' test program.

Calibration by comparison is accomplished by mounting both accelerometers (the secondary standard and the one to be calibrated) to the

Fig. 10-5. Fixture used in calibration of accelerometers by comparison to a standard. (*Courtesy of Endevco Corp.*)

same surface (usually back to back, as shown in Fig. 10-5) and then subjecting that surface to the desired vibration environment. If both accelerometers are linear, the sensitivity of the accelerometer to be calibrated (S_1) is

$$S_1 = S_{\text{Std}} \frac{E_1}{E_{\text{Std}}},$$

in which S_{Std} is the amplitude sensitivity of the secondary standard.
E_1 is the signal produced by the accelerometer to be calibrated.
E_{Std} is the signal produced by the secondary standard.

When an accelerometer is calibrated by comparison, it is most important that the two accelerometers are actually subjected to the same acceleration. This is more difficult than it may appear to be on first thought—particularly with high-acceleration transients. The accelerometers must be carefully mounted on a solid surface as near the same point as is possible.

It is also very important that the acceleration environment used is one for which the secondary standard calibration applies. For example, the secondary standard may have been calibrated under pure sinusoidal-motion conditions, free of transverse acceleration. In this case, when the secondary standard is used for calibration, the motion should be pure sinusoidal, free of transverse acceleration. This means that the acceleration exciter must be carefully constructed, controlled, and checked.

10-6 Other kinds of calibration

As was mentioned in the introduction to this section, complete accelerometer calibration involves more than determination of amplitude sensitivity.

Frequency response is most frequently checked by determining amplitude sensitivity and phase angle over a range of frequencies. Figure 10-6 shows frequency-response data obtained from a piezoelectric accelerometer with a resonance frequency of 33,000 cps.

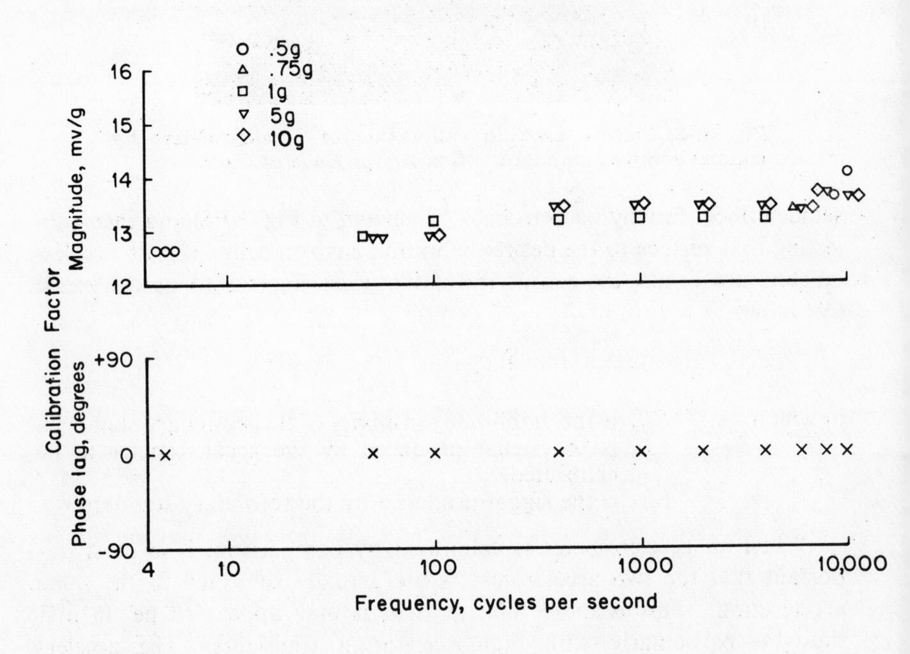

Fig. 10-6. Frequency-response data for a piezoelectric accelerometer. (*Courtesy of ISA, Ref.* [*19*].)

Natural frequency is defined as $\sqrt{K/M}$, but several other related terms are in use. *Resonance frequency* is defined as the frequency of sinusoidal input that produces a maximum response; therefore, resonance can be established by monitoring output as input frequency is varied. This measurement requires a sinusoidal motion generator with frequency capabilities higher than the resonance frequency of the accelerometer to be tested.

Undamped natural frequency or natural frequency is defined as the frequency of sinusoidal input that causes the relative motion between the mass and the case to lag the case (input) motion by 90 deg, i.e., a 90-deg phase angle. This measurement requires a sinusoidal motion generator with frequency capabilities higher than the resonance frequency of the accelerometer to be tested and a method for monitoring phase angle.

Damped natural frequency is defined as the frequency with which the seismic mass will vibrate freely. This is ordinarily determined by impacting the accelerometer and measuring the frequency of the residual signal.

With piezoelectric accelerometers there is little difference between these three values because of the small amount of damping present.

Theoretically, damped natural frequency (f_{n_d}) is related to undamped natural frequency (f_n) by the expression

$$f_{n_d} = f_n\sqrt{1 - h^2},$$

in which h is the damping ratio. For piezoelectric accelerometers, $h < 0.05$.

For a particular piezoelectric accelerometer,* Bouche [19] finds these three values to be

Resonance frequency	=	34,400 cps.
Undamped natural frequency	=	34,500 cps.
Damped natural frequency (with accelerometer mounted)	=	33,100 cps.

With the variable-resistance accelerometers, there may be considerable difference, however, since the damping is often equal to 0.7 of critical; i.e., $h = 0.7$. The method of mounting an accelerometer has an effect on the resonance frequency, and this problem will be discussed in Sect. 11-6.

If the damped natural frequency of an accelerometer is determined by impacting the unmounted accelerometer, the value obtained will, in general, be higher than that obtained by impacting the accelerometer through an anvil to which it is attached. Damped natural frequencies determined with the accelerometer unmounted are misleading. For the

* Endevco Model 2242, Serial Number 7821.

accelerometer discussed previously, Bouche [19] finds the two values differ as shown below:

	Damped Natural Frequency cps
Accelerometer mounted on anvil weighing 0.16 lb	33,100
Accelerometer unmounted	50,000

Transverse sensitivity is defined as the ratio of signal produced per unit of acceleration applied perpendicular to the intended use axis to the signal produced per unit of acceleration applied parallel to the intended use axis. Transverse sensitivity is important because in most test situations there are several components of acceleration present, but the acceleration is to be measured along only one axis.

Transverse sensitivity (K) is measured by deliberately calibrating the accelerometer with the acceleration applied along various axes perpendicular to the intended use axis. The transverse sensitivity is then expressed as the ratio of sensitivity determined under this condition (S_t) to the sensitivity as normally determined, S; i.e.,

$$K = \frac{S_t}{S}.$$

Most important accelerometer characteristics (damping factor, amplitude sensitivity, capacitance, etc.) are affected by environmental factors such as temperature, pressure, etc. Therefore, it may be necessary at times to do some, or all, of the calibration previously discussed under a variety of different environmental conditions. Keast's paper, "Calibration of Accelerometers in a Simulated Space Environment" [20] is an example of this type of problem. Keast calibrated several accelerometers at pressures as low as 5×10^{-5} in. of mercury and at temperatures as low as $-320°$F.

10-7 Accelerometer system calibration

10-7a Accelerometers capable of DC response

Because accelerometers are calibrated in several different ways, the calibration data is given in several different forms. As explained in Sect. 10-2, those accelerometers capable of DC response are most often calibrated under steady-state acceleration conditions, i.e., on a centrifuge, where $a_n = r\omega^2$. In the case of the four-arm-bridge accelerometer, the manufacturer gives the calibration data by giving the bridge resistance (R) and a gage factor (F). Then

$$F = \frac{\Delta R/R}{N}, \tag{10-1}$$

in which $\Delta R/R$ is the change in arm resistance per unit of arm resistance.
N is the number of units of the variable applied. In this case units of acceleration, usually in g units. See Fig. 10-7.

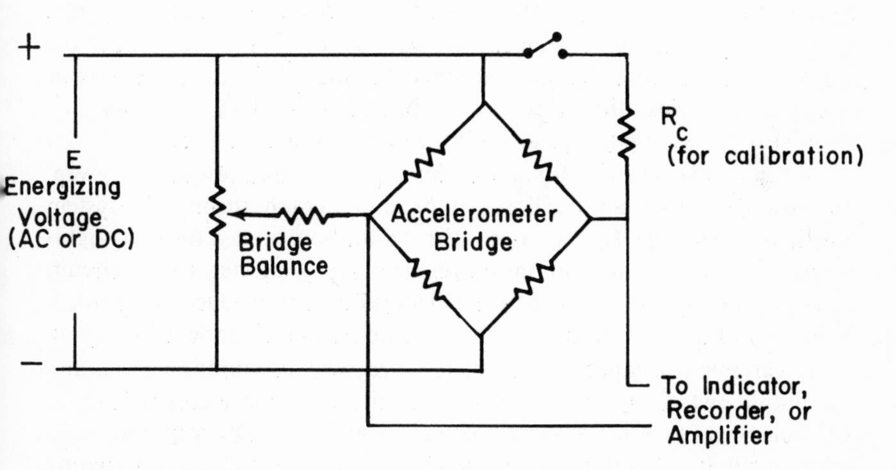

Fig. 10-7. Four-arm-bridge-type accelerometer.

With these two values given, it is possible to use the bridge-circuits equations, previously developed for use with the strain gages, to compute the accelerometer output in terms of either current or voltage.* Specifically,

$$I_L = \frac{FNE}{R + R_L} \tag{10-2}$$

and

$$E_L = \frac{FNE}{\dfrac{R}{R_L} + 1}, \tag{10-3}$$

in which F and N are as previously defined.
E is the bridge supply voltage.
R_L is the resistance of the indicator, recorder, or amplifier.
I_L is the current through the recording instrument.
E_L is the voltage to the recording instrument.

* See Sect. 2-2 for a derivation of bridge-circuit equations.

This system can be calibrated in the same way in which bridge-type strain-gage circuits were calibrated, i.e., by paralleling resistors across one arm of the bridge. The signal simulated is given by the equation

$$N = \frac{R}{4F(R_c + R)}, \tag{10-4}$$

in which R_c is the calibration resistor. In this case the "4" has been added because in the accelerometer the output of all four arms is additive, whereas during calibration a ΔR is produced across one arm only.

It is important to remember that with a four-wire lead system the resistance of lead wires has an effect on calibration if the calibrate resistor is connected across the bridge at the instrument end of the leads, i.e., paralleled across one bridge arm plus lead resistance. See Sect. 2-2f.

When accelerometers, for which this type of calibration data is given, are recorded from an oscilloscope or oscillograph through a system which is capable of DC response, the calibration procedure is straightforward. One or more calibration resistors are connected to the circuit, as shown in Fig. 10-7 and the trace deflection they produce is recorded. Solution of Eq. (10-4) relates the recorded deflection to acceleration signal.

If variable-resistance accelerometers are used in vibration tests, and the output (which will be some form of distorted sine wave) is read on AC voltmeters or other systems that are incapable of DC response, some other method of calibration is necessary. In general, an alternating calibrate signal must be supplied, or the output signal must be related to input acceleration by computation.

One circuit for system calibration which can be used when the indicator is incapable of DC response and when there are unknown circuit parameters such as amplifier gain is shown in Fig. 10-8. To use this system, a calibration signal is applied to the input of the amplifier with the voltage oscillator. The calibration voltage signal is computed by using Eq. (10-3), where the value of N is the acceleration level to be simulated. Thus

$$E_L = \frac{FE}{\frac{R}{R_L} + 1} N. \tag{10-3}$$

In the usual case, where $R_L >> R$, this reduces to

$$E_L = FEN, \tag{10-3a}$$

and hence an exact value for R_L is not necessary. Since the accelerometer bridge supply voltage (E) usually cannot conveniently be measured at the

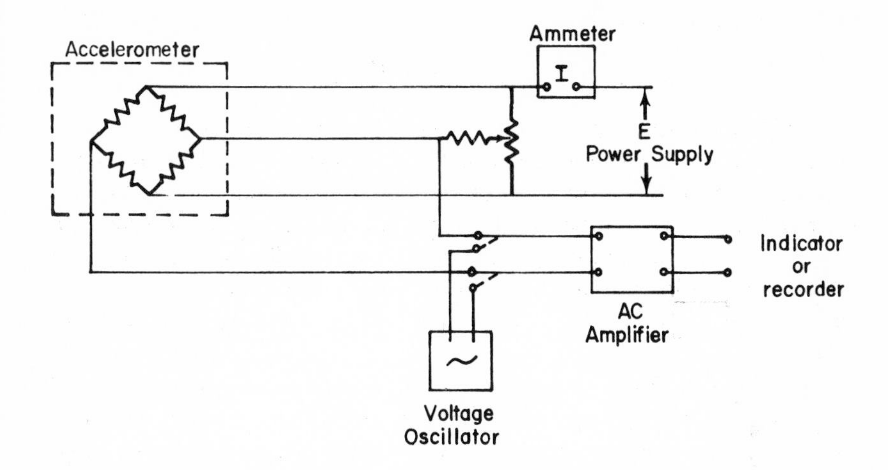

Fig. 10-8. Calibration circuit for variable-resistance accelerometer with AC readout.

accelerometer, a more useful form of this last equation can be obtained by replacing E by IR, where I is the measured supply current. Thus,

$$E_L = (FIR)N. \qquad (10\text{-}3b)$$

Since the fundamental calibration of accelerometers of this type involves relating a DC voltage output to a steady state acceleration input, the calibration relates peak voltage output to peak acceleration input. Hence, Eq. (10-3b) should be written as

$$E_{L_{\text{pk v}}} = (FIR)N_{\text{pk g}}. \qquad (10\text{-}3c)$$

That is, when the calibration signal is inserted as a *peak voltage value*, the value to be used is (FIR) times the zero-to-peak acceleration to be simulated. The relationship between peak, rms, average, and peak-to-peak values associated with a sinusoidal voltage signal are as follows:

$$\text{Rms value} = 0.707 \times \text{peak value.}$$
$$\text{Average value} = 0.637 \times \text{peak value.}$$
$$\text{Peak-peak value} = 2 \times \text{peak value.}$$

If the calibration signal is inserted as an *rms voltage value* the value to be used is

$$E_{L_{\text{rms}}} = 0.707(FIR)N_{\text{pk g}} \qquad (10\text{-}3d)$$

and if the calibration signal is inserted as a "peak-to-peak voltage value" the value to be used is

$$E_{L_{\text{pk-pk volts}}} = 2\,(FIR)N_{\text{pk g}}\ . \tag{10-3e}$$

If the calibration signal and the test signal are read on an AC voltmeter, the reading taken when the calibration signal is applied represents N peak g's regardless of the type of voltmeter (i.e., peak, rms, or peak-to-peak readings). If the calibration signal and test signal are recorded on an oscilloscope or oscillograph, the zero-to-peak deflection (one-half the double amplitude) produced on the record by the calibration signal is equal to the deflection that will be produced by a zero-to-peak acceleration of $N_{\text{pk g}}$.

When the indicator is not capable of DC response, as with an AC voltmeter, but when all circuit parameters are known, it is not necessary to use a calibration signal; the output voltage can be related to input acceleration by Eq. (10-3).

If we remember that variable-resistance accelerometers are effectively calibrated in terms of peak volts output per peak g input, the simplest case involves a peak reading AC voltmeter.

$$E_{\text{pk g}} = \frac{E_{\text{pk reading}}}{(FIR)}.$$

If the signal is read on an rms-reading voltmeter,

$$N_{\text{pk g}} = \frac{E_{\text{rms reading}}}{0.707(FIR)},$$

and if the signal is read on a peak-peak reading voltmeter,

$$N_{\text{pk g}} = \frac{E_{\text{pk-pk reading}}}{2(FIR)}$$

It should be pointed out that in most vibration work the accelerations measured are not of a single frequency; rather, they contain many higher harmonics. For this reason a peak-reading meter with an rms scale *must not be used*, and there is some error even when a true "rms" reading meter is used.* An example will serve to illustrate some of the material just discussed.

---

* See Ref. [21] for analysis of this error. Basically, the difficulty is this: although a true (heating value) rms voltmeter reads the true rms value of a complex wave, there is no fixed relationship between rms and peak value; i.e., rms value $\neq$ 0.707 peak value for a complex wave.

Example 10-1. A variable-resistance accelerometer has been recalibrated on a centrifuge, and the following data are available: R (bridge resistance) = 326.6 ohms.

Applied Acceleration (g)	R_c to produce equivalent signal (ohms)
3.10	500×10^3
7.70	200×10^3
19.1	80×10^3
38.0	40×10^3

Substitution of these values into Eq. (10-4) gives the following values for F:

$$F = \frac{R}{4N(R_c + R)},$$

$$F = \frac{326.6}{(4)(3.10)(500{,}000 + 326.6)} = 52.6 \times 10^{-6},$$

etc.

$$F = 53.0 \times 10^{-6},$$
$$F = 53.5 \times 10^{-6},$$
$$F = 53.7 \times 10^{-6}.$$

Although some nonlinearity is indicated, we shall use the average value of sensitivity

$$F_{\text{Ave}_{3<g<38}} = 53.2 \times 10^{-6}$$

This accelerometer is mounted on a device which is to be tested on an electrodynamic shaker. The circuit is as shown in Fig. 10-9. Since this circuit is not capable of

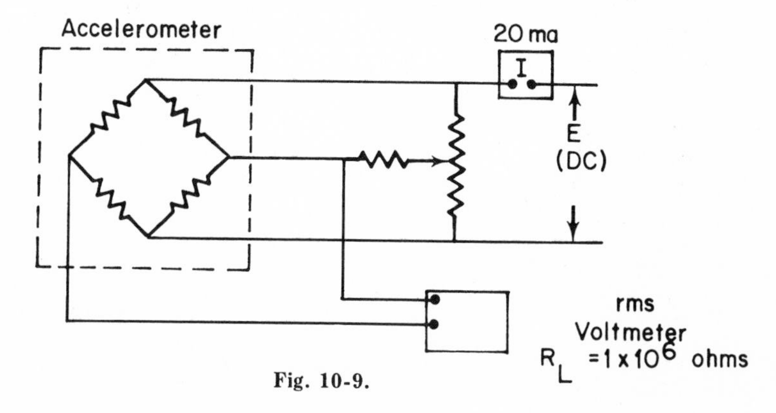

Fig. 10-9.

DC response, we shall relate output signal to input acceleration by computation. Using Eq. (10-3), we obtain

$$E_{L_{pk}} = \frac{FNE}{\dfrac{R}{R_L} + 1} \simeq FNE,$$

or

$$E_{L_{pk}} = (FIR)N_{pk}.$$

The rms output is 0.707 of the peak output, so finally

$$E_{L_{rms}} = 0.707(FIR)N_{pk}.$$

If, during test, a reading of 1500 rms μv is obtained, the acceleration is

$$N = \frac{1500 \times 10^{-6}}{(0.707)(53.2 \times 10^{-6})(20 \times 10^{-3})(326.6)},$$

$$N = 6.11 \text{ zero-to-peak g},$$

or

$$N = \pm 6.11 \text{ g}.$$

10-7b Piezoelectric accelerometers

Because the piezoelectric accelerometers are not capable of DC response, they are generally calibrated by using harmonic (sinusoidal) or transient acceleration conditions. When they are calibrated under harmonic-motion conditions, as on an electrodynamic shaker or vibrating beam,* it is customary to express their sensitivity in terms of rms mv/pk g of acceleration.

$$S_{rms} = X \text{ rms mv/pk g}.$$

If during use in a vibration test an accelerometer so calibrated is read on an rms voltmeter, sensitivity may be established with a minimum of computations. If, however, such an accelerometer is recorded from an oscilloscope or oscillograph, a system calibration to relate trace deflection to acceleration signal is necessary. The calibration signal is generally introduced by means of a voltage generator, as a sinusoidal voltage.†

The calibration signal (E_{cal}) is chosen to represent the desired acceleration signal ($N_{peak\ g}$). Thus

$$E_{cal_{rms\ mv}} = X\frac{\text{rms mv}}{\text{pk g}} \times N_{pk\ g}$$

* See Sect. 10-3.

† The actual calibration circuitry used is discussed later in this same section.

or

$$E_{\text{cal}_{\text{pk mv}}} = \frac{X\dfrac{\text{rms mv}}{\text{pk g}} \times N_{\text{pk g}}}{0.707},$$

or

$$E_{\text{cal}_{\text{pk-pk mv}}} = 2\frac{X\dfrac{\text{rms mv}}{\text{pk g}} \times N_{\text{pk g}}}{0.707}.$$

The *zero-to-peak* deflection (i.e., one-half the double amplitude) produced on the record by this calibration signal is equal to the deflection that will be produced by a zero-to-peak acceleration of N g. An example will illustrate the procedure.

Example 10-2. A piezoelectric accelerometer has been calibrated on a shake table, and the sensitivity is given as 20 rms mv/pk g. This accelerometer and recording system is to be calibrated for a 50-g zero-to-peak acceleration. A harmonic calibration voltage of 1000 rms mv, 20 rms mv/g × 50 g (or 1414 pk mv or 2828 pk-pk mv) is applied to the system and the record shown in Fig. 10-10 is obtained.

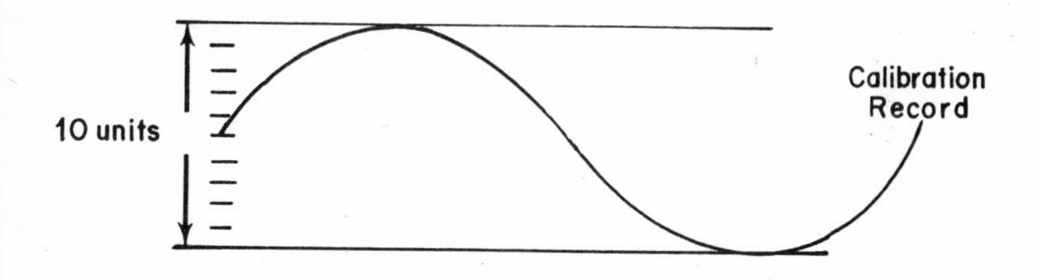

Fig. 10-10.

The calibration record is interpreted as follows:

$$1 \text{ unit of deflection} = \frac{50 \text{ pk g}}{5 \text{ units zero-to-peak deflection}}$$
$$= 10 \text{ g acceleration},$$

i.e., the zero-to-peak acceleration value simulated, (50), divided by zero-to-peak trace deflection, or one-half the double amplitude, (5).

If this calibration were followed by a vibration test which gave the record shown in Fig. 10-11, it would be read as indicated.

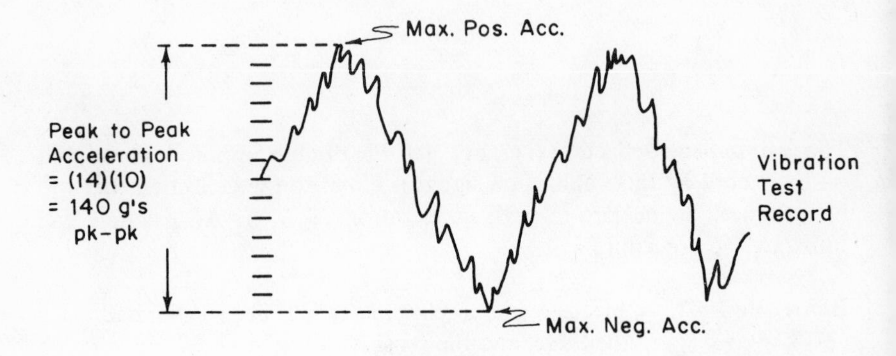

Fig. 10-11.

In general, with a mixed frequency wave the positive and negative peaks will not be of the same magnitudes, and since the zero line is difficult to establish, the individual peak values are not specified. If the calibration were followed by an impact test which gave the record shown in Fig. 10-12, it would be read as indicated.

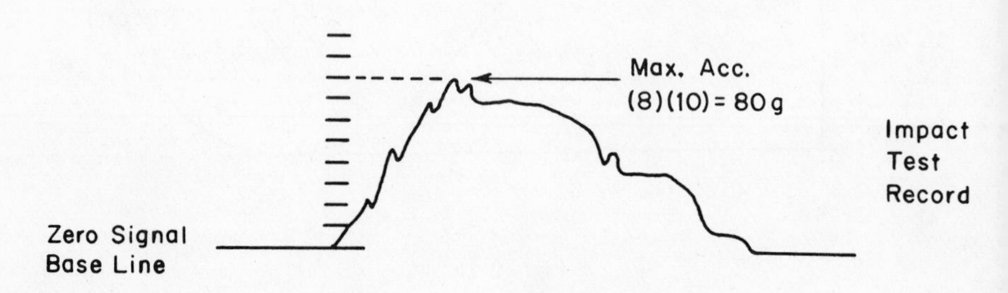

Fig. 10-12.

When accelerometers are calibrated under transient conditions, it is customary to express their sensitivity in terms of zero-to-pk mv/pk g of acceleration, $S_{pk} = \gamma$ pk mv/pk g. This value of sensitivity is, of course, equal to the rms sensitivity value divided by 0.707. ($S_{pk} = S_{rms}/0.707$), and this value can be computed and used regardless of how the accelerometer was calibrated.

Again, for recording-system calibration the calibration signal (E_{cal}) is chosen to represent the desired acceleration signal ($N_{pk\,g}$). Thus

$$E_{cal_{pk\ mv}} = \gamma \frac{\text{pk mv}}{\text{pk g}} \times N \text{ pk g},$$

or

$$E_{cal_{pk\text{-}pk\ mv}} = 2\gamma \frac{\text{pk mv}}{\text{pk g}} \times N \text{ pk g},$$

or

$$E_{cal_{rms\ mv}} = 0.707\gamma \frac{\text{pk mv}}{\text{pk g}} \times N \text{ pk g}.$$

Again, the zero-to-peak deflection (one-half the double amplitude) produced by this calibration signal is equal to the deflection that will be produced by a zero-to-peak acceleration of N g.

An example will illustrate the procedure.

Example 10-3. A piezoelectric accelerometer has been calibrated on a shock pendulum, and the sensitivity is given as 28.28 pk mv/pk g. (*Note:* This is the same accelerometer used in the previous example, and the shock calibration confirms the harmonic motion calibration, i.e.,

$$S_{pk} = \frac{S_{rms}}{0.707} = \frac{20}{0.707} = 28.28.$$

The accelerometer and recording system is to be calibrated for 50 g zero-to-pk acceleration.)

A harmonic calibration voltage of 1414 pk mv, 28.28 pk mv/pk g $\times$ 50 pk g (or 2828 pk-pk mv or 1000 rms mv) is applied, and the record shown in Fig. 10-13 is obtained.

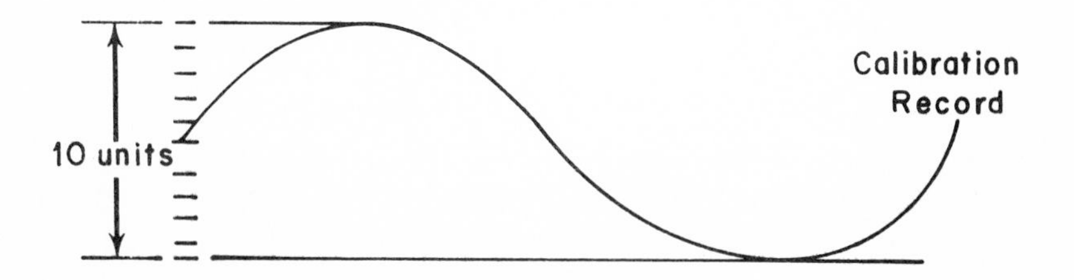

Fig. 10-13.

Again, the calibration record is interpreted as follows:

$$1 \text{ unit deflection} = \frac{50 \text{ pk g}}{5 \text{ units of zero-to-pk deflection}}$$

$$= 10 \text{ g acceleration,}$$

and either vibration or impact records are interpreted just as in the previous example.

With piezoelectric transducers, a system calibration technique comparable in simplicity and accuracy to the parallel-resistance technique used with variable-resistance transducers has not been perfected.

The basic accelerometer sensitivity (picocoulombs/g or mv/g with known capacitance) can be established by any one of the several methods discussed in Sects. 10-3, 10-4, and 10-5. With the basic accelerometer sensitivity known, the problem is to establish the relationship between final recorder signal (probably trace deflection) and acceleration.

Several circuits for system calibration are in use, and, of these, the one using signal substitution is the most direct method when a voltage-amplifier system is to be calibrated. In order that this system calibration technique be understood, it will be necessary to refer again to the equivalent circuit of a piezoelectric crystal, cable, and instrument load; see Fig. 10-14.

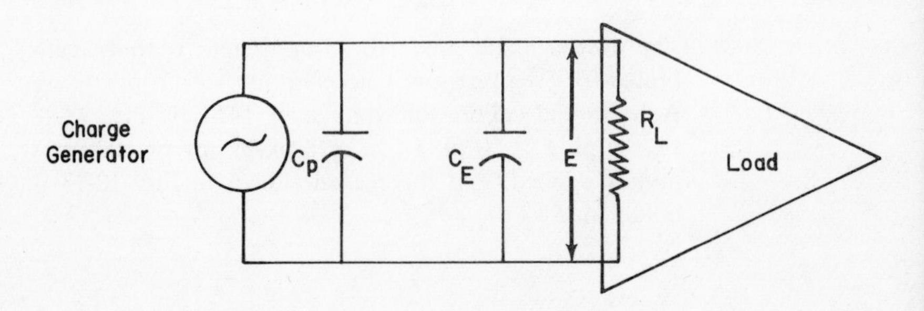

Fig. 10-14. Piezoelectric accelerometer circuit.

During the accelerometer calibration, the following are measured:

$E_{c/g}$ in mv/g = crystal voltage sensitivity with some known external shunt capacitance ($C_E = C_{\text{Std}}$).

C_p in pfd = crystal capacitance.

With these values it is possible to compute

q/g in picocoulombs/g = crystal charge sensitivity;

$$[q/g = E_{c/g}(C_p + C_{\text{Std}})], \tag{10-5}$$

and

$E_{p/g}$ in mv/g = the effective internal crystal voltage sensitivity;

$$\left[E_{p/g} = \frac{q/g}{C_p} = \frac{E_{c/g}(C_p + C_{\text{Std}})}{C_p}\right]. \tag{10-6}$$

In test situations where the voltage sensitivity at the input to a *voltage-amplifier*-type cathode follower is known, the system calibration consists of replacing the accelerometer and every item ahead of the voltage-amplifier-type cathode follower by a voltage generator which will supply a test signal (E_T) to simulate a desired input acceleration (g_T); i.e.,

$$E_T = g_T E_{c/g}.$$

Some examples of this type of situation may be helpful.

Example 10-4. A piezoelectric accelerometer with an internal capacitance of 300 pfd was calibrated by using a 12-ft length of cable, having 30 pfd/ft, into a cathode follower with an input impedance of 1000×10^6 ohms shunted by 20 pfd. The cathode follower has a gain of 0.98. The cathode follower output was measured as 22.0 rms mv/pk g. From this data we compute the following:

$$E_c/g \text{ at cathode follower } \textit{input} = \frac{22}{0.98}$$

$$= 22.45 \text{ rms mv/pk g}.$$

$$C_{\text{Std}} = (12 \times 30 + 20) = 380 \text{ pfd}.$$

Now assume that this accelerometer is to be used in a test where the type and length of cable and the cathode-follower shunt capacitance are the same as were used during calibration; i.e.,

$$C_E = C_{\text{Std}} = 380 \text{ pfd}.$$

To calibrate this system we shall insert a voltage generator ahead of the cathode follower and apply 22.45 rms mv/pk g to be simulated, i.e., to simulate 10 pk g, apply 224.5 rms mv; see Fig. 10-15.

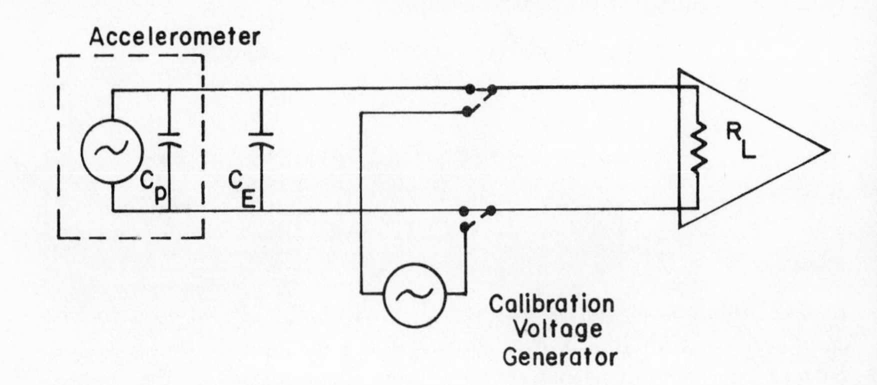

Fig. 10-15. System calibration by signal insertion at the voltage amplifier input.

Example 10-5. Assume that at the time of calibration the accelerometer previously discussed is incorporated into an output standardizing unit, i.e., that shunt capacitance has been added so that the cathode follower *output* is some preselected value—say 10 rms mv/pk g. See Fig. 10-16.

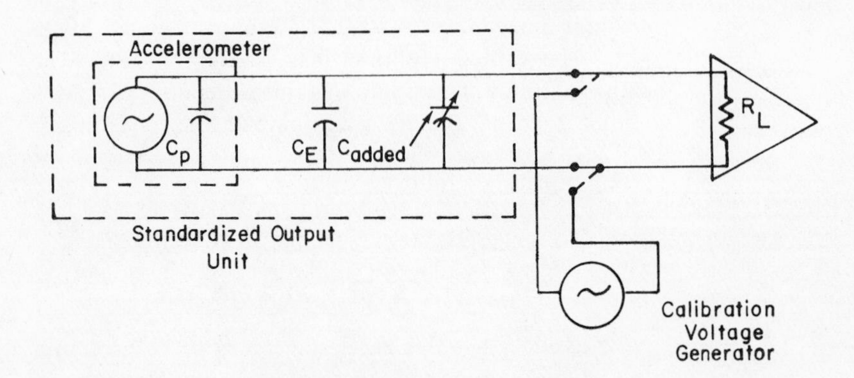

Fig. 10-16. Accelerometer and standardized output circuit.

If this entire standardized output unit is used with a cathode follower having the same input shunt capacitance, the system is again calibrated by inserting a volt-age generator ahead of the cathode follower. In this case we apply 10/0.98 = 10.2 rms mv/pk g to be simulated.

Example 10-6. Consider the use of this same accelerometer with a 20-ft cable of 640 pfd total capacitance connected to a cathode follower with an input shunt capacitance of 15 pfd; i.e.,

$$C_E = 640 + 15 = 655 \text{ pfd.}$$

Calibration will be accomplished in the same way as before (Fig. 10-15), but the calibration voltage to be inserted in this case will be

$$E_{T/g} = \frac{\frac{q}{g}}{C_p + C_E} = \frac{E_{c/g}(C_p + C_{\text{Std}})}{C_p + C_E}$$

$$= \frac{\left(\frac{20}{0.98}\right)(680)}{300 + 655} = 15.95 \text{ rms mv/pk g.}$$

This method of calibration by signal insertion cannot be used if the accelerometer is connected to a *charge* amplifier, since the accelerometer charge is not simulated. Furthermore, in many test situations it is not convenient to determine the voltage sensitivity at the input to a voltage amplifier by measuring the actual value of C_E, and proceeding as in the last example. This is particularly true when long lines, which are exposed to various environments, are used between the accelerometer and the voltage preamplifier. In these situations or when a charge amplifier is used, the circuit for system calibration by signal substitution is slightly altered.

Since the equivalent circuit of a piezoelectric crystal is a *charge* generator shunted by a capacitance, and since this is equivalent to a *voltage* generator with a series capacitance, we may simulate a piezoelectric accelerometer *anywhere* in a system by means of a *voltage* generator and a series capacitance C_s. See Fig. 10-17.

With a voltage amplifier system, the series capacitance used in the signal substitution circuit is equal to the accelerometer crystal capacitance, $C_s = C_p$; the shunt capacitance in the signal substitution circuit is the same as the shunt capacitance in the part of the accelerometer circuit which it replaces ($C_{\text{S.L.}}$), and the applied voltage is the effective internal crystal voltage sensitivity, i.e., the voltage sensitivity ($E_{p/g}$) of the accelerometer with *no* external capacitance.

With a charge amplifier system the series capacitance C_s can have any value. The charge signal simulated is equal to the test voltage applied times the series capacitance.

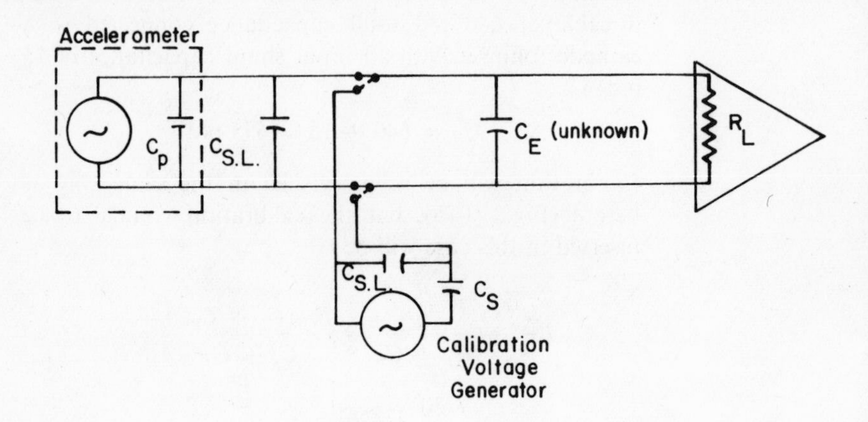

Fig. 10-17. Alternate circuit for signal substitution.

In using this method with a voltage amplifier system, it is first necessary to compute $E_{p/g}$ from the information made available from the accelerometer calibration. Use Eq. (10-6). For the accelerometer and calibration data given in Example 10-4 the values to be used in the signal substitution circuit shown in Fig. 10-17 would be

$$E_{p/g} = \frac{\frac{22}{0.98}(300 + 380)}{300} = 51.0 \text{ rms mv/pk g},$$

or

$$E_{p/g} = \frac{51.0}{0.707} = 72.2 \text{ pk mv/pk g}.$$

The value of C_s to be set in series with the calibration voltage generator is 300 pfd. The value of the shunt capacitance $C_{\text{S.L.}}$ to be used in the calibration circuit is the same as the shunt capacitance that is associated with the disconnected accelerometer leads. The easiest way in which to fulfill this last condition is to use the same kind and length of leads on the calibrator as are attached to the accelerometer.

It should be noted that in this second method it is not necessary to determine the external capacitance (C_E) associated with the long lines and the input stage of the voltage amplifier. It should also be noted that the signal substitution circuit can be added at the amplifier input without changing the circuit; i.e., it is possible to have the value C_E shunted across the load impedance regardless of where the calibration is inserted. See Fig. 10-18 to calibrate; switch (A) is opened and switch (B) is closed.

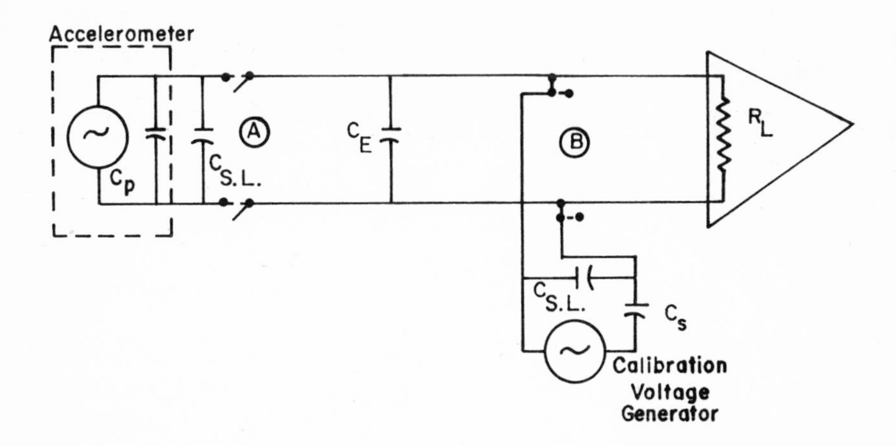

Fig. 10-18. Signal substitution at the voltage amplifier—accelerometer disconnected.

In many cases involving long lines it is not feasible to disconnect the accelerometer during calibration—no switch at position (A) in Fig. 10-18. In this case calibration is still accomplished in the same way, but some additional considerations are necessary if a voltage amplifier is used. The circuit contains more shunt capacitance during calibration than during test; i.e., during calibration the total shunt capacitance is

$$C = C_E + 2C_p + 2C_{\text{S.L.}},$$

but during test

$$C = C_E + C_p + C_{\text{S.L.}}.$$

In many cases involving long lines the difference between these two values is so small that the effect can be neglected. If, however, a high-internal-capacitance accelerometer (some have values of C_p as great as 8000 pfd) is used with moderately long lines, some correction will be required. Any computed correction will require a knowledge of (C_E), and hence defeats the purpose of the calibration method now under discussion.*

A correction which does not require knowledge of C_E can be made as shown in Fig. 10-19. In this case, shunt capacitance of ($C_{\text{S.L.}} + C_p$) is added during test so that the total shunt capacitance will be the same during test as during calibration.

We conclude that system calibration by signal substitution is possible with either long or short leads and does not require the knowledge of the total shunt capacitance in the circuit. It is obvious, however, that when a

* If C_E is known, we can calibrate by using the method discussed in Example 10-4.

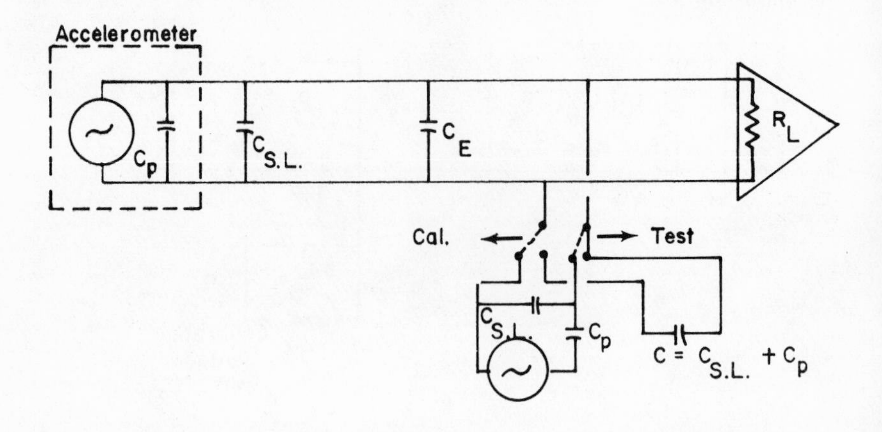

Fig. 10-19. Signal substitution at the voltage amplifier—accelerometer not disconnected.

voltage-amplifier-type cathode follower is used the capacitance must not change from the time of calibration until the time of test. The serious limitation on this type of calibration is that it does not check the condition of the accelerometer; i.e., this calibration will not show whether the accelerometer itself is open, shorted, or operational. Therefore, when this method of system calibration is used, the accelerometer is generally checked for "GO" or "NO GO" by direct mechanical excitation; i.e., hit it.

A method of system calibration which does qualify the accelerometer as well as the remainder of the system has recently been devised. We shall refer to this method as "calibration by simulation."* In this method of system calibration a resistor is inserted in the ground side of the accelerometer cable at the accelerometer location, and a calibration voltage is applied across this resistor. See Fig. 10-20a.

This system may be redrawn as shown in Fig. 10-20b and 10-20c by replacing all shunt capacitances by their effective reactive impedances.

$$Z_p = \frac{1}{2\pi f C_p},$$

$$Z_E = \frac{1}{2\pi f C_E},$$

in which f is the frequency of the calibration signal in cps.

* "Calibration by simulation" is the term used by D. Pennington [22], who gives a detailed analysis of this method and several alternatives.

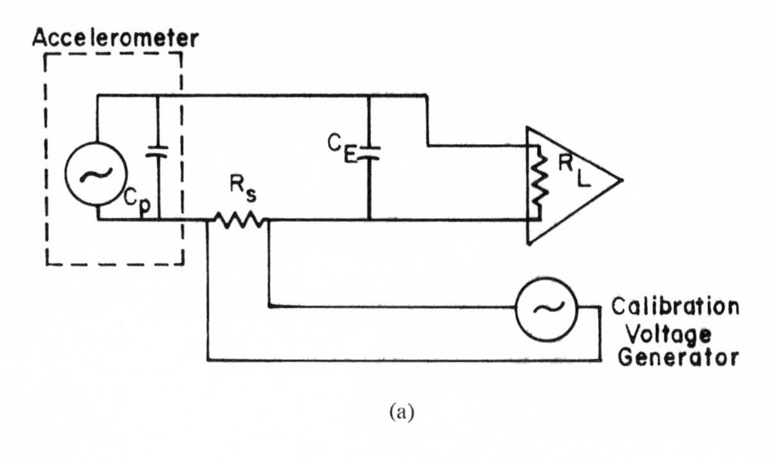

(a)

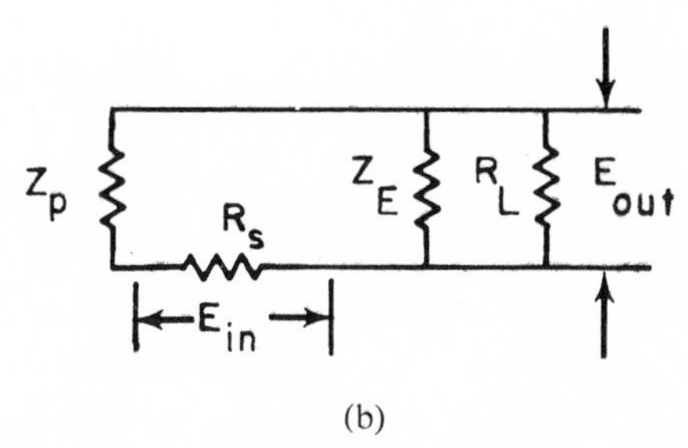

(b)

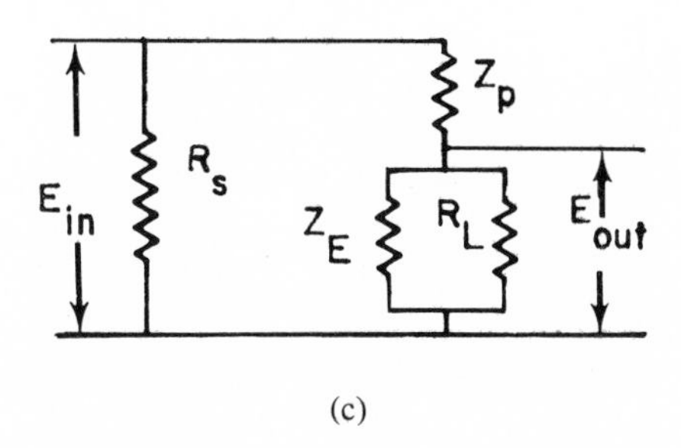

(c)

Fig. 10-20. Voltage simulation circuit.

Referring to Fig. 10-20c, we can see that the ratio of output to input voltage is

$$\frac{E_{\text{output}}}{E_{\text{input}}} = \left(\frac{\dfrac{Z_E R_L}{Z_E + R_L}}{Z_p + \dfrac{Z_E R_L}{Z_E + R_L}} \right) = K. \tag{10-7}$$

System calibration by this method will effectively indicate the condition of all items in the circuit.

1. With both accelerometer and cable operative, $E_{\text{output}} = KE_{\text{input}}$.
2. With accelerometer open, $E_{\text{output}} = 0$.
3. With accelerometer shorted, $E_{\text{output}} = E_{\text{input}}$.
4. With cable inner conductor open, $E_{\text{output}} = 0$.
5. With cable shorted, $E_{\text{output}} = 0$.

Calibration is accomplished by applying an input voltage equal to the desired E_p; an example will illustrate the procedure.

Example 10-7. The same accelerometer used in Example 10-4 is to be wired in the circuit shown in Fig. 10-20a, and the system is to be calibrated by simulation. The calibration is to represent 10 pk g's.

$$C_p = 300 \text{ pfd},$$
$$C_E = 300 \text{ pfd},$$
$$R_L = 1000 \times 10^6 \text{ ohms}.$$

From the calibration data for this accelerometer we compute that

$$E_{p/g} = 51.0 \text{ rms mv/pk g}$$

[use Eq. (10-6)]. Hence, for simulating 10 pk g's we set

$$E_{\text{input}} = 510 \text{ rms mv}.$$

When this system is used, it is more common to apply a DC calibration voltage. In this case

$$E_{p/g} = \frac{51.0}{0.707} = 72.1 \text{ pk mv/pk g},$$

and hence to simulate 10 pk g's we set

$$E_{\text{input}} = 721 \text{ pk mv} = 721 \text{ mv DC}.$$

So that the system will be unaffected by voltage losses in the calibration resistance lead lines, a standardized calibration current is often used. In this example, if a 10 ma DC calibration current is used, the required calibration resistance (R_s) is

$$R_s = \frac{e}{i} = \frac{721 \times 10^{-3}}{10 \times 10^{-3}} = 72.1 \text{ ohms}.$$

Notice that it is not necessary to know C_E to calibrate the circuit. The value of C_E does, of course, affect K [Eq. (10-4)], and it is the value of K that distinguishes between the "GO" conditions (both accelerometer and cable operative) for which $E_{\text{output}} = KE_{\text{input}}$ and the "NO GO" conditions associated with the accelerometer shorted ($E_{\text{out}} = E_{\text{in}}$), or the accelerometer open ($E_{\text{output}} = 0$).

Inspection of Eq. (10-7) will show that as C_E becomes smaller $K \to 1$, and hence it might be difficult to distinguish the "GO" condition from the "NO GO" condition associated with the accelerometer shorted. Even with the shortest cable, this is seldom a problem. For the numbers given in Example 10-7 and with a 1000 cps calibration signal,

$$Z_p = \frac{1}{2\pi f C_p} = \frac{1}{2\pi \times 1000 \times 300 \times 10^{-12}} = 0.53 \times 10^6 \text{ ohms},$$

$$Z_E = \frac{1}{2\pi f C_E} = \frac{1}{2\pi \times 1000 \times 300 \times 10^{-12}} = 0.53 \times 10^6 \text{ ohms},$$

$$K = \frac{\dfrac{Z_E R_L}{Z_E + R_L}}{Z_p + \dfrac{Z_E R_L}{Z_E + R_L}} = \frac{\dfrac{(53 \times 10^4)(10^9)}{10^9}}{53 \times 10^4 + \dfrac{(53 \times 10^4)(10^9)}{10^9}} = 0.5.$$

Further inspection of Eq. (10-7) will show that as C_E becomes larger $K \to 0$, and hence it might be difficult to distinguish the "GO" condition from the "NO GO" condition associated with the accelerometer open.

For the numbers given in Example 10-7, except for the use of 100 ft of cable ($C_E = 100 \times 30 = 3000$ pfd),

$$Z_p = \frac{1}{2\pi f C_p} = \frac{1}{2\pi \times 1000 \times 300 \times 10^{-12}} = 0.53 \times 10^6 \text{ ohms},$$

$$Z_E = \frac{1}{2\pi f C_E} = \frac{1}{2\pi \times 1000 \times 3000 \times 10^{-12}} = 0.053 \times 10^6 \text{ ohms},$$

$$K = \frac{\dfrac{Z_E R_L}{Z_E + R_L}}{Z_p + \dfrac{Z_E R_L}{Z_E + R_L}} = \frac{\dfrac{(5.3 \times 10^4)(10^9)}{10^9}}{53 \times 10^4 + \dfrac{(5.3 \times 10^4)(10^9)}{10^9}} = \frac{5.3}{58.3}$$

$$= 0.091,$$

which means that in the "GO" condition $E_{\text{output}} = 0.091\, E_{\text{input}}$.

With 1000 feet of cable, or with other shunt capacitance added to make C_E = 30,000 pfd,

$$K = 0.01,$$

and $E_{output} = 0.01\ E_{input}$, a value very difficult to distinguish from zero.

The method of system calibration by simulation just discussed will work equally well with a charge amplifier as with a voltage amplifier. The calibration technique is the same, i.e., circuit as in Fig. 10-15a, and $E_{input} = E_{p/g} \times$ g signal desired. However, with a charge amplifier all "NO GO" conditions are shown by zero output, since with either open or short circuits no charge is developed.

The main disadvantages of system calibration by simulation is the fact that two sets of leads must be carried to the accelerometer location. One manufacturer* makes an accelerometer which contains a resistor in its base for calibration by simulation.

10-8 References listed in Chapter 10

1. "American Standard Methods for the Calibration of Shock and Vibration Pickups," S2.2-1959, American Standards Association, Incorporated, 10 East 40th St., New York 16, N.Y.
2. Bouche, R. R., "Calibration of Shock and Vibration Pickups," *The Magazine of Standards* (Mar. 1960), pp. 73–75.
3. Tyzzer, F. G. and H. C. Hardy, "Accelerometer Calibration Technique," *Journal of the Acoustical Society of America*, Vol. 22 (1950), pp. 454–7.
4. Ziegler, C. A., "Electromechanical Pickup Calibration by the Interferometer Method," *Journal of the Acoustical Society of America*, Vol. 25 (1953), pp. 135–7.
5. Rosenberg, J. D., "A Flat Vibration Generator for Accelerometer Calibration," *National Bureau of Standards Report No. 2624* (1953), pp. 85–9.
6. Edelman, S., E. Jones, and E. R. Smith, "Some Developments in Vibration Measurement," *Journal of the Acoustical Society of America*, Vol. 27 (1955), pp. 728–34.
7. Bouche, R. R., "Improved Standard for the Calibration of Vibration Pickups," *Experimental Mechanics* (Apr. 1961), pp. 116–21.
8. Smith, E. R., S. Edelman, E. Jones, and V. A. Schmidt, "Stroboscopic Interferometer for Vibration Measurement," *Journal of the Acoustical Society of America*, Vol. 30, Part 2 (1958), pp. 867–70.
9. Yates, W. A. and M. Davidson, "Wide Range Calibrator for Vibration Pickups," *Electronics*, Vol. 26, Part 2 (Sept. 1953), p. 183.
10. Sulzer, P. G., E. R. Smith, and S. Edelman, "High-Speed Stroboscope for Accelerometer Calibration," *Review of Scientific Instruments*, Vol. 25 (1954), pp 837–8.

* Endevco Corporation.

11. Trent, H. M., "The Absolute Calibration of Electromechanical Pickups," *Journal of Applied Mechanics*, ASME Transactions, Vol. **70** (1948), pp. 49–52.
12. Levy, S. and R. R. Bouche, "Calibration of Vibration Pickups by the Recipocity Method," *Journal of Research of the National Bureau of Standards*, Vol. **57**, No. 4 (1956), pp. 227–43.
13. Conrad, R. W. and I. Vigness, "Calibration of Accelerometers by Impact Techniques," *Proceedings of the Instrument Society of America*, Vol. 8 (1953), pp. 166–70.
14. Perls, T. A., "Tests of Accelerometer Linearity at High Accelerations," *National Bureau of Standards Report No. 2624* (1953), pp. 133–8.
15. Perls, T. A. and C. W. Kissinger, "High G Accelerometer Calibrations by Impact Methods with Ballistic Pendulum, Air Gun, and Inclined Trough," *Proceedings of the Instrument Society of America*, Vol. 9, Part 5 (1954).
16. Bouche, R. R., "The Absolute Calibration of Pickups on a Drop-Ball Shock Machine of the Ballistic Type," *1961 Proceedings of the Institute of Environmental Sciences* (1961), pp. 115–21.
17. Baker, W. E. and R. C. Dove, "Transient Calibration of Piezoelectric Accelerometers," *The Journal of Environmental Sciences* (Oct. 1962), pp. 20, 21, and 24.
18. Palmer, D. F., "An Accurate Shock Calibrator for Accelerometers," *SCTM 96-61 (73)*, Sandia Corporation, Albuquerque, N.Mex. (1961).
19. Bouche, R. R., "High Frequency Response and Transient Motion Performance Characteristics of Piezoelectric Accelerometers," *Instrument Society of America Conference Preprint No. 50-LA-61*, Instrument Society of America.
20. Keast, D. M., "Calibration of Accelerometers in a Simulated Space Environment," *Journal of the Acoustical Society of America*, Vol. 31, Part 1 (1959), pp. 584–7.
21. Adams, P. H., "Effect of Waveform on Ballentine Model 300 VTVM," *SCTM 51-6(16)*, Sandia Corporation, Albuquerque, N.Mex. (Feb. 17, 1960).
22. Pennington, D., "In-Place Calibration of Piezo-Electric Crystal Accelerometer Amplifier Systems," Sixth ISA National Flight Test Instrumentation Symposium, San Diego, Calif. (May 1960).

10-9 Problems

10-1 A centrifuge is used to calibrate accelerometers. The accelerometers are mounted at a radial distance of 20.00 in. The angular velocity is set and measured as 10,000 revolutions/min. If an error of ± 10 rpm is possible, what error results in the acceleration calibration?

10-2 An electrodynamic shaker is used to calibrate accelerometers to 10,000 cps. What would the double amplitude of motion ($2r$) be at 10,000 cps for a peak acceleration of 1000 g's? What would the double amplitude be for 100 g's at 10,000 cps?

10-3 Figure 10-21 shows a steel mass mounted on a gaged force link. A piezoelectric accelerometer is mounted on the top of the steel mass.

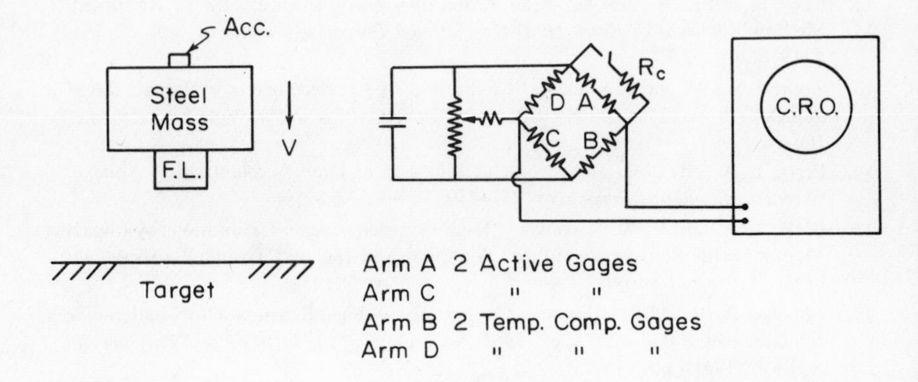

Fig. 10-21.

Force link—Solid Aluminum ($E = 10 \times 10^6$ psi, $\mu = 0.3$, $a = 1$ in.^{2}, height $= \frac{1}{2}$ in.).
4—400 ohm gages bonded longitudinally at 90 deg; $F = 2.0$.

Steel mass = 10 lb.

CRO—Accelerometer channel gain = 50 mv/cm.
Force link channel : a 1×10^6 ohm-resistor (R_c) connected as shown produced a trace deflection of 5 cm.

The peak deflection of the force link trace is 3 cm. The peak deflection of the accelerometer trace is 3.8 cm. What is the accelerometer sensitivity in mv/g?

10-4 Figure 10-22 shows a steel mass mounted on a gaged force link. An accelerometer is mounted on the mass as shown. The mass is dropped 12 ft. from rest. Find the sensitivity of the accelerometer in mv/g.

10-5 A piezoelectric accelerometer has a crystal capacitance of 8000 pfd and a charge sensitivity of 30 picocoulombs per pk g. It is connected in a circuit of unknown shunt capacitance to a cathode follower which has a gain of 0.98. Sketch a circuit to calibrate this system. What rms voltage must be applied to simulate 500 pk g's?

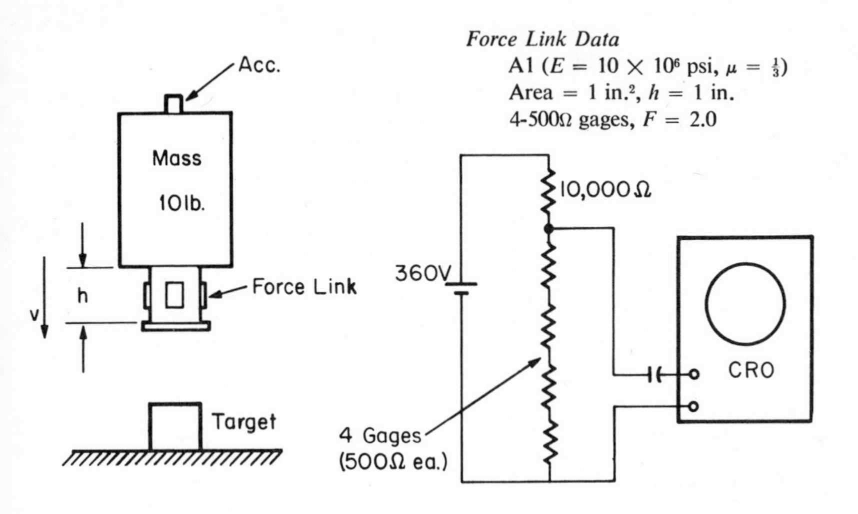

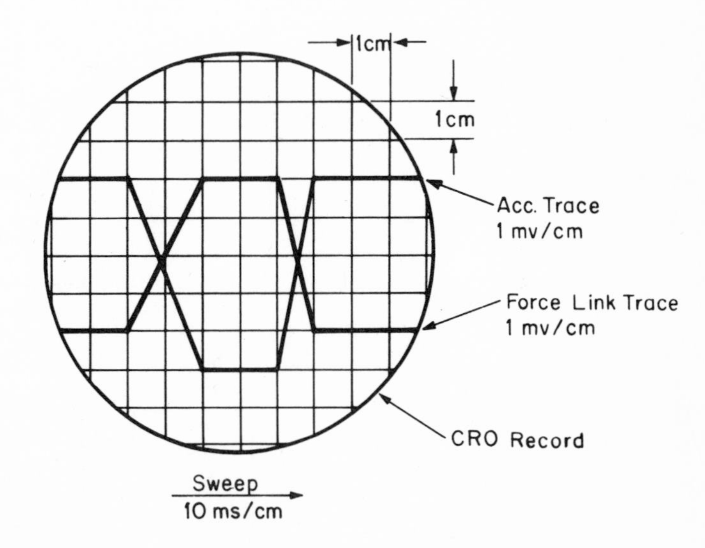

Fig. 10-22.

10-6 Calibration shows that an increase in temperature of 100°F increased the capacitance of a piezoelectric accelerometer from 600 pfd to 750 pfd while the charge sensitivity was increased from 18 to 20 picocoulombs per g. Find the percentage of change in voltage sensitivity associated with this 100°F temperature change (a) if $C_{\text{Ext}} = 600$ pfd and (b) if $C_{\text{Ext}} = 6000$ pfd.

10-7 The apparatus sketch, circuit diagrams, and data taken during the performance of Laboratory Experiment 10-1, Transient Calibration of a Piezoelectric Accelerometer, are given in Figures 10-23 and 10-24. Write the report asked for.

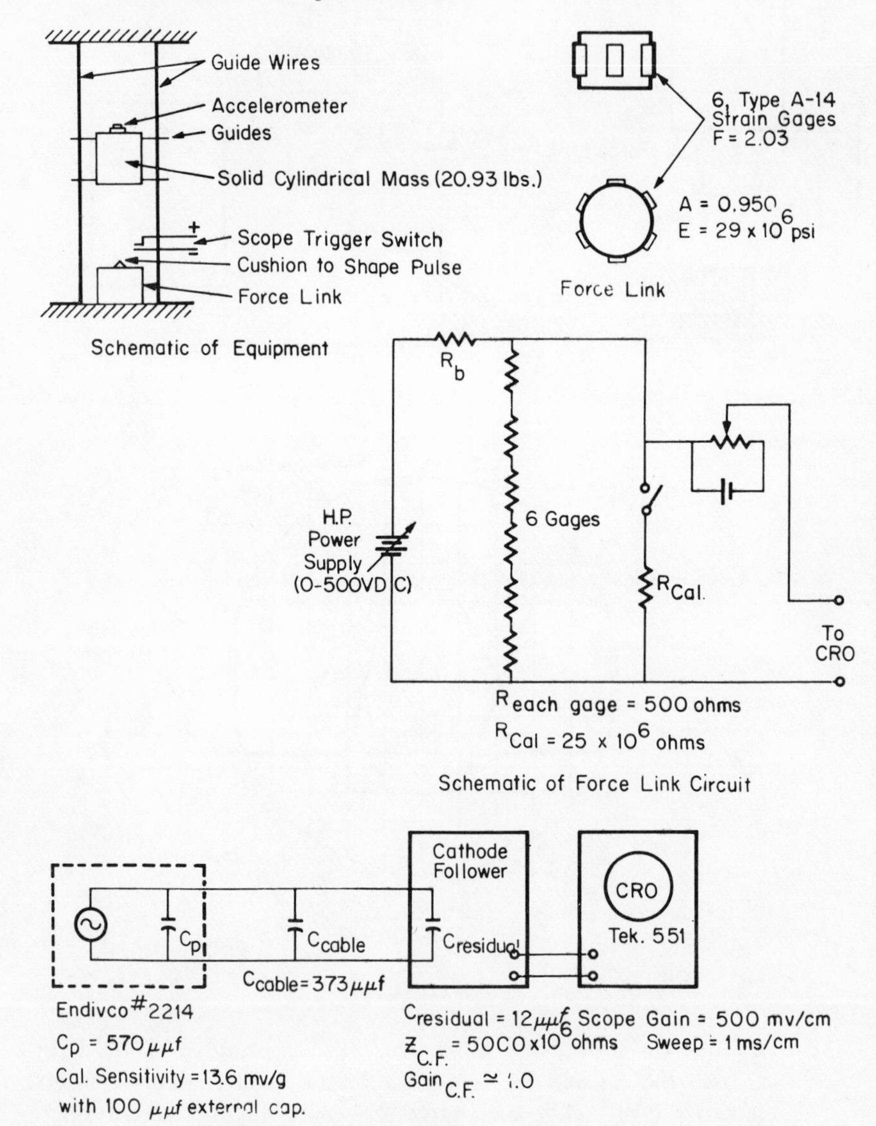

Fig. 10-23. Data sheet for Experiment 10-1.

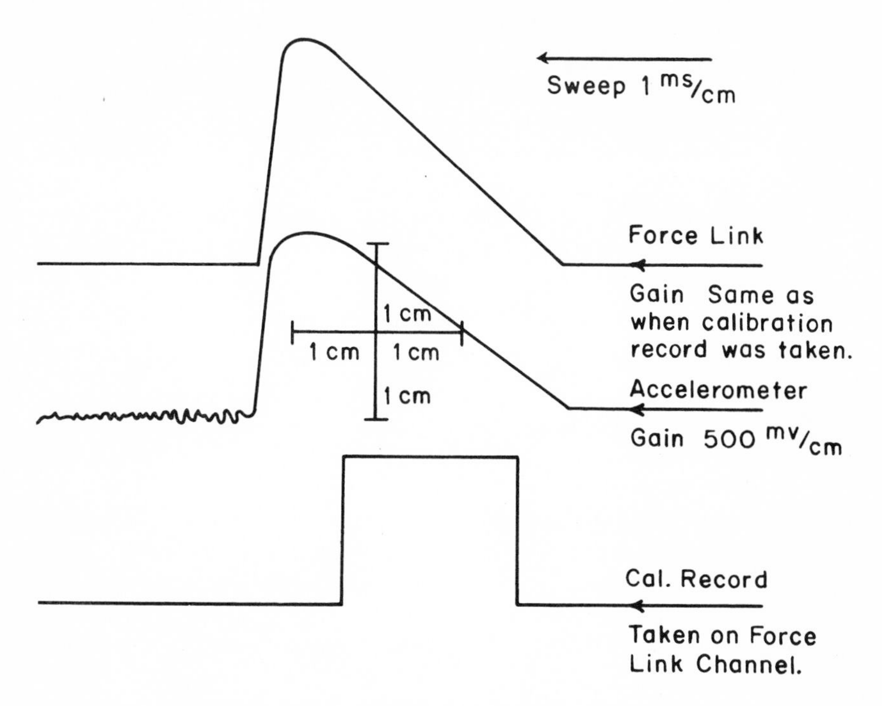

Fig. 10-24. Trace of CRO record for Experiment 10-1.

10-10 Suggested laboratory experiments

Experiment 10-1 Transient calibration of a piezoelectric accelerometer*

EQUIPMENT NECESSARY

1. A piezoelectric accelerometer and cathode follower.
2. A calibrated force link or load cell (the one calibrated in Laboratory Experiment 8-2 may do for this purpose).
3. A dual-beam cathode ray oscilloscope (or two single-beam scopes) and recording camera.
4. A drop tower or other device in which a mass, on which the accelerometer is mounted, can be impacted on the calibrated force link.

---

* Data taken during this experiment are given in Prob. 10-7, so all computations may be conducted as a home problem if desired.

PROCEDURE

1. Mount the accelerometer on a "rigid" mass.
2. Mount the mass in a drop tower so that it can free-fall and impact the calibrated force link.
3. Connect the accelerometer output to one trace of the oscilloscope and the force link output to the other trace.
4. Photograph the signals obtained during a drop test and produced by a calibration signal applied to the force link.

REPORT

1. Trace the signal versus time plot obtained from the force link. Add a force scale and an acceleration scale.
2. Determine the sensitivity of the accelerometer in mv/g.
3. Plot the acceleration-time signal obtained from the accelerometer on the same sheet and to the same acceleration scale as that obtained from the force link.
4. Compare the accelerometer sensitivity determined in this experiment to the value given by the manufacturer (obtained by a harmonic-motion calibration).
5. Discuss the following items as they may be related to this experiment.
   a. Time duration of applied pulse.
   b. Size and construction of the mass on which the accelerometer was mounted.
   c. Size and construction of the force link.
   d. Force link calibrated under static conditions.

CHAPTER 11

Accelerometer Problems, Differentiation and Integration

As is the case with all kinds of transducers, accelerometers must be correctly used in order to give valid data. Suitable methods for mounting, wiring up, switching, and protecting accelerometers against temperature and moisture have been developed by users, and it is profitable to study their results. Other problems, particularly in the field of very high accelerations, acoustic noise and nuclear radiation, have been encountered and studied. In these areas many problems remain unsolved, but, even so, a review of findings to date is useful.

11-1 Humidity and dirt

Most commercially available accelerometers are sealed against moisture and dirt. Protecting and sealing the cables and connectors is up to the user, however. In high-humidity environments, it is usually necessary to pot (mold in plastic—Dow Corning 271 Adhesive is recommended) all cable connectors and cable to accelerometer connections.

With variable-resistance accelerometers, moisture and dirt may introduce shunt resistance which produces a signal which may be indistinguishable from acceleration. With piezoelectric accelerometers, moisture and dirt may lower the load impedance and impair the low-frequency response of the system.

11-2 Temperature effects

The way in which temperature variation affects accelerometers depends on the type of accelerometer. With fluid-damped accelerometers, temperature change produces change in the damping ratio (h) and, therefore, change in the instrument's high-frequency response (see Sect. 9-1). Even the best silicone fluids available undergo significant viscosity changes. Gas damping (see Ref. [6] in Chap. 9) appears promising in this respect, but it has not been entirely successful, because of other problems.

The transducer elements in variable-resistance accelerometers undergo changes in resistance with changes in temperature. This effect can be compensated for electrically, however (see Refs. [1] and [2]).

Unbonded wire, variable-resistance accelerometers (see Fig. 9-17) which have the strain-sensitive element fixed at two separated points are affected by temperature change because of the change in dimensions

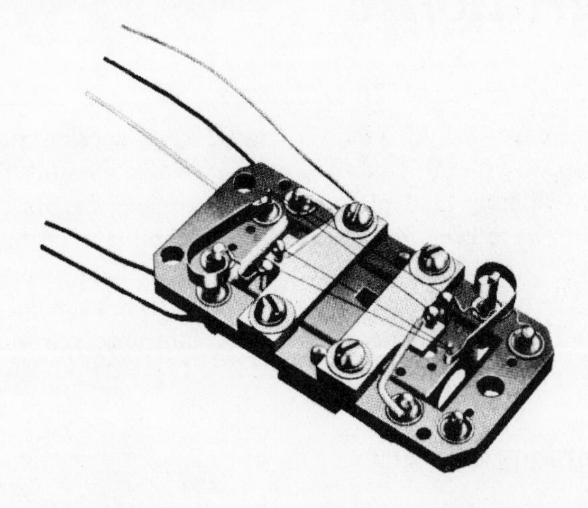

Fig. 11-1. A "zero-length" transducer. (*Courtesy of Statham Instruments, Inc.*)

between these points with temperature. Recently, an unbonded wire accelerometer has been developed in which the wires are fixed at points very close together, and hence this effect is minimized. See Fig. 11-1.

With piezoelectric accelerometers, both charge sensitivity (q/g picocoulombs/g) and crystal capacitance (C_p pfd) are affected by temperature. These, in turn, affect voltage sensitivity (E_c = mv/g), since

$$E_c = \frac{q}{C_p + C_E}.$$

For most piezoelectric materials, q and C_p tend to change in the same sense; i.e., both increase or both decrease with increasing temperature. See Fig. 11-2. Unfortunately, how this affects the voltage sensitivity (E_c)

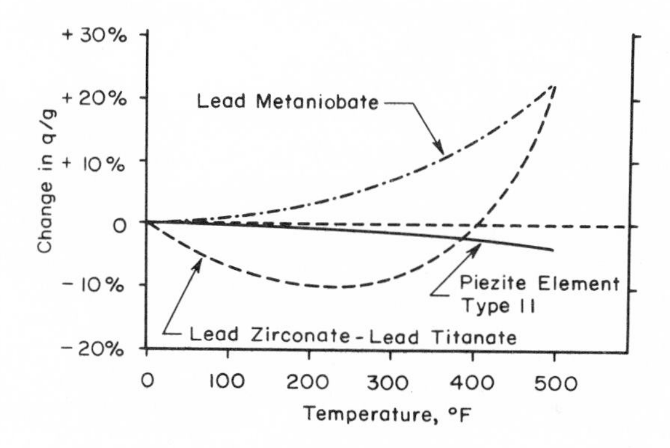

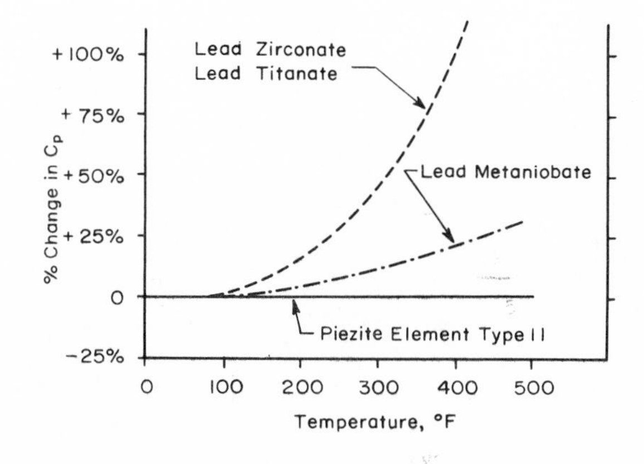

Fig. 11-2. Effect of temperature on crystal capacitance and charge sensitivity. (*Courtesy of Endevco Corp., Ref.* [3].)

depends upon the amount of external shunt capacitance (C_E) in the circuit. Figure 11-3 shows how voltage sensitivity (E_c) varies for a particular

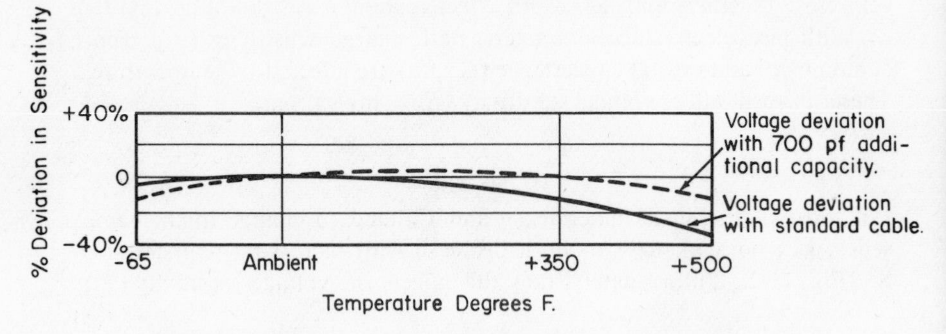

Fig. 11-3. Effect of temperature on voltage sensitivity for an Endevco Type VI crystal element. (*Courtesy of Endevco Corp.*)

crystal when $C_t = C_p$. It is also unfortunate that those piezoelectric materials which show the least change in q and C_p with temperature have very low equivalent voltage sensitivity, $E_p = q/C_p$.

One approach to the problems encountered in using accelerometers at high or low temperatures is to maintain the accelerometer at a constant temperature. Accelerometers which incorporate self-heating or -cooling devices for this purpose have already been mentioned in Sect. 9-2.

Another approach to the use of accelerometers at various temperatures is to calibrate completely the accelerometer at the temperature at which it will be used. If the temperature varies during the test, the required calibration will be extensive and the data reduction will be involved.

11-3 Nuclear-radiation effects

To the authors' knowledge, no studies have been made on the effect of nuclear radiation on variable-resistance accelerometers. However, nuclear-radiation studies made on strain gages should be pertinent.* If the resistance elements are metallic and unbonded, it would appear that very large values of integrated flux ($> 10^{17}$ neutrons/cm^2) can be tolerated, since the gage factor (F) is not affected by smaller doses.

The effect of nuclear radiation on piezoelectrics has been reported. F. T. Rogers [4] reports that when barium titinate ($BaTiO_3$) is subjected to very large values of integrated flux (10^{20} neutrons/cm^2), the dielectric constant is reduced, and the effect of temperature on dielectric constant

* See Sect. 4-2c.

is decreased. Reference [5] reports on the use of a piezoelectric pressure gage in a location where the neutron flux was 10^{12} neutrons/cm²/sec. Transient calibration during steady reactor operation showed that the radiation had little effect on the signal from the piezoelectric crystal. Radiation transients (changes in neutron and gamma ray flux) produced false signals equal to five to ten per cent of the true signal. No apparent crystal damage was produced by an integrated flux of 5×10^{14} neutrons/cm².

11-4 Acoustical sensitivity

A problem of considerable interest is the measurement of vibration of structures in acoustic fields. The vibration may be totally or partially produced by the acoustical energy. When an accelerometer is used in this situation, it is important to know how much of the signal is produced by acceleration of the surface on which the accelerometer is mounted and how much is produced by direct acoustical affect on the seismic mass. The signal not produced by acceleration of the surface of interest must be negligible or must be corrected for. Acoustic sensitivity is defined as accelerometer output in an acoustic environment that is not a measure of acceleration.

A test to determine acoustic sensitivity has proved to be difficult to devise. If an accelerometer is suspended in a noise chamber on a low-frequency mount (this method has been used by some manufacturers), the accelerometer case is subjected to an acceleration which is proportional to the sound pressure; the output is not a measure of acoustic sensitivity. D. W. Bauder and R. J. Klingler [6] have suggested the following method. The accelerometer to be evaluated is mounted in an acoustic chamber as shown in Fig. 11-4.

The reference accelerometer is subjected to at least 40 db ($\frac{1}{100}$) less acoustic output than the test accelerometer (acoustic level at reference accelerometer is monitored with microphone shown), and both accelerometers are subjected to the same acceleration, since the frequency is well below the natural frequency of the connecting link. Therefore, the difference in the output of the two accelerometers is a measure of the acoustical sensitivity of the test accelerometer.

11-5 Zero shift with piezoelectric accelerometers

When piezoelectric accelerometers produce a voltage signal, the average value of which is different from zero, after the input acceleration has

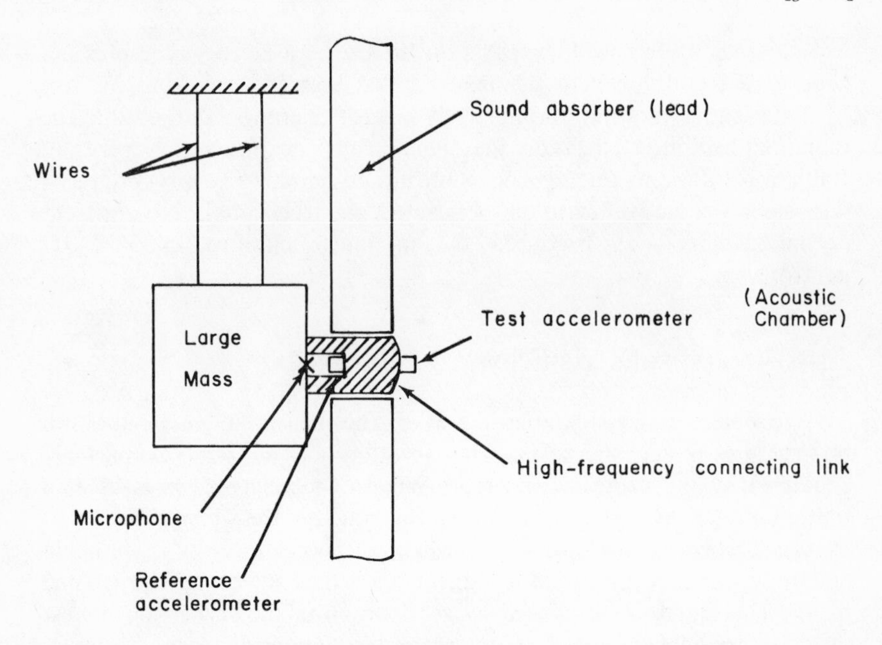

Fig. 11-4. Test facility for determining the acoustical sensitivity of accelerometers.

been reduced to zero, the accelerometer is said to have undergone zero shift. This phenomenon is often observed in test results where high (above 600 g's) accelerations are measured. When it occurs, it makes the interpretation of results impossible.

Since zero shift is detected by a study of the accelerometer record, it is important to distinguish between zero shift and two other kinds of signal distortion, which produce the same effect. In recording transients the record will show negative undershoot if the circuit has too small an $R_L C_T$ time constant (inadequate low-frequency response). This condition, which is associated with long-duration transients of any g level, can be corrected, as explained in Sect. 9-3b. Overloading of a cathode follower or preamplifier will also produce a negative undershoot. As explained in Sect. 9-3c, this condition can be corrected by attenuating the signal by the use of shunt capacitance. True accelerometer zero shift is associated with a signal originating in the accelerometer. There is a difference of opinion as to the exact mechanism which causes zero shift, but the following points meet general agreement:

1. Zero shift occurs only under high ($>$ 600 g's) acceleration conditions.

2. Zero shift may be either positive or negative and may be sufficiently large to make test results meaningless.
3. The amount of zero shift cannot be predicted, even in carefully controlled tests.
4. Tendency to zero shift varies with the piezoelectric material used, with the way in which the crystal is loaded (in compression, bending, or shear), and from one accelerometer to another, even when they are of the same design, same material, etc., i.e., same model of a given manufacturer.

P. E. Scarborough [7] produced zero shift by applying shocks perpendicular to the sensitive axis. He attributes the zero shift in compression-type accelerometers to transverse motion of the seismic mass over the crystal surface, which, in turn, changes the residual compression between mass and crystal. It follows that in the usual test environment zero shift is due to the transverse component of acceleration.

H. J. Jensen [8] suggests that, in addition to the effect of the motion of the seismic mass on the crystal, the electric field generated by strong shocks acts further to polarize artificial piezoelectric materials (those made piezoelectric by application of an electric field during manufacturing), and that this residual polarization contributes to zero shift.

At the present time, the best way to minimize zero shift seems to be to pretest accelerometers under expected test conditions and to discard those which show excessive zero shift.

11-6 Mounting techniques

The way in which an accelerometer is attached to the point of interest is of considerable importance. Ideally, the accelerometer should be mounted so that the accelerometer case becomes a part of the surface at the point of measurement. This would appear to be an easy task, but under high-frequency and high-acceleration conditions almost any type of connection acts as a spring element and permits motion of the accelerometer relative to the test surface. Under favorable environmental conditions, at low g levels (below ten g's), and at low frequencies (below 500 cps), many of the miniature piezoelectric accelerometers may be mounted with double-backed tape.

Accelerometers may be cemented to the test surface with any of several epoxies, with dental cement, or with Eastman 910. A good cement bond is as satisfactory as almost any kind of mechanical connection, but thick bonds and nonhardening cements must not be used.

When it is permissible to drill and tap a hole in the test surface, a threaded stud can be used to join the accelerometer to the test surface. The stud may contain two threaded ends separated by a collar. In this case the stud is torqued down until the collar bears on the test surface; the accelerometer, which contains a tapped hole in its base, is then torqued down until it bears on the stud collar. The stud may be an extension of the accelerometer case. In this case, the accelerometer is torqued down against the mounting surface. All mating surfaces must be flat, smooth, and clean, since torqueing the accelerometer onto an irregular surface may warp the case and change both resonance frequency and sensitivity.

Bouche (Ref. [19] listed in Sect. 10-8) determined the resonance frequency of an accelerometer* mounted in four different ways. By using a steel stud and a film of oil between contact surfaces, resonance frequency (f) was measured as 34,400 cps. Without the oil, $f = 31{,}040$ cps. With a steel stud containing a fiber washer on the collar (for electrical insulation), $f = 29{,}150$ cps. With the accelerometer case bonded to the test surface with Eastman 910, $f = 34{,}300$ cps.

With piezoelectric accelerometers, it is often necessary electrically to isolate the accelerometer case (one side of the accelerometer's electrical system) from the test surface to prevent ground loops which cause electrical noise. Special insulating studs are available for this purpose; in general, these insulating mounts lower the usable frequency range of the accelerometer. Any nonconductive cement will accomplish the same purpose.

11-7 Effect of accelerometer's presence on the acceleration measured

When an accelerometer is used, the information sought is the acceleration that exists at a given point under a given set of conditions. If locating the accelerometer at this point changes the value of acceleration that will be developed under the given set of conditions, the test has lost all meaning. The assumption that the presence of the accelerometer does not affect the acceleration developed is valid in most, but not all, cases. As an example of a difficult situation, a large, heavy accelerometer mounted on thin skin far from support points may have a great influence on the acceleration-versus-frequency results obtained for that point during test.

A first, and good, approximation of the effect of the accelerometer's presence can be made by assuming that the accelerometer acts only to

* Endevco Model 2242.

increase the mass at the point of attachment. The effect that this additional mass (M_A) will have on the resonant frequency of the structure can be computed, provided that the effective mass (M_E) of the structure can be determined. Thus,

$$f_{n_{\text{without accelerometer}}} = \frac{1}{2\pi}\sqrt{\frac{K}{M_E}},$$

$$f_{n_{\text{with accelerometer}}} = f_n^* = \frac{1}{2\pi}\sqrt{\frac{K}{M_E + M_A}}.$$

Then

$$\Delta f_n = \frac{f_n^* - f_n}{f_n} = \sqrt{\frac{M_E}{M_E + M_A}} - 1. \qquad (11\text{-}1)$$

For the case in which M_A is as large as $\frac{1}{10}\, M_E$,

$$\Delta f_n = -\sqrt{\tfrac{10}{11}} - 1 = -0.046,$$

or 4.6 per cent decrease in f_n.

How a decrease in resonant frequency due to the attachment of an accelerometer will affect test results depends on the frequency of the exciting motion or force, and upon the amount of damping present in the structure. If the structure is being excited at a frequency slightly less than the value of resonant frequency, without the accelerometer, then attachment of the accelerometer may lower the resonant frequency to a value such that the structure is being excited at or very near resonance. The magnitude of the effect which this will have on the measured response of the structure will depend upon the amount of damping present in the structure.

For a more exact analysis we consider that attaching an accelerometer at a point adds a rigidly attached mass (the accelerometer case) and a second spring-mounted mass (the seismic element). See Fig. 11-5. Only damping has been neglected in this case.

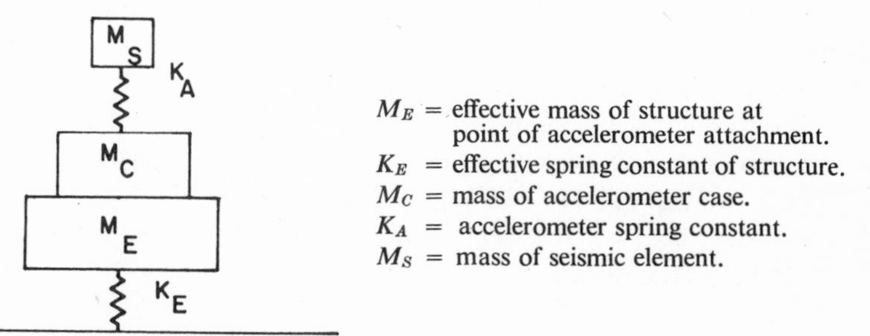

M_S
K_A
M_C
M_E
K_E
M_E = effective mass of structure at point of accelerometer attachment.
K_E = effective spring constant of structure.
M_C = mass of accelerometer case.
K_A = accelerometer spring constant.
M_S = mass of seismic element.

Fig. 11-5. System and accelerometer.

This system can be analyzed by using any one of several techniques used for the solution of two-degrees-of-freedom vibration problems; indeed, this is the common vibration absorber system. Such an analysis* will show that presence of the second spring-supported mass (M_S) will produce two resonant frequencies in place of the original first resonant frequency of the system. Using the terms defined in Fig. 11-5, we find that the frequency equation is

$$\left(\frac{\omega_A}{\omega_{\text{sys}}}\right)^2\left(\frac{\omega}{\omega_A}\right)^4 - \left[1+\left(1+\frac{M_S}{M_C+M_E}\right)\left(\frac{\omega_A}{\omega_{\text{sys}}}\right)^2\right]\left(\frac{\omega}{\omega_A}\right)^2 + 1 = 0, \quad (11\text{-}2)$$

in which ω is the resonant frequencies of the new system, Fig. 11-5.
ω_A is the resonant frequency of the accelerometer.
ω_{sys} is the resonant frequency of the original system with M_C rigidly attached.

(1) *Case I, accelerometer resonant frequency greater than system resonance*

In many cases $M_S << (M_C + M_E)$, since the seismic mass (M_S) is very small even when compared to the case mass (M_C) alone; and

$$\frac{\omega_A}{\omega_{\text{sys}}} \geq 2.5$$

if frequencies as high as ω_{sys} are to be measured, since even with 0.7 of critical damping ω_A must be $\geq 2.5\,\omega_{\text{sys}}$, if the accelerometer is to function as an accelerometer to a frequency of ω_{sys}. A typical case would be

$$\frac{M_S}{M_C + M_E} \leq 0.01, \quad \text{and} \quad \frac{\omega_A}{\omega_{\text{sys}}} \geq 2.5.$$

When these values are used in Eq. (4-26), the two resonant frequencies are

$$\omega = 1.005\omega_A = 2.512\omega_{\text{sys}},$$

and

$$\omega = 0.397\omega_A = 0.992\omega_{\text{sys}}$$

(less than one per cent decrease in ω_{sys}).

It should be remembered that ω_{sys} may be lower than the ω for the original structure because of the addition of the accelerometer case mass (M_C); see Eq. (11-1). The higher resonance ($\omega = 2.512\omega_{\text{sys}}$) is of no importance, because the accelerometer will not function at frequencies above ω_{sys} in any case.

* See Sect. 36, "The Vibration Absorber" in Ref. [1] listed in Sect. 9-4 for development of the equations describing the behavior of the system shown in Fig. 11-5.

(2) *Case II, accelerometer resonant frequency equal to, or less than, system resonance*

If an accelerometer having a low resonant frequency is mounted on a relatively stiff structure (high ω_{sys}), the resonant frequency of the new system (system and accelerometer case plus seismic element) may be considerably reduced.* However, in this case, the accelerometer is only usable to a frequency which is some fraction of ω_A and hence of ω_{sys}. To check the effect of the accelerometer's presence, we need to compare the response of a single-degree-of-freedom system (Fig. 11-5 with accelerometer seismic element removed) to the response of the two-degrees-of-freedom system over the frequency range in which the accelerometer can function. The response equation for the single-degree-of-freedom system is given by the equation

$$\frac{X_{\text{sys}}}{X_o} = \frac{1}{\sqrt{\left[1 - \left(\frac{\omega'}{\omega_{\text{sys}}}\right)^2\right]^2 + \left(2h\frac{\omega'}{\omega_{\text{sys}}}\right)^2}}. \qquad (11\text{-}3)\dagger$$

For zero damping this reduces to

$$\frac{X_{\text{sys}}}{X_o} = \frac{1}{\left[1 - \left(\frac{\omega'}{\omega_{\text{sys}}}\right)^2\right]}. \qquad (11\text{-}3a)$$

The response of the undamped two-degrees-of-freedom system is given by the equation‡

$$\frac{X_{\text{sys}}}{X_o} = \frac{\left[1 - \left(\frac{\omega'}{\omega_A}\right)^2\right]}{\left[1 + \frac{K_A}{K_E} - \left(\frac{\omega'}{\omega_{\text{sys}}}\right)^2\right]\left[1 - \left(\frac{\omega'}{\omega_A}\right)^2\right] - \frac{K_A}{K_E}}, \qquad (11\text{-}4)$$

in which ω' is the frequency of the forcing or driving motion, and X_o is the equivalent static deflection, F/K_E. For the case $\omega_A/\omega_{\text{sys}} = 1$, the region of interest is $\omega'/\omega_{\text{sys}} \leq 0.4$, since the accelerometer will not function properly at frequencies above $0.4\omega_A$ (hence, $0.4\omega_{\text{sys}}$) at the most.

---

* With

$$\frac{\omega_A}{\omega_{\text{sys}}} = 1 \quad \text{and} \quad \frac{M_S}{M_C + M_E} = 0.1,$$

Eq. (11-2) gives $\omega = 0.8\omega_{\text{sys}}$ and $1.25\omega_{\text{sys}}$.

† See p. 65 of Ref. [1] listed in Sect. 9-4.

‡ See p. 128 of Ref. [1] listed in Sect. 9-4.

Equations (11-3a) and (11-4) have been solved for

$$\frac{X_{\text{sys}}}{X_o} \text{ versus } \frac{\omega'}{\omega_{\text{sys}}}$$

in the region where

$$\frac{\omega'}{\omega_{\text{sys}}} \leq 0.4 \qquad \text{and for} \qquad \frac{K_A}{K_E} = 0.1.$$

The results are plotted as Fig. 11-6.

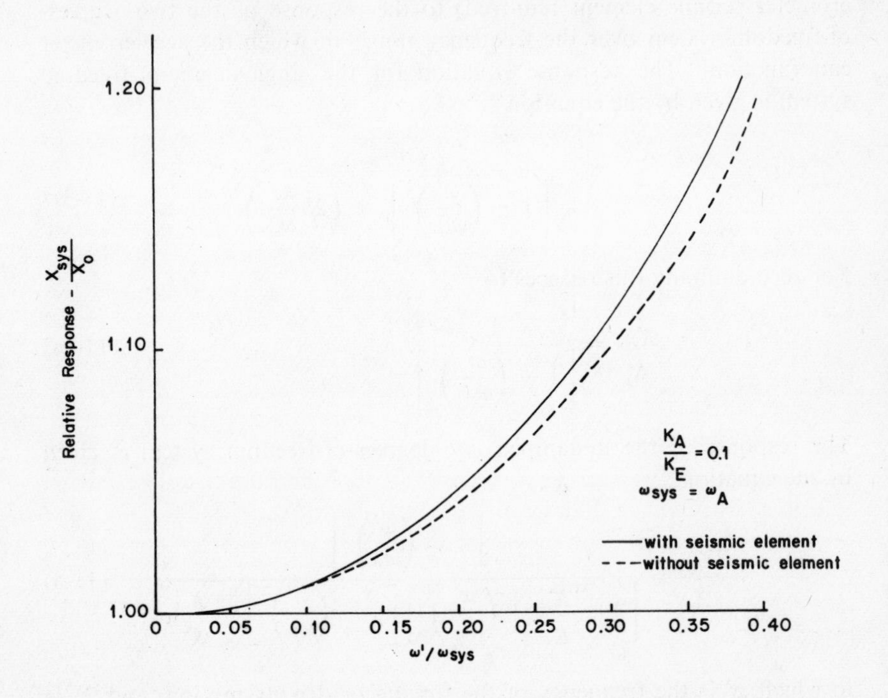

Fig. 11-6. System response with and without a second spring mass added.

With

$$\frac{\omega_A}{\omega_{\text{sys}}} = 1,$$

$K_A/K_E = 0.1$ corresponds to

$$\frac{M_S}{M_C + M_E} \simeq 0.1,$$

since

$$\frac{\omega_A}{\omega_{\text{sys}}} = \frac{\sqrt{\dfrac{K_A}{M_S}}}{\sqrt{\dfrac{K_E}{(M_E + M_C)}}} = 1.$$

Then

$$\frac{K_A M_E}{K_E M_S} \simeq 1, \qquad \text{or} \qquad \frac{K_A}{K_E} \simeq 1 \times \frac{M_S}{M_E} \simeq 0.1$$

if $M_E >> M_C$.

In this case the presence of the seismic mass increases the response by a maximum of two per cent, and in the more usual case with $M_S/(M_C + M_E) \leq 0.01$ the effect will be negligible.

It is difficult to conceive of a case in which the analysis just concluded, that of the accelerometer as a rigid mass (case, M_C) plus a second spring-mounted mass (M_S on K_A), is necessary if the effect of adding a rigid mass [Eq. (11-1)] has already been checked and reduced to an allowable value. Hence, the real problem becomes that of determining the effects of an added rigid mass on the resonant frequency and the resultant effect on the relative response of the system.

In the case where the effective mass of the structure cannot be determined and hence Eq. (11-1) cannot be solved, the effect of the accelerometer's presence can still be checked experimentally. Data is first obtained with the accelerometer located at the point of interest. The test is repeated with the accelerometer and an additional dummy mass equal to the mass of the accelerometer located at the point of interest. If there is a difference in the results obtained, the effect of the accelerometer's presence is measurable, and a lighter accelerometer should be applied and checked.

11-8 Differentiation and integration of motion measurements

The definition of linear velocity (v) and linear acceleration (a) suggests that displacement, velocity, and accelerometer transducers can be used interchangeably to measure displacement, velocity, or acceleration. Specifically, velocity (v) is defined as $v = ds/dt$, and acceleration (a) is defined as $a = dv/dt = d^2s/dt^2$, in which s is position and t is time. Therefore, displacement signals can be differentiated to obtain either velocity or acceleration, and velocity signals can be differentiated to obtain acceleration.

Rearranging and integrating, we obtain

$$S_{1-2} = \int_{t_1}^{t_2} v\,dt = \int_{t_1}^{t_2}\int_{t_1}^{t_2} a\,dt$$

$$v_{1-2} = \int_{t_1}^{t_2} a\,dt,$$

which suggests determining change in displacement by measuring either velocity or acceleration and integrating the signal obtained, and determining velocity change by measuring acceleration and integrating the signal obtained.

If the desired quantity is to be obtained by differentiation, two possibilities suggest themselves. First, we may record the signal from a displacement gage as a displacement-versus-time diagram (Fig. 11-7) and

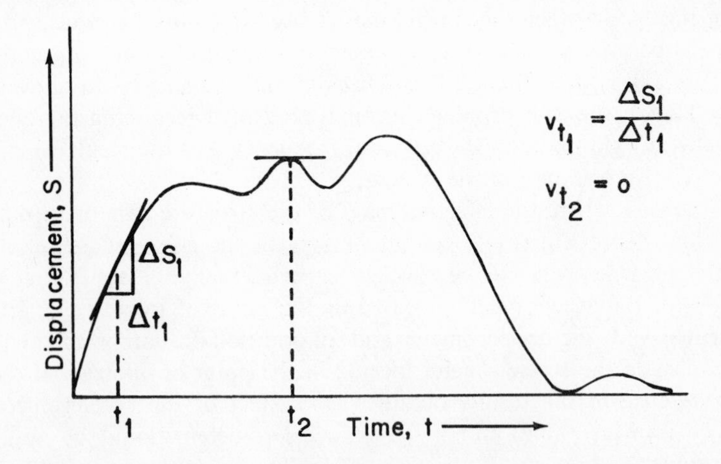

Fig. 11-7. Graphical differentiation of a displacement-time record to obtain velocity.

then differentiate this record. Although essentially this consists of finding the slope of the displacement-time curve, there are several graphical techniques (see Ref. [9]) and mechanical devices for doing this. Second, we may use the signal from the displacement transducer as the input to an electrical differentiating circuit, i.e., a circuit the output of which is the derivative of the input. Here again, there are several circuits which might be used. We shall illustrate and discuss only the simplest; see Fig. 11-8.

The variable voltage (e_i) which is the output signal from the linear potentiometer displacement transducer serves as the input signal to the

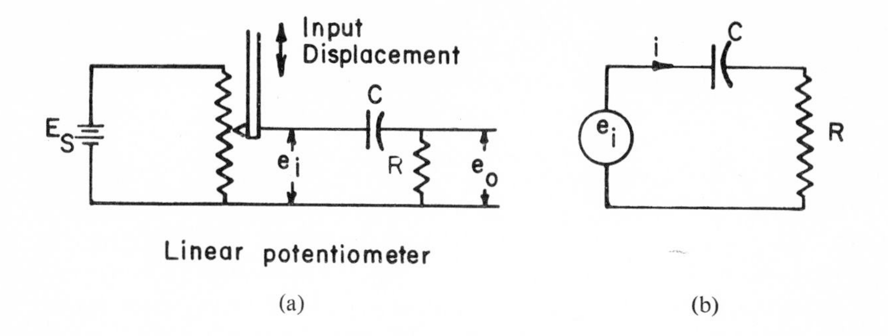

Fig. 11-8. Linear displacement transducer connected to a differentiating circuit to obtain velocity.

differentiating circuit, which consists of a capacitance and resistor in series. Under certain conditions the variable voltage across the resistor (e_o) is proportional to the derivative of the input voltage (e_i) and hence to the input velocity. This can be shown in the following way: the voltage drop around the circuit must equal the applied voltage

$$e_{\text{in}} = iR + \frac{1}{C}\int i\,dt.$$

If the voltage drop across the capacitor is much larger than the drop across the resistor, then

$$e_{\text{in}} \simeq \frac{1}{C}\int i\,dt,$$

which can be differentiated and rewritten as

$$i = C\frac{de_{\text{in}}}{dt}.$$

Now the voltage drop across the resistor is

$$e_{\text{out}} = iR,$$

and, substituting for i from the previous equation, we have

$$e_{\text{out}} = RC\frac{de_{\text{in}}}{dt}.$$

Having shown how velocity may be obtained by differentiation, we must now point out that both of the methods suggested are fraught with difficulties. When the displacement-time curve is differentiated graphically, the errors tend to be largest at the very points of greatest interest, i.e., where the velocity is a maximum or where it is changing rapidly. When the displacement signal is electrically differentiated, the output signal (the desired time derivative) is inherently of lower level than the input signal, and the ratio of signal level to electrical noise level becomes unfavorable. Since to make the voltage drop across the capacitance large compared to the voltage drop across the resistor, both R and C must be small; velocity and acceleration are seldom determined by differentiation.

If the desired motion quantity is to be obtained by integration, there are, again, two possibilities. First, we may record the signal from an accelerometer as an acceleration-time diagram and then integrate this record. Essentially, this consists of finding the area under the acceleration-time curve. Mechanical devices are available for this purpose, but it can be accomplished conveniently with surprising accuracy by the trapezoid rule; see Ref. [9].

Second, we may use the signal from an accelerometer as an input to an electrical integrating circuit, i.e., a circuit the output of which is the integral of the input. We shall begin with the simplest circuit; see Fig. 11-9.

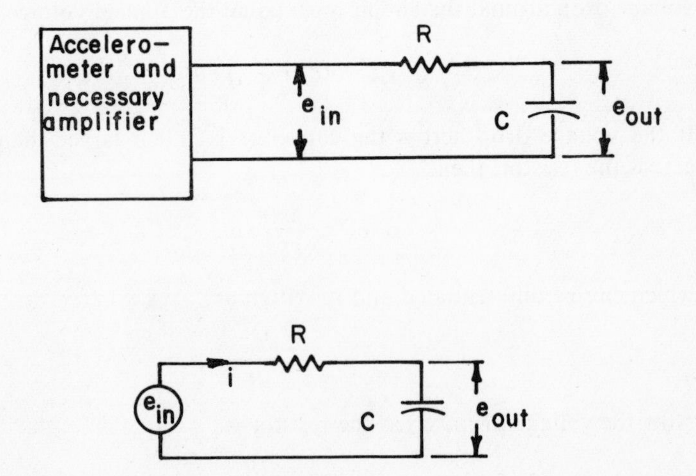

Fig. 11-9. Accelerometer connected to an integrating circuit to obtain velocity change.

The variable voltage (e_i) which is the output signal from the accelerometer system serves as the input signal for the integrating circuit. Under certain conditions the variable voltage across the capacitance (e_o) is proportional to the integral of the input voltage signal (e_i) and hence to the velocity change. This can be shown in the following way: the voltage drop around the circuit must be equal to the applied voltage

$$e_{\text{in}} = {}_iR + \frac{1}{C}\int i\,dt.$$

If the voltage drop across the resistor is much larger than the drop across the capacitance, then

$$e_{\text{in}} \simeq iR.$$

The voltage drop across the capacitance (e_o) can then be approximated by

$$e_o = \frac{1}{C}\int i\,dt \simeq \frac{1}{C}\int \frac{e_{\text{in}}}{R}\,dt,$$

which can be rewritten as

$$e_{\text{out}} \simeq \frac{1}{RC}\int e_{\text{in}}\,dt.$$

With this circuit the output is inherently small, because to function as an integrating circuit both R and C must be large. Fortunately, this circuit can be improved upon in a rather simple manner. In Fig. 11-10 a voltage

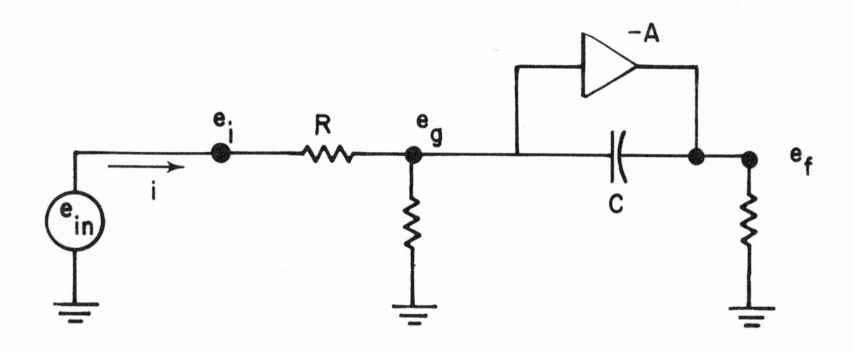

Fig. 11-10. Integrating circuit utilizing a high-gain amplifier.

amplifier with a gain of $-A$ has been connected as shown. (The operational amplifiers commonly used in analog computer circuits are ideal for this purpose.)

In considering this circuit, it is convenient to consider the potential at three points: e_i, e_g, and e_f. The voltage drop across the resistor is

$$e_{ig} = iR,$$

or

$$e_{ig} = \frac{dq}{dt}R, \tag{11-5}$$

since, by definition,

$$i = \frac{dq}{dt},$$

in which q is charge.

The voltage drop across the capacitance is

$$e_{gf} = \frac{q}{C},$$

which can be differentiated to give

$$\frac{dq}{dt} = C\frac{de_{gf}}{dt}. \tag{11-6}$$

Substituting Eq. (11-6) into Eq. (11-5), we have

$$e_{ig} = RC\frac{de_{gf}}{dt},$$

or

$$de_{gf} = \frac{1}{RC}e_{ig}\,dt. \tag{11-7}$$

If the gain of the amplifier is large (i.e., $A \to \infty$), e_g will be small compared to both e_i and e_f, and Eq. (11-7) can be approximated as

$$de_f \simeq \frac{1}{RC}e_i\,dt,$$

or

$$e_f \simeq \frac{1}{RC}\int e_i\,dt. \tag{11-7a}$$

The important point is that the validity of this approximation can be controlled by selection of the amplifier gain.

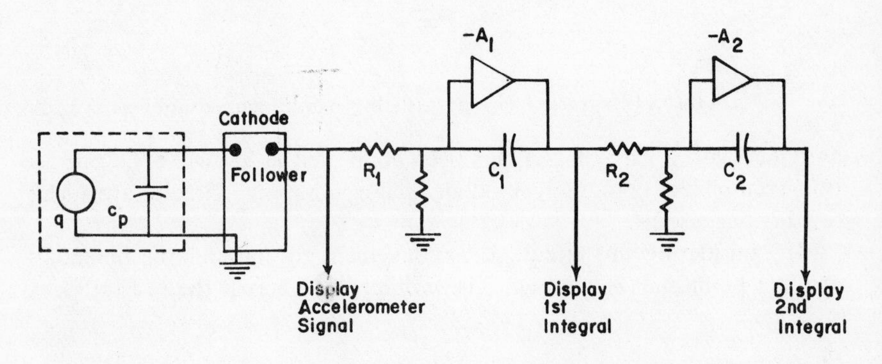

Fig. 11-11. Double-integrating circuit.

Figure 11-11 shows a circuit of this type arranged to double-integrate the output of a piezoelectric accelerometer, thus giving acceleration, velocity, and displacement information simultaneously.

Since integration of acceleration yields change in velocity, it is necessary to have a value of initial velocity in order correctly to interpret records obtained by double integration. Two examples will illustrate this point.

Example 11-1. An accelerometer is mounted on an item which is initially at rest ($v_o = 0$). The item is impacted to produce an acceleration transient. The acceleration-time record is as shown in Fig. 11-12a. If this signal is integrated

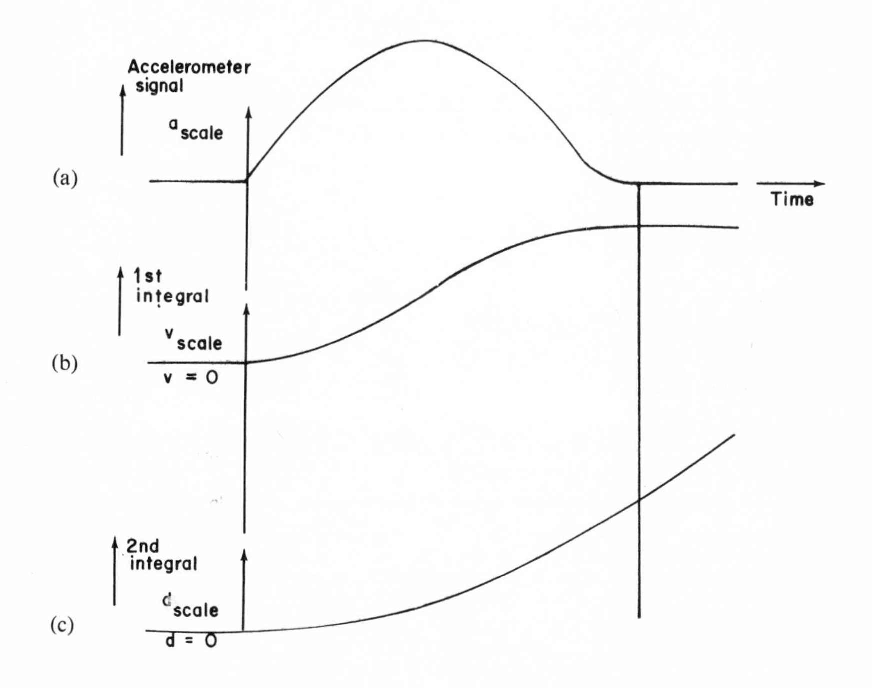

Fig. 11-12.

twice, the resulting traces will be as shown in Figs. 11-12b and c, and velocity and displacement scales can be assigned as shown, since $v_o = 0$ and the position at time $t = 0$ can be taken as $d_o = 0$.

Example 11-2. An accelerometer is mounted on an item which is traveling with a constant velocity of $v_o \neq 0$. The item impacts the earth. The acceleration-time record is as shown in Fig. 11-13a. If this signal is integrated twice, the result-

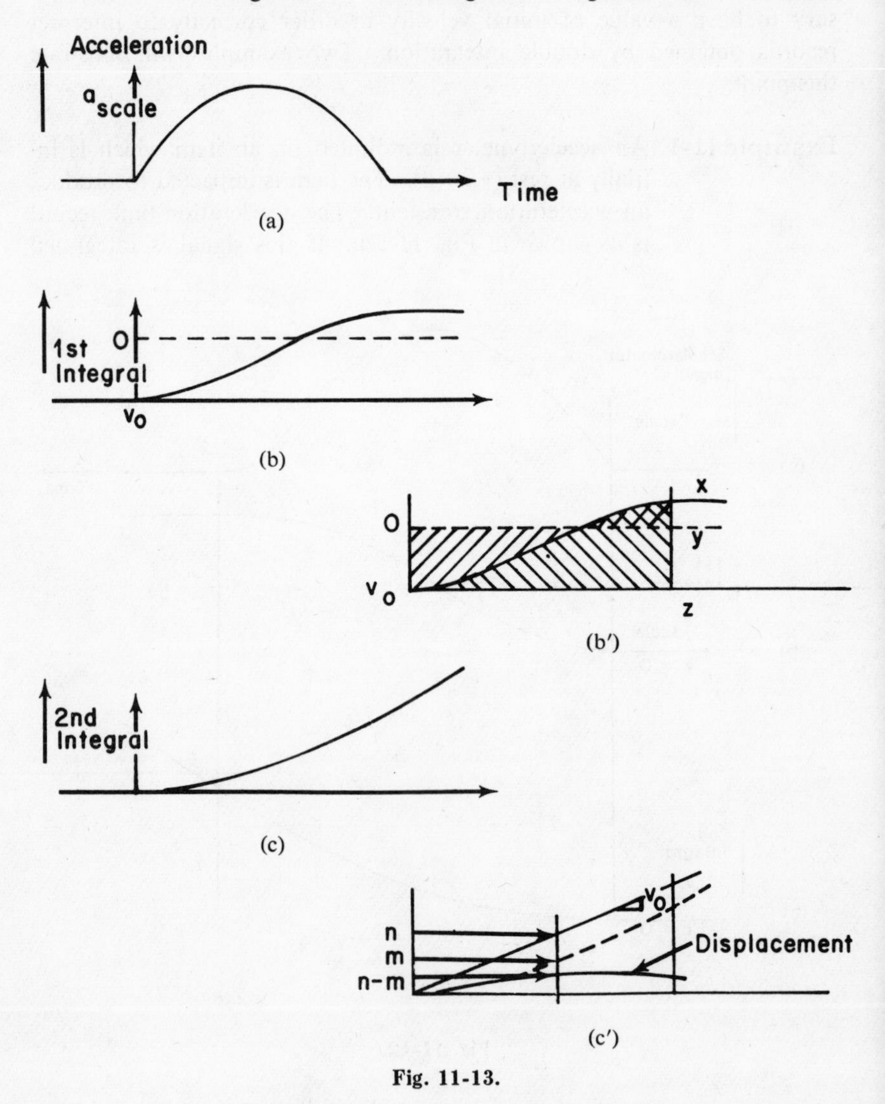

Fig. 11-13.

ing traces will be as shown in Figs. 11-13b and c. In this case the velocity at time $t = 0$ is v_o, and hence the velocity scale must be assigned as shown. When this signal was integrated electrically, the area between the signal and the line v_o(\\\ in Fig. 11-13b′) was summed, thus giving the trace shown in Fig. 11-13c. What is desired is the area between the first integral signal and the line $v = 0$ (/// in Fig. 11-13b′). This desired result can most readily be obtained by recognizing that it is the difference between the area v_o0yz and v_oxz. Drawing the line of slope v_o, shown in Fig. 11-13c′ (the integral of $0y$ from the base v_oz), and plotting the difference between this line and the trace obtained from the second integration (shown dotted in Fig. 11-13c′) gives the desired displacement-time plot.

The integrating circuit shown in Fig. 11-11 can readily be calibrated to establish the constant of proportionalities between the input signal and the first and second integrals. A sinusoidal voltage ($e_o = E_0 \sin \omega t$) is introduced ahead of the first integrating element (R_1). This input signal and the resulting signals at the first and second integral readout points (e_1 and e_2) are recorded.

$$e_o = E_0 \sin \omega t,$$

$$e_1 = K_1 \int e_o\, dt = \frac{K_1 E_0}{\omega} \cos \omega t,$$

or

$$e_{1_{\max}} = E_1 = \frac{K_1 E_0}{\omega},$$

and

$$e_2 = K_2 \int e_1\, dt = \frac{K_2 K_1 E_0}{\omega^2} \sin \omega t,$$

or

$$e_{2_{\max}} = E_2 = \frac{K_2 K_1 E_0}{\omega^2}.$$

The frequency (ω rad/sec) and peak voltage signals are read on each of the three traces (E_0, E_1, and E_2), and the required constants of proportionality are then determined as

$$K_1 = \frac{E_1}{E_0}\omega,$$

and

$$K_2 = \frac{E_2}{E_0}\frac{\omega^2}{K_1} = \frac{E_2}{E_1}\omega.$$

This kind of calibration technique can also be used to check frequency range and phase shift in the integrating circuit.

When this system is connected to an accelerometer, the input signal e_0 is

$$e_0 = S\left(\frac{\text{mv}}{\text{g}}\right) \times \text{Acceleration (g)}.$$

Then

$$e_1 = K_1 \int e_0 \, dt = K_1 S \int a \, dt,$$

and

$$e_2 = K_2 \int e_1 \, dt = K_2 K_1 S \iint a \, dt.$$

11-9 References listed in Chapter 11

1. White, G. E., "Temperature Compensation of Bridge-Type Transducers," *Instrument Notes, No. 5*, Statham Laboratories (Oct.–Nov. 1948).
2. Hefland, B. B. and J. Burns, "Calibration of Resistance Bridge Transducer Circuits Under Temperature Extremes," *Instrument Notes, No. 14*, Statham Laboratories (Mar.–Apr. 1950).
3. Bradley, W., "Performance of Three 500°F Crystal Accelerometers," paper presented at National Telemetering Conference, El Paso, Texas (May 1957).
4. Rogers, F. T., "Effect of Pile Irradiation on the Dielectric Constant of Ceramic Ba Ti O_3." *Journal of Applied Physics*, Vol. 27, No. 9 (Sept. 1956), p. 1066.
5. Unsigned letter appearing in *Technical Data Report dated July 21, 1959*, Endevco Corporation.
6. Bauder, D. W. and R. J. Klingler, A series of letters and memos on Acoustic Sensitivity, Sandia Corporation, Sect. 7323-1 (June 18, 1962).
7. Scarborough, P. E., "Zero Shift in Piezoelectric Transducers," *SCTM 315-59(16)*, Sandia Corporation, Albuquerque, N.Mex. (Oct. 5, 1959).
8. Jensen, H. J., "Zero Shift in Piezoelectric Transducers," a letter in reference to Scarborough's (Ref. [7]) paper, distributed by Sandia Corporation (June 22, 1960).
9. Lipka, J., *Graphical and Mechanical Computation.* New York: John Wiley and Sons, Inc., December 1945.

11-10 Problems

11-1 It has been estimated that the attachment of an accelerometer to a certain light structure lowers the natural frequency of the structure by five per cent. Estimate the effect this will have on the response to forced vibration, (a) if the forcing frequency (ω) is equal to 0.95 times the natural frequency of the original system, i.e., natural frequency without the accelerometer attached, (b) if the forcing frequency (ω) is equal to 0.5 times the natural frequency of the original system, and (c) if the forcing frequency (ω) is equal to 0.1 times the natural frequency of the original system. First, consider the structure to be undamped. Second, consider it to be damped such that $h = 0.2$

11-2 Refer to Prob. 10-4. How long (m sec) after impact is it until the velocity of the mass reaches zero?

11-3 Figure 11-14 shows a rigid mass on which an accelerometer is mounted. The mass free-falls to the target block from a height of 100 in., the accelerometer sensitivity is 10 mv/g, and the record is taken on a CRO with a gain of 400 mv/cm, and a sweep rate of 1000 μsec/cm. By how much is the target block compressed? (See the accelerometer trace in Fig. b.)

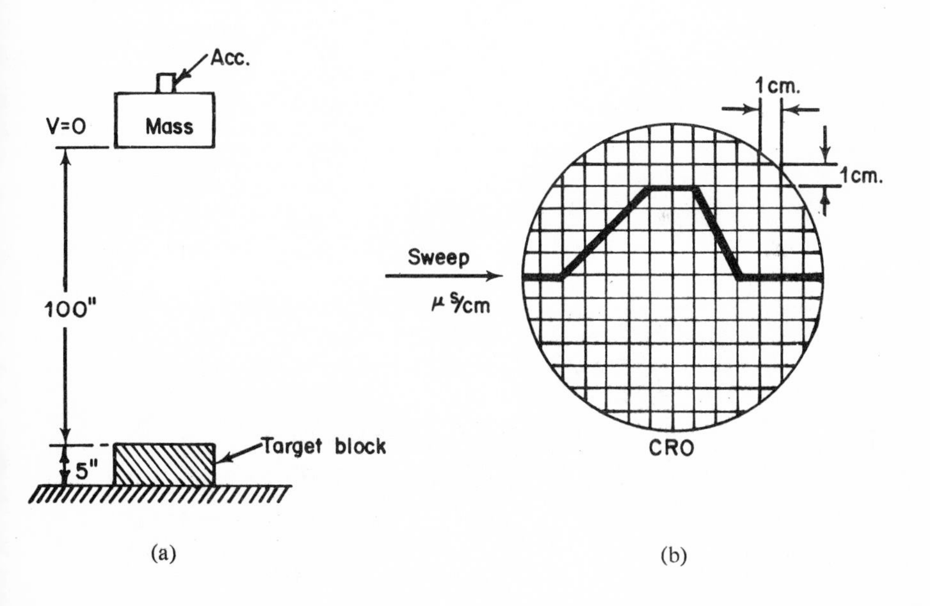

Fig. 11-14.

11-4 The apparatus sketch, circuit diagrams, and data taken during the performance of Laboratory Experiment 11-1, Integration of an Accelerometer Signal, are given. Write the report asked for.

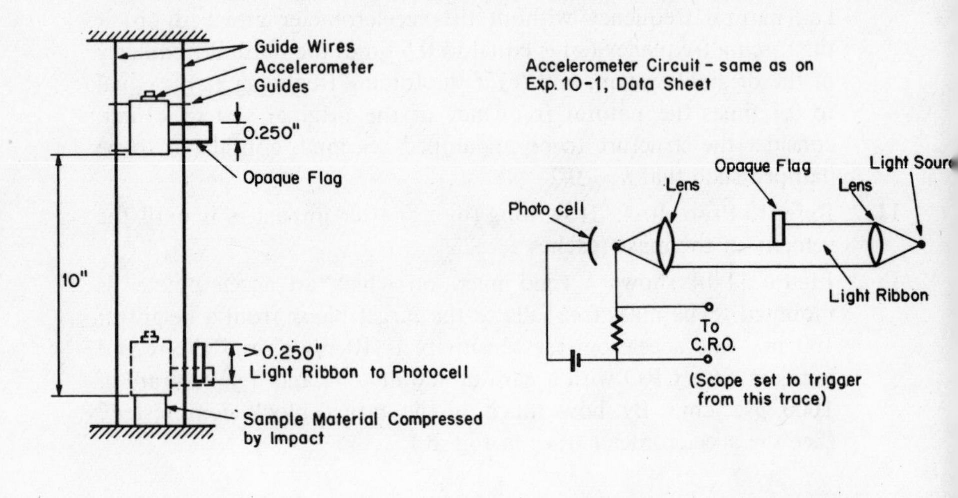

Fig. 11-15. Data sheet for Experiment 11-1.

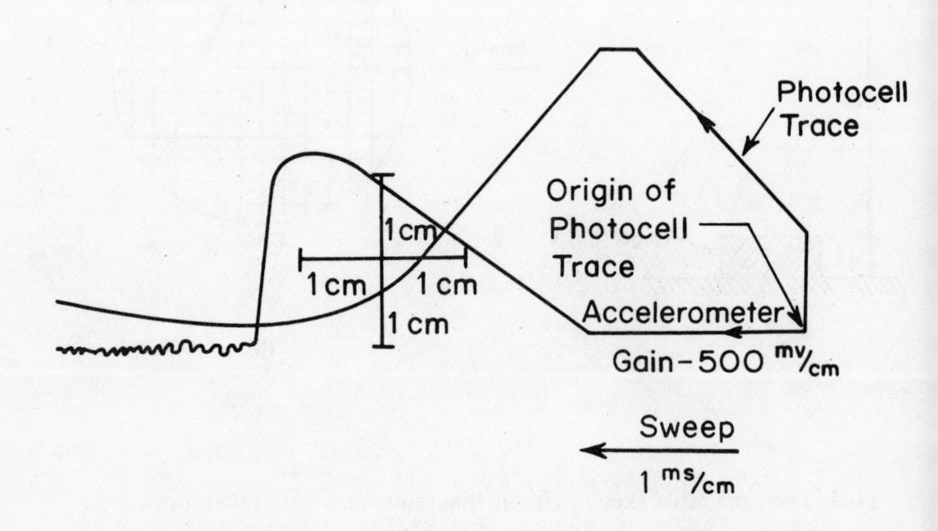

Fig. 11-16. Trace of CRO record for Experiment 11-1.

11-5 The apparatus sketch, circuit diagrams, and data taken during the performance of Laboratory Experiment 11-2, Electrical Integration of an Accelerometer Signal, are given. Write the report asked for.

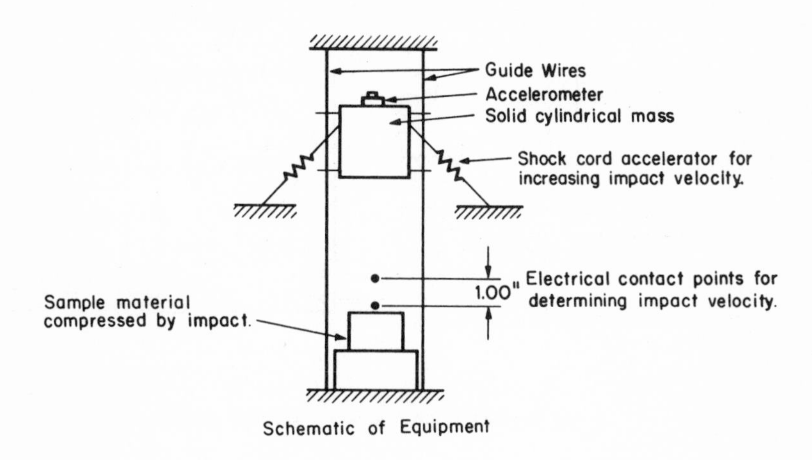

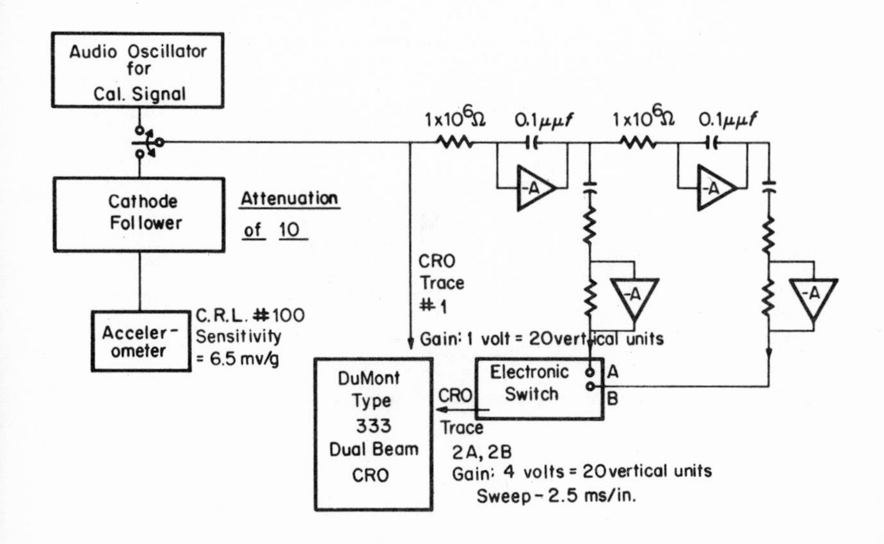

Fig. 11-17. Data sheet for Experiment 11-2.

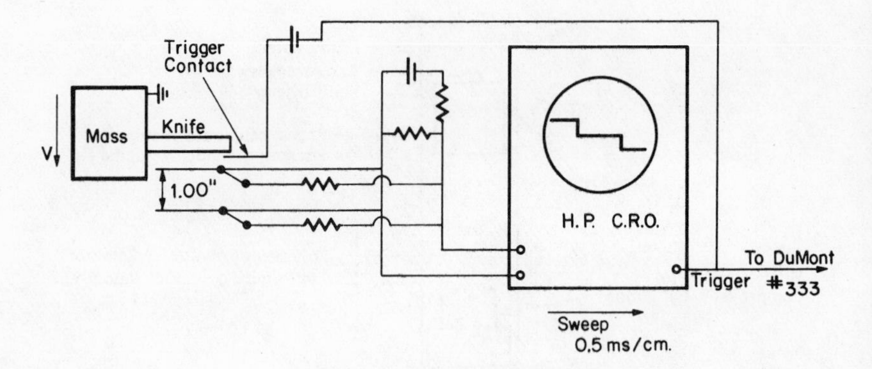

Velocity Meter and Triggering Circuit

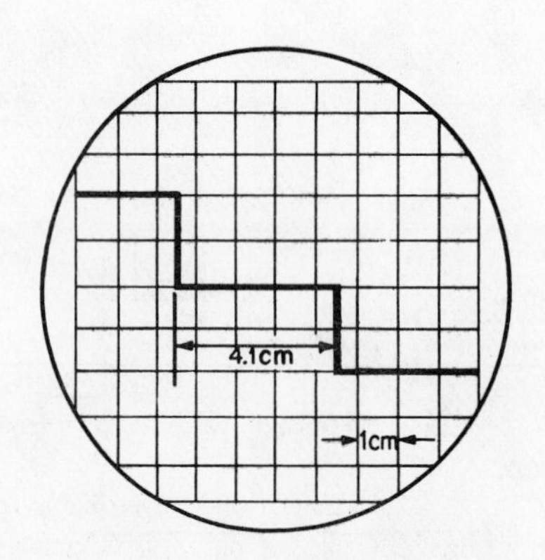

Trace of Velocity Indicator Scope Record

Fig. 11-17. (*Continued.*)

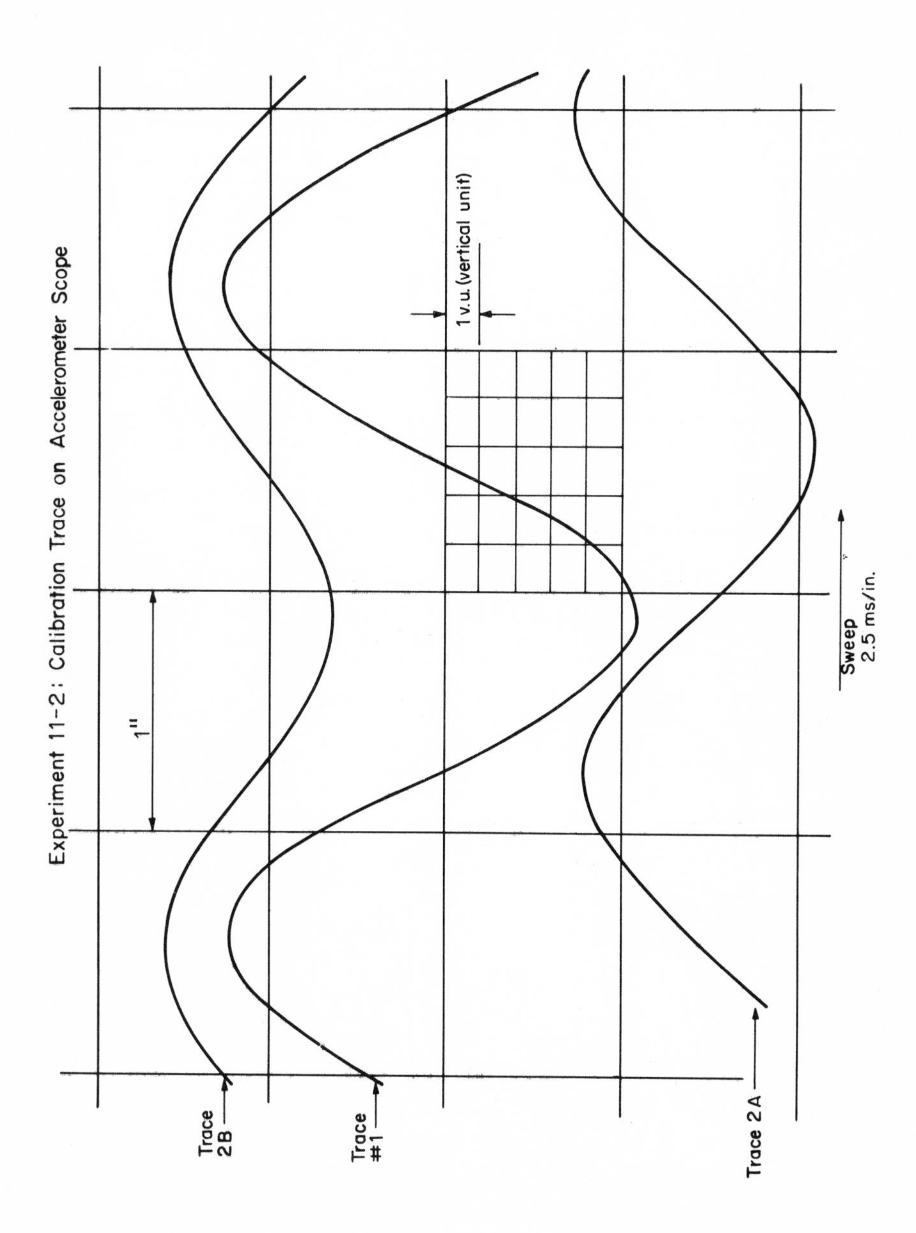

Fig. 11-18. Calibration trace on accelerometer scope, Experiment 11-2.

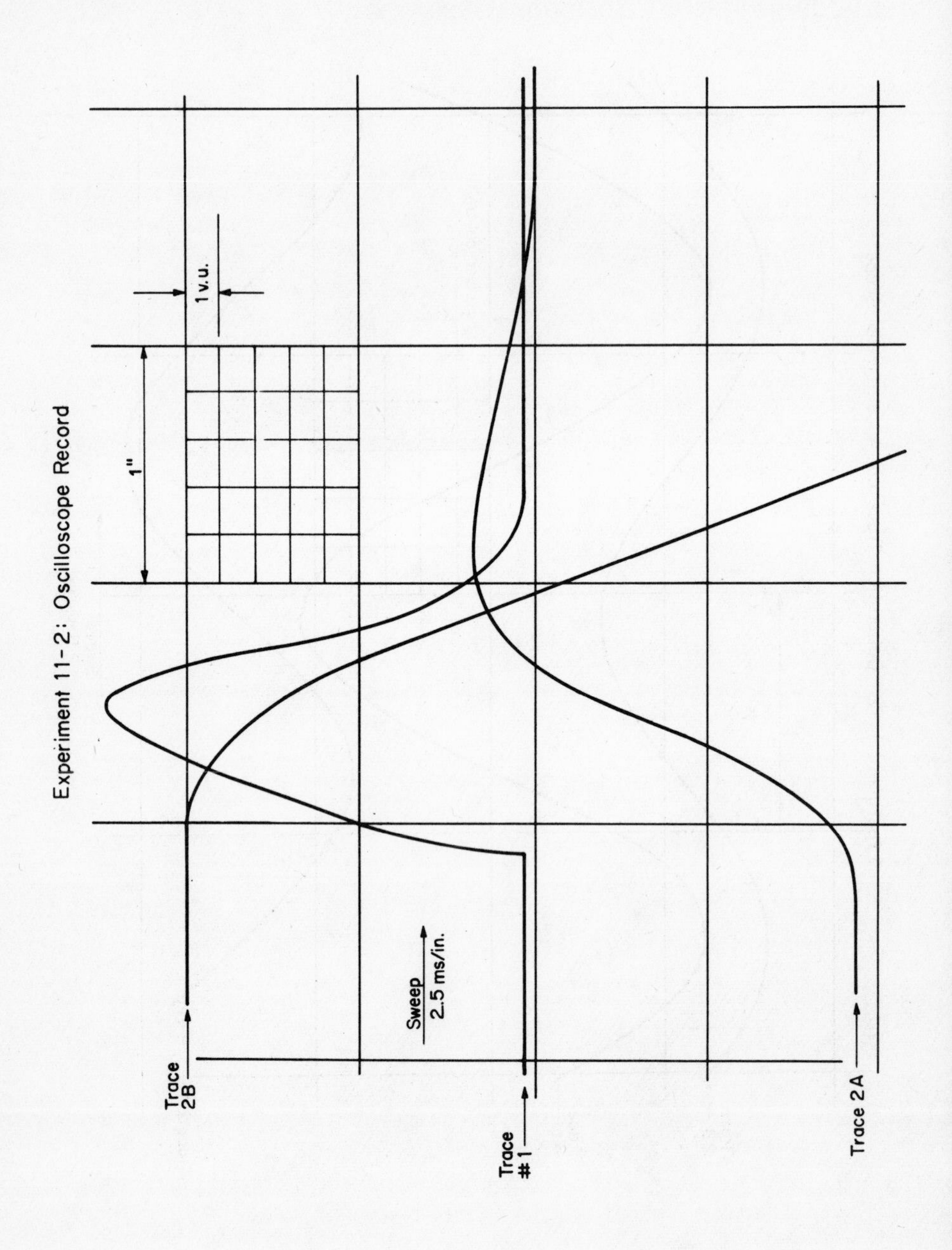

Fig. 11-19. Oscilloscope record for Experiment 11-2.

11-11 Suggested laboratory experiments

Experiment 11-1 Integration of an accelerometer signal*

EQUIPMENT NECESSARY

1. An accelerometer mounted on a mass which can be accelerated (a freely falling mass arrested by a plastic cushion or clay does nicely).
2. A photoelectric system from which displacement versus time is available during the acceleration period.

Or

2′. An arresting system which permits very little rebound and from which total displacement produced during the acceleration period is available. (Dropping a pointed missile into modeling clay gives a good measure of total displacement, but because the acceleration period is likely to be long, good low-frequency response for the accelerometer is essential.)

3. Oscilloscope and oscilloscope camera.

PROCEDURE

1. If a photoelectric system is used for displacement measurements, calibrate this system.
2. For a transient acceleration, record accelerometer signal and photocell signal as functions of time.

Or

2′. Record accelerometer signal as a function of time, and measure maximum displacement.

3. Compute or measure the velocity of the mass at the beginning of the acceleration pulse.

REPORT

1. At the top of a 17×11 sheet, trace accelerometer signal versus time. Add an acceleration scale.
2. Integrate this trace to obtain change in velocity. Plot velocity versus time immediately below the acceleration-time plot.
3. Integrate this trace to obtain displacement. Plot displacement versus time immediately below the velocity-time plot.

* Data taken during this experiment are given in Prob. 11-4, so all computations may be conducted as a home problem if desired.

4. Plot the photoelectric signal to the same displacement scale as used in step 3 above.

Or

4′. Compare the measured total displacement to the value predicted by double integration of the accelerometer signal.
5. Discuss the effect of error in the value used for initial velocity and the effect of inadequate low-frequency response in the accelerometer system.

Experiment 11-2 Electrical integration of an accelerometer signal*

EQUIPMENT NECESSARY

The equipment used in Experiment 11-1 plus an electrical double-integrating circuit and two additional recording channels.

PROCEDURE

1. Calibrate the integrating circuit.
2. During the transient acceleration period record accelerometer signal, first integral, second integral, and photocell signal.

REPORT

1. Plot acceleration-time, velocity-time, displacement-time diagrams with appropriate scales.
2. Discuss results.

Experiment 11-3 Effect of accelerometer location on acceleration measurements

EQUIPMENT NECESSARY

1. One, or more, piezoelectric accelerometer and cathode follower.
2. Oscilloscope and recording camera.
3. A structure which can be subjected to a transient acceleration, with provision for mounting accelerometers at several locations on the structure.

---

* Data taken during this experiment are given in Prob. 11-5; so all computations may be conducted as a home problem if desired.

PROCEDURE

If only one accelerometer is available, a reproducible acceleration transient will be needed. Record the acceleration signal obtained with the accelerometer at several locations on the structure.

REPORT

1. Reproduce all acceleration-time traces to the same acceleration scale.
2. Discuss the results.

INDEX

Index